when AB is 1·5m ...

~~∴ AB i~~

$\frac{1}{1 \cdot 5} \times \cdot 56$

37

$1 \cdot 5 \overline{) \cdot 5 \cdot 6} (\cdot 78$

$15 \overline{) 5 \cdot 6}$

4 9

1 10

1 20

S | A
T | C

A MANUAL OF PRACTICAL MATHEMATICS

MACMILLAN AND CO., Limited
LONDON · BOMBAY · CALCUTTA · MADRAS
MELBOURNE

THE MACMILLAN COMPANY
NEW YORK · BOSTON · CHICAGO
DALLAS · ATLANTA · SAN FRANCISCO

THE MACMILLAN COMPANY
OF CANADA, LIMITED
TORONTO

A MANUAL

OF

PRACTICAL MATHEMATICS

BY

FRANK CASTLE, M.I.Mech.E.

LATE LECTURER IN PRACTICAL MATHEMATICS, MACHINE CONSTRUCTION AND DRAWING
BUILDING CONSTRUCTION AND ENGINEERING SCIENCE, AT THE
MUNICIPAL TECHNICAL INSTITUTE, EASTBOURNE

REVISED EDITION

MACMILLAN AND CO., LIMITED
ST. MARTIN'S STREET, LONDON
1937

First Edition 1903.
Reprinted 1904, 1906, 1908, with additions 1911,
with additions 1916, 1919, 1920, 1925, 1928, 1930, 1932.
Revised Edition 1934. Reprinted 1935, 1937.

PRINTED IN GREAT BRITAIN

PREFACE

ONE of the chief objects of this volume is to bring within the reach of students of ordinary abilities, and to enable them to make practical use of, some portions of what are generally, though with little reason, called "higher" Mathematics. Many mathematical rules, such as those studied under Mensuration to obtain the volume and surface of a sphere, may be obtained by so-called "elementary" methods, but these are frequently only roundabout and troublesome tricks, and are after all merely expedients to evade the simple notation of the Calculus and usually end by assuming the idea of a limit, a conception which my experience shows is quite as difficult for the student to grasp as the underlying principles of the Calculus. Or, take the problem of determining the moment of inertia of a rod: when once the student becomes familiar with the easy language of the Calculus, all the scaffolding, which has to be so carefully and tediously built up to obtain a result if Algebra alone is employed, may be at once discarded.

For these and similar reasons, and to keep the size of the book within reasonable limits, the rudiments of Mathematics—Arithmetic and simple Algebra—are taken for granted, though summaries of the more important elementary results are given at the beginning of each section. The summaries are in every case followed by concrete numerical examples fully worked out and a set of exercises to enable the student to become possessed of the full meaning of each of the terms in the algebraic expressions representing the rules.

The order of treatment merely represents what I have found to be most advantageous in my own classes. Other teachers may find it better to vary the sequence to meet the particular requirements of their own students. Readers who are studying without the help of a teacher are recommended to omit the more difficult sections at the first reading. I should like to direct particular attention to several portions of the book, for, so far as I am aware, the method of treatment therein is now published for the first time. Among these sections are:

(*a*) The identification of the nature of a plotted curve by the use of a strip of celluloid on which a series of standard curves is already drawn; and the method of finding the value of n in the family of curves denoted by $y=x^n$, etc.

(*b*) The method of solution of equations of the form $T=a+by^n$.

(*c*) The graphical methods of dealing with problems in Simple Harmonic Motion expressed by $y=a\cos(\omega t+e)$, or $y=a\sin(bx+c)$.

(*d*) The problems involving addition and subtraction of simple solids.

(*e*) The theory of the Amsler planimeter, of vector notation, and of Fourier's theorem. In this connection I am glad to express my grateful indebtedness to Mr. Joseph Harrison, of the Royal College of Science, for portions of the proofs.

(*f*) The graphical method of obtaining the slope of a curve by means of a set-square and pencil.

(*g*) The geometrical proof that $\frac{dy}{dx}=\frac{dy}{dz}\cdot\frac{dz}{dx}$.

(*h*) The use of arithmetical and geometrical progressions to illustrate the Integral Calculus.

Great importance has been attached throughout the book to fully-worked concrete examples, and of these a very large number is to be found; it is hoped that the student will be able, by means of these examples, to follow intelligently every step of his work.

In order not to overburden the book, I have been compelled to be very brief in some parts, especially in my treatment of the Calculus and of Differential Equations. Students who wish for more detailed information should consult Prof. Perry's *Calculus for Engineers*, where they will find complete guidance in the further study of the subject.

In the preparation of my MSS. and in the passage of the book through the press I have received much assistance from many friends, whose help I am pleased thus to acknowledge. Prof. L. Bairstow, F.R.S., has looked through the MSS. and made many valuable suggestions; Mr. H. J. Woodall has read all the proofs and usefully altered and corrected my work in many places; and Sir Richard Gregory and Mr. A. T. Simmons, B.Sc., have again given me the benefit of their kindly and experienced criticism at every stage in the preparation of the book.

FRANK CASTLE.

On account of the regretted death of Mr. Castle in August, 1928, the preparation of this new issue of his book had to be entrusted to other hands. Mr. F. G. W. Brown, Senior Mathematical Master, West Ham Secondary School, very kindly undertook the necessary revision; and he has taken advantage of the opportunity by bringing many of the older methods more up-to-date, and also supplementing them by some modern ones. Especially has this been done in the case of algebraic, trigonometric and differential equations. For an adequate practical treatment of the Second Order Differential equation, space has been found for the inclusion of a paragraph on the exponential values of the circular functions.

The distinction between the modern meanings attached to the terms *slope* and *gradient* has also been made more precise, and the text rendered consistent throughout without disturbing the general arrangement.

Several typographical errors, which had previously escaped detection, have been corrected, and Fig. 50 has been re-drawn.

The original arrangement and pagination remain, however, as before.

THE PUBLISHERS.

October, 1933.

CONTENTS.

CHAPTER IX.

CHAPTER X.

CHAPTER XI.

CHAPTER XII.

CHAPTER XIII.

CHAPTER XIV.

CHAPTER XV.

CHAPTER XVI.

CHAPTER XVII.

CHAPTER XVIII.

A MANUAL OF PRACTICAL MATHEMATICS.

CHAPTER I.

SIMPLIFICATIONS AND PARTIAL FRACTIONS.

Elementary results and formulae.—The following formulae are probably already familiar to the reader. If not, they should, after verification by actual multiplication, be committed to memory :

$$(a+b)^2=a^2+2ab+b^2\ ;\ (a-b)^2=a^2-2ab+b^2.$$

The two formulae may be combined, thus :

$$\mathbf{(a \pm b)^2=a^2 \pm 2ab+b^2.}$$

These formulae should be equally familiar when other letters are used, such as x, y, etc.

Ex. 1. $(3ax-2ay)^2=(3ax)^2-2\times(3ax)\times(2ay)+(2ay)^2$
$=9a^2x^2-12a^2xy+4a^2y^2.$

Similarly, by multiplication,

$$\mathbf{(a \pm b)^3=a^3 \pm 3a^2b+3ab^2 \pm b^3.}$$
$$\mathbf{(a+b)(a-b)=a^2-b^2.}$$

The last example may be expressed in words by saying: **The product of the sum and difference of two quantities is equal to the difference of their squares.**

Ex. 2. $127^2-123^2=(127+123)(127-123)$
$=250\times4=1000.$

Ex. 3. $9c^2-16(a-b)^2=(3c)^2-\{4(a-b)\}^2$
$=(3c+4a-4b)(3c-4a+4b).$

C

Square of a polynomial.—The square of an expression consisting of three or more terms can be obtained by arranging the terms as in Multiplication, and obtaining the product; but the work is much reduced by noticing the arrangement of the terms in

$$(a+b)^2=a^2+b^2+2ab,$$

and applying the result to any expression containing three or more terms; it is then easy to write down the square required.

Thus, $(a+b+c)^2=a^2+b^2+c^2+2ab+2ac+2bc.$

On the right-hand side the sum of the squares of the three separate terms are followed by twice the products of the first and second, the first and third, and finally of the second and third terms respectively. Similarly,

$$(a+b+c+d)^2=a^2+b^2+c^2+d^2+2ab+2ac+2ad+2bc+2bd+2cd.$$

Other expressions involving squares and cubes should be written down in a similar manner and verified.

Fractional expressions.—In the simplification of fractional expressions, a factor of the denominator of one fraction may be equal to a factor of another denominator with its sign changed. In such cases, it is advisable to change the sign of one of the fractions by multiplying its numerator and denominator by -1. If any fraction requires two such changes the original sign will remain unaltered.

Ex. 1. Simplify

$$\frac{a}{(a-b)(a-c)}+\frac{b}{(b-c)(b-a)}+\frac{c}{(c-a)(c-b)}.$$

It is convenient in fractions of this type to preserve cyclic order in the letters a, b, c; thus a will follow c, and $a-c$ changed to $-(c-a)$. Similarly $b-a$ and $c-b$ will become $-(a-b)$ and $-(b-c)$ respectively. Hence the expression becomes

$$-\frac{a}{(a-b)(c-a)}-\frac{b}{(a-b)(b-c)}-\frac{c}{(c-a)(b-c)}$$

$$=-\frac{a(b-c)+b(c-a)+c(a-b)}{(a-b)(b-c)(c-a)}$$

$$=0.$$

Ex. 2. Simplify $\dfrac{x-2a}{x+a}+\dfrac{2(a^2-4ax)}{a^2-x^2}-\dfrac{3a}{x-a}$.

By changing the sign of the last fraction, the L.C.M. of the denominators becomes a^2-x^2. The expression may then be written

$$\frac{(x-2a)(a-x)+2a^2-8ax+3a(a+x)}{a^2-x^2}$$

$$=\frac{3a^2-2ax-x^2}{a^2-x^2}=\frac{3a+x}{a+x}.$$

When it is required to simplify an expression containing the algebraic sum of three or more given fractions, it is usually convenient to take the L.C.M. of the denominators as a common denominator. But, if this course be always followed, much unnecessary labour will often result. It is sometimes better first to arrange the terms in groups of two or more together and simplify each group before proceeding further.

Ex. 3. Simplify $\dfrac{1}{x-2}-\dfrac{1}{x-3}+\dfrac{1}{x-4}-\dfrac{1}{x-5}$.

Here, following the ordinary rule, the L.C.M. of the denominators would be $(x-2)(x-3)(x-4)(x-5)$, and each numerator would have to be multiplied by three factors. Instead, we may simplify the first two terms,

$$\frac{1}{x-2}-\frac{1}{(x-3)}=\frac{x-3-x+2}{(x-2)(x-3)}=\frac{-1}{(x-2)(x-3)}.$$

In a similar manner, the remaining two terms become

$$\frac{1}{x-4}-\frac{1}{(x-5)}=\frac{-1}{(x-4)(x-5)}.$$

Hence, the given expression is equivalent to

$$-\frac{1}{(x-2)(x-3)}-\frac{1}{(x-4)(x-5)}$$

$$=\frac{-(x^2-9x+20)-(x^2-5x+6)}{(x-2)(x-3)(x-4)(x-5)}$$

$$=\frac{-2(x^2-7x+13)}{(x-2)(x-3)(x-4)(x-5)}.$$

Fractions of the form $\frac{x^3+y^3}{x+y}$ are easily simplified by writing down the factors of the numerator. Thus

$$\frac{x^3+y^3}{x+y}=\frac{(x+y)(x^2-xy+y^2)}{x+y}$$
$$=x^2-xy+y^2.$$

Similarly, $\frac{x^4-y^4}{(x+y)(x-y)}=\frac{(x^2+y^2)(x^2-y^2)}{x^2-y^2}=x^2+y^2,$

and $x^4+x^2y^2+y^4=(x^2+xy+y^2)(x^2-xy+y^2).$

The above examples are simple applications of the following general statements:

Factors.

x^n+y^n is divisible by $x+y$ when n is odd;
x^n-y^n „ „ $x+y$ „ n is even;
x^n-y^n „ „ $x-y$ „ n is either odd or even.

Surd quantities.—In questions dealing with fractions involving surd quantities, simplification is often effected by using one or both of the forms $(a+b)^2=a^2+2ab+b^2$ (i) or $(a^2-b^2)=(a+b)(a-b)$ (ii).

The former may be used in extracting the root of a binomial surd quantity. Some applications are indicated in the following examples:

Ex. 1. Simplify (i) $\frac{1}{\sqrt{20}}$; (ii) $\frac{\sqrt{5}-2}{\sqrt{5}+2}$ and express the result in each case as a decimal fraction. (Given $\sqrt{5}=2{\cdot}2361$.)

(i) Here $\frac{1}{\sqrt{20}}=\frac{\sqrt{20}}{20}=\frac{\sqrt{4\times5}}{2\times10}=\frac{\sqrt{5}}{10}.$

But $\sqrt{5}=2{\cdot}2361$; $\therefore \frac{\sqrt{5}}{10}=0{\cdot}22361.$

(ii) $\frac{\sqrt{5}-2}{\sqrt{5}+2}.$

Multiply numerator and denominator by $\sqrt{5}-2$.

$$\therefore \frac{\sqrt{5}-2}{\sqrt{5}+2}=\frac{(\sqrt{5}-2)(\sqrt{5}-2)}{(\sqrt{5}+2)(\sqrt{5}-2)}.$$

Apply the forms given by (i) and (ii) above,

$$\therefore \frac{(\sqrt{5}-2)(\sqrt{5}-2)}{(\sqrt{5}+2)(\sqrt{5}-2)}=\frac{5-4\sqrt{5}+4}{5-4}=9-4\sqrt{5}=0{\cdot}0556.$$

Ex. 2. Show without extracting roots that $\sqrt{17}+\sqrt{19}$ is less than $6\sqrt{2}$.

Here, if $\sqrt{17}+\sqrt{19}<6\sqrt{2}$,

then, squaring both sides,

$$17+2\sqrt{17\times 19}+19<72;$$

$$\therefore\ 36+2\sqrt{17\times 19}<72,$$

$$\text{or}\ 36+2\sqrt{323}<72.$$

Subtracting 36 from each side and dividing by 2 we obtain

$$\sqrt{323}<18.$$

Squaring both sides $323<324$, which is obviously true.

Ex. 3. Find the value of

$$\frac{3-\sqrt{5}}{(\sqrt{3}+\sqrt{5})^2}+\frac{3+\sqrt{5}}{(\sqrt{3}-\sqrt{5})^2}.$$

As a common denominator take the product of the two denominators. Then

$$\frac{(3-\sqrt{5})(\sqrt{3}-\sqrt{5})^2+(3+\sqrt{5})(\sqrt{3}+\sqrt{5})^2}{(\sqrt{3}+\sqrt{5})^2\times(\sqrt{3}-\sqrt{5})^2}$$

or

$$\frac{(3-\sqrt{5})(3+5-2\sqrt{15})+(3+\sqrt{5})(3+5+2\sqrt{15})}{(3-5)^2}$$

$$=12+5\sqrt{3}=20{\cdot}66.$$

In Ex. 3, and in all similar cases, the numerical values of numerator and denominator may be obtained by using a table of square roots, then the value of each fraction may be obtained by logarithms.

Ex. 4. In the expression $(x-a)^2-(y-b)^2$ put $x=a+b+\frac{(a-b)^2}{4(a+b)}$, and $y=\frac{a+b}{4}+\frac{ab}{a+b}$, and reduce the resulting expression to its simplest form.

$$(x-a)^2-(y-b)^2=(x-a+y-b)(x-a-y+b).$$

Substitute the given values for x and y, thus,

$$(x-a+y-b)=\left(a+b+\frac{(a-b)^2}{4(a+b)}-a+\frac{a+b}{4}+\frac{ab}{a+b}-b\right)$$

$$=\frac{(a-b)^2+(a+b)^2+4ab}{4(a+b)}=\frac{(a+b)^2}{2(a+b)}$$

$$=\frac{a+b}{2}.$$

Similarly, for the second factor,

$$(x-a-y+b)=\left\{a+b+\frac{(a-b)^2}{4(a+b)}-a-\left(\frac{a+b}{4}+\frac{ab}{a+b}\right)+b\right\}$$

$$=\frac{8b(a+b)+(a-b)^2-\{(a+b)^2+4ab\}}{4(a+b)}$$

$$=\frac{8b^2}{4(a+b)}=\frac{2b^2}{a+b}.$$

Hence, $(x-a)^2-(y-b)^2$

$$=\frac{a+b}{2}\times\frac{2b^2}{a+b}$$

$$=b^2.$$

Ex. 5. If $x^2=(x+1)$, show that $x^5=5x+3$.

$$x^5=x^4\times x=(x+1)^2\times x \text{ by substitution,}$$

$$\therefore\ x^5=(x^2+2x+1)x=(3x+2)x,$$

$$\therefore\ x^5=5x+3.$$

Partial fractions.—A single fraction has often to be expressed as the sum of several simpler fractions. Such fractions are called partial fractions.

If necessary, the given fraction must be simplified, and it may be assumed that the denominator can be resolved into its factors. The methods adopted in some easy cases may be seen from the following examples.

Ex. 1. Express in the form of partial fractions $\frac{2x+1}{x^2-5x+6}$.

The factors of the denominator are $(x-2)$ and $(x-3)$.

First write the given fraction in the form:

$$\frac{2x+1}{(x-2)(x-3)}=\frac{A}{x-2}+\frac{B}{x-3}, \quad \text{.....................(1)}$$

where the values of the coefficients A and B are to be determined.

Multiplying both sides of Eq. (1) by $(x-2)(x-3)$, we obtain

$$2x+1\equiv A(x-3)+B(x-2). \quad \text{.....................(2)}$$

By putting in succession $x-3=0$ and $x-2=0$, the numerical values of A and B can be found.

Thus, let $x-3=0$. Then substitute $x=3$ in (2).

$$7=B(3-2);\quad \therefore\ B=7.$$

Again, let $x-2=0$; $\therefore\ x=2$.

Then $5=A(2-3)$, or $A=-5$.

Substitute these values in (1), thus,

$$\frac{2x+1}{(x-2)(x-3)} = -\frac{5}{x-2} + \frac{7}{x-3}.$$

A more general method is as follows :

Writing (2) in the form

$$2x+1 \equiv (A+B)x - 3A - 2B$$

and equating corresponding coefficients,

$$A + B = 2,$$

$$-3A - 2B = 1.$$

Solving these equations for A and B, we obtain

$$A = -5, \quad B = 7$$

as before.

Note that the symbol $\equiv$ means *identically equal to*, i.e. the statement $2x+1 \equiv (A+B)x - 3A - 2B$ is true for *all* values of x.

Ex. 2. Express in partial fractions the fraction $\dfrac{2x+1}{x^3-6x^2+11x-6}$

The denominator is $(x-1)(x-2)(x-3)$,

Let $$\frac{2x+1}{(x-1)(x-2)(x-3)} = \frac{A}{x-1} + \frac{B}{x-2} + \frac{C}{x-3}.$$

Multiply both sides by $(x-1)(x-2)(x-3)$;

$$\therefore\ 2x+1 = A(x-2)(x-3) + B(x-1)(x-3) + C(x-1)(x-2) \quad \ldots(3)$$

Let $x - 1 = 0$; $\therefore\ x = 1$.

Substitute this value for x, then from (3),

$$3 = A(1-2)(1-3) = 2A;$$

$$\therefore\ A = \frac{3}{2}.$$

Similarly, let $x - 2 = 0$; $\therefore\ x = 2$.

Substitute in (3); then

$$5 = B(2-1)(2-3) = -B;$$

$$\therefore\ B = -5.$$

Finally, put $x - 3 = 0$, or $x = 3$;

$$\therefore\ 7 = 2C, \text{ or } C = \frac{7}{2}.$$

Hence, $$\frac{2x+1}{(x-1)(x-2)(x-3)} = \frac{3}{2(x-1)} - \frac{5}{x-2} + \frac{7}{2(x-3)}.$$

Ex. 3. Resolve into partial fractions the single fraction

$$\frac{lx^2+mx+n}{(x-a)(x-b)(x-c)}.$$

Let $$\frac{lx^2+mx+n}{(x-a)(x-b)(x-c)}=\frac{A}{x-a}+\frac{B}{x-b}+\frac{C}{x-c}.$$

Multiply throughout by $(x-a)(x-b)(x-c)$,

$\therefore\ lx^2+mx+n=A(x-b)(x-c)+B(x-a)(x-c)+C(x-a)(x-b).$

Let the factor $x-a=0$, $\therefore\ x=a$;

then, $$la^2+ma+n=A(a-b)(a-c);$$

$$\therefore\ A=\frac{la^2+ma+n}{(a-b)(a-c)}.$$

In a similar manner let $x-b=0$, $\therefore\ x=b$;

then $$B=\frac{lb^2+mb+n}{(b-a)(b-c)}.$$

Finally, if $x-c=0$, we obtain

$$C=\frac{lc^2+mc+n}{(c-a)(c-b)}.$$

If the numerator is of equal, or greater, degree than the denominator, it will be necessary to divide the former by the latter, so that the fraction to be operated upon shall have its numerator of lower degree than its denominator. Also, when the denominator of a fraction contains a factor such as $(x-a)^3$, it is necessary to take several corresponding partial fractions having for their denominators the factors $x-a$, $(x-a)^2$, $(x-a)^3$, etc.

Ex. 4. Resolve into partial fractions

$$\frac{3x+5}{(1-2x)^2}.$$

Let $$\frac{3x+5}{(1-2x)^2}=\frac{A}{1-2x}+\frac{B}{(1-2x)^2}.$$

Multiply both sides by $(1-2x)^2$. Then

$$3x+5=A(1-2x)+B. \quad\text{.............................(1)}$$

Put $1-2x=0$, $$\therefore\ x=\frac{1}{2};$$

$$\therefore\ \frac{3}{2}+5=B,$$

giving $$B=\frac{13}{2}.$$

Substitute this value for B in (1),

$$3x+5-\frac{13}{2}=A(1-2x);$$

$$\therefore\ A=-\frac{3}{2}\left(\frac{1-2x}{1-2x}\right)=-\frac{3}{2}.$$

Or, put $x=0$ in (1), then $5=A+\frac{13}{2}$; $\therefore\ A=-\frac{3}{2}$.

Hence, $$\frac{3x+5}{(1-2x)^2}=\frac{13}{2(1-2x)^2}-\frac{3}{2(1-2x)}.$$

A very useful artifice which may be used in many cases (especially in dealing with factors such as $(x-a)^n$ and often referred to as **repeating factors**) may be shown by an example.

Ex. 5. Resolve into partial fractions

$$\frac{x^3+3x+1}{(1-x)^4}. \quad \text{..................................(1)}$$

Let $1-x=z$; $\therefore\ x=1-z$. Substitute in Eq. (1) and we obtain

$$\frac{(1-z)^3+3(1-z)+1}{z^4}$$

$$=\frac{1-3z+3z^2-z^3+3-3z+1}{z^4}=\frac{5-6z+3z^2-z^3}{z^4}$$

$$=\frac{5}{z^4}-\frac{6}{z^3}+\frac{3}{z^2}-\frac{1}{z}.$$

Then, substituting for z, this result may be written,

$$\frac{5}{(1-x)^4}-\frac{6}{(1-x)^3}+\frac{3}{(1-x)^2}-\frac{1}{1-x}.$$

Thus, in Ex. 4 let $1-2x=z$, $\therefore\ x=\frac{1-z}{2}$;

$$\therefore\ \frac{3x+5}{(1-2x)^2}=\frac{\frac{3}{2}(1-z)+5}{z^2}=\frac{13-3z}{2z^2}$$

$$=\frac{13}{2z^2}-\frac{3}{2z};$$

$$\therefore\ \frac{3x+5}{(1-2x)^2}=\frac{13}{2(1-2x)^2}-\frac{3}{2(1-2x)}.$$

EXERCISES. I.

1. Simplify $$\left(\frac{x^5-1}{x-1}\right)^2-\left(\frac{x^5+1}{x+1}\right)^2$$
and find its numerical value when $x\sqrt{(2+\sqrt{3})}=1$.

2. Find the value of $\sqrt{\left(\frac{\sqrt{5}-2}{\sqrt{5}+2}\right)}$ to three places of decimals.

3. Find the product of $\frac{a}{4}+\frac{\sqrt{ab}}{3}+\frac{b}{9}$ and $\frac{\sqrt{a}}{2}-\frac{\sqrt{b}}{3}$, and find the value of the product when $a=12$ and $b=18$.

4. Simplify $\frac{x^2-8x+12}{3x^2-17x-6}-\frac{2x^2+5x+2}{6x^2+x-1}$, and find its value when $3x=\sqrt{2}-1$.

5. Reduce to its simplest form:
$$\frac{x^3-5x^2-8x+12}{x^4-7x^3+7x^2-7x+6}.$$
Find its value when $x=1+\sqrt{3}$. ($\sqrt{3}=1{\cdot}732$.)

Simplify the following expressions:

6. $\sqrt{(52-7\sqrt{12})}$.

7. $\frac{1-\sqrt{2}+\sqrt{3}}{1+\sqrt{2}+\sqrt{3}}-\frac{1-\sqrt{2}-\sqrt{3}}{1+\sqrt{2}-\sqrt{3}}$.   **8.** $\frac{4\sqrt{2}-3\sqrt{3}}{7-2\sqrt{6}}\times\frac{2\sqrt{2}+\sqrt{3}}{7-2\sqrt{2}}$.

9. If $$\left(\frac{1}{x}+\frac{2}{y}+\frac{1}{z}\right)^2=\frac{(x+2y+z)^2}{xy^2z}$$
show that either $x=z$ or $y^2=zx$.

10. Show that $\left(x-2+\frac{1}{x}\right)\left(x+2+\frac{1}{x}\right)\left(x^2+2+\frac{1}{x^2}\right)=\left(x^2-\frac{1}{x^2}\right)^2$.

11. Given $\sqrt{5}=2{\cdot}236$, express $\frac{1}{\sqrt{20}}$ and $\frac{\sqrt{5}-2}{\sqrt{5}+2}$ as decimals.

12. Find the value of $\left(x+\frac{a}{b}\right)\left(x+\frac{b}{a}\right)-\left(x-\frac{a}{b}\right)\left(x-\frac{b}{a}\right)$ when $x=\frac{1}{a^2+b^2}$.

13. Reduce the following expression to its simplest form: $\left(\frac{a-b}{a+b}\right)-\left(\frac{a}{a-b}+\frac{b}{b-a}\right)^2$; and find its value, expressed as a decimal, when $a=2$ and $b=\sqrt{5}=2{\cdot}236$.

14. Simplify $(a+b+c)^3+6a(a-b-c)(a+b+c)+(a-b-c)^3$.

15. Simplify $\frac{1+2\sqrt{x}}{1-\sqrt{x}}-\frac{1-\sqrt{x}}{1+2\sqrt{x}}$; and find its value to four places of decimals when $3x=1$, having given $\sqrt{3}=1\cdot732$.

16. If $a^2=m+n$, $b^2=n+l$, $c^2=l+m$ and $2s=a+b+c$ show that

$$s(s-a)(s-b)(s-c)=\tfrac{1}{4}(mn+nl+lm).$$

17. Simplify $\frac{x^2-x-2}{x^2-3x+2}+\frac{2x^2+x-3}{2x^2+5x+3}-2$; and find its value to four places of decimals, when $x=1+\sqrt{3}$.

Simplify the expressions:

18. $\frac{[ax^2+(b-c)x+d]^2-[ax^2+(b+c)x+d]^2}{[ax^2+(b+e)x+d]^2-[ax^2+(b-e)x+d]^2}$.

19. $\frac{(x+y)^2+2(x^2-y^2)+(x-y)^2}{(x^4-2x^2y^2+y^4)\left\{\frac{1}{(x-y)^2}+\frac{2}{x^2-y^2}+\frac{1}{(x+y)^2}\right\}}$.

Resolve into factors:

20. $12x^2-25xy+12y^2$.

21. $a^8+a^4b^4+b^8$.

22. $x^4+x^2y^2+y^4-2xy-1$.

23. Show that a is a factor of the expression

$$(a+b)^2(a^2+c^2)-(a+c)^2(a^2+b^2).$$

Resolve into factors the following expressions:

24. $20x^2-x-30$.

25. $2xy+7x+6y+21$.

26. $5x^2-(7+15a)x+21a$.

27. $x^4-1-4(x-1)$.

Simplify the following expressions:

28. $$\left(a-\frac{a-b}{1+ab}\right)\times\frac{a}{b}\div\left(1+\frac{a(a-b)}{1+ab}\right).$$

29. $$\frac{x^2-x}{x^2-1}\times\frac{(x+1)^2-(x-1)^2}{2x}-\left(\frac{x}{x+1}-1\right)+\left(\frac{x^3-1}{x^2-1}-1\right)$$

30. Given $\sqrt{2}=1\cdot4142$, and $\sqrt{3}=1\cdot7321$, find the value of $\frac{1}{\sqrt{6}-\sqrt{2}}$ correct to three places of decimals, using a contracted method of multiplication.

31. Find the value of

$$\frac{3-\sqrt{5}}{(3+\sqrt{5})^2}+\frac{3+\sqrt{5}}{(3-\sqrt{5})^2}.$$

32. If $z=\sqrt{(x^2+y^2)}$ show that

$$\frac{x+y+z}{-x+y+z}=\frac{x-y+z}{x+y-z}.$$

33. Show that

$$\frac{z^2}{a^2+b^2}+\frac{a^2+b^2}{a^2b^2}\left(x-\frac{za^2}{a^2+b^2}\right)^2=\frac{x^2}{a^2}+\left(\frac{z-x}{b}\right)^2.$$

Express in partial fractions:

34. $\frac{2x-5}{(x-2)(x-3)}$.

35. $\frac{7x-1}{1-5x+6x^2}$.

36. $\frac{9}{(x-1)(x+2)^2}$.

37. $\frac{x-13}{x^2-2x-15}$.

38. $\frac{x-5}{x^2-x-2}$.

39. $\frac{x+37}{x^2+4x-21}$.

40. $\frac{5x-18}{x^2-7x+12}$.

41. $\frac{3x^2-10x-4}{(x-2)(x-4)}$.

42. $\frac{2x^3-11x^2+12x+1}{(x-1)(x-2)(x-3)}$.

43. $\frac{5+2x-3x^2}{(x^2-1)(x+1)}$.

Resolve into factors:

44. $x^2+0\cdot4x-4\cdot37$.

45. $a^2(b-c)+b^2(c-a)+c^2(a-b)$.

46. $x^2+6x-520$.

47. x^2-24.

48. $84x^2-525y^2$.

49. $x^2-8\cdot92x+18\cdot4$.

Simplify the following expressions:

50. $\frac{x^2+6x-7}{x^2+3x-4}\div\frac{x^2+4x-21}{2x+8}$.

51. $\frac{x^3+7x^2+4x-12}{x^3+6x^2-2x-12}$.

52. $\frac{1-3x+2x^2}{1-4x+x^2+6x^3}$. Express the resulting fraction as the sum of two simpler fractions.

53. $\frac{x^2-x-2}{x^2-3x+2}+\frac{2x^2+x-3}{2x^2+5x+3}-2$. Find its value to three significant figures when $x=1+\sqrt{3}$.

54. Resolve the fraction $\frac{46+13x}{12x^2-11x-15}$ into the sum, or difference, of two simpler fractions.

CHAPTER II.

MEASUREMENT OF ANGLES AND THE SIMPLE RATIOS.

Measurement of angles.—In the measurement of length, a certain distance is selected as a unit, and the number of times a given length contains the unit length is the measure of its length. In like manner, the magnitude of an angle is estimated by the number of times it contains the unit angle. The two angular units adopted are the **degree** and the **radian**.

Let AE be a line free to move about a centre A. Any point in the line such as D (Fig. 1) will eventually describe a circle. If we assume such a circle to be divided into 360 equal parts then the lines joining any two consecutive points on the circumference to the centre A will enclose an angle of one degree, which is written 1°.

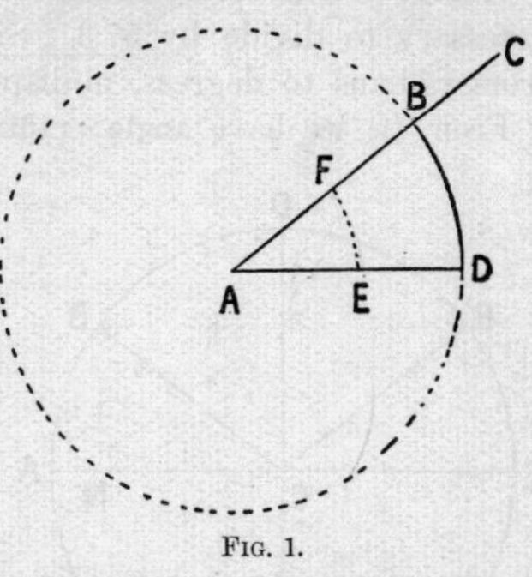

FIG. 1.

A degree is divided into 60 minutes and a minute into 60 seconds. An angle of thirty degrees, twenty minutes, and fifteen seconds would be written $30° 20' 15''$.

The actual distance described by B will be proportional to the amount of turning from the initial position, also for the same angle the arc described is proportional to the radius, hence the measure of an angle is denoted by $k\frac{\text{arc}}{\text{radius}}$; where k

is a constant whose value depends on the particular system adopted. Thus $k=1$ in the *radian* system, and $k=180\div$ratio of circumference to diameter, in the *degree* system.

Assume AB, Fig. 1, a line initially coincident with the line AD, to be rotated about a centre A into the position AB, through an angle which may be denoted by θ.

To ascertain the magnitude of the angle, draw with A as centre an arc of a circle cutting AD in E and AB in F. Then the ratio $\frac{\text{arc}}{\text{radius}}$ is called the measure of the angle in radians,

$$\therefore\ \textbf{angle in radians}=\frac{\textbf{arc}}{\textbf{radius}}. \qquad \text{(i)}$$

The measure of the angle will obviously be unity when the numerator is equal to the denominator, or when the length of arc DB is equal to the radius AD.

The unit angle is called a **radian**, and its value is $\frac{180^\circ}{\pi}$, or is equal to $57^\circ\ 17'\ 45''$ nearly, or about $57^\circ\cdot 3$.

Hence, to convert to radians an angle given in degrees, it is necessary to divide by 57·3. Similarly, to convert an angle from radians to degrees, multiply by 57·3.

From (i) we have **angle × radius = arc.**

Hence, when any two of the three terms are given the remaining term may be obtained.

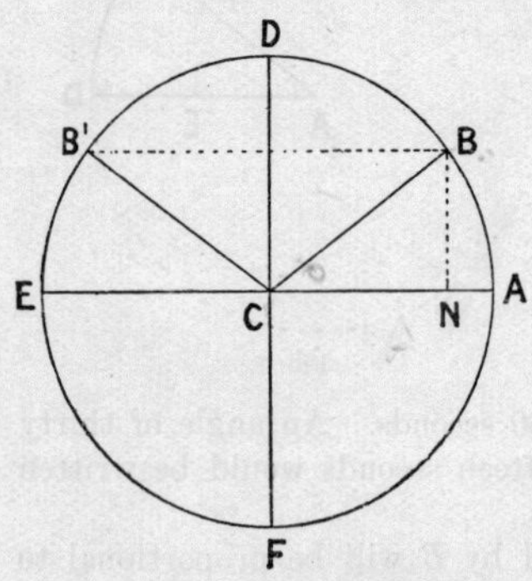

Fig. 2.—Ratios of angles.

Ratios of angles.—The ratios of an angle designated as **sine, cosine,** and **tangent,** abbreviated into sin, cos, and tan, are probably already familiar to the reader. It is only necessary to refer briefly to the definitions.

When the rotating line (Fig. 2) moving in a direction opposite to the hands of a clock comes into the position CB, then, if BN be drawn perpendicular to CN and meeting CA in N, and the angle NCB

be represented by θ, we have for the triangle the following relations:

$$\sin\theta = \frac{NB}{CB}, \quad \cos\theta = \frac{CN}{CB}, \quad \tan\theta = \frac{NB}{CN}.$$

Also $\quad \sin^2\theta + \cos^2\theta = 1$, since $NB^2 + CN^2 = CB^2$.

The reciprocals of each of these ratios are also important and are as follows:

$$\text{cosecant}\,\theta = \frac{1}{\sin\theta} = \frac{CB}{NB}. \quad \text{secant}\,\theta = \frac{1}{\cos\theta} = \frac{CB}{CN}.$$

$$\text{cotangent}\,\theta = \frac{1}{\tan\theta} = \frac{CN}{NB}.$$

The abbreviations cosec θ, sec θ, and cot θ, are used for these ratios. Also, referring to Fig. 1, it is easily seen that

$$\sec^2\theta = 1 + \tan^2\theta \quad \text{and} \quad \text{cosec}^2\theta = 1 + \cot^2\theta.$$

The ratios of the sine, cosine, and tangent for 30°, 45°, and 60° are very important, and are so often required in calculations that it is necessary to remember their numerical values.

Ratios for 60°, 30°.—One of the best methods is to draw (or better, mentally to picture) an equilateral triangle ABC (Fig. 3), with each of its sides say 2 units length. If from the vertex C a perpendicular CD be drawn to the opposite side, then, as ADC is a right-angled triangle, the length of CD is

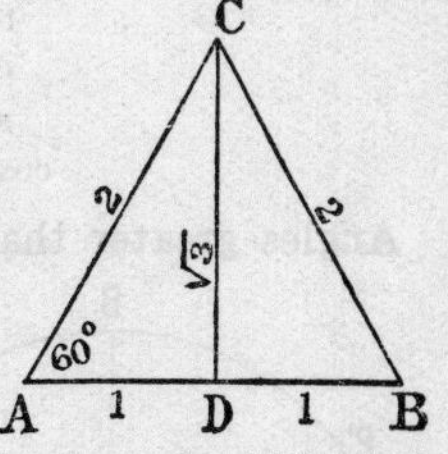

FIG. 3.—Angles of 30° and 60°.

$$\sqrt{2^2 - 1^2} = \sqrt{3}.$$

Hence $\quad \sin A = \sin 60° = \frac{\sqrt{3}}{2}, \quad \cos 60° = \frac{1}{2}, \quad \tan 60° = \sqrt{3}.$

The angle ACD is an angle of 30°. Hence we get the ratios

$$\sin 30° = \frac{1}{2}, \quad \cos 30° = \frac{\sqrt{3}}{2}, \quad \tan 30° = \frac{1}{\sqrt{3}}.$$

Ratios for 45°.—Draw a right-angled triangle in which one side AB is equal to the other side BC. Then ABC is an isosceles triangle and the angles at A and C are in each case 45°. If in Fig. 4 the lengths of the sides AB and BC be denoted by 1, then

$$AC = \sqrt{2}.$$

FIG. 4.—Angle of 45°.

Hence
$$\sin 45^\circ = \frac{1}{\sqrt{2}},$$
$$\cos 45^\circ = \frac{1}{\sqrt{2}},$$
$$\tan 45^\circ = 1.$$

Complementary angles.—Two angles are said to be complementary when their sum is 90° (a right angle).

Ex. Let $A = 30°$, $B = 60°$, then, as we have **found above**,

$$\sin A = \cos B, \text{ and } \cos A = \sin B;$$

these relations hold generally, and we have

$$\begin{aligned}
\sin A &= \cos(90^\circ - A),\\
\cos A &= \sin(90^\circ - A),\\
\tan A &= \cot(90^\circ - A),\\
\cot A &= \tan(90^\circ - A),\\
\sec A &= \operatorname{cosec}(90^\circ - A),\\
\operatorname{cosec} A &= \sec(90^\circ - A).
\end{aligned}$$

Angles greater than 90°.—The ratios of the sine, cosine, tangent, etc., which are all positive for angles not exceeding 90°, may or may not be positive for angles greater than 90°.

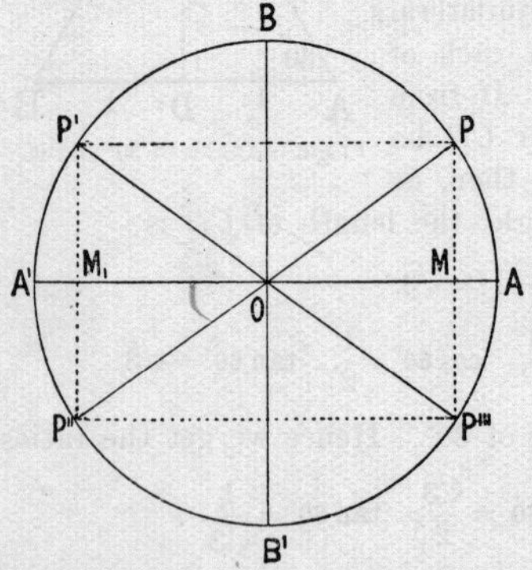

FIG. 5.—Ratios of angles greater than 90°.

The conventions adopted are as follows: If a circle be drawn as in Fig. 5 and also horizontal and vertical diameters, as AA', BB', then all distances measured to the right of the line BB' are said to be **positive**, and those to the left are said to be **negative**.

Distances measured upwards from AA' are positive, those

downwards are negative. The revolving line itself is always positive, but angles are reckoned positive or negative according as the revolving line rotates in the opposite or the same direction as the hands of a watch. Thus, if AP be one-twelfth of the circumference, then, joining P to O, the angle POA is an angle of 30°. If $M_1P'=MP$ the angle AOP' is 150°, and

$$\sin 150^\circ = \frac{M_1P'}{OP} = \frac{MP}{OP} = \frac{1}{2}.$$

The perpendicular M_1P' is measured in a positive direction; OM_1 is measured in a negative direction;

$$\therefore \cos 150^\circ = \frac{OM_1}{OP'} = -\frac{\sqrt{3}}{2}.$$

In a similar manner, if $A'OP''$ is an angle of $180^\circ + 30^\circ = 210^\circ$, both sine and cosine are negative. Finally, corresponding to the position P''', the sine of the angle is negative and the cosine is positive.

As the tangent is the ratio of sine to cosine, it follows that when the sine and cosine have the same sign, either positive or negative, the tangent is positive, but is negative when the sine and cosine have different signs. Some values are given in the following table; these should be carefully verified.

Collecting the results for the points P, P', P'', and P''' we find

Angle	30°	150°	210°	330°
sin	$\frac{1}{2}$	$\frac{1}{2}$	$-\frac{1}{2}$	$-\frac{1}{2}$
cos	$\frac{\sqrt{3}}{2}$	$-\frac{\sqrt{3}}{2}$	$-\frac{\sqrt{3}}{2}$	$\frac{\sqrt{3}}{2}$
tan	$\frac{1}{\sqrt{3}}$	$-\frac{1}{\sqrt{3}}$	$\frac{1}{\sqrt{3}}$	$-\frac{1}{\sqrt{3}}$

General values.—It has been seen that an angle is traced out by the revolution of a line, from coincidence with another line into a second position; and, as the angle may be traced out by any number of revolutions of the line, it follows that for a given value of a trigonometrical ratio there is an indefinite number of angles. But corresponding to a given angle there is only one value for each ratio.

If n is used to denote any integer, $2n$ represents an **even** number, and $2n+1$ or $2n-1$ an **odd** number; positive and negative values may be ensured by using the symbol $(-1)^n$.

$(-1)^n$ is $+1$ when n is even including zero, and is -1 when n is odd.

To find a general expression for all the angles which have a given sine or cosecant—

Let CP, a line initially coincident with CB, move into a position CP, so that the angle BCP is θ; if CP_1 is another position of CP so that $P_1B_1 = PB$, the two angles BCP and B_1CP_1 are equal, and $\sin\theta = \sin(180° - \theta)$.

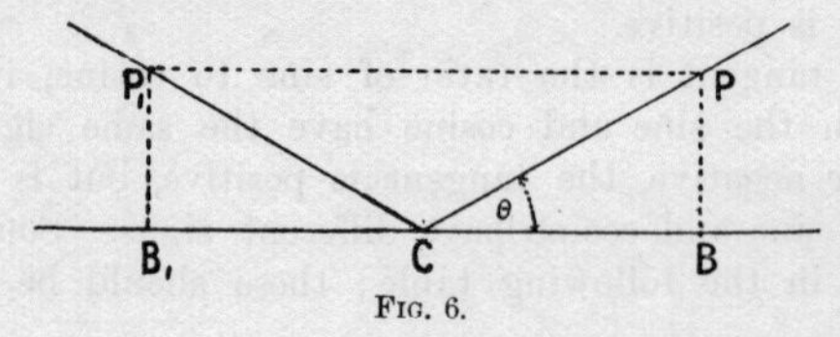

FIG. 6.

These angles may be increased by any number of revolutions of the line CP, that is by any multiple of four right angles, or $2n\pi$. It will then be obvious that all angles having the same sine, or cosecant, are included in the formulae

$$n\pi + (-1)^n\theta.$$

In a similar manner, all the angles which have a given cosine, or secant, are included in the formulae

$$2n\pi \pm \theta.$$

And all the angles which have a given tangent, or cotangent, are included in the general formula

$$n\pi + \theta.$$

Graphical measurement of angles.—In graphical work in which angles occur, the magnitudes should be set out, or measured, as accurately as possible. Thus, when two sides and the included angle of a triangle are given, the two sides may be marked off as accurately as a good scale will permit, but the results obtained will be inaccurate if an error is made in setting out the given angle.

The usual method adopted in setting out a given angle is to use some form of **protractor.** These are made both in the form of a rectangle and of a semicircle, but are rarely sufficiently accurate to enable the results obtained by them to be more than a check on calculated values. The most accurate results are probably obtained by using a good scale, a pair of compasses, and either a table of chords of angles or a table of tangents, Table VI. (pp. 536-7).

Table of chords.—To set out a given angle at A (Fig. 7), make the base AB equal, on any convenient scale, to, say, 10 units; with A as centre and AB as radius, describe an arc, and with B as centre and radius equal to ten times (because AB

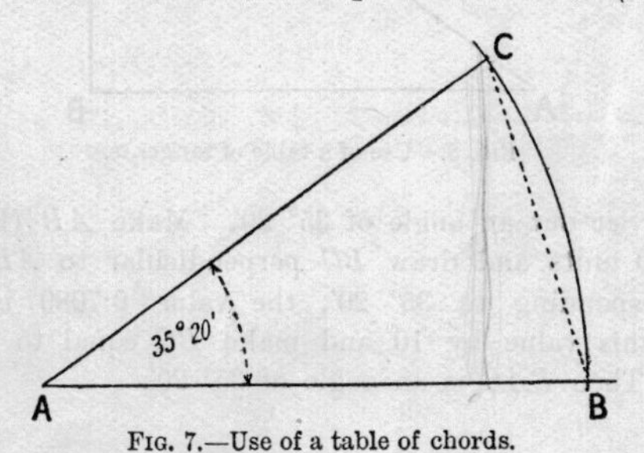

FIG. 7.—Use of a table of chords.

has been made 10 units long) the length of the chord corresponding to the given angle as shown in Table VIII. on p. 540, describe an arc intersecting the former in C; join A to C. Then BAC is the angle required.

Ex. 1. Set out at a given point, A, an angle of 35° 20′.

Measure off AB equal to 10 inches, and describe an arc with A as centre and AB as radius. Opposite the angle 35° 20′ in Table VIII. the value 0·607 is tabulated. Multiplying this by 10 we obtain 6·07. With B as centre and a radius 6·07, describe an arc BC intersecting the former in C. Join A to C. Then BAC is an angle of 35° 20′.

The converse of this exercise, *i.e.* given an angle to obtain its measure, will not present much difficulty. Either of the lines meeting at the vertex of the angle may be assumed as base and a length of 10 units marked off. Then, with this distance as radius, an arc of a circle may be drawn cutting both the lines enclosing the angle. The chord can be measured and divided by 10, finally by referring to Table VIII. the numerical measure of the angle is ascertained.

Table of tangents.—An angle can be determined graphically when the numerical value of its tangent is known.

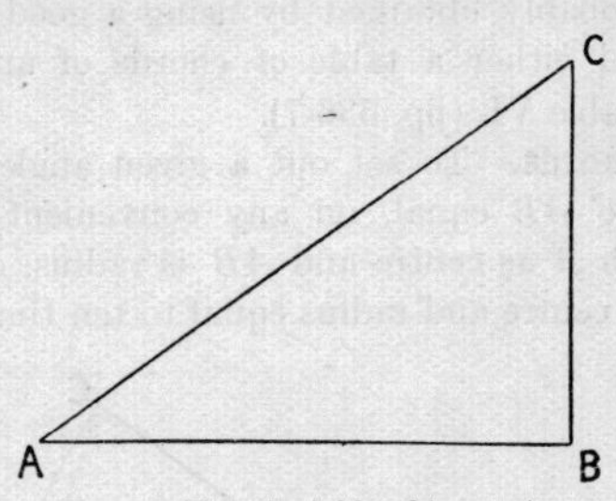

FIG. 8.—Use of a table of tangents.

Ex. 2. Set out an angle of 35° 20′. Make AB (Fig. 8) equal to (say) 10 units and draw BC perpendicular to AB. In Table VI., corresponding to 35° 20′, the value 0·7089 is tabulated. Multiply this value by 10 and make BC equal to 7·089. Join A to C. Then BAC is an angle of 35° 20′.

EXERCISES. II.

1. Express seven-sixteenths of a right-angle in radians.

2. What is meant by the radian measure of an angle? How many degrees and minutes are there in an angle whose radian measure is $\frac{5}{6}$?

3. Express in radians an angle of 240° and express in degrees the angle $\frac{2\pi}{3}$ (radians).

4. The difference of two angles is 10°, the radian measure of their sum is 2; find the radian measure of each angle.

5. Find the distance in miles between two places on the Equator which differ in longitude by 6° 18′, assuming the Earth's equatorial diameter to be 7926 miles.

6. What is the unit of radian measure? Find the length of that part of a circular railway curve which subtends an angle of $22\frac{1}{2}°$ to a radius of a mile.

7. Write down the values of sin 132°, cos 226°, tan 326°.

8. Write down the values of sin 165°, cos 132°, tan 198°.

9. Write in a table the values of the sine, cosine, and tangent of the following angles, 23°, 123°, 233°, 312°, 383°.

Find the measure in radians of an angle of 384°.

10. Trace the variations in sign and magnitude of $\cos A - \sin A$, as A varies from 0° to 180°.

11. Find the two least values of θ if $\sin\theta = \sqrt[3]{\frac{a}{b}}$ where $a = 2{\cdot}12$, $b = 6{\cdot}47$.

12. The geographical mile being a minute of latitude on the surface of the Earth, supposed spherical, prove that the circumference of the Earth is 21600 geographical miles.

13. Find in degrees and minutes the angle which at the centre of a circle of 8 ft. radius subtends an arc of 10 ft. length.

14. A disc revolves 300 times a minute; how many radians is that per second? If the disc is 3 ft. diameter, how fast (in feet per second) will a point on its rim move?

15. The winding drum of a colliery is 10 feet in diameter and revolves ten times a minute, at what rate is the cage raised or lowered?

16. The earth being assumed to be a perfect sphere, and a geographical mile being defined as the length of an arc of the sea which subtends an angle of 1′ at the centre of the earth, show that the earth's radius is approximately equal to 3438 geographical miles.

17. Express in radian measure the least angle of an isosceles triangle, in which the vertical angle is one-half of each of the angles at the base.

18. The radius of a railway curve is 1·5 miles. Find the angle turned through in 40 sec., in radians and degrees, by a train travelling at 50 miles per hour.

19. If a railway train changes its direction through 25° in a distance of 300 ft. What is the average radius of the line?

CHAPTER III.

RATIOS OF THE SUM AND DIFFERENCE OF ANGLES.

Trigonometrical ratios.—In considering trigonometrical ratios, it should be carefully borne in mind that in all except the simplest case of the acute angle, it is of the utmost importance to be quite clear in regard to the direction in which the various lines are drawn. When this is made out, there will be no difficulty in dealing with angles of any magnitude.

Any angle such as XAP (Fig 9) traced by a line AP, initially coincident with a fixed line AX, and rotating about a fixed point A in the opposite direction to the hands of a clock (or anti-clockwise), may, as has been seen, be expressed numerically by the number of *degrees* or *radians* in the angle, or simply be indicated by a letter, such as A.

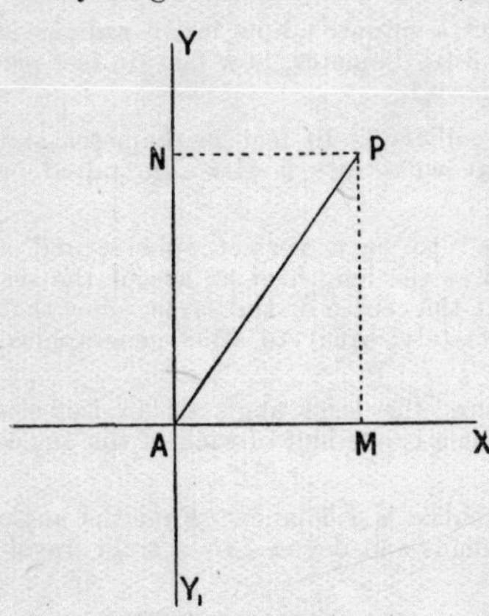

FIG. 9.—Projection of a line.

Such a line as AP carries with it a number of associated lines, or ratios, and although these are probably familiar to the reader, it may be useful to refer briefly to them here, and especially to indicate how, by means of such ratios, angles of any magnitude may be represented.

If from P, a line PM be drawn perpendicular to AX and meeting AX in M, and similarly PN is drawn perpendicular to AY, then AM is called the **projection** of AP on AX; and AN the projection on AY. The following ratios are at once obtained:

$$\frac{MP}{AP}=\sin A, \quad \frac{AM}{AP}=\cos A, \quad \frac{MP}{AM}=\tan A,$$

if $AP=r$, then the projection $AM=r\cos A$; or, **the projection of a line of length r on another to which it is inclined at an angle A is $r\cos A$.**

Since AP may denote the edge view of an area, the preceding statement may be applied to an area.

The angle $APM=NAP$ (Fig. 9);

$$\sin A=\frac{PM}{AP}=\frac{AN}{AP}.$$

But $$\frac{AN}{AP}=\cos NAP=\cos(90°-A)=\sin A.$$

Hence, the projection of a vector r on an axis AX to which it is inclined at an angle A, is $r\cos A$; and on the axis AY, or axis of y, is $r\sin A$. The two projections just referred to are called the **rectangular components of the vector AP.**

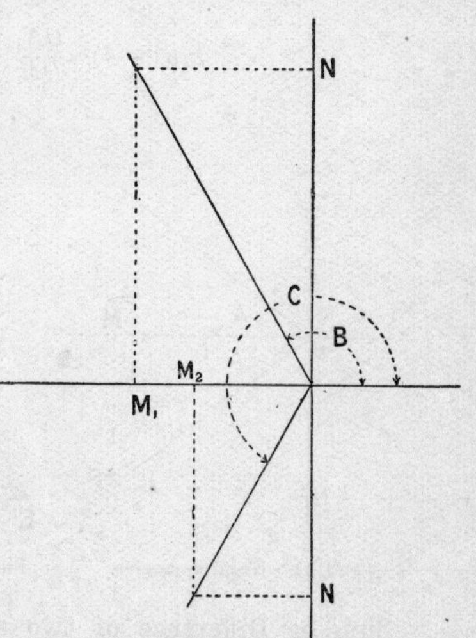

FIG. 10.—Rectangular components.

In the case of an obtuse angle B (Fig 10), the projection is in the negative direction, and the cosine is negative. The sine remains positive. Thus, if B is 120°,

$$\cos 120° = -\cos 60°;$$
$$\sin 120° = \sin 60°;$$
$$\tan 120° = -\tan 60°.$$

For an angle between 180° and 270°, say the angle C, the projections giving the sine and cosine of C are both negative, while the tangent is positive.

Finally, for an angle between 270° and 360°, it will easily be made out from its projections that the sine is negative, the cosine is positive, and the tangent is therefore negative.

Negative angles.—As already indicated, positive angles are angles formed by the rotation of a line in the opposite direction to the hands of a clock. It is, however, sometimes convenient to deal with angles formed by a line rotating in the opposite direction, or clockwise. Such angles are called **negative angles.** Thus, an angle of 340° could be obtained by the rotating line describing an angle of 340° in a positive direction, or an angle of 20° in a negative direction.

The ratios for such angles (Fig. 11) are found by the same rule as for positive angles.

$$\text{Thus } \cos(-A) = \frac{OM}{OP} \text{ and is positive,}$$

$$\sin(-A) = \frac{ON_1}{OP} \text{ and is negative,}$$

$$\tan(-A) = \frac{ON_1}{OM} \text{ and is negative.}$$

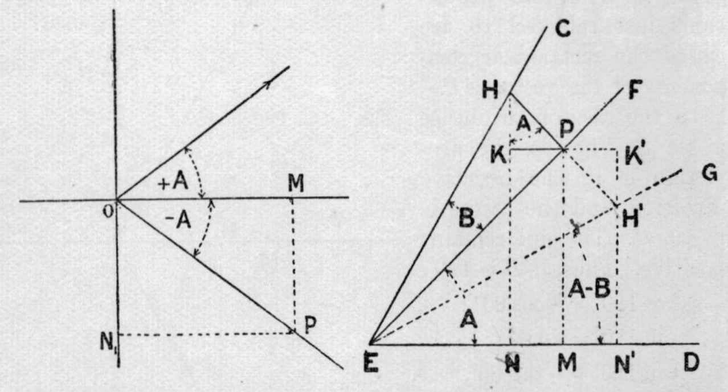

FIG. 11.—Negative angles.

FIG. 12.—Sum and difference of angles.

Sum or Difference of two angles.—Let DEF (Fig. 12) denote an angle A, and FEC an angle B. At any point P in EF, draw PH at right angles to EF, meeting EC in H.

Draw HN and PM perpendicular to DE, and PK parallel to DE.

As the angle KPE is equal to A, and KPH is complementary to KHP and to KPE, it follows that the angle KHP is equal to A.

We have
$$\sin(A+B)=\frac{NH}{EH}=\frac{NK+KH}{EH}=\frac{MP+KH}{EH}$$
$$=\frac{MP}{EP}\cdot\frac{EP}{EH}+\frac{KH}{HP}\cdot\frac{HP}{EH}$$
$$=\sin A\cos B+\cos A\sin B;$$

similarly,
$$\cos(A+B)=\frac{EN}{EH}=\frac{EM-NM}{EH}=\frac{EM-KP}{EH}$$
$$=\frac{EM}{EP}\cdot\frac{EP}{EH}-\frac{KP}{PH}\cdot\frac{PH}{EH}$$
$$=\cos A\cos B-\sin A\sin B.$$

If the angle FEG is equal to B, then the angle DEG is $A-B$.

$$\therefore\ \sin(A-B)=\frac{N'H'}{EH'}=\frac{N'K'-H'K'}{EH'}$$
$$=\frac{MP-H'K'}{EH'}$$
$$=\frac{MP}{EP}\cdot\frac{EP}{EH'}-\frac{HK'}{PH'}\cdot\frac{PH'}{EH'}$$
$$=\sin A\cos B-\cos A\sin B.$$

The result may also be obtained by writing $-B$ for B in the preceding.

In a similar manner,

$$\cos(A-B)=\cos A\cos B+\sin A\sin B.$$

So, too,
$$\tan(A+B)=\frac{\sin(A+B)}{\cos(A+B)}$$
$$=\frac{\sin A\cos B+\cos A\sin B}{\cos A\cos B-\sin A\sin B}.$$

By dividing numerator and denominator by $\cos A \cos B$, we obtain

$$\frac{\dfrac{\sin A \cos B}{\cos A \cos B}+\dfrac{\cos A \sin B}{\cos A \cos B}}{\dfrac{\cos A \cos B}{\cos A \cos B}-\dfrac{\sin A \sin B}{\cos A \cos B}}=\frac{\tan A+\tan B}{1-\tan A \tan B}.$$

The last result may also be obtained geometrically as follows :—

$$\tan(A+B)=\frac{NH}{EN}=\frac{NK+KH}{EM-NM}=\frac{MP+KH}{EM-KP}$$

Then, by dividing numerator and denominator by EM,

$$=\frac{\dfrac{MP}{EM}+\dfrac{KH}{EM}}{1-\dfrac{KP}{KH}\dfrac{KH}{EM}}.$$

But from the similar triangles PHK and PEM,

$$\frac{KH}{HP}=\frac{EM}{EP} \text{ or } \frac{KH}{EM}=\frac{HP}{EP};$$

$$\therefore \tan(A+B)=\frac{\tan A+\tan B}{1-\tan A \tan B}.$$

By proceeding in a similar manner, we find

$$\tan(A-B)=\frac{\tan A-\tan B}{1+\tan A \tan B}.$$

Tests of the above formulae should be worked out by the student, using simple ratios, and the results obtained checked by reference to Table VI.

Thus, if $A=45°$, $B=30°$, then $A+B=75°$.

$$\tan(A+B)=\frac{\tan 45°+\tan 30°}{1-\tan 45° \tan 30°},$$

$$=\frac{1+\dfrac{1}{\sqrt{3}}}{1-\dfrac{1}{\sqrt{3}}}=\frac{\sqrt{3}+1}{\sqrt{3}-1}=\frac{4+2\sqrt{3}}{2}=2+\sqrt{3}.$$

Thus, $\tan 75° = 3·7321$, and referring to Table VI. opposite $\tan 75°$ we find this value tabulated.

Again, $A - B = 15°$,

$$\therefore \tan(A-B) = \frac{\tan 45° - \tan 30°}{1 + \tan 45° \tan 30°},$$

$$= \frac{1 - \frac{1}{\sqrt{3}}}{1 + \frac{1}{\sqrt{3}}} = 2 - \sqrt{3};$$

$$\therefore \tan 15° = 0·2679,$$

and this is the value found in Table VI.

We have now found the following relations connecting simple with compound angles.

$$\sin(A+B) = \sin A \cos B + \cos A \sin B, \quad \text{.........(1)}$$

$$\sin(A-B) = \sin A \cos B - \cos A \sin B, \quad \text{.........(2)}$$

$$\cos(A+B) = \cos A \cos B - \sin A \sin B, \quad \text{.........(3)}$$

$$\cos(A-B) = \cos A \cos B + \sin A \sin B. \quad \text{.........(4)}$$

These results may be combined thus,

$$\mathbf{\sin(A \pm B) = \sin A \cos B \pm \cos A \sin B,}$$

$$\mathbf{\cos(A \pm B) = \cos A \cos B \mp \sin A \sin B,}$$

$$\mathbf{\tan(A \pm B) = \frac{\tan A \pm \tan B}{1 \mp \tan A \tan B}.} \quad \text{.........(5)}$$

By adding (1) and (2) we obtain,

$$\sin(A+B) + \sin(A-B) = 2 \sin A \cos B. \quad \text{.........(6)}$$

We may conveniently replace $A+B$ by P, and $A-B$ by Q.

$$\therefore A+B=P,$$

$$A-B=Q,$$

or,

$$2A = P+Q, \quad \therefore A = \frac{P+Q}{2},$$

$$2B = P-Q, \quad \therefore B = \frac{P-Q}{2}.$$

Hence, by the appropriate modification of formulae (1) to (4), we obtain

$$\sin P + \sin Q = 2 \sin \frac{P+Q}{2} \cos \frac{P-Q}{2},$$

$$\sin P - \sin Q = 2 \cos \frac{P+Q}{2} \sin \frac{P-Q}{2},$$

$$\cos P + \cos Q = 2 \cos \frac{P+Q}{2} \cos \frac{P-Q}{2},$$

$$\cos Q - \cos P = 2 \sin \frac{P+Q}{2} \sin \frac{P-Q}{2}.$$

These results may be expressed in words:

sum of two sines = twice the sine of half sum × cosine of half difference of the angles;

difference of two sines = twice the cosine of half sum × sine of half difference of the angles;

sum of two cosines = twice the cosine of half sum × cosine of half difference of the angles;

difference of two cosines = minus twice the sine of half sum × sine of half difference.

Formulae connecting an angle and the double angle.—If in the preceding formulae A is equal to B, then

$$\sin 2A = 2 \sin A \cos A,$$

$$\cos 2A = \cos^2 A - \sin^2 A$$

$$= 2\cos^2 A - 1 = 1 - 2\sin^2 A,$$

and $$\tan 2A = \frac{2 \tan A}{1 - \tan^2 A}.$$

We may replace $2A$ by A, if we also replace A by $\frac{A}{2}$;

$$\therefore \sin A = 2 \sin \frac{A}{2} \cos \frac{A}{2},$$

$$\cos A = 2\cos^2 \frac{A}{2} - 1 = 1 - 2\sin^2 \frac{A}{2}.$$

The preceding results may also be obtained in a more direct manner as follows:

Let NOP (Fig. 13) be the angle A, and NOQ be the angle B. Draw the line OR bisecting the angle POQ.

Then, angle NOR
$$=B+\tfrac{1}{2}(A-B)$$
$$=\tfrac{1}{2}(A+B).$$

Draw PRQ perpendicular to OR.

From points P, R, Q draw the perpendiculars PM, RL, and QN.

Then $ML=LN$.

Sum of the projections of OP and OQ on $OX=$ 2 (projection of OR), or

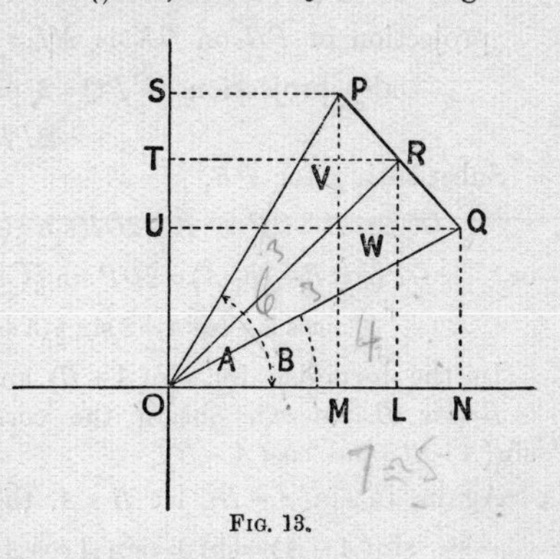

FIG. 13.

$$OP\cos A+OQ\cos B=2OR\cos\tfrac{1}{2}(A+B). \qquad (1)$$

Also $$OR=OP\cos POR=OP\cos\tfrac{1}{2}(A-B).$$

Substituting this value of OR in (1)

$$OP\cos A+OQ\cos B=2OP\cos\tfrac{1}{2}(A+B)\cos\tfrac{1}{2}(A-B).$$

As ORP and ORQ are equal and similar triangles, $OP=OQ$. Hence, dividing both sides by OP;

$$\therefore\ \mathbf{\cos A+\cos B=2\cos\tfrac{1}{2}(A+B)\cos\tfrac{1}{2}(A-B).}$$

By projecting on the axis OY we can obtain the sum of two sines.

Thus, the projections of OP and OQ on OY is twice the projection of OR on OY;

$$\therefore\ OS+OU=2\times OT,$$

or $$OP\sin A+OQ\sin B=2\times OR\sin\tfrac{1}{2}(A+B),$$

but $$OR=OP\cos POR=OP\cos\tfrac{1}{2}(A-B);$$

$$\therefore\ OP\sin A+OQ\sin B=2\times OP\sin\tfrac{1}{2}(A+B)\cos\tfrac{1}{2}(A-B);$$

$$\therefore\ \mathbf{\sin A+\sin B=2\sin\tfrac{1}{2}(A+B)\cos\tfrac{1}{2}(A-B).}$$

From Fig. 13 it is seen that;

Projection of OQ on OX=projection of OP on OX together with projection of PQ on OX;

$$\text{projection of } OQ \text{ on } OX = OQ\cos B;$$
$$\text{,, } \quad OP \text{ on } OX = OP\cos A;$$
$$PQ = 2PR \text{ and } PR = OP\sin\tfrac{1}{2}(A-B);$$
$$\text{projection of } PR \text{ on } OX \text{ is } ML = RV = PR\sin\tfrac{1}{2}(A+B);$$
$$\text{also projection of } PQ = 2 \text{ projection of } PR$$
$$= 2PR\sin\tfrac{1}{2}(A+B).$$

Substituting for PR,

$$OQ\cos B = OP\cos A + 2OP\sin\tfrac{1}{2}(A+B)\sin\tfrac{1}{2}(A-B),$$

or $$OP(\cos B - \cos A) = 2OP\sin\tfrac{1}{2}(A+B)\sin\tfrac{1}{2}(A-B);$$

$$\therefore \mathbf{\cos B - \cos A = 2\sin\tfrac{1}{2}(A+B)\sin\tfrac{1}{2}(A-B).}$$

In the formulae for $\sin(A+B)$ and $\cos(A+B)$, by writing $-B$ for B we can obtain the corresponding formulae for $\sin(A-B)$ and $\cos(A-B)$.

Again, in $\sin(A-B)$, let $B=A$, then

$$\sin(A-A) = \sin 0 = \sin A\cos A - \cos A\sin A = 0.$$

In $\cos(A-B)$ let $B=A$,

$$\cos(A-A) = \cos 0 = \cos A\cos A + \sin A\sin A$$
$$= \cos^2 A + \sin^2 A = 1.$$

Inverse Ratios.—A very convenient method of writing $\sin\theta = \frac{5}{7}$ is to write it in the form $\theta = \sin^{-1}\frac{5}{7}$ which is read as the angle, the sine of which is $\frac{5}{7}$; this is also sometimes written arc sin $\frac{5}{7}$. Thus, if $\sin\theta = 0{\cdot}4848$, this may be written either as $\theta = \sin^{-1} 0{\cdot}4848$ or $\text{arc}\sin 0{\cdot}4848$. Similarly $\tan y = 0{\cdot}364$ may be written $y = \tan^{-1} 0{\cdot}364$ or $y = \text{arc}\tan 0{\cdot}364$.

Numerical values.—We may use the formulae now obtained to find the numerical value of $\sin 15°$, $\cos 75°$, $\sin 75°$, $\cos 15°$, etc.

$$\sin 15° = \sin(45° - 30°) = \sin 45°\cos 30° - \cos 45°\sin 30°$$
$$= \frac{1}{\sqrt{2}} \times \frac{\sqrt{3}}{2} - \frac{1}{\sqrt{2}} \times \frac{1}{2}$$
$$= \frac{\sqrt{3}-1}{2\sqrt{2}}.$$

As $\cos 75° = \sin 15°$ this result is also the value of $\cos 75°$. Or, we may proceed to find the value of $\cos 75°$ as follows:

$$\cos 75° = \cos(45° + 30°) = \cos 45° \cos 30° - \sin 45° \sin 30°$$

$$= \frac{\sqrt{3} - 1}{2\sqrt{2}} \text{ as before.}$$

$$\cos 15° = \cos(45° - 30°) = \cos 45° \cos 30° + \sin 45° \sin 30°$$

$$= \frac{1}{\sqrt{2}} \times \frac{\sqrt{3}}{2} + \frac{1}{\sqrt{2}} \times \frac{1}{2}$$

$$= \frac{\sqrt{3} + 1}{2\sqrt{2}},$$

and hence $$\sin 75° = \cos 15° = \frac{\sqrt{3} + 1}{2\sqrt{2}}.$$

The two fractions $\frac{\sqrt{3} \pm 1}{2\sqrt{2}}$ may be simplified in the usual way.

Thus, $$\frac{\sqrt{3} - 1}{2\sqrt{2}} = \frac{\sqrt{2}(\sqrt{3} - 1)}{4} = \frac{\sqrt{6} - \sqrt{2}}{4}.$$

The values of $\sqrt{6}$ and $\sqrt{2}$ can be at once obtained by logarithms or from a table of square roots;

$$\therefore \quad \frac{\sqrt{6} - \sqrt{2}}{4} = \frac{1 \cdot 0352}{4} = 0 \cdot 2588.$$

Referring to Table IV., pp. 532-3, opposite $\sin 15°$ we find this value tabulated.

In a similar manner we have

$$\sin 75° = \frac{\sqrt{3} + 1}{2\sqrt{2}} = \frac{\sqrt{6} + \sqrt{2}}{4} = 0 \cdot 9659,$$

and this agrees with the value tabulated. Proceeding in this manner the student can make exercises for himself, taking various numerical data from Table IV., then obtain the sine, cosine, or tangent of the sum or difference of any two angles.

Thus, if $A = 20°$ and $B = 43°$.

Then $\sin(A + B) = \sin(20° + 43°)$

$$= \sin 20° \cos 43° + \cos 20° \sin 43°$$

$$= 0 \cdot 3420 \times 0 \cdot 7314 + 0 \cdot 9397 \times 0 \cdot 6820$$

$$= 0 \cdot 2501 + 0 \cdot 6409 = 0 \cdot 8910.$$

Referring to Table IV. we find that this value corresponds to $\sin 63°$;

$$\therefore \sin(20° + 43°) = \sin 63°.$$

From the formula

$$\sin(A+B) = \sin A \cos B + \cos A \sin B,$$

we have (when $A = B$)

$$\begin{aligned}\sin 2A &= \sin A \cos A + \cos A \sin A \\ &= 2 \sin A \cos A.\end{aligned}$$

Similarly, $\cos 2A = 2\cos^2 A - 1 = 1 - 2\sin^2 A.$

We can, in like manner, proceed to find the values of $\sin 3A$ and $\cos 3A$.

Thus,

$$\begin{aligned}\sin 3A &= \sin(2A + A) \\ &= \sin 2A \cos A + \cos 2A \sin A \\ &= (2 \sin A \cos A) \cos A + (1 - 2\sin^2 A) \sin A \\ &= 2 \sin A (1 - \sin^2 A) + \sin A - 2\sin^3 A \\ &= 3 \sin A - 4 \sin^3 A.\end{aligned}$$

Similarly,

$$\begin{aligned}\cos 3A &= \cos(2A + A) \\ &= \cos 2A \cos A - \sin 2A \sin A \\ &= (2\cos^2 A - 1) \cos A - (2 \sin A \cos A) \sin A \\ &= 2\cos^3 A - \cos A - (2 \sin^2 A \cos A) \\ &= 4\cos^3 A - 3 \cos A.\end{aligned}$$

By using the ratios for known angles such as 15°, 30°, 45°, tests of the formulae for the double angle can be obtained.

Ex. 1. Given $\sin 30° = \frac{1}{2}$; find $\sin 60°$, $\tan 60°$.

$$\begin{aligned}\sin 60° &= 2 \sin 30° \cos 30° \\ &= 2 \times \frac{1}{2} \times \frac{\sqrt{3}}{2} = \frac{\sqrt{3}}{2}.\end{aligned}$$

$$\tan 60° = \frac{2 \times \tan 30°}{1 - \tan^2 30°} = \frac{\frac{2}{\sqrt{3}}}{1 - \frac{1}{3}} = \sqrt{3}.$$

Ex. 2. Given $\sin A = \frac{3}{5}$; find $\sin 2A$, $\cos 2A$, and $\tan 2A$.

$$\cos A = \pm\sqrt{1 - \left(\frac{3}{5}\right)^2} = \pm\frac{4}{5}.$$

Taking the positive sign, then,

$$\sin 2A = 2 \times \frac{3}{5} \times \frac{4}{5} = \frac{24}{25}.$$

$$\cos 2A = 1 - 2\sin^2 A$$

$$= 1 - 2 \times \frac{9}{25} = \frac{7}{25}.$$

$$\tan 2A = \frac{\sin 2A}{\cos 2A} = \frac{24}{7}.$$

The preceding formulae for multiple angles may be used to verify various trigonometrical identities.

Ex. 3. Prove the following statements:

(i) $\frac{\sin A + \sin B}{\cos A + \cos B} = \tan \frac{1}{2}(A + B).$

(ii) $\frac{\sin\theta + \sin(\theta+\phi) + \sin(\theta+2\phi)}{\cos\theta + \cos(\theta+\phi) + \cos(\theta+2\phi)} = \tan(\theta+\phi).$

(i) $$\frac{\sin A + \sin B}{\cos A + \cos B} = \frac{2\sin\frac{A+B}{2}\cos\frac{A-B}{2}}{2\cos\frac{A+B}{2}\cos\frac{A-B}{2}}$$

$$= \tan\frac{1}{2}(A+B).$$

(ii) The given expression may be written

$$\frac{\{\sin(\theta+2\phi) + \sin\theta\} + \sin(\theta+\phi)}{\{\cos(\theta+2\phi) + \cos\theta\} + \cos(\theta+\phi)}$$

$$= \frac{2\sin(\theta+\phi)\cos\phi + \sin(\theta+\phi)}{2\cos(\theta+\phi)\cos\phi + \cos(\theta+\phi)}$$

$$= \frac{\sin(\theta+\phi)(1+2\cos\phi)}{\cos(\theta+\phi)(1+2\cos\phi)} = \tan(\theta+\phi).$$

It will be noticed that the sum or difference of any two sines, or cosines, can be obtained in the form of a product.

Ex. 4. $\sin 6A + \sin 4A = 2\sin\left(\frac{6A+4A}{2}\right)\cos\left(\frac{6A-4A}{2}\right)$

$$= 2\sin 5A\cos A.$$

Ex. 5. $\sin 5A - \sin 3A = 2\cos\left(\frac{5A+3A}{2}\right)\sin\left(\frac{5A-3A}{2}\right)$

$$= 2\cos 4A \sin A.$$

Similarly, $\cos 6A + \cos 4A = 2\cos 5A \cos A,$

and $\cos 3A - \cos 5A = 2\sin 4A \sin A.$

The preceding direct process must be clearly understood, then the converse process (*e.g.* given a product to obtain a sum or difference) will not present much difficulty.

Ex. 6. Express $2\sin 5A \cos A$ as the sum of two sines.

Let

$$2\sin 5A \cos A = \sin x + \sin y = 2\sin\tfrac{1}{2}(x+y)\cos\tfrac{1}{2}(x-y),$$

then $\tfrac{1}{2}(x+y) = 5A$ and $\tfrac{1}{2}(x-y) = A.$

or $x+y = 10A;$

also $x-y = 2A:$

$$\therefore x = 6A,$$

$$y = 4A.$$

Hence, we obtain

$$\sin 6A + \sin 4A = 2\sin 5A \cos A.$$

Ex. 7. To show that $a = b\cos C + c\cos B.$

Given $\frac{a}{\sin A} = \frac{b}{\sin B} = \frac{c}{\sin C} = k$ say, and $A+B+C = 180°.$

Hence, $a = k\sin A, \qquad (1)$

$b = k\sin B, \qquad (2)$

$c = k\sin C. \qquad (3)$

Multiplying (2) by $\cos C$ and (3) by $\cos B$ we have

$$b\cos C = k\sin B\cos C$$

$$c\cos B = k\sin C\cos B$$

adding

$$b\cos C + c\cos B = k(\sin B\cos C + \cos B\sin C)$$

$$= k\sin(B+C) = k\sin A,$$

because $\sin(B+C) = \sin A;$

$$\therefore b\cos C + c\cos B = k\sin A = a.$$

In like manner we can obtain

$$a\cos C + c\cos A = b$$

$$a\cos B + b\cos A = c.$$

EXERCISES. III.

1. Given $\cos A = \frac{3}{5}$, $\cos B = \frac{12}{13}$. Find $\sin(A+B)$ and $\cos(A+B)$.

2. The cosines of two angles of a triangle are $\frac{3}{5}$ and $\frac{12}{13}$ respectively; find the sine and cosine of the remaining angle.

3. Prove that $\cos 20° \cos 40° \cos 60° \cos 80° = \frac{1}{16}$.

4. Prove that $\cos 20° + \cos 100° + \cos 140° + \cos 90° = 0$.

5. From the relations $a = b\cos C + c\cos B$, $b = a\cos C + c\cos A$, $c = a\cos B + b\cos A$; show that $a^2 = b^2 + c^2 - 2bc\cos A$.

6. Write down the formulae for sine and cosine of the sum and difference of any two angles, and prove any one of them.

If $x = \sin^{-1} 0{\cdot}4848$ and $y = \tan^{-1} 0{\cdot}364$, find the value of $\cos(x+y)$.

7. If $\cos\alpha = \dfrac{3}{5}$ and $\cos\beta = \dfrac{4}{5}$, find the values of $\cos\dfrac{\alpha-\beta}{2}$ and $\cos^2\dfrac{\alpha+\beta}{2}$ the angles α and β being positive acute angles.

8. Prove the formula

$$\sin(A-B) = \sin A\cos B - \cos A\sin B,$$

and write down the corresponding formula for $\cos(A-B)$.

If $\sin A = 0{\cdot}8$ and $\sin B = 0{\cdot}6$, find the numerical values of $\sin(A-B)$ and $\cos(A-B)$.

9. Prove the formulae

(i) $\dfrac{\sin 3A - \sin A}{\cos 3A + \cos A} = \tan A$.

(ii) $4(\cos^3 10° + \sin^3 20°) = 3(\cos 10° + \sin 20°)$.

10. A and B are the angles of a triangle. Given $\cos A = \frac{3}{4}$, show how to construct the angle A, and find the sine, tangent, and cotangent of A.

11. Show that

(i) $\sin(A+B) + \sin(A-B) = 2\sin A\cos B$.

(ii) $\cos(A+B) + \cos(A-B) = 2\cos A\cos B$.

(iii) $\sin 70° = \sin 10° + \sin 50°$.

12. If $\sin(A+B) = 0{\cdot}8$, and $\sin(A-B) = 0{\cdot}6$, find the value of $\tan 2A$.

13. Prove that

(i) $\sin 80° = \sin 40° + \sin 20°$.

(ii) $\dfrac{\cos 2\alpha + \cos 12\alpha}{\cos 6\alpha + \cos 8\alpha} + \dfrac{\cos 7\alpha - \cos 3\alpha}{\cos\alpha - \cos 3\alpha} + 2\dfrac{\sin 4\alpha}{\sin 2\alpha} = 0$.

(iii) $\dfrac{\sin\alpha+\sin\beta+\sin(\alpha+\beta)}{\sin\alpha+\sin\beta-\sin(\alpha+\beta)}=\cot\dfrac{\alpha}{2}\cot\dfrac{\beta}{2}.$

(iv) $\tan 4\theta=\dfrac{4\tan\theta(1-\tan^2\theta)}{1-6\tan^2\theta+\tan^4\theta}.$

14. Prove that

$$\frac{\tan^3\theta}{1+\tan^2\theta}+\frac{\cot^3\theta}{1+\cot^2\theta}=\frac{1-2\sin^2\theta\cos^2\theta}{\sin\theta\cos\theta}.$$

Show that

15. $\cos\beta\cos(2\alpha+\beta)=\cos^2(\alpha+\beta)-\sin^2\alpha.$

16. $\dfrac{\cos x}{1-\tan x}+\dfrac{\sin x}{1-\cot x}=\sin x+\cos x.$

17. $2+4\cot^2 2A=\tan^2 A+\cot^2 A.$

18. $\tan(A+B)=\dfrac{\sin^2 A-\sin^2 B}{\sin A\cos A-\sin B\cos B}.$

19. (a) Find the numerical values of the sine and cosine of angles $22\frac{1}{2}^\circ$ and 75° respectively; (b) given $\sqrt{2}=1{\cdot}414$ and $\sqrt{6}=2{\cdot}449$, calculate the numerical value of $27+32\sin 195^\circ$.

20. Show that in a triangle ABC, $c=a\cos B+b\cos A$, when the angles A and B are acute, and when one of them (A) is obtuse. Given $a=6$, $b=6$, $c=10$, find $\cos C$, and from it find C.

21. Show that $\sin(A+B)=\sin A\cos B+\sin B\cos A$, using the relation $c=a\cos B+b\cos A$, having given $A+B+C=180^\circ$.

22. In the triangle ABC, if M is the middle point of BC, show that $4AM^2=b^2+c^2+2bc\cos A$.

If BC is 6 inches long, find the length of AM, when

$$\tan C=5\tan B=9\cot A.$$

23. Show how the formula for $\tan(A+B)$ in terms of $\tan A$, $\tan B$, may be deduced from the formulae for $\sin(A+B)$ and $\cos(A+B)$.

24. Prove that $\cos(135^\circ+A)+\sin(135^\circ-A)=0$.

If $\tan A=\dfrac{\sqrt{3}}{4-\sqrt{3}}$, and $\tan B=\dfrac{\sqrt{3}}{4+\sqrt{3}}$, prove that $\tan(A-B)=0{\cdot}375$.

25. Assuming that

$$\left.\begin{aligned}\sin(A+B)&=\sin A\cos B+\cos A\sin B\\ \cos(A+B)&=\cos A\cos B-\sin A\sin B\end{aligned}\right\},$$

find in terms of the ratios of A the values of $\sin 2A$, $\cos 2A$, $\tan 2A$, $\sin\dfrac{A}{2}$, $\cos\dfrac{A}{2}$, and $\tan\dfrac{A}{2}$.

26. If $\cos\theta=\dfrac{3}{5}$, determine the values of $\cos 2\theta$, $\sin 2\theta$, $\cos\dfrac{\theta}{2}$.

CHAPTER IV.

TRIGONOMETRICAL EQUATIONS.

Solution of Trigonometrical equations.—An equality of two expressions involving trigonometrical ratios, which is only true for certain definite values of an unknown angle, is called a **trigonometrical equation.** The process of solving such an equation is in many respects similar to that adopted in an algebraical equation. The object is to find a value, or values, of the unknown angles which will satisfy the given equation.

Having obtained such an equation in its simplest form, so that a trigonometrical ratio (such as sine, cosine, or tangent) is on the left of the equation and its numerical value on the right, the angle can be ascertained from Tables IV., V., VI. The process may be seen from the following examples.

Ex. 1. What are the values of A less than 360° which satisfy the equation $2\cos A+1=0$.

$$\text{Here } 2\cos A=-1;$$

$$\therefore \cos A=-\tfrac{1}{2},$$

$$\text{or } A=120^\circ \text{ or } 240^\circ.$$

The general value is given by

$$\theta \text{ rads.} =(2n+1)\pi \pm \frac{\pi}{3}$$

$$\text{or } A^\circ=(2n+1)\,180^\circ \pm 60^\circ.$$

Ex. 2. Find a series of values of A which satisfy the equation $\sin A=\frac{1}{3}$.

$$\sin A=\tfrac{1}{3}=0{\cdot}3333.$$

From Table IV. $0{\cdot}3333=\sin 19^\circ\ 28'$.

Hence one angle is $19^\circ\ 28'$.

All the angles whose sine is $\frac{1}{3}$ may be obtained from the formula $n\pi+(-1)^n\theta$.

Thus, when $n=0$, $A=19° 28'$,

„ $n=1$, $A=160° 32'$,

„ $n=2$, $A=379° 28'$,

„ $n=3$, $A=520° 32'$, etc., etc.

Ex. 3. Solve the equation $4\cos\theta+3\sin\theta=2{\cdot}5$.

Let R and α be two positive constants, such that,

$$4\cos\theta+3\sin\theta\equiv R\cos(\theta-\alpha). \quad\text{..................(i)}$$

Now $\cos(\theta-\alpha)=\cos\theta\cos\alpha+\sin\theta\sin\alpha$,

$$\therefore\ 4\cos\theta+3\sin\theta\equiv R\cos\theta\cos\alpha+R\sin\theta\sin\alpha.$$

This will only be true if the respective coefficients of $\cos\theta$ and $\sin\theta$ are the same on both sides,

$$\therefore\ R\cos\alpha=4 \quad\text{and}\quad R\sin\alpha=3. \quad\text{..................(ii)}$$

By squaring and adding to eliminate α,

$$R^2=16+9=25, \quad\text{or}\quad R=5.$$

Also from (ii), by division, to eliminate R,

$$\tan\alpha=0{\cdot}75,$$

so that $\alpha=36° 52'$ from Table VI, (p. 536).

Hence (i) becomes

$$4\cos\theta+3\sin\theta\equiv 5\cos(\theta-36° 52'),$$

and the given equation reduces to

$$\cos(\theta-36° 52')=0{\cdot}5;$$

$\therefore$ Smallest positive value of $(\theta-36° 52')=60°$;

$\therefore$ General value of $(\theta-36° 52')=n.\ 360°\pm60°$;

$$\therefore\ \theta=n.\ 360°\pm60°+36° 52'$$
$$=96° 52' \quad\text{or}\quad 336° 52',$$

if $0°<\theta<360°$.

The above is a general method for equations of the form

$$a\cos\theta+b\sin\theta=c.$$

Ex. 4. Solve the equation $\sqrt{3}\cot\theta=2\operatorname{cosec}\theta-1$.

Multiply out by $\sin\theta$, then,

$$\sqrt{3}\cos\theta=2-\sin\theta, \quad\text{or}\quad \sqrt{3}\cos\theta+\sin\theta=2,$$

i.e. $\cos(\theta-30°)=1$, by the method of *Ex.* 3;

$$\therefore\ \theta-30°=n.\ 360°\pm0°;$$

$$\therefore\ \theta=n.\ 360°+30°=30°, 390°, \ldots .$$

Ex. 5. Find all the positive values of θ not exceeding 180° which satisfy the following equations :

$$(a)\ 8\sin^3\theta - 7\sin\theta + \sqrt{3}\cos\theta = 0\,;$$
$$(b)\ \sin 3\theta + \cos 5\theta = \cos\theta.$$

(*a*) $8\sin^3\theta - 7\sin\theta + \sqrt{3}\cos\theta = 0.$

Since $4\sin^3\theta = 3\sin\theta - \sin 3\theta$ (p. 32) ;

$\therefore$ the given equation becomes

$$2\sin 3\theta + (\sin\theta - \sqrt{3}\cos\theta) = 0,$$

Let $\sin\theta - \sqrt{3}\cos\theta \equiv R\sin(\theta - \alpha)$, then, by the method of *Ex.* 3, $R = 2$, and $\alpha = 60°$;

$$\therefore\ \sin 3\theta + \sin(\theta - 60°) = 0$$

after dividing out by 2.

But $\sin 3\theta + \sin(\theta - 60°) = 2\sin\tfrac{1}{2}(3\theta + \theta - 60°)\cos\tfrac{1}{2}(3\theta - \theta + 60°)$

$$= 2\sin(2\theta - 30°)\cos(\theta + 30°)$$

from p. 28 ;

$$\therefore\ \sin(2\theta - 30°)\cos(\theta + 30°) = 0,$$

so that $\sin(2\theta - 30°) = 0$, or $\cos(\theta + 30°) = 0$;

$\therefore\ 2\theta - 30° = n.\,180° + (-1)^n\,0°$, or $\theta + 30° = n.\,360° \pm 90°$;

$\therefore\ \theta = n.\,90° + 15°$, or $\theta = n.\,360° \pm 90° - 30°$,

hence $\theta = 15°, 105°, \ldots,$ or $\theta = 60°, \ldots.$

Hence the values are 15°, 60°, 105°.

(*b*) $\sin 3\theta + \cos 5\theta = \cos\theta$;

$$\therefore\ \sin 3\theta - \cos\theta + \cos 5\theta = 0\,;$$
$$\therefore\ \sin 3\theta - 2\sin 3\theta\sin 2\theta = 0.$$

or $\sin 3\theta(1 - 2\sin 2\theta) = 0$;

$\therefore\ \sin 3\theta = 0$, or $\sin 2\theta = \tfrac{1}{2}$;

$\therefore\ 3\theta = n.\,180° + (-1)^n 0°$, or $2\theta = n.\,180° + (-1)^n 30°$;

$\therefore\ \theta = 0°, 60°, 120°, \ldots,$ or $\theta = 15°, 75°, \ldots.$

Hence, the values are 0°, 15°, 60°, 75°, 120°.

Elimination.—In trigonometrical, as in algebraical equations, from a sufficient number of distinct and independent equations one or more unknown terms may be eliminated. For this purpose the relations between trigonometrical ratios, such as $\sin^2\theta + \cos^2\theta = 1$, $\sec^2\theta = 1 + \tan^2\theta$, etc., are very important. The following examples will serve to illustrate some of the processes which may be adopted.

Ex. 1. Eliminate θ between the equations

$$a \sin \theta + b \cos \theta = m; \quad \text{.......................(i)}$$
$$a \cos \theta - b \sin \theta = n. \quad \text{..........................(ii)}$$

First eliminate $\cos \theta$ by multiplying (i) by a, (ii) by b, and subtracting, then,

$$(a^2 + b^2) \sin \theta = am - bn.$$

Similarly by eliminating $\sin \theta$ between (i) and (ii),

$$(a^2 + b^2) \cos \theta = bm + an.$$

Now, since $\sin^2\theta + \cos^2\theta = 1$,

$$\therefore \ (a^2 + b^2)^2 = (am - bn)^2 + (bm + an)^2$$
$$= a^2m^2 - 2abmn + b^2n^2 + b^2m^2 + 2abmn + a^2n^2$$
$$= (a^2 + b^2)(m^2 + n^2);$$
$$\therefore \ a^2 + b^2 = m^2 + n^2.$$

Ex. 2. Eliminate ϕ between the equations

$$x = 2b \cos \phi \cos 2\phi - b \cos \phi; \quad \text{.....................(i)}$$
$$y = 2b \cos \phi \sin 2\phi - b \sin \phi. \quad \text{......................(ii)}$$
$$x = 2b \cos \phi (2 \cos^2\phi - 1) - b \cos \phi$$
$$= b(4 \cos^3\phi - 3 \cos \phi) = b \cos 3\phi;$$
$$y = 4b \sin \phi \cos^2\phi - b \sin \phi$$
$$= 4b \sin \phi (1 - \sin^2\phi) - b \sin \phi$$
$$= b(3 \sin \phi - 4 \sin^3\phi) = b \sin 3\phi;$$

$\therefore$ By squaring and adding,

$$\therefore \ x^2 + y^2 = b^2.$$

Ex. 3. Given $p^2 + q^2 = \sin^2\theta$.

Show that $p^2 + \left(\dfrac{pq}{1 + \cos \theta}\right)^2 + \dfrac{(q^2 + \cos \theta + \cos^2\theta)^2}{(1 + \cos \theta)^2} = 1$;

$$i.e.\ (1 + \cos \theta)^2(p^2 - 1) + p^2q^2 + (q^2 + \cos \theta + \cos^2\theta)^2 = 0.$$

Let $k = 1 + \cos \theta$, then

$$q^2 + \cos \theta + \cos^2\theta = \sin^2\theta - p^2 + \cos \theta + \cos^2\theta = k - p^2, \quad \text{......(i)}$$

and

$$\cos^2\theta = 1 - \sin^2\theta = 1 - p^2 - q^2. \quad \text{.....................(ii)}$$

$\therefore$ Given expression becomes

$$k^2(p^2 - 1) + p^2q^2 + (k - p^2)^2 \quad \text{from (i)}$$
$$= k^2p^2 + p^2q^2 - 2kp^2 + p^4$$
$$= p^2(k - 1)^2 - p^2 + p^2q^2 + p^4$$
$$= p^2(1 - p^2 - q^2) - p^2 + p^2q^2 + p^4 = 0. \quad \text{from (ii)}$$

Ex. 4. If $p = 1 + \sin^2\theta$ and $q = 1 + \cos^2\theta$, show that

$$2(p^3 + q^3) + 9q^2 = 27(1 + \cos^4\theta).$$

By addition $p + q = 1 + \sin^2\theta + 1 + \cos^2\theta = 3$, and $$p=1+1-\cos^2\theta=2-\cos^2\theta.$$

But $$p^3+q^3=(p+q)^3-3pq(p+q)=27-9pq$$
$$=27-9(2-\cos^2\theta)(1+\cos^2\theta)$$
$$=9-9\cos^2\theta+9\cos^4\theta;$$
$$\therefore\ 2(p^3+q^3)+9q^2=18-18\cos^2\theta+18\cos^4\theta+9(1+\cos^2\theta)^2$$
$$=27(1+\cos^4\theta).$$

EXERCISES. IV.

Find values less than 180° which will satisfy each of the following equations:

1. $5\tan^2 x-\sec^2 x=11.$
2. $2\cos 4A\sin A=\sqrt{2}\cos 4A.$
3. $\cos^2 A+2\sin^2 A-\frac{5}{2}\sin A=0.$
4. $\tan A+3\cot A=4.$
5. $2\sin^2 A-5\cos A=4.$
6. $\sin 7x-\sin x=\sin 3x.$
7. (i) $17\sin\theta=15\sin 63°\,18'$; (ii) $\cos\theta=\cos 37°\,59'\cos 153°\,18'$; (iii) $\tan 2\theta=-\sin 52°\,2'$.
8. $2\sin^2 A-(1+\sqrt{3})\sin 2A+2\sqrt{3}\cos^2 A=0.$
9. $\sin^2 x+\cos^2 x=3\cos x.$
10. $\cos x+\sqrt{3}\sin x=1.$
11. $4\tan x=\sqrt{3}\sec^2 x.$
12. $\tan x\tan 2x=1.$
13. $\tan^2 x-(1+\sqrt{3})\tan x+\sqrt{3}=0.$
14. $\cos 3A+\cos 5A+\sqrt{2}(\cos A+\sin A)\cos A=0.$

15. What is the value of θ less than 360° which satisfies the equations; $5\sin\theta+3=0$, and $5\cos\theta+4=0$.

16. Find a value of θ which satisfies the equation
$$\sin\theta+2\cos\pi+4\tan\frac{\pi}{4}=1.$$

17. If $\cos 41°\,24'=\frac{3}{4}$ find an angle θ which satisfies the equation
$$4\cos 2\theta+3=0.$$

18. Find the value or values of θ less than 180° which satisfy the equations:
(i) $2\cos\theta+1=0$, (ii) $\tan\theta+1=0$, (iii) $13\sin\theta=3$.

19. Find the values of θ between 0° and 180° which satisfy the equation $$\tan^4\theta-4\tan^2\theta+3=0.$$

20. The sine of $26°\,24'=0{\cdot}4446$. Write down the values of $\cos 243°\,36'$ and $\sin 333°\,36'$.

21. Find the four least positive values of θ which satisfy the equation $$2\tan^2 2\theta = 4{\cdot}5.$$

22. Calculate the values of θ between 0° and 360° which satisfy the equation $$1{\cdot}7\tan^2\theta - 14{\cdot}4 = 0.$$

23. It is known that A and B are each less than 90°. If

$$A = \tan^{-1}\frac{5}{6} \text{ and } \tan 2B = \sqrt{2{\cdot}165}$$

find the values of A and B correct to the nearest minute.

24. Find the least positive value of B which satisfies the equation $$24\tan^2 B - 15 = 0.$$

25. Find a positive value of θ less than 180° which will satisfy the equation

$$\sin\theta = \frac{h}{2a}\left(\frac{w}{w - w'}\right)^{\frac{1}{2}}$$

$$\text{when } \frac{h}{a} = \frac{3121}{4183} \text{ and } \frac{w'}{w} = \frac{719}{1719}.$$

26. Solve the equation $$5\tan^2 x + \sec^2 x = 7.$$

27. Calculate the value of θ less than 180° which satisfies the equation $$\cos\theta = \cos 45^\circ \cos 139^\circ\, 6'.$$

28. Find all the positive values of θ less than 360° which satisfy the equation $$4\sin^2\theta - 2\sin\theta - 1 = 0.$$

29. Show that $8(\sin^2 42^\circ - \cos^2 78^\circ) = \sqrt{5} + 1.$

30. Find a value of θ which will satisfy each of the following equations: (*a*) $2\sin^2\theta = 3\cos\theta$, (*b*) $1 + 2\sin^2\theta = 2\cos^2\theta$.

31. Determine the least value of ϕ which will satisfy the equation $$\sqrt{3}\tan^2\phi + 1 = (1 + \sqrt{3})\tan\phi.$$

32. Find the two least positive values of A and B such that $\sin A + \sin B = \frac{1}{2}$ and $24\tan^2 2B - 15 = 0$.

33. Prove that $\cos 9^\circ - \sin 39^\circ - \cos 69^\circ + \sin 99^\circ = \sin\frac{9\pi}{20}$.

34. Find the least positive value of B which satisfies the equation $$24\tan^2 2B - 14{\cdot}97 = 0.$$

35. If $4\cot 2\theta = \cot^2\theta - \tan^2\theta$, prove that all possible values of θ are given by $$\theta = n\pi \pm \frac{\pi}{4}.$$

36. Find a value of θ which satisfies the equation $$5\cos\theta + 7\sin\theta = 5{\cdot}915.$$

37. Find the values of A which satisfy the equation $$\cos 8A - \cos 5A + \cos 3A = 1.$$

CHAPTER V.

INDICES. LOGARITHMS.

Indices.—The letter or number, placed near the top and to the right of a quantity, which expresses the power of a quantity, is called the index. Thus, in a^5, a^7, a^9, the numbers 5, 7, and 9, are called the **indices** of a, and are read as "a to the power five," "a to the power seven," etc. Similarly a^b denotes a to the power b. There are three index rules or laws.

First index rule.—To multiply together different powers of the same quantity, add the index of one to the index of the other. To divide different powers of the same quantity, subtract the index of the divisor from the index of the dividend.

$$\text{Thus, } a^3 \times a^2 = (a \times a \times a)\,(a \times a) = a^{3+2} = a^5.$$

Ex. 1. $a^3 \times a^5 = a^{3+5} = a^8$.

Ex. 2. $a^2 \times a^3 \times a^4 = a^{2+3+4} = a^9$.

These results may be expressed in a more general manner as follows:

$$a^m = (a \times a \times a \ldots \text{to } m \text{ factors})$$

and $$a^n = (a \times a \times a \ldots \text{to } n \text{ factors}),$$

$$\therefore\ a^m \times a^n = (a \times a \times a \ldots \text{to } m \text{ factors})\,(a \times a \times a \ldots \text{to } n \text{ factors})$$
$$= (a \times a \times a \ldots \text{to } m+n \text{ factors})$$
$$= a^{m+n}.$$

This most important rule has been shown to be true when $m=3$ and $n=5$. Other values of m and n should be assumed, and a further verification obtained.

Also $$\frac{a^5}{a^3} = \frac{a \times a \times a \times a \times a}{a \times a \times a} = a^{5-3} = a^2.$$

Similarly $$\frac{a^m}{a^n} = \frac{a \times a \times a \text{ to } m \text{ factors}}{a \times a \times a \text{ to } n \text{ factors}} = a^{m-n}.$$

In like manner, the product of any number of positive or negative integers m, n, p,... is given by

$$a^m \times a^n \times a^p \ldots = a^{m+n+p+\ldots}.$$

It is often found convenient to use both fractional and negative indices in addition to those described.

The meaning attached to fractional and negative indices is such that the previous rule holds for them also. When one fractional power of a quantity is multiplied by another fractional power, the fractional indices are added; and when one fractional power is divided by another the fractional index of the latter is subtracted from that of the former.

$$a^{\frac{1}{2}} \times a^{\frac{1}{2}} = a^{\frac{1}{2}+\frac{1}{2}} = a^1 = a,$$

$$a^{\frac{1}{3}} \times a^{\frac{1}{3}} = a^{\frac{2}{3}}\ ;\ a^{\frac{1}{3}} \times a^{\frac{1}{3}} \times a^{\frac{1}{3}} = a^{\frac{1}{3}+\frac{1}{3}+\frac{1}{3}} = a^1 = a.$$

Hence, the meaning to attach to $a^{\frac{1}{2}}$ is the square root of a; to $a^{\frac{2}{3}}$ is the cube root of a squared ; and to $a^{\frac{1}{3}}$ the cube root of a.

Thus, $\sqrt{a}$ can be written as $a^{\frac{1}{2}}$,

$\sqrt[3]{a}$ can be written as $a^{\frac{1}{3}}$.

Also,
$$\frac{1}{\sqrt{a}} = a^{-\frac{1}{2}},$$

and
$$\frac{1}{\sqrt[3]{a}} = a^{-\frac{1}{3}}.$$

Again,
$$\frac{a^{\frac{1}{3}}}{a^{\frac{1}{2}}} = a^{\frac{1}{3}} \times a^{-\frac{1}{2}} = a^{\frac{1}{3}-\frac{1}{2}} = a^{-\frac{1}{6}}.$$

Also,
$$\frac{a^{\frac{1}{3}}}{a^{\frac{1}{3}}} = a^{\frac{1}{3}-\frac{1}{3}} = a^0.$$

Similarly,
$$\frac{a^3}{a^3} = \frac{a \times a \times a}{a \times a \times a} = a^{3-3} = a^0.$$

Generally, since $a^m \times a^n = a^{m+n}$ is true for all values of m and n. If n be 0, then

$$a^m \times a^0 = a^{m+0} = a^m\ ;$$

$$\therefore\ a^0 = \frac{a^m}{a^m} = 1.$$

Again $\left(\frac{a}{b}\right)^n = \frac{a}{b} \cdot \frac{a}{b} \ldots$ to n factors $= \frac{a^n}{b^n}$.

If $a=1$, then $\left(\frac{1}{b}\right)^n = \frac{1}{b^n}$.

Similarly $a^m \times a^{-m} = \frac{a^m}{a^m} = a^0 = 1$.

Hence, any quantity except zero raised to the power 0 is equal to 1.

Second index rule.—To obtain a power of a power, multiply the two indices.

Ex. 1. To obtain the cube of a^2 we have

$$(a^2)^3 = (a \times a)(a \times a)(a \times a) = a^{2 \times 3} = a^6,$$

where the index is the product of the indices 2 and 3.

Ex. 2. Find the value of $(2{\cdot}15^2)^3$.

$$(2{\cdot}15^2)^3 = 2{\cdot}15^{2 \times 3}$$
$$= 2{\cdot}15^6 = 98{\cdot}72,$$

or, expressing this rule as a formula,

$$(a^m)^n = a^{mn},$$

$\therefore$ *a quantity a^m may be raised to a power n by using as an index the product mn.*

To show that $(a^m)^n = a^{mn}$.

$$(a^m)^n = a^m \times a^m \ldots \text{ to } n \text{ factors};$$

but each a^m contains a repeated m times, therefore

$$(a^m)^n = a \times a \ldots \text{ to } mn \text{ factors};$$
$$\therefore (a^m)^n = a^{mn}.$$

If we assume m to be 4 and n to be 2,

$$(a^m)^n = (a^4)^2 = (a \times a \times a \times a)(a \times a \times a \times a)$$
$$= a^{4 \times 2} = a^8.$$

Ex. 3. Which is greater $\sqrt{3}$ or $\sqrt[3]{5\frac{1}{5}}$?

Raise each of the given quantities to the sixth power;

$$\therefore (3^{\frac{1}{2}})^6 = 3^3 = 27$$

$$\{(5\tfrac{1}{5})^{\frac{1}{3}}\}^6 = (5\tfrac{1}{5})^2 = (\tfrac{26}{5})^2 = 27{\cdot}04.$$

Hence $\sqrt[3]{5\frac{1}{5}}$ is greater than $\sqrt{3}$.

Third index rule.—To raise a product to any power raise each factor to that power.

Ex. 1. $(abcd)^m = a^m \times b^m \times c^m \times d^m$.

Ex. 2. Let $a=1$, $b=2$, $c=3$, $d=4$, and $m=2$.

Then $$(abcd)^m = (1 \times 2 \times 3 \times 4)^2 = 1^2 \times 2^2 \times 3^2 \times 4^2$$
$$= 24^2 = 576.$$

In fractional indices, the index may be written either in a fractional form or the root symbol may be used. The general form is $a^{\frac{m}{n}}$. This may be written in the form $\sqrt[n]{a^m}$, which is read as *the nth root of a to the power m.*

Ex. 3. $2^{\frac{5}{3}} = \sqrt[3]{2^5} = \sqrt[3]{32} = 3 \cdot 174.$

Ex. 4. Find the values of $8^{\frac{2}{3}}$, $64^{-\frac{1}{2}}$, $4^{-\frac{3}{2}}$.

Here $$8^{\frac{2}{3}} = \sqrt[3]{8^2} = \sqrt[3]{64} = 4.$$
$$64^{-\frac{1}{2}} = \frac{1}{\sqrt{64}} = \frac{1}{8}.$$
$$4^{-\frac{3}{2}} = \frac{1}{4^{\frac{3}{2}}} = \frac{1}{\sqrt{64}} = \frac{1}{8}.$$

Ex. 5. Find the value of $64^{\frac{1}{2}} + 4^{1 \cdot 5} + 2^{2 \cdot 5} + 27^{\frac{1}{3}}$.

Here $$64^{\frac{1}{2}} = 8,\ 4^{1 \cdot 5} = 4^{\frac{3}{2}} = 64^{\frac{1}{2}} = 8,$$
$$2^{2 \cdot 5} = 2^{\frac{5}{2}} = 32^{\frac{1}{2}} = 5 \cdot 656,$$
$$27^{\frac{1}{3}} = 3.$$

Hence $$64^{\frac{1}{2}} + 4^{1 \cdot 5} + 2^{2 \cdot 5} + 27^{\frac{1}{3}} = 24 \cdot 656.$$

Ex. 6. Find, to two places of decimals, the value of $x^2 - 5x^{\frac{1}{2}} + x^{-2}$, when $x=5$.

Here $$x^2 - 5x^{\frac{1}{2}} + x^{-2} = 25 - 5\sqrt{5} + \frac{1}{5^2}$$
$$= 25 - \frac{10}{2} \times 2 \cdot 236 + 0 \cdot 04 = 13 \cdot 86.$$

Ex. 7. Solve the equations
$$\frac{27^x}{9^y} = 1. \ldots\ldots\ldots\ldots(\text{i}) \qquad \frac{81^y}{3^x} = 243. \ldots\ldots\ldots\ldots(\text{ii})$$

From (i) $\therefore\ 3^{3x} = 3^{2y}$; $\qquad \therefore\ 3x = 2y. \ldots\ldots\ldots\ldots(\text{iii})$

From (ii) $$3^{4y} = 3^x \times 3^5 = 3^{x+5};$$
$$\therefore\ 4y = x + 5. \ldots\ldots\ldots\ldots(\text{iv})$$

Combining (iii) and (iv) $3x = 12y - 15 = 2y$;
$$\therefore\ 10y = 15,\ y = \frac{3}{2},\ x = 1.$$

EXERCISES. V.

1. Simplify $\dfrac{\left(\frac{3}{2}\right)^{\frac{1}{2}}-\left(\frac{3}{2}\right)^{\frac{3}{2}}}{6^{\frac{1}{2}}+\left(\frac{2}{3}\right)^{\frac{1}{2}}}$.

2. Show that $x^{\frac{2}{3}}+y^{\frac{2}{3}}+4z^2$ is one of the factors of

$$x^2+y^2-4z^2\,(3x^{\frac{2}{3}}y^{\frac{2}{3}}-16z^4).$$

3. Multiply together $x^{\frac{1}{n}}-x^{-\frac{1}{n}}$ and $x^{\frac{2}{n}}+1+x^{-\frac{2}{n}}$.

4. Divide

$$x^{12}+\frac{1}{x^{12}}+6\left(x^8+\frac{1}{x^8}\right)+15\left(x^4+\frac{1}{x^4}\right)+20 \text{ by } x^6+\frac{1}{x^6}+3\left(x^2+\frac{1}{x^2}\right).$$

5. Express $\sqrt{x}+\sqrt[4]{(xy)}+\sqrt{y}$ with fractional indices and multiply it by $x^{-\frac{1}{2}}+x^{-\frac{1}{4}}y^{-\frac{1}{4}}+y^{-\frac{1}{2}}$.

Simplify

6. $\sqrt[6]{(a^3b\sqrt[5]{a^3bc})^5}$.

7. $[a^{-1}b\{a^{-4}b^3(a^3b\sqrt{ab})^2\}^{\frac{1}{3}}]^{-1}$.

8. Solve the equations

$$18y^x-y^{2x}=81\,;$$
$$3^x=y^2.$$

9. (*a*) Assuming that $a^m\times a^n=a^{m+n}$ is true for all values of m and n, find the meaning of the symbols a^{-4} and $a^{-\frac{1}{4}}$.

(*b*) Simplify $(x^{-\frac{1}{3}}y^{-\frac{1}{4}})^{-6}$.

(*c*) Find the product of

$$x^{-\frac{1}{6}}y^{-\frac{2}{6}} \text{ and } \frac{x^{\frac{1}{2}}y^{\frac{2}{3}}}{\sqrt[6]{x^2y^3}}\div x^{\frac{1}{6}}y^{-\frac{1}{6}}.$$

10. Divide $x-256y^3$ by $4x^{-\frac{1}{4}}+y^{-\frac{3}{4}}$.

11. Multiply $a+b^{\frac{2}{3}}+c^{\frac{1}{2}}-b^{\frac{1}{3}}c^{\frac{1}{4}}-c^{\frac{1}{4}}a^{\frac{1}{2}}-a^{\frac{1}{2}}b^{\frac{1}{3}}$ by $a^{\frac{1}{2}}+b^{\frac{1}{3}}+c^{\frac{1}{4}}$.

12. (i) Prove that

$$\frac{x^{\frac{3}{2}}+y^{\frac{3}{2}}+xy(x^{-\frac{1}{2}}+y^{-\frac{1}{2}})}{x^{\frac{3}{2}}-y^{\frac{3}{2}}-xy(x^{-\frac{1}{2}}-y^{-\frac{1}{2}})}=\frac{x+y}{x-y}.$$

(ii) Find the value of

$$x^3+2y^3+2z^3+6xyz, \text{ when } x=y+z=\sqrt[3]{4}.$$

13. Find the value of $1+2^{-2}+2^{-3}\times 5^{-1}+2^{-7}+2^{-8}$.

Simplify the following expressions:

14. $\left(\dfrac{a^{\frac{3}{4}}b^{\frac{7}{4}}}{a^{\frac{2}{3}}b^{\frac{1}{2}}}\right)^{-\frac{1}{5}} \times \{\sqrt[3]{(a^{-2})}\,\sqrt[6]{(b^{-1})}\}^2.$ **15.** $\{ab^2(ab^3)^{\frac{1}{2}}(a^2b^3)^{\frac{1}{6}}\}^{\frac{1}{2}}.$

16. (i) $\dfrac{pq^{-1}+p^{-1}q+2}{p^{\frac{1}{3}}q^{-\frac{1}{3}}+p^{-\frac{1}{3}}q^{\frac{1}{3}}-1}.$ (ii) $\sqrt{(x^{-\frac{5}{3}}y^3z^{-\frac{2}{3}})} \div \sqrt[3]{(x^{\frac{1}{2}}y^4z^{-1})}.$

17. $(x^{-\frac{1}{3}}y^{-\frac{1}{4}})^{-6} \times y^{-\frac{3}{2}}.$

18. $(a^{\frac{2}{3}} - a^{\frac{1}{3}}b^{\frac{3}{4}} + b^{\frac{3}{2}})(a^{\frac{2}{3}} + a^{\frac{1}{3}}b^{\frac{3}{4}} + b^{\frac{3}{2}})$, and find its value when $a=3$, $b=4$.

19. Find the value of $\sqrt{\dfrac{5}{x}} - \sqrt[3]{-x}$, when $x=0{\cdot}008$.

Logarithms.—Logarithms of numbers consist of an integral part which may be positive, negative, or zero, called the index or **characteristic**, and a decimal part called the **mantissa.** Referring to Table II. the reader will find that opposite each of the numbers from 10 to 99 four figures are placed; these are *positive numbers* and each set of four is called a *mantissa.*

The *characteristic* has to be supplied when writing down the logarithm of any given number. Logarithmic tables have been calculated for all numbers from 1 to 100,000 giving seven or more figures in the mantissa, but for all practical purposes the numbers in such a table as that referred to, and known as *four-figure logarithms,* are very convenient.

By means of the numbers 10 to 99 in the left hand column with (a) those along the top of the table, and (b) those in the difference column on the right, the logarithm of any number consisting of four significant figures can be written down.*

* The numerical values of logarithms increase much more rapidly and the numbers in the difference columns are greater in the earlier part of Table II. than elsewhere, and there is more liability to error here than at any other place. Several methods may be devised to make such a table uniformly accurate, one is to calculate two or more columns of differences for each of the ten horizontal rows (10-20). Another method is as follows:

Let N denote a given number, write down $\log\dfrac{N}{2}$, and finally add $\log 2$.

Ex. Find $\log 11{\cdot}78$.

Using seven-figure logarithms, $\log 11{\cdot}78 = 1{\cdot}0711453$.
From Table II., $\log 11{\cdot}78 = 1{\cdot}0712$, the last figure is in error.
Using the rule: $\dfrac{11{\cdot}78}{2} = 5{\cdot}89$; $\therefore \log 5{\cdot}89 + \log 2 = 1{\cdot}0711$.

In logarithms, all numbers are expressed as the powers of some number called the **base.**

The logarithm of a number to a given base is the index showing the power to which that base must be raised to give the number.

Let N denote any number, and a the given base, then if by raising a to some power x we can obtain N,

$$N=a^x \qquad \text{.......................................(1)}$$

Thus, if the base be 2, then $2^3=8$; or, 3 is the logarithm of 8 to the base 2. This can be expressed as $\log_2 8=3$.

Also, as $64=2^6=4^3=8^2$.

Hence 6 is the log of 64 to the base 2,

3 " " " 4,

2 " " " 8.

These facts may, as just indicated, be expressed thus:

$$\log_2 64=6, \quad \log_4 64=3, \quad \log_8 64=2,$$

using in each case the abbreviation log for logarithm.

Characteristic and Mantissa.—As will be seen from the preceding paragraphs any number can be used as base; but the system of logarithms in which the base is 10 (known as common logarithms) is that generally used. It is then only necessary to print in a table the decimal part, or mantissa; the characteristic can be written by inspection.

As the base is 10, Eq. (1) above may be written

$$N=10^x;$$

$$\therefore \log_{10} N=x.$$

Substituting powers of 10 for N,

$$1=10^0; \quad \therefore \log 1=0.$$

Also $10=10^1; \quad \therefore \log 10=1.$

Again $100=10^2; \quad \therefore \log 100=2.$

Again as 0·1, 0·01, and 0·001 can be written in the form $\frac{1}{10}$ or 10^{-1}, $\frac{1}{100}$ or 10^{-2}, $\frac{1}{1000}$ or 10^{-3} respectively,

$$\therefore \log 0{\cdot}1=\log 10^{-1}=-1,$$

$$\log 0{\cdot}01=\log 10^{-2}=-2,$$

and $\log 0{\cdot}001=\log 10^{-3}=-3.$

The **mantissa** in the tables is always a positive number. In order, therefore, to preserve its character, and to indicate that the negative sign attaches to the characteristic alone, we write the negative sign over the characteristic. Thus, log 0·1 is not written -1 but as $\bar{1}$, and $\log 0{\cdot}01 = \bar{2}$. In the preceding cases only the characteristic has been inserted, for each mantissa consists of a series of ciphers.

$$\log 1 = 0{\cdot}0000$$
$$\log 10 = 1{\cdot}0000$$
$$\log 100 = 2{\cdot}0000$$
$$\log 0{\cdot}01 = \bar{2}{\cdot}0000, \text{ etc.}$$

As the logarithm of 1 is 0, and log 10 is 1, it is clear that the logarithms of all numbers between 1 and 10 will consist only of a series of figures after the decimal point. Thus, $\log 3 = 0{\cdot}4771$ indicates that if we raise 10 to the power 0·4771 we obtain 3, or $10^{0\cdot4771} = 3$.

In a similar manner, 300 might be written as $10^2 \times 10^{0\cdot4771}$;

$$\therefore\ 300 = 10^{2\cdot4771}.$$

Thus, we write $\log 300 = 2{\cdot}4771.$

Similarly, $0{\cdot}0003 = \frac{3}{10000} = 3 \times 10^{-4}$;

$$\therefore\ 0{\cdot}0003 = 10^{\bar{4}\cdot4771},$$

or $\log 0{\cdot}0003 = \bar{4}{\cdot}4771.$

The most convenient rule by which the characteristic may be found is as follows. **The characteristic of any number greater than unity is positive, and is less by one than the number of figures to the left of the decimal point. The characteristic of a number less than unity is negative, and is greater by one than the number of zeros which follow the decimal point.**

Ex. Write down log 30 and log 0·00003.

Here $\log 30 = 1{\cdot}4771,$

and $\log 0{\cdot}00003 = \bar{5}{\cdot}4771.$

Multiplication.—Add the logarithms of the multiplier and multiplicand together; the sum is the logarithm of their product. The number corresponding to this logarithm, called the antilog, is the product required.

Let a and b denote two numbers.

Let $\log a = x$ and $\log b = y$;

$$\therefore \ a = 10^x, \ b = 10^y,$$

$$a \times b = 10^{x+y},$$

$$\text{or} \quad \log_{10} ab = x + y = \log a + \log b.$$

Ex. 1. Multiply $0{\cdot}03056 \times 0{\cdot}4105$.

From Table II., $\log 305 = 4843$

Diff. col. for 6 $\quad 9$

$\therefore \log 0{\cdot}03056 = \bar{2}{\cdot}4852$

Similarly, $\log 0{\cdot}4105 = \bar{1}{\cdot}6133$

log of product $= \bar{2}{\cdot}0985$

From Table III., antilog $0{\cdot}098 = 1253$

Diff. col. for 5, $\quad 1$

$\therefore$ antilog $\cdot 0985 = 1254$

The numerical part of the product is 1254, and the characteristic is $\bar{2}$.

Hence $\quad 0{\cdot}03056 \times 0{\cdot}4105 = 0{\cdot}01254$.

Division.—Subtract the logarithm of the divisor from the logarithm of the dividend and the result is the logarithm of the quotient of the two numbers. The number corresponding to this logarithm is the quotient required.

Let a and b be the two numbers.

Let $\quad \log a = x$ and $\log b = y$;

$$\therefore \ a = 10^x \quad b = 10^y.$$

Hence $$\frac{a}{b} = \frac{10^x}{10^y} = 10^{x-y},$$

$$\text{or} \ \log \frac{a}{b} = x - y = \log a - \log b.$$

Ex. 1. Divide 30·56 by 4·105.

Let z denote the value required;

$$\log z = \log 30{\cdot}56 - \log 4{\cdot}105$$
$$= 1{\cdot}4852 - 0{\cdot}6133 = 0{\cdot}8719;$$
$$\therefore \ z = 7{\cdot}446.$$

Hence $\quad 30{\cdot}56 \div 4{\cdot}105 = 7{\cdot}446$.

Involution.—**To obtain the power of a number, multiply the logarithm of the number by the index representing the power required; the product is the logarithm of the number required.**

Let $\log a = x.$

Then $a = 10^x.$

And $a^n = (10^x)^n = 10^{xn};$

$$\therefore \log_{10} a^n = nx = n \log a.$$

Ex. 1. Find the value of $4{\cdot}105^{1{\cdot}23}$.

Let z denote the value required.

$$\log z = 1{\cdot}23 \log 4{\cdot}105 = 1{\cdot}23 \times 0{\cdot}6133$$
$$= 0{\cdot}7544 = \log 5{\cdot}680;$$
$$\therefore z = 5{\cdot}680.$$

It should be carefully noticed that the logarithm of a decimal number consists of a negative characteristic and a positive mantissa.

Evolution.—**To obtain the root of a number, divide the logarithm of the number by the number which indicates the root.**

Ex. 1. Find the cube root of 32·4.

Let x denote the value;

$$\therefore x = (32{\cdot}4)^{\frac{1}{3}};$$
$$\log x = \tfrac{1}{3} \log 32{\cdot}4 = \tfrac{1}{3} \times 1{\cdot}5105 = 0{\cdot}5035 = \log 3{\cdot}188;$$
$$\therefore x = 3{\cdot}188.$$

No difficulty will be experienced when, as in the preceding example, the characteristic and mantissa are both positive. But, as already indicated, although the characteristic may be negative, the mantissa remains positive, and a little alteration in form is necessary, in order to make such a logarithm exactly divisible by the number.

Ex. 2. Find the fifth root of 0·0324.

Assume $x = (0{\cdot}0324)^{\frac{1}{5}};$

$$\log 0{\cdot}0324 = \bar{2}{\cdot}5105.$$

To make this exactly divisible we increase the characteristic to $\bar{5}$, and make the necessary correction. Thus,

$$\bar{2}{\cdot}5105 = \bar{5} + 3{\cdot}5105.$$

Hence $\log x = \tfrac{1}{5}(\bar{5} + 3{\cdot}5105) = \bar{1}{\cdot}7021 = \log 0{\cdot}5036;$

$$\therefore x = 0{\cdot}5036.$$

The alteration may be made as suggested; but, after a little practice, the steps indicated are most easily carried out mentally. To extract say the 1·065th root of 0·0324, it is advisable to make the mantissa of the logarithm negative in order to carry out the division indicated and finally to make the mantissa positive before referring to the table of antilogs for the result.

When it is required to raise a number less than unity to a negative power, it will usually be found most convenient to make the mantissa of the logarithm negative before proceeding to multiply.

Ex. 3. Calculate the value of $0{\cdot}04105^{-2{\cdot}3}$.

Log $0{\cdot}04105 = \bar{2}{\cdot}6133$, in which the characteristic is negative, but the mantissa is positive. When both are made negative

$$\bar{2}{\cdot}6133 = -2 + 0{\cdot}6133 = -1{\cdot}3867;$$

Let x denote the value required.

$$\therefore \log x = -2{\cdot}3 \times (-1{\cdot}3867) = 3{\cdot}1894 = \log 1546;$$

$$\therefore x = 1546.$$

Ex. 4. Compute the value of $(5)^a + (3)^b + (0{\cdot}042)^c$, where $a = 2{\cdot}43$, $b = -0{\cdot}246$ and $c = 0{\cdot}476$.

Let x denote the value required. Then substitute the given values,

$$x = 5^{2{\cdot}43} + 3^{-0{\cdot}246} + 0{\cdot}042^{0{\cdot}476}.$$

As the three terms are connected by the signs of addition it is necessary to evaluate each separately and afterwards to add.

Thus, $\log 5^{2{\cdot}43} = 2{\cdot}43 \log 5 = 0{\cdot}6990 \times 2{\cdot}43 = 1{\cdot}6986 = \log 49{\cdot}96;$

$$\therefore 5^{2{\cdot}43} = 49{\cdot}96$$

$$\log 3^{-0{\cdot}246} = -0{\cdot}246 \log 3 = 0{\cdot}4771 \times (-0{\cdot}246)$$

$$= -0{\cdot}1174 = \bar{1}{\cdot}8826 = \log 0{\cdot}7632;$$

$$\therefore 3^{-0{\cdot}246} = 0{\cdot}7632.$$

Again, $\log 0{\cdot}042 = \bar{2}{\cdot}6232 = -1{\cdot}3768.$

Hence, $\log 0{\cdot}042^{0{\cdot}476} = -1{\cdot}3768 \times 0{\cdot}476 = -0{\cdot}6554$

$$= \bar{1}{\cdot}3446 = \log 0{\cdot}2211;$$

$$\therefore 0{\cdot}042^{0{\cdot}476} = 0{\cdot}2211.$$

Adding all the separate terms

$$x = 49{\cdot}96 + 0{\cdot}7632 + 0{\cdot}2211 = 50{\cdot}94.$$

Napierian logarithms.—The system of logarithms employed by Napier, the discoverer of logarithms, and called the **Napierian** or **Hyperbolic system**, is used in all theoretical investigations and very largely in practical calculations. The base of this system is the number which is the sum of the series

$$1+1+\tfrac{1}{2}+\frac{1}{2\times 3}+\frac{1}{2\times 3\times 4}+\ldots \text{ (p. 289)};$$

this sum to five figures is 2·7183. Usually the letter e is used to denote this number, as for example log 2 to base 10 would be written $\log_{10}2$ or more simply as $\log 2$, but the hyperbolic logarithm of 2 is written as $\log_e 2$.

Transformation of logarithms.—A system of logarithms calculated to a base a may be transformed into another system in which the base is b.

Let N be a number. Its logarithms in the first system we may denote by x and in the second system by y.

Then $$N=a^x=b^y \text{ or } b=a^{\frac{x}{y}};$$

$$\therefore\ \frac{x}{y}=\log_a b \text{ and } \frac{y}{x}=\frac{1}{\log_a b}=\log_b a.$$

Hence, if the logarithm of any number in the system in which the base is a be multiplied by $\frac{1}{\log_a b}$, we obtain the logarithm of the number in the system in which the base is b.

The common logarithms have been calculated from the Napierian logarithms. Let l and L be the logarithms of the same number in the common and Napierian systems respectively, then

$$l=\frac{1}{\log_e 10}L,$$

$$\log_e 10=2{\cdot}30258509\ldots\ldots=2{\cdot}3026 \text{ approx.},$$

and $$\frac{1}{2{\cdot}30258509}=0{\cdot}43429448\ldots\ldots=0{\cdot}4343 \text{ approx.}$$

Hence, the common logarithm of a number may be obtained by multiplying the Napierian logarithm of the same number by 0·4343....

To convert common into Napierian logarithms multiply by 2·3026 instead of the more accurate number 2·30258509.

The preceding rules will be best understood by a careful study of a few examples.

Ex. 1. Log 10 to base e is 2·3026.

$$\therefore \log_e 10 = 2{\cdot}3026,$$

or

$$e^{2\cdot3026} = 10.$$

From this relation any number which is a power of 10 may be expressed as a power of e. Thus, $\log 19{\cdot}5 = 1{\cdot}29$.

$$\therefore 19{\cdot}5 = 10^{1\cdot29} = e^{2\cdot3026\times1\cdot29} = e^{2\cdot9703},$$

or

$$\log_{10} 19{\cdot}5 = 1{\cdot}29, \ \log_e 19{\cdot}5 = 2{\cdot}9703.$$

Ex. 2. Find $\log_e 3$ and $\log_e 8{\cdot}43$.

$$\therefore \log_e 3 = 0{\cdot}4771 \times 2{\cdot}3026 = 1{\cdot}0986,$$

$$\log_{10} 8{\cdot}43 = 0{\cdot}9258;$$

$$\therefore \log_e 8{\cdot}43 = 0{\cdot}9258 \times 2{\cdot}3026 = 2{\cdot}1317.$$

Ex. 3. Find log 13 to base 20.

Here $\log 13 = 1{\cdot}1139$, also $\log 20 = 1{\cdot}3010$.

$$\therefore \log_{20} 13 = \frac{1{\cdot}1139}{1{\cdot}3010} = 0{\cdot}8562.$$

Methods of computation.—Careful attention should be given to the *method* adopted in carrying out all computations. These should in all cases be so arranged that any results obtained can be checked from time to time as the work proceeds. Finally, where possible, any convenient rough check should be used to make sure that the result obtained is a reasonable one. In working with four-figure logarithms, the results obtained are only approximate; they give results true to three significant figures, the fourth figure although not necessarily accurate is usually not far wrong. When greater accuracy is required, five, six, or seven-figure logarithms should be used.

Ex. 4. Find the value of

$$3{\cdot}142^{1\cdot3} \times 0{\cdot}063 \times 10{\cdot}17^{-0\cdot09}.$$

Denoting the value required by x we have

$$x = 3{\cdot}142^{1\cdot3} \times 0{\cdot}063 \times 10{\cdot}17^{-0\cdot09};$$

$$\begin{aligned} \therefore \log x &= 1{\cdot}3 \log 3{\cdot}142 + \log 0{\cdot}063 - 0{\cdot}09 \log 10{\cdot}17 \\ &= 1{\cdot}3 \times 0{\cdot}4972 + \bar{2}{\cdot}7993 - 0{\cdot}09 \times 1{\cdot}0072 \\ &= 0{\cdot}64636 + \bar{2}{\cdot}7993 - 0{\cdot}09065 \\ &= \bar{1}{\cdot}3550 = \log 0{\cdot}2265; \end{aligned}$$

$$\therefore x = 0{\cdot}2265.$$

Ex. 5. The relation between Q, the quantity of water in cubic feet per second passing over a triangular gauge notch, and H, the height, in feet, of the surface of the water above the bottom of the notch, is given by $Q \propto H^{\frac{5}{2}}$.

When H is 1, Q is found to be 2·634. What is the value of Q when H is 4?

If the area of the reservoir supplying the notch is 80000 square feet, find the time in which a volume of water 80000 square feet in area and 3 inches in depth will be drawn off when H remains constant and equal to 4 ft.

The relation between Q and H may be written $Q = kH^{\frac{5}{2}}$, where k is a constant.

$$\text{When } H \text{ is } 1,\ Q = k \times 1;\ \therefore\ k = 2{\cdot}634.$$

$$\text{When } H \text{ is } 4,\ Q = 2{\cdot}634 \times 4^{\frac{5}{2}},$$

$$\text{or } \log Q = \log 2{\cdot}634 + \tfrac{5}{2}\log 4 = 1{\cdot}9259;$$

$$\therefore\ Q = 84{\cdot}31 \text{ cub. ft.}$$

$$\text{Volume of water} = \frac{80000 \times 3}{12} = 20000 \text{ cub. ft.}$$

$$\text{Time required} = \frac{20000}{84{\cdot}31 \times 60} = 3{\cdot}953 \text{ minutes.}$$

Ex. 6. If pv^k is constant; and if $p=1$ when $v=1$, find for what value of v, p is 0·2. Do this for the following values of k, 0·8, 0·9, 1·0, 1·1.

Let c denote the constant, then $pv^k = c$.

Substituting the simultaneous values $p=1$, $v=1$;

$$\therefore\ 1^k = c;\ \therefore\ c = 1.$$

Thus when $p = 0{\cdot}2$ we have

$$0{\cdot}2v^k = 1;$$

$$\therefore\ v = 5^{\frac{1}{k}};$$

$$\therefore\ v = 5^{\frac{10}{8}} = 5^{1{\cdot}25}.$$

$$\log v = 1{\cdot}25 \log 5 = 0{\cdot}8738;$$

$$\therefore\ v = 7{\cdot}476.$$

Similarly, when k has the values 0·9, 1·0, and 1·1, corresponding values of v are found to be 5·98, 5, and 4·32 respectively.

Ex. 7. In steam vessels of the same kind it is found that the relation between H, the horse power; V, the speed in knots; and D, the displacement in tons, is given by $H \propto V^3 D^{\frac{2}{3}}$.

Given $H = 35640$, $V = 23$, and $D = 23000$,

find the probable numerical value of H when V is 24.

The relation may be written in the form

$$H=kV^3D^{\frac{2}{3}}, \text{ where } k \text{ is a constant.}$$

To find the value of k, substitute the given quantities

$$35640=k\times(23)^3\times(23000)^{\frac{2}{3}};$$

$$\therefore\ k=\frac{35640}{23^3\times 23000^{\frac{2}{3}}}.$$

To find H when V is 24 we have

$$\begin{aligned}H&=k\times 24^3\times(23000)^{\frac{2}{3}}\\&=35640\times\left(\frac{24}{23}\right)^3\times\left(\frac{23000}{23000}\right)^{\frac{2}{3}}\\&=35640\times\left(\frac{24}{23}\right)^3.\end{aligned}$$

$$\begin{aligned}\log H&=\log 35640+3(\log 24-\log 23)\\&=4{\cdot}5519+0{\cdot}0555=4{\cdot}6074=\log 40500;\\&\therefore\ H=40500.\end{aligned}$$

Ex. 8. In any class of turbine, if P is the power of the water, n the rate of revolution, H the height of the fall, and R the average radius at the place where water enters the wheel, then it is known that for all sizes

$$n\propto H^{1{\cdot}25}P^{-0{\cdot}5}, \quad\ldots\ldots\ldots\ldots\ldots\text{(i)}$$

$$R\propto P^{0{\cdot}5}H^{-0{\cdot}75}. \quad\ldots\ldots\ldots\ldots\ldots\text{(ii)}$$

In the list of a particular maker a turbine for a fall of 6 feet, 100 horse-power, 50 revolutions per minute, is 2·51 feet radius. By means of this n and R may be calculated for all the other turbines of the list. Find n and R for a fall of 20 feet and 75 horse-power.

Here $$n=kH^{1{\cdot}25}P^{-\frac{1}{2}}, \quad\ldots\ldots\ldots\ldots\ldots\text{(iii)}$$
where k is a constant.

Substituting the given values,

$$50=k\times(6)^{1{\cdot}25}\times(100)^{-\frac{1}{2}};$$

$$\therefore\ k=\frac{500}{6^{1{\cdot}25}}.$$

When H is 20, P is 75; to find n, we have, from (iii),

$$n=500\times\left(\frac{20}{6}\right)^{1{\cdot}25}\times(75)^{-\frac{1}{2}};$$

$$\begin{aligned}\therefore\ \log n&=\log 500+1{\cdot}25(\log 20-\log 6)-\tfrac{1}{2}\log 75\\&=2{\cdot}4150;\\&\therefore\ n=260.\end{aligned}$$

In a similar manner, from (ii),

$$R=kP^{0\cdot5}H^{-0\cdot75};\quad\text{(iv)}$$

$$\therefore\ k=\frac{2\cdot51}{10}\times(6)^{0\cdot75}.$$

Substituting this value for k in (iv), we have, when H is 20 and P is 75,

$$R=2\cdot51\times\left(\frac{6}{20}\right)^{0\cdot75}\times\left(\frac{75}{100}\right)^{0\cdot5}$$

$$=2\cdot51\times(0\cdot3)^{0\cdot75}\times(0\cdot75)^{0\cdot5};$$

$$\therefore\ \log R=0\cdot3997+\bar{1}\cdot6078+\bar{1}\cdot9375=\bar{1}\cdot9450;$$

$$\therefore\ R=0\cdot881.$$

Logarithms of trigonometrical ratios.—In Table IX. the sine, cosine, tangent, etc., for angles of a degrees from 0° to 90° are tabulated. In addition, by means of the numbers arranged in a horizontal direction, and by the columns of difference, the value of any of the above ratios can be obtained to the nearest minute. These ratios give the magnitude of all such angles with the conventions referred to in Chap. II. Having obtained the required number from the table, operations involving multiplication, division, involution, and evolution can be carried out in the usual manner.

Ex. 1. From Table IX. find the values of

$$\sin 161°,\ \tan 127°,\ \text{and}\ \cos 104°.$$

As shown on p. 17, $\sin A=\sin(180°-A)$.

Hence $\sin 161°=\sin(180°-161°)=\sin 19°$,

and $\sin 19°=0\cdot3256=\sin 161°$.

$$\tan 127°=-\tan(180°-127°)=-\tan 53°.$$

Hence, from Table IX, $\tan 127°=-1\cdot3270$.

Similarly, $\cos 104°=-\cos(180°-104°)=-\cos 76°$;

$$\therefore\ \cos 104°=-0\cdot2419.$$

Ex. 2. Find the value of

$$\sin 161°\tan^2 127°\div\sqrt[3]{(\cos 104°)}.$$

Since $\cos 104°=-\cos 76°$,

this may be written as

$$x=-\sin 19°\tan^2 53°\div\sqrt[3]{(\cos 76°)}.$$

From Table IX. $\sin 19^\circ = 0\cdot3256$,

$$\tan 53^\circ = 1\cdot3270,$$

$$\cos 76^\circ = 0\cdot2419.$$

Now $$-x = \sin 19^\circ \tan^2 53^\circ \div \sqrt[3]{(\cos 76^\circ)}.$$

$$\therefore \log(-x) = \log 0\cdot3256 + 2\log 1\cdot3270 - \tfrac{1}{3}\log 0\cdot2419$$

$$= \bar{1}\cdot5127 + 2\times 0\cdot1229 - \tfrac{1}{3}(\bar{1}\cdot3836)$$

$$= \bar{1}\cdot5127 + 0\cdot2458 - \bar{1}\cdot7945$$

$$= \bar{1}\cdot9640;$$

$$\therefore x = -0\cdot9204.$$

Ex. 3. Find the values of

$$m = \frac{5400}{\pi}\log_e\frac{1+\sin l}{1-\sin l} \quad \ldots\ldots\ldots\ldots\ldots\ldots\ldots\ldots\text{(i)}$$

When $l = 0^\circ, 35^\circ, 65^\circ$. ....(*a*), (*b*), (*c*)

(*a*) When $l = 0^\circ$, $m = 0$.

(*b*) When $l = 35^\circ$; $\sin 35^\circ = 0\cdot5736$.

Substituting in (i),

$$m = \frac{5400}{\pi}\log_e\frac{1\cdot5736}{0\cdot4264}$$

$$= \frac{5400}{\pi}\left(0\cdot1970 - \bar{1}\cdot6298\right)2\cdot303$$

$$= \frac{5400}{\pi}\times 0\cdot5672\times 2\cdot303$$

$$= 2246.$$

(*c*) Similarly, when $l = 65^\circ$

$$m = \frac{5400}{\pi}\log_e\frac{1\cdot9063}{0\cdot0937} = 5180.$$

Ex. 4. If $a = 5$, $b = 200$, $c = 600$, $g = -0\cdot1745$ radian, find the value of

$$ae^{-bt}\sin(ct+g). \quad \ldots\ldots\ldots\ldots\ldots\ldots\ldots\ldots\text{(i)}$$

(*a*) When $t = 0\cdot001$.

(*b*) When $t = 0\cdot01$.

(*c*) When $t = 0\cdot1$.

Denoting the value of the given expression by y, and substituting the given values, we have

$$y = 5e^{-200t}\sin(600t - 0\cdot1745). \quad \ldots\ldots\ldots\ldots\ldots\ldots\text{(ii)}$$

(*a*) When t is 0·001, we have, from (ii),

$$y = 5e^{-0\cdot2} \sin(0\cdot6 - 0\cdot1745) = 5e^{-0\cdot2} \sin(0\cdot4255).$$

From Table VII., or by multiplying 0·4255 by 57°·3, we find 0·4255 radians to be 24° 23′.

$$\therefore \log y = \log 5 - 0\cdot2 \log e + \log \sin 24° 23'$$
$$= 0\cdot6990 - 0\cdot0869 + \bar{1}\cdot6157 = 0\cdot2278 = \log 1\cdot69;$$
$$\therefore y = 1\cdot69.$$

(*b*) When t is 0·01, we have, from (ii),

$$y = 5e^{-2} \sin(6 - 0\cdot1745) = -5e^{-2} \sin 26° 12'.$$
$$\log(-y) = 0\cdot6990 - 0\cdot8686 + \bar{1}\cdot6449 = \bar{1}\cdot4753 = \log 0\cdot2987;$$
$$\therefore y = -0\cdot2987.$$

(*c*) When t is 0·1,

$$y = 5e^{-20} \sin(60 - 0\cdot1745) = -5e^{-20} \sin 7° 44';$$
$$\therefore \log(-y) = 0\cdot6990 - 8\cdot686 + \bar{1}\cdot1290 = \bar{9}\cdot1420 = \log 1\cdot387 \times 10^{-9},$$
$$y = -0\cdot1387 \times 10^{-8}, \text{ or, } 0\cdot000000001387.$$

Ex. 5. Solve the equations,

$$\text{(i) } 7^x = 3y, \quad \text{(ii) } 6^x = 5y.$$

Dividing (i) by (ii), we have

$$\left(\frac{7}{6}\right)^x = \left(\frac{3}{5}\right) = 0\cdot6;$$
$$\therefore x(\log 7 - \log 6) = \log 0\cdot6,$$

or
$$x(0\cdot8451 - 0\cdot7782) = \bar{1}\cdot7782,$$

or
$$0\cdot0669x = \bar{1}\cdot7782 = -0\cdot2218;$$
$$\therefore x = -\frac{2218}{669} = -3\cdot31.$$

Substituting this value in Eq. (ii), we have

$$5y = 6^{-3\cdot31};$$
$$\therefore \log y = -3\cdot31 \log 6 - \log 5$$
$$= -3\cdot31 \times 0\cdot7782 - 0\cdot6990$$
$$= \bar{4}\cdot7251;$$
$$\therefore y = 0\cdot000531.$$

Hence the values are $x = -3\cdot31$, $y = 0\cdot000531$.

Some simple artifices.—When a given algebraic or other expression contains terms connected by the signs of addition and subtraction, the terms must be separately evaluated and afterwards added or subtracted as required.

By means of a few simple artifices it is sometimes possible to change such expressions into the form of products and quotients.

The artifices are not, however, of much value except in those cases where many examples of the same kind have to be evaluated.

Ex. 1. Calculate the value of the expression,

$$a^{\frac{3}{5}}\sin\theta(a^2-b^2)^{-\frac{1}{2}},$$

when $a=11{\cdot}78$, $b=5{\cdot}67$, $\theta=0{\cdot}4712$ radians.

From Table IX. 0·4712 radians $=27°$. Hence, if x denotes the value of the given expression

$$x=(11{\cdot}78)^{\frac{3}{5}}\sin 27°(11{\cdot}78+5{\cdot}67)^{-\frac{1}{2}}(11{\cdot}78-5{\cdot}67)^{-\frac{1}{2}}$$

$$=(11{\cdot}78)^{\frac{3}{5}}\times 0{\cdot}454\times(17{\cdot}45\times 6{\cdot}11)^{-\frac{1}{2}};$$

$$\therefore\ \log x=\tfrac{3}{5}\log 11{\cdot}78+\log 0{\cdot}454-\tfrac{1}{2}(\log 17{\cdot}45+\log 6{\cdot}11)$$

$$=0{\cdot}6427+\bar{1}{\cdot}6571-\tfrac{1}{2}(1{\cdot}2417+0{\cdot}7860)$$

$$=0{\cdot}2998-1{\cdot}0138=\bar{1}{\cdot}2860=\log 0{\cdot}1932;$$

$$\therefore\ x=0{\cdot}1932.$$

Again, in dealing with quantities of the form a^2+b^2, we may use $\tan\theta=\frac{b}{a}$; and, as $\tan\theta$ may have any value, the solution is always possible. Thus, if $\tan\theta=\frac{b}{a}$,

$$a^2+b^2=a^2\left(1+\frac{b^2}{a^2}\right)=a^2(1+\tan^2\theta)$$

$$=a^2\sec^2\theta,$$

a form adapted to logarithmic computation.

In a similar manner the fraction $\frac{a-b}{a+b}$ becomes $\tan\left(\frac{\pi}{4}-\theta\right)$.

Ex 2. Evaluate $a^{\frac{3}{5}} \sin\theta\,(a^2+b^2)^{-\frac{1}{2}}$,
when $a=11{\cdot}78$, $b=5{\cdot}67$, $\theta=0{\cdot}4712$ radians.

In Table IX., 0·4712 radians corresponds to 27° and sin 27° = 0·4540.

Putting $$\tan\phi=\frac{b}{a}=\frac{5{\cdot}67}{11{\cdot}78}=0{\cdot}4812.$$

From Table IX., ϕ is found to be 25° 42′.

Now $$a^2+b^2=a^2\sec^2\phi=\frac{a^2}{\cos^2\phi},$$
and $\cos 25^\circ\,42'=0{\cdot}9011$.

Hence, if x denotes the value of the given expression, we have

$$x=(11{\cdot}78)^{\frac{3}{5}}\sin 27^\circ\,(a^2\div\cos^2\phi)^{-\frac{1}{2}}$$
$$=(11{\cdot}78)^{\frac{3}{5}}\times 0{\cdot}454\times\frac{0{\cdot}9011}{11{\cdot}78}.$$
$$\log x=\tfrac{3}{5}\log 11{\cdot}78+\log 0{\cdot}454+\log{\cdot}9011-\log 11{\cdot}78$$
$$=0{\cdot}6427+\bar{1}{\cdot}6571+\bar{1}{\cdot}9547-1{\cdot}0712$$
$$=\bar{1}{\cdot}1833;$$
$$\therefore\ x=0{\cdot}1525.$$

EXERCISES. VI.

Find the value of

1. $2{\cdot}625^{2{\cdot}5}\times 0{\cdot}0625\times 16{\cdot}06^{-0{\cdot}083}$. **2.** $23{\cdot}07\times 0{\cdot}1354$, $2307\div 1{\cdot}354$.

3. How many ciphers are there between the decimal point and the first significant figure in $(0{\cdot}0504)^{10}$?

Evaluate

4. $\dfrac{(0{\cdot}07197)^{\frac{1}{3}}}{\sqrt[5]{27}}$. **5.** (i) $\sqrt[5]{0{\cdot}02348}$; (ii) $\left(\dfrac{5}{7}\right)^{0{\cdot}1345}$.

6. Find without using tables the value of x for which
$$\log x=3\log 18-4\log 12.$$

7. Calculate the numerical value of
$$(0{\cdot}084)^{\frac{1}{5}}\div(0{\cdot}34)^3.$$

8. Evaluate $2{\cdot}307^{0{\cdot}65}-23{\cdot}07^{-1{\cdot}25}$.

9. In the formula $L=(D+d)\left\{\dfrac{\pi}{2}+\theta+\dfrac{1}{\tan\theta}\right\}$,

given $$\sin\theta=\frac{D+d}{2c},$$
find the value of L when $c=20$ ft., $D=6$ ft., and $d=3$ ft.

10. The loss of energy E through friction of every pound of water flowing with velocity v through a straight circular pipe of length l ft. and diameter d ft. is given by $0{\cdot}0007 lv^2 \div d$.

Given $v = 8{\cdot}5$ ft. per sec., $l = 3000$ ft., $d = 6$ inches, find E.

11. Find the value of E from the formula

$$E = \frac{4}{3} \frac{wl^3}{\pi d \times a^4},$$

when $w = 15$, $l = 18{\cdot}23$, $d = 3$, $a = \frac{3}{8}$.

12. If $x = e^{\mu\theta}$, find x when $e = 2{\cdot}718$, $\mu = 0{\cdot}4$, $\theta = \pi = 3{\cdot}142$.

Also find x when $\mu = 0{\cdot}7$ and $\theta = 180°$.

Evaluate

13. $\sqrt{\dfrac{8^{\frac{1}{5}} \times 11^{\frac{1}{3}}}{\sqrt[4]{18} \times \sqrt[5]{9}}}.$ **14.** $\dfrac{(21{\cdot}43)^2 \times 3{\cdot}142 \times 0{\cdot}0642}{1{\cdot}236 \times \sqrt{0{\cdot}004376}}.$

15. From the equation

$$P = \frac{806300 \times t^{2{\cdot}19}}{L \times D},$$

find P when $t = \frac{1}{2}$, $L = 20$, $D = 36$.

Also find the value of P when t^2 is used instead of the more accurate value $t^{2{\cdot}19}$.

16. The relation between p and v may be expressed by

$$\text{(i) } pv = c, \quad \text{(ii) } pv^{1{\cdot}0646} = c, \quad \text{(iii) } pv^{1{\cdot}13} = c.$$

If when p is $1{\cdot}5$, $v = 1$, find p in each case when $v = 3{\cdot}5$.

Also find in each case the value of v when p is $0{\cdot}5$.

17. If $w = 144\{p_1(1 + \log_e r) - r(p_3 + 10)\}$ and if $p_1 = 100$, $p_3 = 17$, find w when r is $1\frac{1}{2}$, 2, 3, 4.

18. Compute $2{\cdot}307^{0{\cdot}65}$ and $23{\cdot}07^{-1{\cdot}25}$.

19. To what base would the numbers given in Table II. have logarithms double those actually given?

20. Find the square root of

$$\frac{\sqrt[3]{0{\cdot}0125} \times \sqrt{31{\cdot}15}}{0{\cdot}00081}.$$

21. Evaluate $\dfrac{(7{\cdot}25)^{\frac{1}{3}} \times 1{\cdot}005}{(0{\cdot}0874)^2}$.

22. Evaluate I from the formula

$$I = I_0\left(\frac{t_1^2}{t_0^2} \frac{W_0 + W_1}{W_0} - 1\right),$$

given $I_0 = 88{\cdot}2$, $t_0 = 1{\cdot}29$, $t_1 = 1{\cdot}64$, $W_1 = 6{\cdot}4$, $W_0 = 44{\cdot}1$.

23. Find x and y from the equations

$$\log_{10} x^3 + \log_{10} y^2 = \bar{1}\cdot 4571,$$
$$\log_{10} x - \log_{10} y = 0\cdot 2300.$$

24. Find the value of one root of the equation

$$(4)^{2x} - 8(4)^x + 12 = 0.$$

25. Find to three decimal places a value of x which satisfies the equation $$5^{x+2} = 8^{2x-1}.$$

26. Find $\log\left(\frac{64}{35}\right)^{\frac{5}{6}}$ and $\log \sqrt[6]{62\cdot 5}$.

Solve the equations

27. $$2^x = 9.$$

28. $$x^5 = \frac{11\cdot 6 \times 0\cdot 4785}{0\cdot 0278}.$$

29. Evaluate E from the formula $E = \frac{Wl^3}{48 I \delta}$, given $W = 16$, $l = 20$, $I = \frac{\pi}{64}(0\cdot 373)^4$ and $\delta = 2\cdot 44 \div 25\cdot 4$.

30. Find the value of x correct to three places of decimals that satisfies the equation $7^x = 3^{x+1} \div 2^{x-2}$.

31. Solve the equation $105^x = 100$.

32. Find the logarithms of

$$\sqrt[5]{6}\,; \quad \frac{2}{3}\sqrt[3]{14\cdot 4}\,; \quad \frac{72}{125}\sqrt{270} \times \frac{3}{16}\sqrt[3]{625}.$$

33. Find the logarithms to base e of

$$\text{(i)}\ \frac{8}{\sqrt{27}}, \quad \text{(ii)}\ \frac{3e^2}{512}, \quad \text{(iii)}\ \sqrt{\frac{2}{3}} \times \sqrt[3]{\frac{9}{16}} \times \sqrt[4]{\frac{64}{27}}.$$

34. Prove that $7\log\frac{16}{15} + 5\log\frac{25}{24} + 3\log\frac{81}{80} = \log 2.$

35. Solve the equation

$$\left(\frac{1}{2}\right)^{x+4} = (25)^{3x+2}.$$

36. If $$Q = 1000\sqrt{\frac{D^5 H}{GL}},$$

and if $$D = \tfrac{3}{4}, \quad H = 0\cdot 4, \quad L = 10, \quad Q = 145$$

be a set of simultaneous values, find D when

$$H = 2, \quad L = 5000, \quad Q = 465.$$

What is the value of the constant G?

37. Find the value of

$$\log_e \frac{\sqrt{(1+x)}+\sqrt{(1-x)}}{\sqrt{(1+x)}-\sqrt{(1-x)}}, \text{ when } x=0{\cdot}62.$$

38. Evaluate

$$\frac{E\cos\left[pt-\tan^{-1}\frac{2p\pi\cos\beta}{n^2-p^2}\right]}{\sqrt{n^4+2n^2p^2\cos 2\beta+p^2}},$$

when $E=100$, $n=5$, $p=3$, $\beta=\frac{\pi}{6}$, $t=1{\cdot}2$.

39. Find V and v from the equations

$$V=\frac{(88{\cdot}51)(\sqrt{R}-0{\cdot}3)}{\sqrt{\frac{1}{\sin\theta}-\log_e\frac{1}{\sin\theta}-1{\cdot}6}}-0{\cdot}084(\sqrt{R}-0{\cdot}03),$$

$$v=60\sqrt{R\sin\theta}+120R^{\frac{2}{3}}\sin^{\frac{2}{3}}\theta;$$

(i) when $R=8$, $\theta=0{\cdot}02$;

(ii) when $R=2{\cdot}56$, $\theta=0{\cdot}144$.

40. Find to four significant figures the value of

$$\sin 116^\circ \tan^2 218^\circ \div \sqrt[3]{(\cos 102^\circ)}.$$

41. Some particulars of steam vessels are given. Assuming in each case the relation H.P. $\propto V^3D^{\frac{2}{3}}$ to hold, where H.P. denotes the horse-power at a speed of V knots and displacement D in tons, find in each case the probable H.P. necessary to give a speed of 24 knots for same displacement.

Name.	H.P.	V	D
(i) Paris, - -	20000	20·25	15000
(ii) Teutonic, -	18000	19·50	13800
(iii) Campania, -	30000	22·10	19000
(iv) Kaiser, - -	28000	22·62	20000
(v) Oceanic, -	28000	20·50	28500
(vi) Deutschland,	35640	23·0	23000

42. When water pours over a triangular notch $Q \propto H^{\frac{5}{2}}$ (where Q denotes the number of cubic feet per sec., and H the height of the surface in feet), when H is 2, Q is 14·9, find the number of gallons per minute when H is 4.

43. Find the value of $10e^{-0\cdot7t}\sin(2\pi ft+0\cdot6)$ when f is 225 and t is 0·003.

44. Find the value of $a^p+b^q+c^r$ when $a=5$, $b=3$, $c=0\cdot042$, $p=2\cdot43$, $q=-0\cdot246$, $r=0\cdot476$.

45. Evaluate $(x^2-y^2)z^{-\frac{4}{5}}\tan 40°$ when

$$x=50\cdot9,\ y=14\cdot8,\ z=29\cdot29.$$

46. If p is the pressure and u the volume in cubic feet of 1 lb of steam, then from $pu^{1\cdot0646}=479$ find u when p is 150.

47. If
$$y=\log_e\frac{1+x+x^2}{1-2x+x^2}+2\sqrt{3}\tan^{-1}\frac{2x+1}{\sqrt{3}},$$

find the values of y which correspond to the following values of x

$$x=0,\ x=0\cdot4,\ x=1.$$

Assume that the given angle is acute.

48. Solve the equation

$$(2\cdot065)^{-0\cdot048x}=0\cdot826.$$

Evaluate

49. (i) $(0\cdot9415\times2\cdot304)^{1\cdot72}$ (ii) $(0\cdot9415\times2\cdot304)^{-1\cdot72}$.

50. $y=ae^{-bx}\sin(cx+d)$

when $a=6$, $b=30$, $x=0\cdot5$, $c=4$, $e=2\cdot718$, $d=-0\cdot1$.

51. $y=e^{-kt}\sin(pt+q)$

when $k=0\cdot1$, $p=0\cdot3$, $q=0\cdot2$, $e=2\cdot718$.

(i) when $t=1$, (ii) when $t=5$.

52. If $y=\frac{c}{2}\left(e^{\frac{x}{c}}+e^{-\frac{x}{c}}\right)$ and $s=\frac{c}{2}\left(e^{\frac{x}{c}}-e^{-\frac{x}{c}}\right)$.

Find c, y and x, when $s=290$, $y=50+c$.

53. The loss of pressure of water flowing with velocity v in a pipe of diameter d and length l is equal to h ft. of water where

$$\frac{h}{l}=\frac{m}{d^{1\cdot16}}\times\frac{v^n}{64\cdot4}.$$

m and n are constants.

Given $l=100$, $d=2$, if when $v=6$, $h=1\cdot12$ and $v=8$, $h=1\cdot99$. Find values of m and n.

CHAPTER VI.

EQUATIONS.

Equations.—A statement that two arithmetical, or algebraical, expressions are equal is called an **equation.**

Identity.—When an equality exists between two quantities, and the **two expressions are equal for all values** of the quantities involved, such a statement is called an **identity,** thus

$$a(b+c)=ab+ac,$$

$$(a+x)^2=a^2+2ax+x^2,$$

$$(a+b)(a-b)=a^2-b^2,$$

are examples of **identities.**

Equation.—An algebraic expression in which an equality or relation exists between certain known and unknown quantities, which is only true for certain values of the quantities involved, constitutes an **equation.** Known quantities may be indicated by the letters a, b, c, etc., and unknown quantities by the letters x, y, z.

An equation consists of two equal parts, one on the left, the other on the right of the sign of equality, and the equation will still be true when both sides are:

(i) Equally increased, or diminished; which is the same in effect as taking a quantity from one side of an equation and placing it on the other with altered sign.

(ii) Equally multiplied, or divided; this includes changing the signs of all the terms by multiplying both sides of the equation by -1.

Degree of an equation.—When a given equation expressed in its simplest form contains only the first power of one, or more, unknown quantities, it is called a **simple equation.** All such equations are said to be of the **first degree** or **linear equations.**

Similarly, if an equation contains the second power of an unknown quantity, it is called a **quadratic** equation. If it contains the third power it is called a **cubic** equation, etc.

Solution of an equation.—The symbol $f(x)$ is used to denote any expression which involves a variable quantity x, and is read as a **function** *of* x.

If y stands for the value of such a function, then we may write $y=f(x)$; and by giving a series of numerical values to x, a corresponding series of values can be obtained for y.

Thus, $2x-16$, $2x^2-8x+6$, $x^3-3x^2-10x+24$,

may be called functions of x. The highest power of x in the first is one; it is two in the second, and three in the third. Hence, these may be described as of the *first*, *second*, and *third* degree, respectively.

If a given equation be written in the form $f(x)=0$, and the substitution of any quantity a satisfies the equation, then $x-a$ is a **factor**; or, $x=a$ is a **root** of the equation. Such an equation is said to be solved when all those values of x are found which when substituted in the expression makes it vanish or makes one side identical with the other. Again, if by giving two different values to x, results are obtained with different signs, the curve joining the plotted points would obviously intersect the axis of x at some intermediate point, that is to say at least one root of the given equation lies between the assigned values of x.

As a simple example let $f(x)=2x-16$; then, if y denotes the value of the function, $y=2x-16$.

Let $x=9$; then, $2x-16=18-16=2$.

Again, let $x=7$; then, $2x-16=14-16=-2$.

Hence, the root lies between these values.

By substituting $x=8$, it is found that this value satisfies the given equation; and therefore $x=8$ is the root required.

Ex. 1. $$\frac{3x}{4}+\frac{x}{2}+3=3x-4.$$

First subtract 3, and next subtract $3x$ from each side, and we obtain
$$\frac{3x}{4}+\frac{x}{2}-3x=-7.$$

Multiplying both sides of the equation by 4, then
$$3x+2x-12x=-28;$$
$$\therefore\ -7x=-28;$$
$$x=\frac{-28}{-7}=4.$$

To prove that this value of x satisfies the given equation, it is only necessary to substitute 4 for x, and each side is seen to be equal to 8.

Instead of subtraction we may remove any term, or terms, from one side of an equation to the other; or, in other words, we may **transpose** a term, or terms, taking care to alter the sign, or signs, as in the case of the terms 3 and $3x$ in the preceding example. Hence, for the solution of a given simple equation we may deduce the following rule:

Transpose all the unknown quantities to the left and all the known quantities to the right-hand side of the equation. Simplify if necessary, and finally divide by the coefficient of the unknown quantity.

Some of the methods which may be used in the solutions of equations may be seen from the following examples:

Ex. 2. $$\frac{12}{x}+\frac{1}{12x}=\frac{29}{24}.$$

Multiply both sides by $24x$;
$$\therefore\ 288+2=29x,$$
$$\therefore\ 29x=290,$$
$$\therefore\ x=10.$$

Ex. 3. Solve $$\frac{\sqrt{4x+1}+\sqrt{4x}}{\sqrt{4x+1}-\sqrt{4x}}=9. \quad \text{.....(i)}$$

This is a typical example in which, if we multiply out and afterwards proceed to square, troublesome expressions result. We may, however, avoid these as follows:

Let $u=\sqrt{4x+1}$, and $v=\sqrt{4x}$, then the equation becomes, after multiplying out by $u-v$,

$$u+v=9u-9v,$$

or $$10v=8u, \quad i.e.\ 5v=4u;$$

$\therefore$ By squaring, $$25v^2=16u^2,$$

$$i.e.\ 100x=64x+16.$$

$$\therefore x=\frac{4}{9}.$$

Fractional equations.—In the solution of equations involving fractions it is in many cases advisable to commence by clearing of fractions. This may be effected by multiplying by the L.C.M. of the denominators.

Ex. 4. Solve $\dfrac{x+3}{x+4}-\dfrac{x-1}{2x-1}=\dfrac{1}{2}.$

Multiply out by $2(x+4)(2x-1)$, then

$$2(x+3)(2x-1)-2(x-1)(x+4)=(x+4)(2x-1).$$

$$\therefore 4x^2+10x-6-2x^2-6x+8=2x^2+7x-4,$$

or $$-3x=-6,$$

i.e. $$x=2.$$

In some cases it is more convenient to simplify each side of the equation, as in the following example.

Ex. 5. Solve $\dfrac{x-15}{x-16}-\dfrac{x-4}{x-5}=\dfrac{x-6}{x-7}-\dfrac{x+5}{x+4}.$

This may be written in the form

$$1+\frac{1}{x-16}-\left(1+\frac{1}{x-5}\right)=1+\frac{1}{x-7}-\left(1+\frac{1}{x+4}\right),$$

or $$\frac{1}{x-16}-\frac{1}{x-5}=\frac{1}{x-7}-\frac{1}{x+4};$$

$$\therefore \frac{x-5-x+16}{(x-5)(x-16)}=\frac{x+4-x+7}{(x+4)(x-7)},$$

or $$\frac{11}{(x-5)(x-16)}=\frac{11}{(x+4)(x-7)},$$

or $$(x+4)(x-7)=(x-5)(x-16),$$

$$x^2-3x-28=x^2-21x+80;$$

$$\therefore 18x=108, \therefore x=6.$$

Ex. 6. Solve $\sqrt{4a+x}-\sqrt{x}=2\sqrt{b+x}$.

Square both sides.

$$4a+2x-2\sqrt{4ax+x^2}=4(b+x).$$

Transpose and divide by 2;

$$\therefore \sqrt{4ax+x^2}=-x+2(a-b).$$

Square both sides.

$$4ax+x^2=x^2-4x(a-b)+4(a-b)^2;$$

$$\therefore x(8a-4b)=4(a-b)^2,$$

$$\text{or } 4x(2a-b)=4(a-b)^2;$$

$$\therefore x=\frac{(a-b)^2}{2a-b}.$$

In the preceding, and in all cases where the solution of an equation is obtained by the processes of involution or evolution, it is necessary to test whether the value obtained satisfies the given equation.

EXERCISES. VII.

Solve the equations:

1. $\frac{2x}{15}+\frac{x-6}{12}-\frac{3x}{20}=1\frac{1}{2}$.

2. $\frac{1}{2}(x-1)-\frac{1}{3}(2-x)+\frac{1}{4}(x+1)=x$.

3. $\frac{5}{2}-\frac{x+4}{11}=x+\frac{1}{2}$.

4. $\frac{x+3}{4}-\frac{x-3}{5}=\frac{x-5}{2}-2$.

5. $\frac{2x-5}{4}-\frac{x-2}{6}=\frac{x}{7}-\frac{1}{4}$.

6. $\frac{3x+5}{7}-\frac{6x+5}{9}=x-\frac{2}{3}$.

7. $\frac{x+2}{3}+2=\frac{x+4}{5}+\frac{x+6}{7}$.

8. $\frac{3x-13}{8}-\frac{4x+6}{9}=1-\frac{x-1}{10}$.

9. $\frac{3x-1}{3}+\frac{5}{12}=\frac{x}{4}+\frac{2x+1}{5}$.

10. $\frac{1}{(x-1)(x-2)}+\frac{1}{(x+1)(x+2)}=\frac{2}{(x-1)(x+2)}$.

11. $\frac{x-\frac{1}{2}}{x-1}-\frac{3}{5}\left(\frac{1}{x-1}-\frac{1}{3}\right)=\frac{23}{10(x-1)}$.

12. $\frac{ax}{b}-\frac{1}{b}\left(\frac{1}{c}+x\right)+d=\frac{d}{b}\left(bx-\frac{1}{cd}\right)-\frac{x}{b}+\frac{a}{b}$.

13. $\frac{3}{7}(6x-7)+\frac{1-7x}{6}=x$.

14. $\frac{2x+1}{3}-\frac{3x-2}{4}=\frac{x-2}{6}$.

Solve the equations:

15. $11(x-5)-5(x-11)=5\frac{1}{4}$.

16. $0{\cdot}1x+\dfrac{0{\cdot}05x-0{\cdot}08}{0{\cdot}3}=0{\cdot}88-\dfrac{0{\cdot}03x-0{\cdot}08}{0{\cdot}5}$.

17. $\dfrac{x+a}{x-c}=\dfrac{a+c}{a-c}$.

18. $\sqrt{x+7}=\sqrt{x}+1$.

19. $\dfrac{a}{bx}+\dfrac{b}{ax}=a^2+b^2$.

20. $\dfrac{a-x}{bc}+\dfrac{b-x}{ac}+\dfrac{c-x}{ab}=0$.

21. $\dfrac{(x+a)^3-(x-a)^3}{2a}=3(x+a)^2-5a^2$.

22. $\dfrac{xa}{b}+\dfrac{xb}{a}=a^2+b^2$.

23. $\dfrac{1}{a(x-b)}+\dfrac{1}{b(x-c)}=\dfrac{1}{a(x-c)}$.

24. $\dfrac{5x-9}{\sqrt{5x}-3}=x+3$.

25. $\sqrt{(x+4)}+\sqrt{(2x+10)}=\sqrt{2}$.

26. $\sqrt{x}+\sqrt{x+3}=\dfrac{5}{\sqrt{x+3}}$.

27. $(x+3)^3-3(x+2)^3+3(x+1)^3-x^3=x+3$.

Problems producing equations.—When told in words how to deal arithmetically with a given quantity, it is of importance to be able to state the matter algebraically. The true meaning of such a question, or problem, must in the first place be perfectly understood and its conditions exhibited by algebraical symbols in the clearest manner possible. The following are a few typical examples of problems of this kind.

Ex. 1. Twice a certain number exceeds four-fifths of its half by 40. Find the number.

Let x denote the number; then, twice the number is $2x$. Also four-fifths of its half is $\frac{4}{5}\times\frac{x}{2}$.

Hence, by the question

$$2x-\frac{4}{5}\times\frac{x}{2}=40;$$

$$\therefore\ 20x-4x=400,$$

$$\text{or } 16x=400;$$

$$\therefore\ x=\frac{400}{16}=25.$$

Substituting this value the equation is satisfied.

Ex. 2. The total length of 4 pieces of copper wire is 50 feet; the second is twice, the third three times, and the fourth is four times as long as the first. Find the length of each piece.

If x denotes the number of feet in the first,
then $2x$,, ,, ,, second,
$3x$,, ,, ,, third,
and $4x$,, ,, ,, fourth;

$$\therefore\ x+2x+3x+4x=50,$$

$$10x=50;\ \therefore\ x=5 \text{ ft.}$$

The lengths are 5, 10, 15 and 20 ft. respectively.

Ex. 3. In ascending a mountain, a man took half as long again to climb the second third as he did to climb the first third, and a quarter as long again for the last third as for the second third; he took altogether 5 hours 50 minutes. Find the time he spent on the first third of the journey.

If x denotes the time taken for the first third,
then $\frac{3}{2}x$,, ,, ,, second third,
and $\frac{5}{4}\times\frac{3}{2}x$,, ,, ,, last third.

Also 5 hours 50 minutes = 350 minutes.

Hence $$x+\tfrac{3}{2}x+\tfrac{15}{8}x=350;$$

$$\therefore\ 35x=8\times 350,$$

$$x=80 \text{ minutes.}$$

The time spent on the first third = 1 hour 20 minutes.

Ex. 4. The sides of a triangle ABC are together 61 miles long; BC is $\frac{5}{6}$th of AB and 3 miles longer than CA. Find the lengths of the sides severally.

Let x denote the length of AB.
Then $\frac{5}{6}x$ will denote the length of BC,
and $\frac{5}{6}x-3$,, ,, AC.

Hence $$x+\tfrac{5}{6}x+\tfrac{5}{6}x-3=61;$$

$$\therefore\ 16x=384, \text{ or } x=24.$$

Also $$\tfrac{5}{6}x=20, \text{ and } \tfrac{5}{6}x-3=17.$$

The three sides are 24, 20 and 17 respectively.

Ex. 5. The perimeter of a triangle is 22 feet, the base is 3 feet longer than one side, and 5 feet longer than the other. Find the lengths of the sides.

Let x denote the length of the base. Then $x-3$ and $x-5$ are the lengths of the sides.

$$\therefore \; x+x-3+x-5=22,$$

$$3x=30, \quad x=10,$$

and the sides are 7 and 5.

EXERCISES. VIII.

1. A person is walking with uniform speed, and when he has completed half his journey he increases his pace in the ratio of 3 to 2, and arrives at his destination 40 minutes earlier than he would otherwise have done. How long was he walking the first half?

2. A and B distribute £60 each among a certain number of persons. A relieves 40 persons more than B does, and B gives to each person 5 shillings more than A. How many persons did A and B relieve?

3. Two cyclists, A and B, ride a mile race. In the first heat A wins by 6 seconds. In the second heat A gives B a start of $58\frac{2}{3}$ yards and wins by 1 second. Find the rates of A and B in miles per hour.

4. At present B's age is to A's in the ratio of 4 to 3; but fifteen years ago it was in the ratio of 3 to 2. Find their ages.

5. Divide £490 among A, B and C, so that B shall have £2 more than A, and C as many times B's share as there are shillings in A's share.

6. I have thought of a number; I multiply it by $2\frac{1}{3}$ and add 7 to the product; I then multiply the result by 8 times the number thought of; next I divide by 14 and subtract from the quotient 4 times the number thought of; I thus obtain 2352. What number did I think of?

7. A distributes £180 in equal sums amongst a certain number of people. B distributes the same sum in equal portions amongst 40 persons fewer, but gives to each person £6 more than A does. How much does A give to each person?

8. A traveller starts from A towards B at 12 o'clock and another starts at the same time from B towards A. They meet at 2 o'clock, at 24 miles from A? and the one arrives at A while the other is still 20 miles from B. What is the distance between A and B?

9. A man walks a certain distance in 4 hours. If he were to reduce his rate by one-sixteenth he would walk one mile less in that time. What is his rate?

10. If one part of £400 is put out at 4 per cent. and the other part at 5 per cent., and if the yearly income be £18. 5*s*., what are the parts?

11. A sum of money amounts to £546 in three years at simple interest, and to £726 in 7 years. Find the sum and the rate per cent.

12. A sum of £23. 14*s*. is divided between *A*, *B* and *C*. If *B* gets 20 per cent. more than *A*, and 25 per cent. more than *C*, how much does each get?

13. A man spends £1000 of his capital, and then spends $\frac{2}{5}$ of the remainder; then after receiving a legacy of £100 he has half his original capital. Find its amount.

14. A person has £1750 invested so as to bring in an annual income of £77; part is lent on a mortgage at 4 per cent., the rest on loan at 5 per cent. How much is in the mortgage?

15. Show that the square of the sum of any two consecutive numbers is greater by 1 than four times the product of the numbers.

16. Show that the cube of the sum of any two numbers is equal to the sum of their cubes together with three times their product multiplied by their sum.

Simultaneous equations.—Equations containing two or more unknown quantities are called **simultaneous** equations. The simplest case occurs when each of two given equations contains the first power only of the two unknown quantities; in such an equation, if values of one variable are assumed, then corresponding values of the other can be calculated. When there are two distinct and independent equations, only one pair of values will simultaneously satisfy both equations. Equations of this kind which are to be satisfied by the same pair of values of x and y are called **simultaneous equations.**

Ex. 1. $2x+5y=48$,.. ....(i)

This may be written in the form $y=\frac{48-2x}{5}$; and if we substitute values 0, 1, 2 .. for x, corresponding values of y can be calculated and the assemblage of plotted points will lie in a straight line.

If, in addition to (i), we have the equation,

$$3x+4y=44, \quad \text{(ii)}$$

then the equations (i) and (ii) form a pair of simultaneous equations, and the process of solving them simply consists in finding those simultaneous values of the variables x and y which will satisfy the given equations.

First method.—Three methods may be used, the first, which should always be used, being the most important. (*a*) By multiplication, or division, the coefficients of x, or y, are made the same in both equations. Then, by addition, or subtraction, an equation involving only one unknown quantity is obtained, and this may be solved in the usual manner.

Thus, multiplying Eq. (i) by 4 and Eq. (ii) by 5,

$$15x+20y=220 \quad \text{(iii)}$$

$$8x+20y=192$$

By subtraction $$7x = 28;$$

$$\therefore\ x=\frac{28}{7}=4.$$

Substitute this value of x in (i) and we get

$$5y=48-2x=40;$$

$$\therefore\ y=\frac{40}{5}=8.$$

Hence, the pair of values $x=4$, $y=8$, satisfies the given equations. This result should be verified by substituting the values obtained in the given equations.

Second method.—The values of x and y may be obtained by substitution.

Thus, given $2x+5y=48$ (i), $3x+4y=44$ (ii).

From (i), $y=\frac{48-2x}{5}$.

Substituting this value in (ii),

$$3x+4\frac{(48-2x)}{5}=44.$$

Multiply both sides by 5;

$$\therefore\ 15x+192-8x=220;$$

$$\therefore\ 7x=220-192=28,$$

$$\text{or } x=4.$$

Substitute this value of x in (i) or (ii), then y is found to be 8.

Third method.—From each of the two given equations a value for y in terms of x may be obtained. Then, by equating the two values so obtained, another equation is obtained involving only x, and this may be solved in the manner shown for equations of one variable.

Ex. 2. Solve

$$3x-\frac{y}{2}=5, \quad \text{(i)}$$

$$\frac{x}{3}+\frac{y}{4}=3. \quad \text{(ii)}$$

From (i) $\frac{y}{2}=3x-5$; $\quad \therefore\ y=6x-10. \quad$ (iii)

From (ii) $\frac{y}{4}=3-\frac{x}{3}$; $\quad \therefore\ y=12-\frac{4x}{3}. \quad$ (iv)

Equating (iii) and (iv), we have

$$6x-10=12-\frac{4x}{3};$$

$$\therefore\ 6x+\frac{4x}{3}=22,$$

or

$$22x=66;$$

$$\therefore\ x=3.$$

Substituting this value for x in (iii) or (iv), we obtain $y=8$.

Elimination.—From two distinct and independent equations containing two unknown quantities, one unknown can be eliminated by the processes just referred to, the resulting equation will then consist of an unknown and a known quantity, and its solution can be effected in the usual manner.

Similarly, three equations containing three unknown quantities may be reduced to two equations containing two unknowns. Then the two can be reduced to one equation containing only one unknown; and from this, the value of that unknown quantity is obtained and the remaining two found by substitution.

Ex. 3. Solve the simultaneous equations,

$$2x+4y=20, \quad \text{(i)}$$

$$3x+2y=18. \quad \text{(ii)}$$

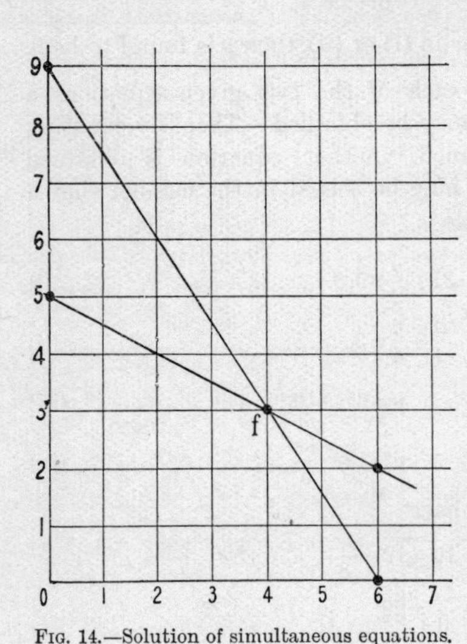

FIG. 14.—Solution of simultaneous equations.

From (i) $y=-\frac{1}{2}x+5$. When

$x=6,\ y=-3+5=2$.

When

$x=0,\ y=5$.

By plotting these values the line (i) is obtained.

Similarly, from (ii), when

$x=6,\ y=0$;

and $x=0,\ y=9$.

By plotting these values the lines can be drawn through the plotted points; f the point of intersection of the two lines (Fig. 14) is a point common to both lines and the co-ordinates of point f, $x=4$ and $y=3$ are the values which satisfy the given equations.

Ex. 4. Solve the equations,

$$2x+3y=13 \quad \text{(i)}$$

$$2x+3y=17. \quad \text{(ii)}$$

These form two distinct equations; but, assuming a series of values 0, 1, 2, etc., for x, and calculating corresponding values of y, it will be found that none of the values obtained from (i) coincide with those from (ii). In other words, simultaneous values of x and y satisfying the two equations cannot be obtained. On plotting, it is seen that the two lines are parallel.

Thus (i) may be written $y=\frac{13-2x}{3}$.

When $x=2,\ y=3$; and when $x=5,\ y=1$.

The line passing through the points $x=2$, $y=3$, and $x=5$, $y=1$, or (2, 3) (5, 1) is shown at ab (Fig. 15).

From (ii),

$$y=\frac{17-2x}{3}.$$

When

$$x=1,\ y=5;$$

and when

$$x=7,\ y=1.$$

The line is indicated by cd (Fig. 15).

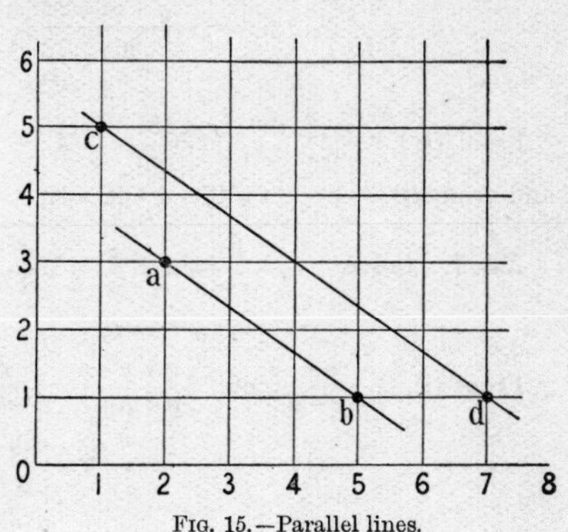

FIG. 15.—Parallel lines.

Some of the artifices which may be usefully employed in the solution of equations may be seen from the following examples.

Ex. 5.

$$x+y=c, \quad \text{(i)}$$
$$ax=by. \quad \text{(ii)}$$

Multiply (i) by b and add to (ii)

$$x(a+b)=bc;$$

$$\therefore\ x=\frac{bc}{a+b}.$$

From (i),

$$y=c-x=c-\frac{bc}{a+b}$$
$$=\frac{ac}{a+b}.$$

Ex. 6.

$$x+2y+3z=17, \quad \text{(i)}$$
$$2x+3y+\ z=12, \quad \text{(ii)}$$
$$3x+\ y+2z=13. \quad \text{(iii)}$$

Multiply (i) by 2 and subtract Eq. (ii) from it;

$$\therefore\ 2x+4y+6z=34$$
$$\underline{2x+3y+\ z=12}$$
$$y+5z=22 \quad \text{(iv)}$$

Multiply (ii) by 3 and (iii) by 2 and subtract;

$$\therefore\ 6x+9y+3z=36$$
$$\underline{6x+2y+4z=26}$$
$$7y-\ z=10. \quad \text{(v)}$$

Multiply (v) by 5 and add to (iv);

$$\therefore\ 35y-5z=50$$
$$y+5z=22$$
$$36y=72,$$
$$y=2.$$

From (iv), $z=\dfrac{22-2}{5}=4$;

and from (i), $x=17-4-12=1$.

Ex. 7. Solve $\dfrac{x}{b+c-a}=\dfrac{y}{c+a-b}=\dfrac{z}{a+b-c}$, ...(i)

$x+y+z=n$. ....(ii)

From (i), $\dfrac{x}{b+c-a}=\text{etc.}=\dfrac{x+y+z}{a+b+c}=\dfrac{n}{a+b+c}$ from (ii);

$$\therefore\ x=\frac{n(b+c-a)}{a+b+c},$$
$$y=\frac{n(c+a-b)}{a+b+c},$$
$$z=\frac{n(a+b-c)}{a+b+c}.$$

In many cases it is more convenient to solve for $\dfrac{1}{x}$ and $\dfrac{1}{y}$... instead of x, y.

Ex. 8. Solve $\dfrac{5}{x}+\dfrac{7}{y}=2$, ...(i)

$5x+y=xy$. ....(ii)

Divide both sides of equation (ii) by xy.

$\dfrac{1}{x}+\dfrac{5}{y}=1$. ....(iii)

Multiply (iii) by 5 and subtract (i) from it;

$$\therefore\ \frac{18}{y}=3,$$

giving $y=6$.

Substitute this value in (i).

$$\frac{5}{x}=2-\frac{7}{6}=\frac{5}{6};$$
$$\therefore\ x=6.$$

It is better to keep the fractional form. The attempt to clear the equations from fractions would introduce a new term xy.

EXERCISES. IX.

Solve the equations:

1. $\frac{x-3}{5}=\frac{y-7}{2}$; $11x=13y$.

2. $3x-2y=2x+3y=26$.

3. $\frac{x+4}{7}-\frac{x-y-1}{4}=2x-4$,
$2y-4-\frac{3x-2y}{3}=3x$.

4. $x+\frac{1}{2}y=4$,
$y+2z=12$,
$\frac{3}{5}z-\frac{2}{3}x=1$.

5. $12x+11y=12$,
$42x+22y=40{\cdot}5$.

6. $\frac{x}{3}+5=\frac{2y}{3}$,
$y-x=\frac{x}{3}$.

7. $2x+\frac{y}{3}=x+12$,
$y-x+20=\frac{x+40}{2}$.

8. $\left.\begin{aligned}7x-4y&=b-a,\\ 8y+21x&=5p-3a-2b.\end{aligned}\right\}$

9. $\frac{5}{2}x-\frac{2}{3}y=9=\frac{5}{3}y-x$.

10. $2x+3y=13$, $5x-3y=1$.

11. $x+2y=3$, $2x-3y=3$.

12. $\left.\begin{aligned}3x+2y+5z&=1,\\ 5x+3y-2z&=2,\\ 2x-5y-3z&=7.\end{aligned}\right\}$

13. $\left.\begin{aligned}3{\cdot}4x-0{\cdot}02y&=0{\cdot}01,\\ x+0{\cdot}2y&=0{\cdot}6.\end{aligned}\right\}$

14. $y=\frac{x}{m}+am$, $y-2am=-m(x-am^2)$.

15. $ax-by=2ab$, $2bx+2ay=3b^2-a^2$.

16. $\left.\begin{aligned}x+y&=a+b,\\ bx+ay&=2ab.\end{aligned}\right\}$

17. $\left.\begin{aligned}\frac{a}{x}+\frac{b}{y}&=cd,\\ \frac{b}{x}-\frac{a}{y}&=ef.\end{aligned}\right\}$

18. $\left.\begin{aligned}\frac{x-a}{b-a}&=\frac{y+b}{a+b},\\ \frac{x+a}{a-b}&=\frac{y-b}{a+b}.\end{aligned}\right\}$

19. $x+y+z=6$, $2x+y-z=1$, $3x-y+z=4$.

20. $\frac{x}{a}+\frac{y}{b}=1$, $\frac{x}{3a}+\frac{y}{6b}=\frac{2}{3}$.

21. $\left.\begin{aligned}&x-y+z=n,\\ &\frac{x}{b+c-a}=\frac{y}{c+a-b}=\frac{z}{a+b-c}.\end{aligned}\right\}$

22. $\left.\begin{aligned}y+z&=x+4a,\\ z+x&=y+2a,\\ x+y&=z.\end{aligned}\right\}$

23. Solve the simultaneous equations :

$$\text{(i) } y^2=px,\ y=mx+\frac{p}{4m};$$

$$\text{(ii) } \frac{x}{2}+\frac{y}{3}+\frac{z}{4}=\frac{x}{3}+\frac{y}{4}+\frac{z}{5}=\frac{x}{4}+\frac{y}{5}+\frac{z}{6}=1.$$

24. From the relation $y=\dfrac{3x^2-10x+9}{5x^2-16x+14}$,

prove that y is never greater than $\frac{2}{3}$ nor less than $\frac{1}{2}$, for real values of x.

Problems producing simultaneous equations.—In preceding examples the conditions of a given problem have been expressed in terms of one unknown quantity x. It is, however, much easier in many problems, and indeed indispensable in others, to use two or more unknown quantities. These are usually expressed by the letters x, y, z, ... In such equations it is necessary to obtain as many independent equations as there are unknown quantities involved. From these the solution is effected either by elimination or by substitution.

Ex. 1. If 9 horses and 7 cows sell for £300 and 6 horses and 13 cows sell for the same amount, what is the price of each?

(a) Let x denote the price of a horse, then $300-9x$ is the price of 7 cows.

$$\therefore\ \frac{300-9x}{7} \text{ is the price of each cow.}$$

Also, in the second case, $\dfrac{300-6x}{13}$ is the price of each cow.

$$\therefore\ \frac{300-9x}{7}=\frac{300-6x}{13};$$

$$\therefore\ x=£24, \text{ and } \frac{300-9x}{7}=£12.$$

(b) Let x denote the price of a horse and y the price of a cow.

Then $9x+7y=300.$ ....(i)

Also $6x+13y=300.$ ....(ii)

Multiply (i) by 2 and (ii) by 3 and subtract;

$$\therefore\ 18x+39y=900$$
$$18x+14y=600;$$
$$25y=300$$
$$\therefore\ y=£12.$$

And by substitution in (i), $x=£24.$

Ex. 2. A number consisting of three digits (those in the tens' and hundreds' places being equal) is 49 times the sum of its digits. If the order of the digits be reversed, the number so formed will be less than the original number by 297. Find the original number.

Let x, y and z denote the three digits. Then, the number required is represented by $100x+10y+z$. Also the sum of the digits is $x+y+z$.

Hence, $$100x+10y+z=49(x+y+z). \quad \text{(i)}$$

The number reversed would be $100z+10y+x$;

$$\therefore\ (100x+10y+z)-(100z+10y+x)=297. \quad \text{(ii)}$$

Also, as the digits in the tens' and hundreds' places are equal,

$$x=y. \quad \text{(iii)}$$

Substituting from (iii) in (i),

$$12x=48z, \text{ or } x=4z. \quad \text{(iv)}$$

Also, from (ii), $$x-z=3;$$

$$\therefore\ x=z+3.$$

Substituting this value in (iv), and we find

$$12(z+3)=48z;$$

$$\therefore\ 36z=36, \text{ or } z=1.$$

Hence, from (iv), $$x=4=y,$$

and the number required is 441.

Ex. 3. If 3 thalers exceed 11 francs and 59 francs exceed 16 thalers, the excess in each case being a halfpenny, find the English equivalents of the thaler and the franc.

Let x denote the value of a thaler and y the value of a franc.

Then, from the first condition,

$$3x-11y=\tfrac{1}{2}. \quad \text{(i)}$$

Also $$-16x+59y=\tfrac{1}{2}. \quad \text{(ii)}$$

Multiplying (i) by 16 and (ii) by 3 and adding,

$$y=9{\cdot}5.$$

Substituting in (i), $$3x=\tfrac{1}{2}+(11\times 9{\cdot}5)=105;$$

$$\therefore\ x=35.$$

Hence, the value of a thaler is $35d.$, and of a franc is $9\tfrac{1}{2}d.$

Ex. 4. The receipts of a railway company are apportioned as follows: 49 per cent. for working expenses, 10 per cent. for the reserved fund, a guaranteed dividend of 5 per cent. on one-fifth of the capital, and the remainder, £40,000, for division amongst the holders of the rest of the stock, being a dividend at the rate of 4 per cent. per annum. Find the capital and the receipts.

Let C denote the capital and R the receipts; 41 %, or $0 \cdot 41R$, is available for dividend. Of this $\frac{1}{20}$ of $\frac{C}{5}$, or $0 \cdot 01C$, goes to pay guaranteed dividend;

$\therefore$ $0 \cdot 41R - 0 \cdot 01C$ remains for ordinary dividend;

$$\therefore \; 0 \cdot 41R - 0 \cdot 01C = 40000. \quad \text{.................................(i)}$$

Also $$0 \cdot 8C = 25 \times 40000;$$

$$\therefore \; C = \pounds 1{,}250{,}000.$$

Substituting in (i),

$$0 \cdot 41R - 12500 = 40000;$$

$$\therefore \; R = \frac{5250000}{41} = \pounds 128048.\ 15s.\ 7d.$$

When the data of a problem furnishes only one equation involving two unknown quantities, the ratio between the two may in some cases be obtained.

Ex. 5. An alloy of copper, zinc, and tin contains 91 per cent. of copper, 6 of zinc, and 3 of tin. A second alloy containing copper and tin only is fused with the first, and the resulting alloy is found to contain 88 per cent. of copper, 4·875 of zinc, and 7·125 of tin. Find the proportion of copper and tin in the second alloy.

We may assume that in order to form the resulting alloy x parts of the second alloy are fused with 100 parts of the first. Then, as there is no zinc in the second alloy, we have the relation,

$$6 = \frac{4 \cdot 875}{100}(100 + x);$$

$$\therefore \; 4 \cdot 875x = 600 - 487 \cdot 5 = 112 \cdot 5;$$

$$\therefore \; x = \frac{112500}{4875} = \frac{300}{13}.$$

Thus, in the resulting $\frac{1600}{13}$ parts of new alloy we have $\frac{88}{100} \times \frac{1600}{13}$ parts of copper.

Hence $\left(88 \times \frac{16}{13} - 91\right)$ parts of copper come from second alloy, and in like manner $\left(7 \cdot 125 \times \frac{16}{13} - 3\right)$ parts of tin come from second alloy;

therefore proportion is $$\frac{\left(88 \times \frac{16}{13} - 91\right)}{7 \cdot 125 \times \frac{16}{13} - 3} = \frac{225}{13} \div \frac{75}{13} = \frac{3}{1}.$$

Ex. 6. The total increase in the number of undergraduates of a certain university in a recent year over the number in the preceding year was $2\frac{1}{2}$ per cent. In the number of resident undergraduates there was an increase of 4 per cent., and in the number of non-resident undergraduates a decrease of 11 per cent. Find the ratio of the number of non-resident to the number of resident undergraduates.

Let x denote the number of resident undergraduates, and y the number of non-resident in the latter year, then we have, considering the ratio in the former year,

$$\frac{100}{104}x+\frac{100}{89}y=\frac{100}{102\cdot5}(x+y),$$

or
$$89\times1025x+104\times1025y=89\times1040(x+y);$$

$$\therefore\ 89x=936y,$$

$$\frac{x}{y}=\frac{936}{89}.$$

Ex. 7. The perimeter of a right-angled triangle is six times as long as the shortest side. Find the ratio of the two perpendicular sides.

Let c denote the hypotenuse, a the shortest side, and b the remaining side.

Then $a+b+c=6a$, or $b+c=5a$. ....(1)

Also $a^2+b^2=c^2$.

Hence, substituting from (1),

$$c^2=(5a-b)^2$$
$$=25a^2-10ab+b^2;$$

$$\therefore\ a^2+b^2=c^2=25a^2-10ab+b^2,$$

or
$$24a^2=10ab;$$

$$\therefore\ \frac{a}{b}=\frac{5}{12}.$$

Ex. 8. An examiner has marked a set of papers; the highest number of marks is 185, the lowest 42. He desires to change all his marks according to a linear law converting the highest number of marks into 250 and the lowest into 100; show how he may do this, and state the converted marks for papers already marked 60, 100, 150.

Let $y=ax+b$ denote the linear law, where y denotes the

number of marks on the new system, and x denotes the number of marks on the old system.

Then, substituting the given values, we have

$$250 = 185a + b \quad \text{(i)}$$
$$100 = 42a + b \quad \text{(ii)}$$

Subtracting, $150 = 143a$;

$$\therefore\ a = \frac{150}{143};$$

and from (ii), $b = 100 - \frac{42 \times 150}{143} = \frac{8000}{143}$.

Hence, if y_1, y_2 and y_3 denote the respective number of marks,

then $$y_1 = \frac{150}{143} \times 60 + \frac{8000}{143} = 118 \cdot 9,$$

$$y_2 = \frac{150}{143} \times 100 + \frac{8000}{143} = 160 \cdot 8,$$

$$y_3 = \frac{150}{143} \times 150 + \frac{8000}{143} = 213 \cdot 3.$$

Ex. 9. The electrical resistance of a wire of given material varies directly as the length and inversely as the area of the cross section of the wire.

Find the ratio of the electrical resistance of a wire 50 metres long and weighing 75 grams to that of a wire, of the same material, 100 ft. long and weighing one ounce.

1 metre = 39·37 inches, and 1 kilog. = 2·2 lbs.

Let l denote the length, d thickness of the wire.

Electrical resistance $\propto \frac{l}{d^2}$, *i.e.* $\frac{l}{r^2}$.

Weight $(w) = \rho\pi r^2 l$.

Electrical resistance of wire

$$= m\frac{l}{r^2} = m\frac{l}{\frac{w}{\rho\pi l}} = \frac{ml^2\pi\rho}{w},$$

where m is a constant.

Electrical resistance of first wire

$$= \frac{m\rho\pi(50 \times 39 \cdot 37)^2}{\frac{75}{1000} \times 2 \cdot 2} = \frac{m\rho\pi(50 \times 3937)^2}{75 \times 22},$$

where weight and length are reduced to pounds and inches respectively.

Similarly, resistance of second wire

$$=\frac{m\rho\pi(100\times 12)^2}{\frac{1}{16}}=16m\rho\pi(100\times 12)^2$$

Required ratio

$$=\frac{m\rho\pi(50\times 3937)^2}{75\times 22}\div 16m\rho\pi(100\times 12)^2=1\cdot 0193.$$

EXERCISES. X.

1. In a certain fraction the difference between the numerator and denominator is 12, but if each be increased by 5 the value of the fraction becomes $\frac{3}{4}$. What is the fraction?

2. If a mixture of gold and silver in which 0·875 is gold, is worth £15. What will be the value of a mixture of equal weight in which 0·625 is gold? Assuming that the value of gold is 16 times that of silver.

3. If a fraction be such that its denominator exceeds twice its numerator by unity, prove that if its numerator and denominator be each increased by unity, the result will be $\frac{1}{2}$.

4. When unity is added both to the numerator and to the denominator of a certain fraction the result is $\frac{3}{2}$; but when unity is subtracted the result is 2. Find the fraction.

5. Divide £1015 among A, B and C, so that B shall receive £5 less than A, and C as many times B's share as there are shillings in A's share.

6. Two passengers have together 500 lbs. of luggage and are charged 5*s.* and 5*s.* 10*d.* respectively for the excess above the weight allowed. If the luggage had all belonged to one of them he would have been charged 15*s.* 10*d.* How much luggage is a passenger allowed free of charge?

7. A sum of £3000 is to be divided among A, B and C. If each had received £1000 more than he actually does, the sums received would be proportional to the numbers 4, 3, 2. Determine the actual shares.

8. Divide 279 into two parts; such that one-third of the first part is less by 15 than one-fifth of the second part.

9. A person lends £5000 at a certain rate of interest. At the end of one year the principal is repaid together with the interest. He then spends £25, and lends the remainder at the same rate of interest as before. At the end of one year more the principal and interest amount to £5382; find the rate of interest.

10. A sum of money amounts to £546 in three years at simple interest, and to £726 in seven years. Find the sum and rate per cent.

11. A body is made up partly of brass and partly of iron; if the brazen parts had been iron, and the iron parts brass, its weight would have been $\frac{21}{19}$ths of what it actually is. Given that the weights of equal volumes of brass and iron are as 9 to 7, find how much of the volume is of iron, and how much of brass.

12. Divide the number 500 into two parts such that the sum of $\frac{1}{5}$th the greater and $\frac{1}{7}$th the smaller shall be less than the difference of the parts by 60.

13. The volumes of two right cylinders are as 11 : 8, the height of the first is to that of the second as 3 : 4. If the base of the first has an area 16·5 sq. ft., what is the area of the base of the second?

14. Between one census and the next, the native population of a town increased by 8 per cent., while the foreigners decreased from 200 to 150. The increase in the total population was 7 per cent.; what was the total population of the second census?

Quadratic equations.—As already indicated (p. 68), when a given equation expressed in its simplest form involves the *square* of the unknown quantity it is called a **quadratic** equation. Such an equation may contain only the square of the unknown quantity, or it may include both the square and the first power.

Ex. 1. Solve the equation $x^2 - 16 = 0$.

$$\therefore \; x^2 = 16, \quad x = \pm 4.$$

It is necessary to insert the double sign before the value obtained for x, as both $+4$ and -4 when squared give 16.

The solution of a given quadratic equation containing both x^2 and x can be effected by one of the three following methods.

First method.—The method most widely known, and generally used, may be stated as follows:

Bring all the terms containing x^2 and x to the left-hand side of the equation, and the remaining terms to the right-hand side.

Simplify, if necessary, and divide all through by the coefficient of x^2.

Finally, add the square of one-half the coefficient of x to both sides of the equation, take the square root of both sides, and the required roots can be readily obtained.

Ex. 2. Solve the equation $x^2 - 11x - 26 = 0$.

$$x^2 - 11x = 26 \qquad \text{(i)}$$

Add to each side the square of one-half the coefficient of x;

$$\therefore \; x^2 - 11x + \left(\frac{11}{2}\right)^2 = 26 + \frac{121}{4} = \frac{225}{4},$$

or

$$\left(x - \frac{11}{2}\right)^2 = \left(\frac{15}{2}\right)^2;$$

$$\therefore \; x - \frac{11}{2} = \pm\frac{15}{2}; \qquad \text{(ii)}$$

$$\therefore \; x = \frac{11}{2} \pm \frac{15}{2} = 13 \text{ or } -2.$$

Second method.—What may be termed the second and the third methods of solution may be indicated in the following manner. Where the given equation can be resolved into factors, then the value of x which makes either of these factors vanish, is a value of x which satisfies the given equation.

Ex. 3. Solve the equation $x^2 - 11x - 26 = 0$.

Since $$x^2 - 11x - 26 = (x+2)(x-13) = 0,$$

$$x - 13 = 0, \text{ when } x = 13,$$

$$\text{and } x + 2 = 0, \text{ when } x = -2.$$

Hence $x = 13$ or $x = -2$ is a solution of the equation and 13 and -2 are the roots of the given equation.

Third method.—A given equation can be written in the form $y = f(x)$, p. 68. Substitute values for x and calculate corresponding values of y. Plot on squared paper and draw a curve through the plotted points. Then **as a function can only change sign when x passes through one of its roots,** it follows that the points of intersection of the curve with the axis of x are the roots required.

The general solution may be obtained as follows:—

$f(x)$ may be written $\quad ax^2 + bx + c = 0.$

Then $$x^2 + \frac{b}{a}x = -\frac{c}{a}.$$

Adding to each side the square of half the coefficient of x, or $\left(\frac{b}{2a}\right)^2$, we have

$$x^2+\frac{b}{a}x+\left(\frac{b}{2a}\right)^2=\frac{b^2}{4a^2}-\frac{c}{a}=\frac{b^2-4ac}{4a^2};$$

$$\therefore\ x=-\frac{b}{2a}\pm\frac{\sqrt{b^2-4ac}}{2a} \quad\text{.................... (i)}$$

The following important cases occur.

If b^2 is greater than $4ac$, i.e. $b^2>4ac$, there are two values of x, or roots, satisfying the given equation and the curve cuts the axis in two points.

If $b^2=4ac$ the two roots are equal and the curve touches the axis; each is $-\frac{b}{2a}$.

If $b^2<4ac$, there are no real values which satisfy the given equation, and the roots are said to be imaginary, and the curve does not meet the axis.

Ex. 4. $2x^2-8x+6=0$.

Solving this equation in the usual manner, the roots of the equation are found to be 1 or 3.

Or, by substitution in the formula,

$$x=-\frac{b}{2a}\pm\frac{\sqrt{b^2-4ac}}{2a},$$

$a=2,\ b=-8,\ c=6$;

$$\therefore\ x=\frac{8}{4}\pm\frac{\sqrt{64-4\times2\times6}}{4}$$

$$=2\pm1=1 \text{ or } 3.$$

Ex. 5. $2x^2-4x+2=0$.

$$x=\frac{4}{4}\pm\frac{\sqrt{16-4\times2\times2}}{4};$$

$$\therefore\ x=1.$$

In this equation $b^2=4ac$.

Ex. 6. $2x^2-4x+3=0$.

Here $a=2,\ b=-4,\ c=3$.

$$x=\frac{4}{4}\pm\frac{\sqrt{16-4\times2\times3}}{4}.$$

Here $b^2<4ac$, and the roots are imaginary.

All these results are readily understood by using squared paper.

Let $y=f(x)$, then for a series of values of x the corresponding values of y can be calculated. The curve passing through the plotted points will for all positive values of y lie above the axis of x and below for negative values. In passing from positive to negative values the curve must obviously cross, or intersect, the axis of x. Each such point gives a value of x which satisfies the given equation, or, is a root of the equation.

Thus, by making the graph of $y=f(x)$, and measuring the intercepts on the axis of x, we may obtain approximately the values of x which make y equal to zero.

By assuming values of x in the neighbourhood of such a point, or points, and plotting the values obtained for y to a larger scale, a solution of a given equation to any desired degree of accuracy can be obtained.

The two points of intersection may coincide; the axis of x is then a tangent to the curve. This corresponds to the case of equal roots.

The plotted curve may not touch, or intersect, the axis of x; the values or roots of the given equation are then said to be imaginary.

Ex. 7. Solve the equation $x^2-4{\cdot}79x+4{\cdot}843=0$.

Let $y=x^2-4{\cdot}79x+4{\cdot}843$.

When $x=0,\ y=4{\cdot}843$;

when $x=1,\ y=1{\cdot}053$.

Substitute other values for x; calculate values of y and tabulate as follows:

x	0	1	2	3	4
y	4·843	1·053	- 0·737	- 0·527	1·683

From the tabulated values of x and y a change of sign is seen to occur in passing from $x=1$ to $x=2$, and again from $x=3$ to $x=4$. It is clear that one root lies between each pair of these values. Plot the tabulated values of x and y, the curve representing the equation passes through the plotted points and intersects the axis of x at points E and F (Fig. 16). By measuring the distances of these points from the origin we obtain the values of x, or roots which satisfy the equation. These are found to be 1·45 and 3·34 respectively. If required to find the numerical values of the roots to a higher order of

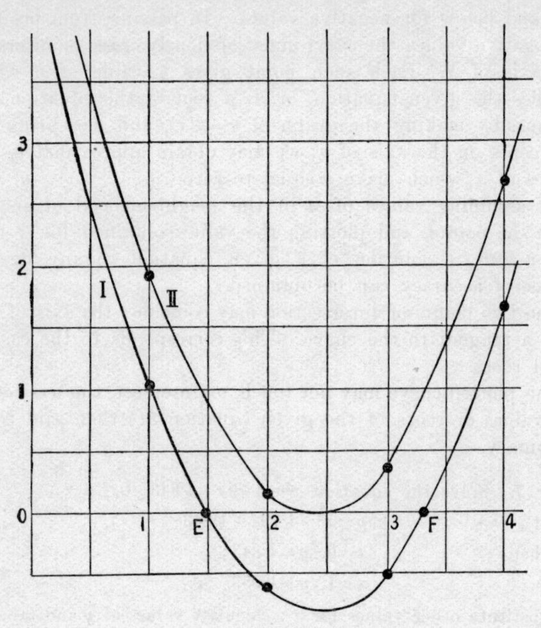

FIG. 16.

accuracy than three figures, then the curve near to E and F may be plotted to a larger scale, and the values of x determined to any necessary degree of accuracy.

Ex. 8. Solve the equation $x^2 - 4{\cdot}79x + 5{\cdot}736025 = 0$.

As before, values of y corresponding to various values of x should be calculated and tabulated as follows:

x	0	1	2	3	4
y	5·736	1·946	0·156	0·366	2·576

Plot these values and draw a curve passing through the plotted points. It touches the axis of x at the point $x=2\cdot395$ (approx.). It will be noticed that in this case $b^2=4ac$, as on p. 90.

If the value of c is increased, b and a remaining the same, then the roots are imaginary, and the curve does not cut the axis of x.

Another graphical method may be used to obtain the solution of a quadratic equation.

Let the equation be,

$$x^2-bx+c=0. \qquad \text{(i)}$$

Set off on squared paper from any convenient point O a distance $OA=b$; draw AB, equal to c, and OD, equal to unity, perpendicular to OA (Fig. 17).

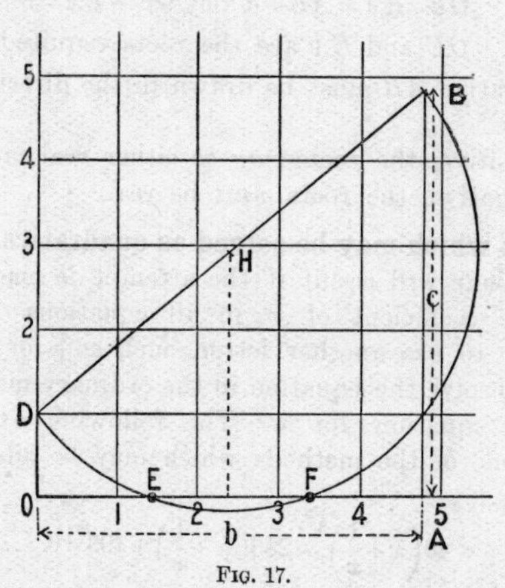

FIG. 17.

Join DB; and on DB as diameter describe a semicircle. The two points of intersection of the semicircle with the line OA are two roots required.

Ex. 9. Solve the equation, $x^2-4\cdot79x+4\cdot843=0$.

Comparing this equation with (i) it is seen that $b=4\cdot79$, $c=4\cdot843$. Hence, make $OA=4\cdot79''$ and $AB=4\cdot843.''$ Finally, $OD=1''$. Join BD. Then a semicircle described on BD as diameter cuts the line OA at points E and F, where $OE=1\cdot45''$ and $OF=3\cdot34''$, giving the two values required.

Ex. 10. Solve the equation $x^2 - 4{\cdot}79\,x + 5{\cdot}736 = 0$.

Setting off AB equal to $c = 5{\cdot}736$, the semicircle, on DB as diameter, touches OA approximately, or, in other words, the two points of intersection are coincident, and the quadratic has two equal roots. If c be increased, b remaining constant, the semicircle moves away from the line OA, and the roots become imaginary.

A proof of the preceding construction may be obtained as follows:

Let D' denote the point of intersection of the semicircle with the vertical through B. Then because the centre of the semicircle bisects DB, $OE = FA$, and $AD' = OD =$ unity.

By property of chords of a circle $AF \,.\, AE = AD' \,.\, AB$;

$$\therefore\ OE \,.\, EA = AB = c, \text{ but } OE + EA = b;$$

$$\therefore\ OE \text{ and } EA \text{ are the roots required.}$$

If c is negative AB must be drawn in the direction opposite to OD.

If c is positive, the roots *may be* either real or imaginary.

If c is negative, the roots *must* be real.

Equations which may be solved as quadratics.—Much unnecessary labour will result if the attempt is made to obtain unity as the coefficient of x^2 in all equations. It may be found better to use another letter, such as y or z, and then to proceed to solve the equation in the ordinary manner, finally solving the equation for x. The following examples will illustrate some of the methods which may be adopted:

Ex. 11. Solve

$$40\left(x + \frac{1}{x}\right)^2 - 286\left(x + \frac{1}{x}\right) + 493 = 0. \quad \text{(i)}$$

Put

$$y = x + \frac{1}{x}. \quad \text{(ii)}$$

The equation becomes

$$40y^2 - 286y = -493;$$

$$\therefore\ y^2 - \frac{143}{20}y = -\frac{493}{40};$$

$$\therefore\ y^2 - \frac{143}{20}y + \left(\frac{143}{40}\right)^2 = -\frac{493}{40} + \left(\frac{143}{40}\right)^2 = \frac{729}{1600};$$

$$\therefore\ y = \frac{143}{40} \pm \frac{27}{40} = \frac{17}{4}, \text{ or } \frac{29}{10}.$$

From (ii), $$\frac{17}{4}=x+\frac{1}{x};$$

$$\text{or } x^2-\frac{17}{4}x=-1,$$

$$\therefore\ x=\frac{17}{8}\pm\frac{15}{8}=4,\ \text{or}\ \frac{1}{4}.$$

Putting $$x+\frac{1}{x}=\frac{29}{10},$$

then $$x=2\tfrac{1}{2},\ \text{or}\ \frac{2}{5}.$$

Hence the values are **4, $\frac{1}{4}$, $2\frac{1}{2}$, or $\frac{2}{5}$.**

Ex. 12. Solve the equations :

(i) $(x^2-4x+3)^2-8(x^2-4x+3)=0$,

(ii) $2x^2-5x+\dfrac{21}{2x^2-5x}=10$.

(i) Take out the common factor (x^2-4x+3),

then $$(x^2-4x+3)(x^2-4x+3-8)=0,$$

i.e. $$(x^2-4x+3)(x^2-4x-5)=0.$$

Hence, by factorising each quadratic factor,

$$(x-3)(x-1)(x-5)(x+1)=0,$$

from which

$$x=3,\ 1,\ 5\ \text{or}\ -1.$$

(ii) Let $y=2x^2-5x$, then

$$y+\frac{21}{y}=10,$$

or $$y^2+21=10y;$$

$$\therefore\ y^2-10y+21=0,$$

or $$(y-7)(y-3)=0.$$

Putting back the value of y,

$$(2x^2-5x-7)(2x^2-5x-3)=0,$$

i.e. $$(2x-7)(x+1)(2x+1)(x-3)=0;$$

$$\therefore\ x=3{\cdot}5,\ -1,\ -0{\cdot}5\ \text{or}\ 3.$$

Ex. 13. Solve $x^2+\frac{9}{x^2}-4\left(x+\frac{3}{x}\right)-6=0.$

Let $$y=x+\frac{3}{x},$$

then $$y^2=x^2+6+\frac{9}{x^2}, \quad \text{or} \quad x^2+\frac{9}{x^2}=y^2-6.$$

Hence the equation becomes
$$y^2-6-4y-6=0,$$
or $$y^2-4y-12=0,$$
i.e. $$(y-6)(y+2)=0,$$
giving $$y=6 \text{ or } -2.$$
When $y=6$,
$$x+\frac{3}{x}=6,$$
i.e. $$x^2-6x+3=0;$$
$$\text{or} \quad (x-3)^2=6,$$
$$\therefore x=3\pm\sqrt{6}.$$
Similarly when $y=-2$,
$$x^2+2x+3=0, \quad \text{or} \quad (x+1)^2=-2,$$
hence the roots are imaginary, since $\sqrt{-2}$ is unreal.

The values satisfying the given equation are
$$x=3\pm\sqrt{6}=5{\cdot}45, \ 0{\cdot}55.$$

Equations reducible to quadratics.—Equations of the fourth degree can in some cases be solved as two quadratic equations.

Ex. 14. Solve (i) $x^4-17x^2+16=0,$

(ii) $(x-4)(x+5)(x-6)(x+7)=504.$

(i) By factorisation, the equation becomes
$$(x^2-1)(x^2-16)=0;$$
$$\therefore x^2=1 \quad \text{or} \quad 16,$$
so that $$x=\pm 1 \quad \text{or} \quad \pm 4.$$

(ii) Noting that $-4+5=-6+7$, the equation becomes
$$(x^2+x-20)(x^2+x-42)=504,$$
or $$(x^2+x)^2-62(x^2+x)+840=504;$$
$$\therefore (x^2+x)^2-62(x^2+x)+336=0,$$
hence $$(x^2+x-6)(x^2+x-56)=0,$$
or $$(x-2)(x+3)(x-7)(x+8)=0;$$
$$\therefore x=2, \ -3, \ 7 \quad \text{or} \quad -8.$$

Relations between the coefficients and the roots of a quadratic equation.—In the preceding examples we have been able, from a given quadratic equation, to find the roots, or the values, which satisfy the given equation. The converse of this is often required, *i.e.* to form a quadratic equation with given roots.

It has been already seen that if we can resolve the left-hand side of the given equation, when reduced to its simplest form, into factors, then the value of x which makes either of these factors zero, is a value of x which satisfies the given equation.

Thus, the roots of the equation $(x-\alpha)(x-\beta)=0$ are α and β.

Conversely, an equation having for its roots α and β is

$$(x-\alpha)(x-\beta)=0.$$

Hence, if α and β denote the roots of the equation,

$$ax^2+bx+c=0.$$

We have $\quad ax^2+bx+c\equiv a(x-\alpha)(x-\beta)$;

$$\therefore\ ax^2+bx+c\equiv a(x^2-\alpha x-\beta x+\alpha\beta)$$
$$=a\{x^2-(\alpha+\beta)x+\alpha\beta\}.$$

Comparing coefficients on both sides

$$a(\alpha+\beta)=-b \text{ and } a\alpha\beta=c;$$

$$\therefore\ \alpha+\beta=-\frac{b}{a} \text{ and } \alpha\beta=\frac{c}{a};$$

therefore, when the coefficient of x^2 is unity, the sum of the roots is equal to the coefficient of x with its sign changed; and the product of the roots is equal to the remaining term.

Ex. 15. Form the quadratic equations having roots 1 and 4.

Here $\quad (x-1)(x-4)=x^2-5x+4$;

$\therefore$ Required equation is $x^2-5x+4=0$.

Ex. 16. Form the quadratic equation having roots

$$-3+\sqrt{2} \text{ and } -3-\sqrt{2}.$$

Here we have $(x+3-\sqrt{2})(x+3+\sqrt{2})=(x+3)^2-2$;

$\therefore$ the required equation is $x^2+6x+7=0$.

Ex. 17. Form the quadratic equation having roots a and $\frac{1}{a}$.

Here $$(x-a)\left(x-\frac{1}{a}\right);$$

$$\therefore \text{ required equation is } x^2-\frac{a^2+1}{a}x+1=0.$$

EXERCISES. XI.

Solve the equations:

1. $x^2-5x+4=0$.
2. $x^2-6x+8=0$.
3. $x^2+7x+12=0$.
4. $x^2-7{\cdot}08x+11{\cdot}875=0$.
5. $x^2-6{\cdot}09x+9{\cdot}179=0$.
6. $\frac{x}{2}+\frac{x-4}{x+4}=\frac{x}{3}$.
7. $\frac{5}{x}+\frac{x-7}{x^2}=\frac{11}{9}$.
8. $\frac{3x^2-27}{x^2+3}+\frac{90+4x^2}{x^2+9}=7$.
9. $x^2+6x-35=0$.
10. $\frac{9}{x}+\frac{25x}{x-1}+9=0$.
11. $m\left(x-\frac{1}{x}\right)+n\left(x+\frac{1}{x}\right)=0$.
12. $\frac{1}{x+a}+\frac{1}{x+b}=\frac{1}{a-x}+\frac{1}{b-x}$.

13. Prove that the roots of $x^2+px+q=0$ are equal when $p^2-4q=0$; also that one is half the other, if $9q=2p^2$.

14. If α and β are the roots of the equation $x^2+px+q=0$, express $\alpha^2+\beta^2$ and $\alpha^3+\beta^3$ in terms of p and q.

15. Solve the quadratic equation
$$x=\frac{16}{15}+\frac{1}{x}.$$

Solve the equations:

16. $x^2+\frac{1}{x^2}+\frac{1}{3}\left(x+\frac{1}{x}\right)=3\frac{5}{12}$.

17. $x^2+y^2+4x-6y-13=0$,
$3x-2y-1=0$.

18. Find the roots of the equation $x^2+7x\sqrt{2}=60$, first in a surd form and then in a decimal form.

19. Form the quadratic equation whose roots are $3+\sqrt{2}$ and $3-\sqrt{2}$.

Solve the equations:

20. $x+a=\sqrt{\{a^2+x\sqrt{(2x^2-a^2)}\}}$.

21. $2x^2-3x-\sqrt{(4x^2-6x-1)}=2$.

22. $x^4-4x^2+3=0$.

23. $x+\dfrac{4a}{x+1}=2a+1.$ **24.** $x^2-5x+6=24-2\sqrt{(x^2-5x+6)}.$

25. $x+\dfrac{1}{x}=2(1+\sqrt{2}).$ **26.** $x^2+4x+\sqrt{(x^2+4x+10)}=2.$

27. $\dfrac{2x-3}{5}+\dfrac{1}{7}\left(5x-\dfrac{6x+4}{5x+1}\right)=x+\dfrac{5x+8}{3x-14}+\dfrac{1}{3}\left(\dfrac{x}{7}+\dfrac{x-9}{5}\right).$

28. $x^2+2\sqrt{x^2+2x+3}=12-2x.$

29. $cx+\dfrac{ac}{a+b}=(a+b)x^2.$ **30.** $2{\cdot}3x^2-6{\cdot}72x-13{\cdot}6=0.$

31. $0{\cdot}24x^2-4{\cdot}37x-8{\cdot}97=0.$

32. $zx=y^2,\ x+y+z=21,\ x^2+y^2+z^2=189.$

33. $x^3-2x^2-3x+4=0.$ **34.** $x^2-5{\cdot}17x+5{\cdot}985=0.$

35. $x=1+\cfrac{1}{2+\cfrac{1}{1+x}}.$ **36.** $\dfrac{1}{1+x}+\dfrac{1}{2+x}=\dfrac{1}{1-x}+\dfrac{1}{2-x}.$

37. $x^2+\dfrac{1}{x^2}+x+\dfrac{1}{x}=4.$

38. Find to three places of decimals, by the use of squared paper, the roots of the equation $x^2-5{\cdot}45x+7{\cdot}181=0.$

39. $x^2-2x\sqrt{3}+2=0.$

40. Show that if A and B are the roots of the equation $x^2-px+q=0$, then will $p=A+B$ and $q=AB$. Form the equation whose roots are 27 and -13.

41. Prove that the equation

$$\frac{(x^2-x+1)^3}{x^2(x-1)^2}=\frac{(a^2-a+1)^3}{a^2(a-1)^2}$$

is satisfied by

$$x=a,\ \frac{1}{a},\ \frac{a-1}{a},\ \frac{a}{a-1},\ \frac{1}{1-a},\ 1-a.$$

42. Prove that the roots of the equation

$$x^4-4x^2+1=0$$

are

$$\pm\sqrt{\left(\frac{\sqrt{3}+1}{\sqrt{3}-1}\right)}\ \text{ and }\ \pm\sqrt{\left(\frac{\sqrt{3}-1}{\sqrt{3}+1}\right)}.$$

Simplify these roots to a form suitable for numerical computation, and calculate each of them to three decimal places.

Simultaneous Quadratics.—Equations involving the squares of two unknown, or variable, quantities, such as x^2 and y^2, may be solved by methods similar in many respects to those adopted in the case of equations of the first degree. That is to say, we can, by multiplication, division, or substitution, obtain an equation involving only one unknown quantity. From this equation the value of the unknown quantity can be determined, and by substitution the value of the remaining unknown can be found.

If a given equation contains a factor of the form $x+y$, we may proceed to obtain $x-y$, and finally the separate values of x and y may be obtained by addition or subtraction.

Ex. 1. $x+y=11, \qquad \text{(i)}$

$xy=30. \qquad \text{(ii)}$

From (i), $x^2+2xy+y^2=121 \qquad \text{(iii)}$

Multiply (ii) by 4, $4xy \quad =120 \qquad \text{(iv)}$

Subtract (iv) from (iii); $\therefore\ x^2-2xy+y^2= \ 1,$

or $x-y=\pm 1.$

Hence, $x+y=11,$

$x-y=\pm 1;$

With the upper sign

$$\left.\begin{aligned} x+y&=11, \\ x-y&=\ 1, \end{aligned}\right\} \text{gives } x=6,\ y=5,$$

With the lower sign

$$\left.\begin{aligned} x+y&=\ 11, \\ x-y&=-1, \end{aligned}\right\} \text{gives } x=5,\ y=6.$$

Ex. 2. Solve the equations

$x^2+xy=84, \qquad \text{(i)}$

$xy+y^2=60. \qquad \text{(ii)}$

Adding (i) and (ii),

$$x^2+2xy+y^2=144;$$

$$\therefore\ x+y=\pm 12.$$

Also from (i), $x(x+y)=84.$

and from (ii), $y(x+y)=60;$

Substitute, $\therefore\ \pm 12x=84$ and $\pm 12y=60;$

$\therefore\ x=\pm 7$ and $y=\pm 5.$

The values required are $x=7,\ y=5,\ x=-7,\ y=-5.$

Ex. 3. Solve $x^3+4xy+y^3=38, \quad \text{......(i)}$

$x+y=2. \quad \text{......(ii)}$

From (ii), $y=2-x$. Substitute in (i);

$$\therefore\ x^3+4x(2-x)+(2-x)^3=38,$$
$$\text{or } 2x^2-4x-30=0;$$
$$\therefore\ x^2-2x-15=0,$$
$$\text{or } (x-5)(x+3)=0.$$

Hence $x=5$, or -3; and from (ii), $y=-3$, or 5.

Or, we may proceed as follows:

The given equation is $x^3+y^3+4xy=38$;

$$\therefore\ (x+y)(x^2-xy+y^2)+4xy=38.$$

But from (ii), $x+y=2$;

$\therefore$ by division $x^2-xy+y^2+2xy=19$,

$$\text{or } (x+y)^2-xy=19,$$
$$xy=-15.$$

And thus, from (ii), $x-y=8$;

$$\therefore\ x=5,\ y=-3,\ x=-3;\ y=5.$$

It will be noticed that this solution gives a method by which the order of one equation may sometimes be reduced by using the other.

EXERCISES. XII.

1. $x^2-2x+y^2-2y=14,\quad xy=5.$

2. $x^2-4y^2=8,\quad 2(x+y)=7.$

3. $3x^2+5xy-7x-3y=128,\quad 3y-2x=2.$

4. $3x+y=15,\quad 2x^2-3y^2=5.$

5. $\left.\begin{array}{r} x^2+xy-6y^2=6, \\ x^2+5xy+6y^2=30. \end{array}\right\}$

6. $\dfrac{1}{x}+\dfrac{1}{y}=\dfrac{x+y}{12}=\dfrac{7}{x+y+5}.$

7. $\left.\begin{array}{r} x^2-xy-y^2=\dfrac{xy}{15}, \\ x-y=2. \end{array}\right\}$

8. $4(x^2-y^2)=35,\ x-2y=2.$

9. $x^2+y=51,\ 2x^2+y^2=102.$

10. $\left.\begin{array}{r} \sqrt{(x+y)}+\sqrt{(x-y)}=5, \\ \sqrt{(x^2-y^2)}=4{\cdot}5. \end{array}\right\}$

11. $\left.\begin{array}{r} x^2+y=8, \\ 3x+2y=7. \end{array}\right\}$

12. $\left.\begin{array}{r} x^{-1}+y^{-1}+z^{-1}=13, \\ y^{-1}-x^{-1}=1, \\ x^{-1}y^{-1}-2z^{-1}=0. \end{array}\right\}$

13. $\left.\begin{array}{r} x^3+y^3+z^3-3a^3=0, \\ x+y+z=0, \\ x^2y+b^3=0. \end{array}\right\}$

14. $\left.\begin{array}{l} x+y+z=yz=12, \\ x^2=y^2+z^2. \end{array}\right\}$

15. $\left.\begin{array}{l} xy+x+y=7, \\ xz+x+z=8, \\ yz+y+z=17. \end{array}\right\}$

16. $\left.\begin{array}{r} x^2y+xy^2=0{\cdot}18, \\ x^3+y^3=0{\cdot}189. \end{array}\right\}$

17. $2y^2=2x^2+1=xy+2.$

Problems leading to quadratic equations.—One of the greatest difficulties experienced by a beginner in Algebra is to express the conditions of a given problem by means of algebraic symbols. The equations themselves may be obtained more or less readily, since the conditions are generally similar to those already explained, but some difficulty may be experienced in the interpretation of the results derived from quadratic equations. Since a quadratic equation which involves one unknown quantity has two solutions, and simultaneous quadratics involving two unknown quantities may have four solutions, it is clear that ambiguity may arise. It will be found, however, that although the equations may have four solutions, only one solution is as a rule applicable to the particular problem. The fact that several solutions can be found and only one applies to the problem is due to the circumstance that algebraic language is far more general than ordinary methods of expression. Usually no difficulty will be experienced in deciding which of the solutions is applicable to the problem in hand.

Ex. 1. A person bought a number of articles for £80; if he had received four more for the same price, they would have cost him £1 each less than he paid. What number did he buy?

Let x denote the given number.

Then the price of each is $\frac{80}{x}$.

If four more could be obtained for the same price, the price of each would be $\frac{80}{x+4}$.

That is,
$$\frac{80}{x+4}=\frac{80}{x}-1.$$

Multiplying both sides of the equation by $x(x+4)$,

$$80x = 80(x+4) - x^2 - 4x;$$

$$\therefore\ x^2 + 4x = 320,$$

$$x^2 + 4x + 2^2 = 320 + 4 = 324;$$

$$\therefore\ x = -2 \pm 18 = 16, \text{ or } -20.$$

It is obvious that 16 is the number required.

The value -20 does not correspond with the conditions of the problem, and is therefore not admissible.

Ex. 2. An arrow is projected vertically upwards with a velocity of 96 feet per second. After what time is it at a distance of 80 feet above the ground?

The relation between initial velocity (V), space described (S), and time (t) is given by the equation

$$S = Vt - \frac{1}{2}gt^2.$$

Take $g = 32$ and substitute the given values:

$$80 = 96t - \frac{1}{2} \times 32 \times t^2;$$

$$\therefore\ 16t^2 - 96t = -80,$$

or

$$t^2 - 6t + 3^2 = -5 + 9 = 4;$$

$$\therefore\ t = 3 \pm 2 = 5, \text{ or } 1.$$

Both values are admissible; the value one second indicating that the arrow is at the height of 80 feet at the end of the first second. It continues to rise until it reaches its greatest height and then begins to descend, and is at a height of 80 feet above the ground at the end of 5 seconds.

Ex. 3. Find two numbers whose difference is 8 and product 240.

Let x denote the least number, then $x+8$ is the greater.

Then

$$x(x+8) = 240,$$

or

$$x^2 + 8x = 240.$$

Hence,

$$x^2 + 8x + (4)^2 = 240 + 16 = 256,$$

$$x = -4 \pm 16 = 12,$$

and $x+8=20$, the greater number.

The rejected solution is $x = -20$, the greater number being $x+8 = -12$.

Ex. 4. If in the equation $ax^2+bx+c=0$, the relations between a, b and c are such that $a+b+3=0$, and $2a-c+1=0$, what must be the value of a in order that one of the roots may be 5, and what is then the value of the other root?

In the given equation $ax^2+bx+c=0$.

On substituting the given values,

$$25a+5b+c=0, \quad \text{.........(i)}$$
$$a+b+3=0, \quad \text{.........(ii)}$$
$$2a-c+1=0. \quad \text{.........(iii)}$$

Multiply (ii) by 5 and subtract from (i),

we obtain $$20a+c-15=0, \quad \text{.........(iv)}$$
$$2a-c+\ 1=0$$

Add (iii) and (iv), $$22a-14=0;$$
$$\therefore\ a=\frac{7}{11}.$$

And by substitution, $$c=\frac{25}{11},\ b=-\frac{40}{11};$$

$$\therefore\ \frac{7}{11}x^2-\frac{40}{11}x+\frac{25}{11}=0.$$

This is the form of the equation corresponding to the conditions of the problem; $\therefore\ 7x^2-40x+25=0$,

or $$(7x-5)(x-5)=0;$$
$$\therefore\ x=5, \text{ or } \frac{5}{7}.$$

Ex. 5. If $z=ax-by^3x^{\frac{1}{2}}$.

If $z=1{\cdot}32$ when $x=1$ and $y=2$,

and if $z=8{\cdot}58$ when $x=4$ and $y=1$,

find a and b. Then find z when $x=2$ and $y=0$.

Substitute the given values

$$1{\cdot}32=\ a-8b \quad \text{.........(i)}$$
$$8{\cdot}58=4a-2b \quad \text{.........(ii)}$$

Multiply (i) by 4 and subtract from (ii),

$$\therefore\ 3{\cdot}3=30b,$$
$$b=0{\cdot}11, \text{ and from (i) } a=2{\cdot}2.$$

Or, use the positive sign,

$$8{\cdot}58=4a+\ 2b$$
$$5{\cdot}28=4a+32b$$
$$3{\cdot}3=-30b;\quad \therefore\ b=-0{\cdot}11,\ a=2{\cdot}2.$$

Hence, the given relation becomes

$$z=2{\cdot}2x\mp0{\cdot}11y^3x^{\frac{1}{2}}.$$

When $x=2$, $y=0$, then $z=2{\cdot}2\times2=4{\cdot}4$.

In forming a system of algebraic equations of second degree from given data, it is, as in simple equations, a matter of little importance in many cases whether the given conditions are expressed in terms of one or more variables, but, in general, it is better to employ as few as possible.

Ex. 6. Find a proper fraction such that twice the denominator exceeds the square of the numerator by 2, and the product of the sum and difference of the numerator and denominator is 325.

Let $\frac{x}{y}$ denote the given fraction, then

$$x^2 = 2y - 2. \qquad \text{(i)}$$

Also, $$(y+x)(y-x) = 325, \qquad \text{(ii)}$$

or $$y^2 - x^2 = 325. \qquad \text{(iii)}$$

Add (iii) to (i);

$$\therefore\ y^2 = 2y + 323,$$

or $$y^2 - 2y - 323 = 0;$$

$$\therefore\ (y-19)(y+17) = 0;$$

$$\therefore\ y = 19, \text{ or } y = -17.$$

Substitute these values for y in (i),

when $y = 19$, $$x^2 = 38 - 2 = 36;$$

$$\therefore\ x = \pm 6.$$

when $y = -17$, $$x^2 = -34 - 2;$$

$$\therefore\ x = \pm\sqrt{-36}.$$

The latter value is clearly not admissible.

Hence, the fraction is $\frac{6}{19}$.

Ex. 7. There are two positive numbers whose sum is 6, and the ratio of the first to the second exceeds the ratio of the second to the first by 2; find the numbers.

Let x denote one number and y the other. Then the first condition that the sum of the two numbers is 6 gives the relation

$$x + y = 6. \qquad \text{(i)}$$

Also $$\frac{x}{y} - \frac{y}{x} = 2,$$

or $$x^2 - y^2 = 2xy. \qquad \text{(ii)}$$

Squaring both sides of (i),

$$x^2 + 2xy + y^2 = 36. \qquad \text{(iii)}$$

Adding (iii) to (ii), $2x^2=36,$

$$x=\pm 3\sqrt{2};$$

and from (i), $y=6\pm 3\sqrt{2}.$

The value of x $-3\sqrt{2}$ is inadmissible, since both numbers are positive. Hence, the two numbers are $3\sqrt{2}$ and $6-3\sqrt{2}$.

Ex. 8. A person lends £1500 in two separate sums, at the same rate of interest. The first sum is repaid, with interest, at the end of eight months, and amounts to £936; the second sum is repaid, with interest, at the end of 10 months and amounts to £630. Find the separate sums lent and the rate of interest.

Let x and y denote the two sums lent, and r denote the rate per £ per annum;

$$\therefore\ x+y=1500, \quad \text{.........(i)}$$

$$x+\frac{2}{3}rx=936, \quad \text{.........(ii)}$$

and

$$y+\frac{5}{6}ry=630; \quad \text{.........(iii)}$$

From (ii), $x(3+2r)=2808;\ \therefore\ x=\frac{2808}{3+2r}.$

From (iii), $y(6+5r)=3780;\ \therefore\ y=\frac{3780}{6+5r}.$

Substituting in (i), $\therefore\ \frac{2808}{3+2r}+\frac{3780}{6+5r}=1500,$

or $1250r^2+1575r-99=0;\ \therefore\ (50r-3)(25r+33)=0.$

The only admissible value is $r=\frac{3}{50}=\frac{6}{100}.$

This gives, $x=£900,\ y=£600.$

Ex. 9. Twice the area of the square on the diagonal of a rectangle equals five times the area of the rectangle; find the ratio of the sides.

Let x and y denote the two sides of the rectangle.

Area of rectangle $=xy$.

Twice the area of the square on the diagonal is $2(x^2+y^2)$.

Then

$$5xy=2(x^2+y^2);$$

$$\therefore\ 2x^2+2y^2-5xy=0,$$

or

$$x^2+y^2-\frac{5}{2}xy=0;$$

$$\therefore\ \left(x-\frac{1}{2}y\right)\left(x-2y\right)=0.$$

Hence, $x:y=1:2$ or $2:1$.

Hence, the sides are as $2:1$.

Ex. 10. When two equal rectangles are placed side by side it is found that the diagonal of the rectangle thus formed is three halves of the diagonal of one of the given rectangles. Find the ratio of the sides of one of the given rectangles.

Let the two rectangles be placed so as to form one rectangle $ABGF$ (Fig. 18).

Let the side $BC=x$ and the side $BA=y$.

$$BF=\sqrt{(2x)^2+y^2},\ BD=\sqrt{(x^2+y^2)}.$$

But $\quad BF=\frac{3}{2}BD$;

$$\therefore \sqrt{4x^2+y^2}=\frac{3}{2}\sqrt{x^2+y^2}.$$

Squaring,

$$4x^2+y^2=\frac{9}{4}(x^2+y^2),$$

or $\quad 16x^2+4y^2=9x^2+9y^2$;

$$\therefore 7x^2=5y^2.$$

$$\frac{x^2}{y^2}=\frac{5}{7};$$

$$\therefore \frac{x}{y}=\sqrt{\frac{5}{7}}.$$

Giving $\quad x:y=\sqrt{5}:\sqrt{7}.$

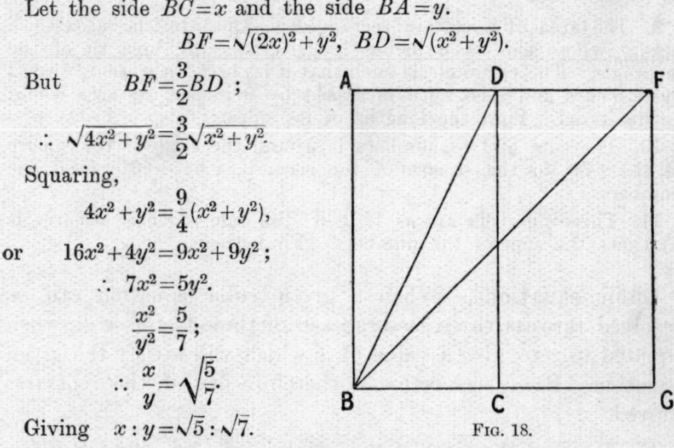

Fig. 18.

EXERCISES. XIII.

1. Eight more articles can be obtained for £1 when the price is 5s. less per dozen. Find the price.

2. The area of a rectangle is equal to the area of a square whose side is three inches longer than one of the sides of the rectangle. If the breadth of the rectangle be diminished by one inch and its length increased by two inches, the area is unaltered. Find the lengths of the sides.

3. The product of two numbers is 48 and the difference of their squares is to the sum of their cubes as 13 to 217. Find the numbers.

4. The diagonal of a rectangular field is to its length as 13 to 12, and its area is 4860 square yards. Find its length and breadth.

5. A certain sum of money had to be divided equally among 100 persons. If the sum had been increased by £5, each person would have received 5 per cent. more. What was the sum?

6. The area of a square, with the addition of 31 square feet, is equal to the area of a rectangle the sides of which are 2 and 3 feet respectively greater than the sides of the square. Find the length of a side of the square.

7. If a certain room were half as broad again as it is, it would be square; and if it were 3 ft. longer and 2 ft. wider its area would be 6 square yards greater than it is. Find its length and breadth.

8. Find two numbers such that their product is 91, and the difference of their squares is to the difference of their cubes as 20 to 309.

9. The area of a certain rectangle is equal to the area of a square whose side is 6 inches longer than the breadth of the rectangle. The rectangle is such that if its breadth were decreased by 3 inches and its length increased by 9 inches, its area would be unaltered. Find the lengths of its sides.

10. The sum of two numbers is 5, and the ratio of the square of the first to the square of the second is as 1 : 3. Find the numbers.

11. Three numbers are as 1, 2, 3: the sum of their squares is 63 times the sum of the numbers. Find them.

Cubic equations.—When a given cubic equation can be resolved into its three factors, each of these factors will, when equated to zero, give a value of x which will satisfy the given equation. Each such value is therefore one of the roots required.

Ex. 1. Find the roots of the equation $x^3-3x^2-10x+24=0$

$$x^3-3x^2-10x+24=(x-2)(x+3)(x-4).$$

Put each of the factors equal to zero, then

$$x-2=0\ ;\ \therefore\ x=2\ ;$$

$$x+3=0, \text{ or } x=-3\ ;\ x-4=0\ ;\ \therefore\ x=4.$$

Hence, the roots of the given equation are 2, -3, 4.

One method, which may often be used with a given cubic equation, is to bring all the terms of the equation to the left-hand side and simplify if necessary. Then, if by inspection, or by trial, one root can be obtained, the remaining roots may be obtained by solving the resulting quadratic equation.

Ex. 2. Solve the equation $x^3+3x^2-6x=8$.

Bring all the terms to the left-hand side, and the equation becomes $x^3+3x^2-6x-8=0$.

By trial $x=2$ satisfies the equation; hence, $x-2$ is a factor. Dividing the given equation by $x-2$, we obtain $x^2+5x+4=0$, the factors of which are $(x+1)(x+4)$. Hence, the roots of the equation are $x=2$, -1 and -4.

The methods just indicated become very laborious when the roots of an equation are not whole numbers; in such cases, as well as in those referred to, the values can be obtained by using squared paper.

Thus, Ex. 1 may be written in the form

$$y=x^3-3x^2-10x+24.$$

Put $x=1$, 2, etc. The following values of y can be obtained:

x	-3	-2	-1	0	1	2	3	4	5
y	0	24	30	24	12	0	-6	0	24

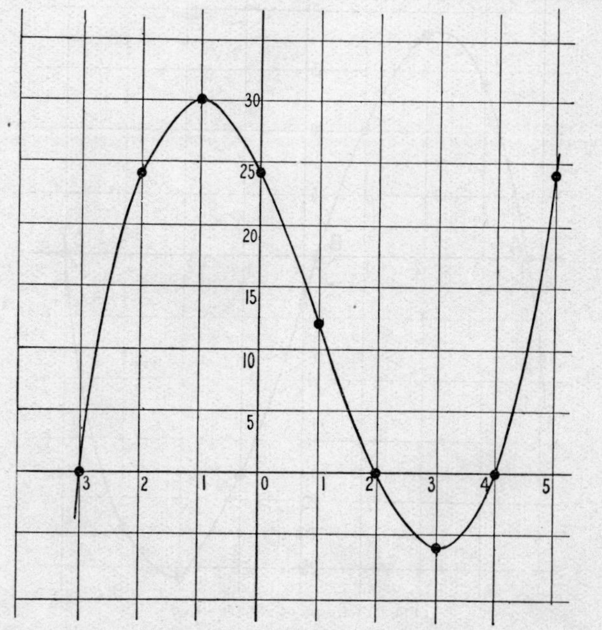

FIG. 19.—Graph of $x^3-3x^2-10x+24=0$.

Plot these values on squared paper and draw a fair curve through the plotted points as in Fig. 19. Then the curve is seen to intersect the axis of x at the three points $x = -3$, 2 and 4, and these are the roots required. It should be noticed that on one side of each of these points the value of x gives a positive value for y and on the other a negative value; hence, we know that if for two assumed values of x the corresponding values of y are different in sign, then the root required lies somewhere between these values. If necessary, that portion of the curve lying between these assumed values may be plotted to a larger scale and the value of x obtained to any desired degree of accuracy.

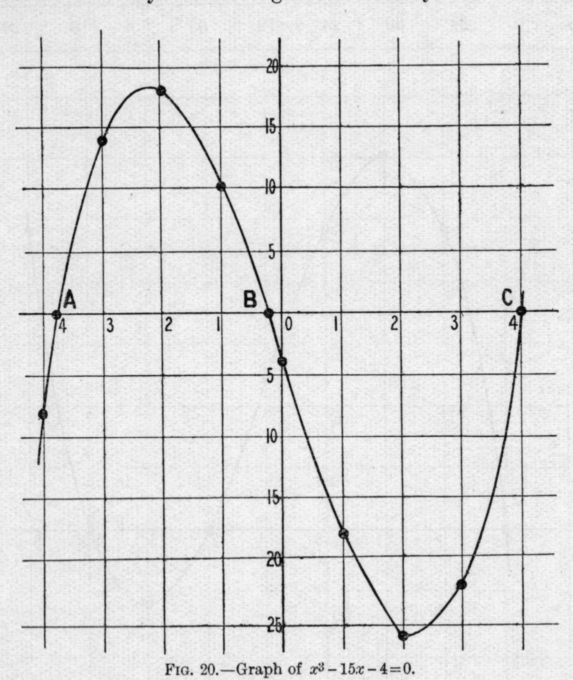

FIG. 20.—Graph of $x^3 - 15x - 4 = 0$.

Ex. 3. Solve the equation $x^3 - 15x - 4 = 0$.

Let $y = x^3 - 15x - 4$. Substituting the values 0, 1, 2, ... etc., for x, values of y can be calculated and tabulated as follows:

x	-4	-3	-2	-1	0	1	2	3	4	5
y	-8	14	18	10	-4	-18	-26	-22	0	46

Plot these values; then the curve passing through the plotted points (Fig. 20) is found to cross the axis of x between $x=-3$ and $x=-4$; also between 0 and -1, and at $x=4$. The values of x corresponding to $y=0$ can thus be obtained.

The roots of the given equation are found to be

$$x=-3{\cdot}732, \quad -0{\cdot}268, \quad 4.$$

Ex. 4. Solve the equation $x^3-0{\cdot}25x-15=0$.

We may write $\qquad x^3-0{\cdot}25x-15=y-y_1=0,$

where $\qquad y=x^3, \qquad$ ....(i)

and $\qquad y_1=0{\cdot}25x+15. \qquad$ ....(ii)

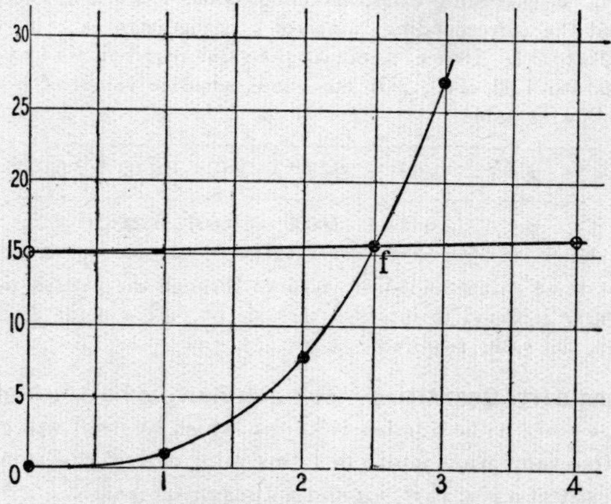

FIG. 21.—Intersection of $y=x^3$ and $y_1=0{\cdot}25x+15$.

The solution is given when $y-y_1=0$ or the value of x determined by the point of intersection of the curve denoted by (i) and the line denoted by (ii). Thus, for values of x and corresponding values of y, the former will give a curve passing through the plotted points; the latter, a straight line. The points of intersection of the line and curve will give values of x which will satisfy the given equation.

Thus, from (i), when

$$x=0,\ y=0;\ x=1,\ y=1;\ x=2,\ y=8;\ x=3,\ y=27.$$

From (ii), $x=0$, $y_1=15$; when $x=4$, $y_1=16$.

Plotting the former values we obtain the graph of $y=x^3$, the intersection of which with the graph of the latter values gives a point of intersection at f (Fig. 21), where the value of $x=2{\cdot}5$, and this is one of the roots required. Other examples may be treated in like manner.

If the given equation contains not only x^3 but also x^2, instead of a straight line we should have a second curve to be plotted; the intersection would give the value, or values, required.

Ex. 5. Find a value of x which satisfies the equation

$$x^2-5\log_{10}x-2{\cdot}531=0.$$

As in the preceding cases, assuming values 1, 1·5, 2·0, 2·1 for x, we find the corresponding values of y change sign as x increases from 2·0 to 2·1. Hence, to obtain the value required, we may take x equal to 1·99, 2·00, 2·01 etc., and calculate values of y as in the following table:

x	1·99	2·00	2·01	2·02	2·03
y	-0·065	-0·036	-0·007	0·023	0·052

Plot these values and draw a curve through the plotted points. The curve is found to intersect the axis of x at a point $x=2{\cdot}012$. This is the value required.

Imaginary Quantities.—The quadratic $x^2+a^2=0$ leads to $x=\pm\sqrt{-a^2}$; as no number is known which by itself will give a negative value when multiplied, this value of x may be supposed to consist of a real part $\pm a$ and an imaginary part $\sqrt{-1}$.

Graphically.—The real part $+a$ is measured in the direction OA (Fig. 5, p. 16), and the part $-a$ in the direction OA'; the multiplication by $\sqrt{-1}$ may be taken to denote the rotation of a line OA through 90° into the position OB, and multiplication by $(\sqrt{-1})^2$ as the rotation of OA through 180° into the position

OA'. Similarly, $(\sqrt{-1})^3$ corresponds to a rotation through 270° to OB' and $(\sqrt{-1})^4$ through 360° to the initial position OA.

It is usual to write $\sqrt{-1}=i$, so that $i^2=-1$, $i^3=-1\times i=-i$, $i^4=(-1)^2=+1$, $i^5=1\times i=i$ etc. Thus in the quadratic

$$ax^2+bx+c=0,$$

when b^2 is less than $4ac$ (p. 90) the imaginary roots may be written in the form $x=-\frac{b}{2a}\pm\frac{1}{2a}i\sqrt{4ac-b^2}$.

EXERCISES. XIV.

Solve the equations:

1. $x^3-12x^2-96x+512=0$.

2. $x^3-2x^2-3x+4=0$.

3. $8x^3-6x^2-3x+1=0$.

Find two roots of the equation:

4. $x^3-3a^2x+2a^3=0$.

Solve the equations:

5. $x^3-19x-30=0$.

6. $x^3-15x-4=0$.

7. $x^3-91x-330=0$.

8. $x^3-12x^2+36x=7$.

9. Find to two places of decimals the real positive root of

$$x^3+2x^2-4=0.$$

Find one root of each of the following equations:

10. $x^3+6x=20$.

11. $x^3-2x=5$.

12. $x^3-6x^2+18x=22$.

13. $x^3+9x-16=0$.

14. Show by plotting $y=x^4-4x^3-4x^2+16x+1$ between $x=-2$ and $x=4$ that the equation $x^4-4x^3-4x^2+16x+1=0$ has four real roots.

Find to two decimal places the value of the root which is numerically the greatest of the four.

15. Find two roots of the equation $x^3-12x=16$.

16. Show by plotting that the equation $x^3-2{\cdot}4x^2-3x+7{\cdot}2=0$ has three real roots, and find the least positive value of x which satisfies the given equation.

17. Solve the equation $x^3-3x^2+2{\cdot}6=0$.

18. Find a value of x which satisfies the equation

$$x^2-5\log_{10}x-2{\cdot}531=0.$$

CHAPTER VII.

GRAPHS. SOME APPLICATIONS OF SQUARED PAPER.

Graphs.—Any expression involving a variable, such as x, as well as known or unknown constants, may be briefly expressed by $f(x)$ [read as—function x].

Thus, we may write $f(x)=x^2-7x+12$.

The value of such a function may be denoted by y. Or $y=f(x)$, which is read as "y is a function of x."

Taking, for example, the former case

$$y=f(x)=x^2-7x+12,$$

then, by substituting various values for x, the corresponding values of y can be calculated. The various values of y thus depend on those given to x, and x is called the **independent variable** and y the **dependent variable.**

The line, straight or curved, which passes through the plotted points is called the **graph** of the function.

In many cases a few points are all that are necessary to enable such a curve to be drawn with sufficient accuracy. In the case of a straight line, two points are sufficient. It may be assumed that the reader is already familiar, from his previous work, with the linear equation

$$y=a+bx, \quad \text{..............................(1)}$$

in which, when x has the value 0, $y=a$, and the line makes the intercept on the axis of y equal to a.

If a is zero, the equation becomes $y=bx$, and denotes a line passing through the origin.

Use of squared paper.—When two variable quantities are connected by a relation such as $y=f(x)$, then, for assumed values of one, corresponding values of the other *can be calcu-*

lated. Using a sheet of squared paper, two convenient lines at right angles are assumed as axes, the simultaneous values may be represented by dots, or small crosses, and finally a curve passing through the plotted points may be drawn free-hand or by means of a flexible strip of metal or wood. In a similar manner, a series of *experimental results* may be plotted and a curve drawn so as to pass as evenly as possible among the points. In other words, about an equal number of the results should lie on each side of any small portion of the curve. Such a curve may be assumed to give the most trust-worthy average for the constants in a general formula, the amount of deviation of any observation from this curve may in the majority of cases, be assumed to be due to errors of observation.

In all cases, except the equation of the first degree, in which the curve connecting the plotted point becomes a straight line, it is difficult to obtain the relation, or law, connecting x and y.

By means of various artifices—some of which may be seen from the following examples—it is possible by plotting the logarithms x and y, or their reciprocals, etc., instead of their numerical values, to replace the curve by a straight line. From such a line the best average values for the two constants a and b in the equation $y=a+bx$ can be obtained.

Thus, if two variables x and y are connected by the relation $y=ax^n$, where a and n are known constants, then when a is known or assumed, the curves corresponding to various values of n can be drawn.

Thus, the equation $\mathbf{y}=\mathbf{ax}^n$ becomes, when $a=1$, $\mathbf{y}=\mathbf{x}^n$. Giving various values 1, 2, 3, $\frac{1}{2}$, $\frac{1}{3}$, etc., to the index n, then functions of the form $y=x^3$, $y=x^{\frac{1}{3}}$, etc., are obtained. Assuming values 0, 1, 2 ... for x, corresponding values of y can be found. The curves can be plotted, and are shown in Fig. 22. It will be seen that the curves $y=x^3$, $y=x^{\frac{1}{3}}$, and the straight line $y=x$ all intersect at the same point (1, 1).

It will also be noticed that, as the value of n is increased, the curve approaches closer and closer to the axis of x. Diminishing the value of n produces a similar effect with regard to the axis of y. This fact is of some importance in proceeding to plot tabulated values of x and y, and more particularly to obtain the law, or relation, between x and y. Thus, if on plotting given values, a curve somewhat of the nature of the curve marked $n=2$ (Fig. 22) is obtained, then it would at once suggest that the numerical magnitude of n be diminished. If, on doing so, a curve of the form $\left(n=\frac{1}{2}\right)$ results, the probable value of n would lie somewhere between the two assumed values.

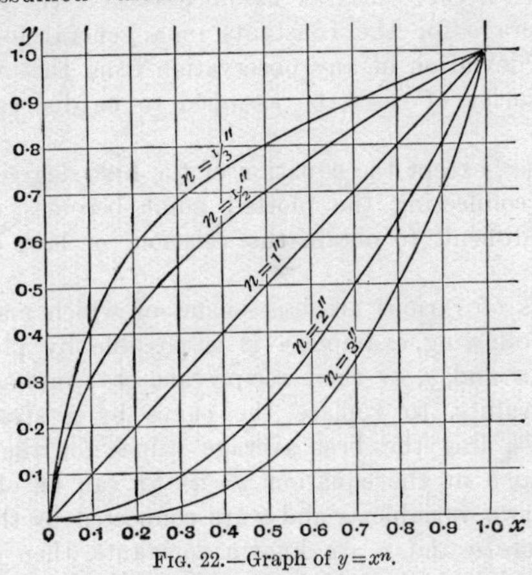

FIG. 22.—Graph of $y=x^n$.

In drawing a set, or family, of curves, as they are sometimes called, similar to the preceding examples, it will be found advantageous to use coloured pencils or crayons. Thus, the line "$n=1$" may be indicated in red; the curves below, where n is an integer, say in blue and green alternately; those above, where n is fractional, in green or yellow.

A good plan would be to draw on a piece of **transparent celluloid** a series of **standard curves** such as $y=x^n$ for various values of n, marking on each the value of n. This can be placed on a curve drawn through a series of plotted points, and the coincidence with one of the curves will suggest a probable value of n.

An important case of $y=ax^n$ ....(i)
occurs when n is negative. The equation then becomes

$$y=ax^{-n},$$

or

$$yx^n=a.$$

Assume a series of values for n, then for various values of x, corresponding values of y may be calculated, and the curves plotted.

When $n=-1$, then (i) becomes

$$xy=a \quad \text{.................................(ii)}$$

For a definite numerical value for a the curve may be plotted.

The relation expressed by (ii) gives approximately the curve of expansion for a gas such as air at constant temperature, and is often taken to represent the curve of expansion of superheated or saturated steam.

If p and v denote the *pressure* and *volume* respectively of a gas, instead of the form shown by (ii), the equation is usually written $pv=\text{constant}=c$, and is known as **Boyle's Law**; c is a constant, this is either given, or may be obtained from a pair of simultaneous values of p and v.

Ex. 1. Plot the curve $xy=9$;

$$\therefore y=\frac{9}{x}. \quad \text{................................(ii)}$$

From (ii),
when $x=1$, $y=9$;
,, $x=2$, $y=4\cdot5$;
,, $x=\frac{1}{1000}$, $y=9000$;

$\therefore$ when x is very small,
y is very great.

Thus, let $x=\frac{1}{1000000}$,
then $y=9000000$.

When $x=0$, then $y=\frac{9}{0}$, or is infinite in value. In other words, the curve gets nearer and nearer to the axis oy as the value of x is diminished, but does

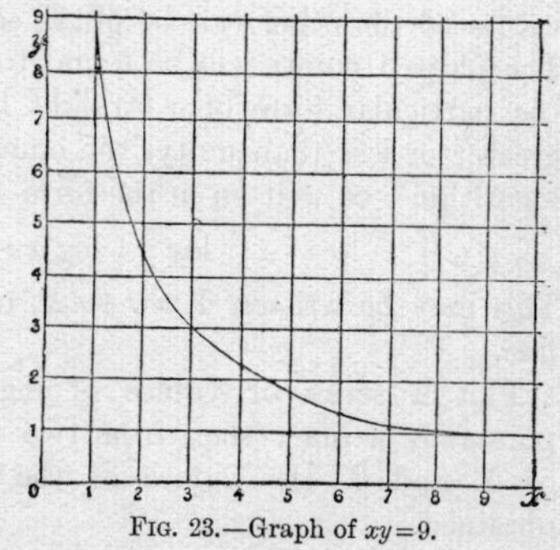

Fig. 23.—Graph of $xy=9$.

not reach the axis at any finite distance from the origin. This is expressed by the symbols $y=\infty$ when $x=0$.

As Eq. (ii) can be written $x=\frac{9}{y}$ it follows as before that when $y=0$, $x=\infty$.

The two lines, or axes, ox and oy are called **asymptotes**, and are said to meet (or touch) the curve at an infinite distance.

Arranging in two columns a series of values of x and corresponding values of y obtained from Eq. (ii), we obtain,

Values of x,	0	1	2	3	4	5	6	7	8	9
Corresponding values of y,	∞	9	4·5	3	2·25	1·8	1·5	1·3	1·13	1

Plot these values of x and y on squared paper; the curve or graph passing through the plotted points is a **hyperbola**, as in Fig. 23.

One of the most important curves with which an engineer is concerned is given by the equation $pv^n=c$, where p denotes the pressure and v the volume of a given quantity of gas.

The constant c and index n depend upon the substance used; *i.e.* whether it is steam, air, etc.

When, as in the preceding example, the values of c and n are known then for various values of one variable, corresponding values of the other can be obtained, and these can be plotted. The plotted points will be found to lie on a curve, which takes the particular form of a straight line when $n=1$. When n is greater or less than unity, the equation $y=ax^n$ may, by taking logarithms, be written in the form

$$\log y=\log a+n\log x. \quad \text{.......................(i)}$$

This may be written $Y=C+nX$, or the equation to a straight line.

Plot a series of values of $\log y$ and $\log x$ and join the points by a line; then from two pairs of simultaneous values of Y and X the values of the constant a and n may be obtained.

It is not of course essential that the letters x and y should denote the two variables. Other letters, such as p and v

(the initial letters of pressure and volume); Q and H; etc., may be used with advantage to suggest at once the quantities to which reference is made.

The converse problem may be stated: given various simultaneous values of p and v to calculate the numerical values of c and n.

To do this it is necessary to write the equation $pv^n = c$ in the form $\log p + n \log v = \log c$.

Plot $\log p$ and $\log v$ and draw a straight line lying evenly among the plotted points, and from two simultaneous values of p and v the values of c and n may be found.

To take the case of the gas in the cylinder of a steam or gas engine as an example: the pressure and volume are connected by an equation of the form $pv^n = \text{constant}$; from Tables the pressure corresponding to any given volume can be obtained, but unless the entries in such a table are very numerous it often happens that the volume corresponding to a given pressure, or the pressure corresponding to a given volume, cannot be found. The only means by which the required data can be arrived at is by a process of interpolation. When values of p and v are plotted on squared paper and the curve lying among the plotted points is drawn, intermediate values can be at once obtained from the curve. The process of interpolation simply consists in reading from a given value of p, or v, the corresponding value of the remaining quantity.

One objection to such a method is that errors may occur in plotting such a curve; another difficulty is experienced in reading the results with sufficient accuracy. When the constants n and c in the general formula are found, values intermediate between those given by observation and, in some cases, even beyond them may be obtained by calculation. Some of the artifices which may be adopted to replace a curve by a straight line may be seen from the following examples:

Ex. 2. The keeper of a restaurant finds when he has G guests in a day, his total daily expenditure (for rent, taxes, wages, wear and tear, food and drink) is E pounds and the total of his daily receipts is R pounds. The following numbers are averages obtained by examination of his books on many days:

G	210	270	320	360
E	16·7	19·4	21·6	23·4
R	15·8	21·2	26·4	29·8

Find E and R and the day's profits, if he has 340 guests. What number of guests per day gives him just no profit? What simple algebraic law seems to connect E, R, P the profit, and G?

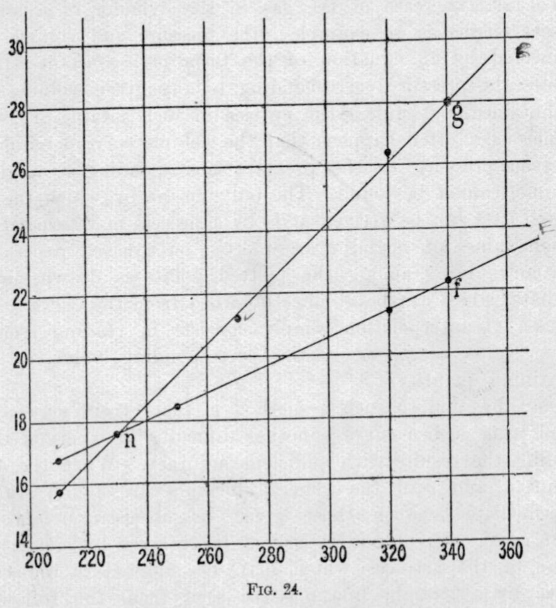

FIG. 24.

On plotting the given values of G and E, and G and R, it is seen that the curve joining the points is in each case a straight line; hence, the relation between E and G may be expressed by

$$G = a + bE, \quad \text{(i)}$$

and between R and G by $G = c + dR$. ....(ii)

Substitute in (i) the values at f and n (Fig. 24),

$$340 = a + 22{\cdot}6b \quad \text{(iii)}$$

$$230 = a + 17{\cdot}3b$$

By subtraction,

$$110 = 5{\cdot}3b;$$

$$\therefore b = \frac{110}{5{\cdot}3} = 20{\cdot}75.$$

Substitute this for b in (iii) and obtain $a = -129$. Hence, the relation between E and G may be written,

$$G = 20{\cdot}75E - 129.$$

Again, we may, in like manner, find the values of the constants c and d in Eq. (ii), by substituting the values at g and n;

$$\therefore 340 = c + 28\ d$$

$$230 = c + 17{\cdot}3d$$

$$110 = 10{\cdot}7d;$$

$$\therefore d = \frac{110}{10{\cdot}7} = 10{\cdot}28.$$

By substituting this value, we find $c = 52{\cdot}2$.

Hence, the required relation is $G = 52{\cdot}2 + 10{\cdot}28R$.

It will be obvious that the profit will be $R - E$. At the point n in the diagram R is equal to E; hence, 230 guests gives just no profit.

In this manner we may find $P = 0\ 05G - 11{\cdot}5$.

Hence, the day's profits when the restaurant keeper has 340 guests is given by $P = 0{\cdot}05 \times 340 - 11{\cdot}5 = £5{\cdot}5$.

Ex. 3. Plot the curve $y = \dfrac{7{\cdot}35x}{1 + 3{\cdot}2x}$.

Calculate the average value of y from $x = 0$ to $x = 8$.

When $x = 2$, $y = \dfrac{7{\cdot}35 \times 2}{1 + 3{\cdot}2 \times 2} = \dfrac{14{\cdot}7}{7{\cdot}4} = 1{\cdot}986$.

When x is 0, 1, ..., values of y can be calculated and tabulated as follows:

x	0	1	2	3	4	5	6	7	8
y	0	1·75	1·986	2·08	2·13	2·162	2·183	2·199	2·211

To obtain the average value we may use Simpson's Rule (p. 199).

Thus, sum of end ordinates 2·211,
,, even ,, 8·191,
,, odd ,, 6·299.

Area from $x=0$ to $x=8$ is

$$\tfrac{1}{3}(2{\cdot}211+8{\cdot}191\times4+6{\cdot}299\times2)=47{\cdot}573\div3=15{\cdot}86.$$

But average value of y multiplied by length of base = area;

$$\therefore \text{ average value of } y=\frac{15{\cdot}86}{8}=1{\cdot}982.$$

In some cases, when the expression $f(x)$ consists of several terms it may be advisable to arrange the various parts in a table and afterwards to add these to obtain the value of y. The method may be illustrated by a simple example as follows:

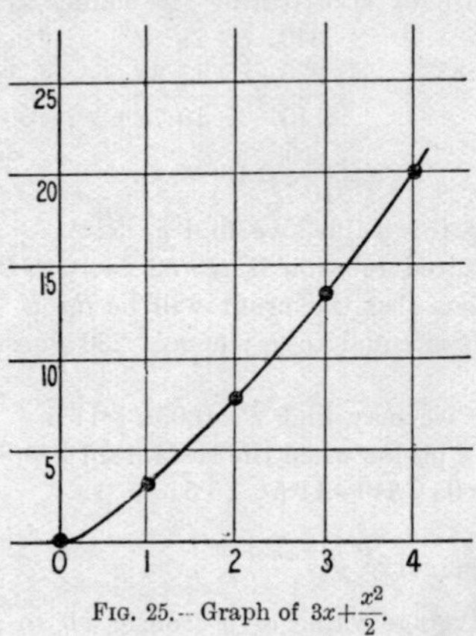

FIG. 25.—Graph of $3x+\frac{x^2}{2}$.

Ex. 4. Draw the graph of the function $y=3x+\frac{x^2}{2}$.

The separate parts of the equation may be arranged in vertical columns. For various values of x the results should be obtained

x	0	1	2	3	4
$3x$	0	3	6	9	12
$\frac{x^2}{2}$	0	0·5	2	4·5	8
y	0	3·5	8	13·5	20

and tabulated, and finally, by adding the numbers together in the vertical columns, the values of y are obtained. Plotting the tabulated values of x and y, a curve, as in Fig. 25, is obtained.

Ex. 5. Experiments made to determine the (water) skin resistance of planks whose wetted surface is 100 square feet, yield the following results:

V = Speed per minute	200	400	600	800
R = Total resistance in lbs.	3·28	11·7	24·6	41·7

Test whether the relation between R and V can be expressed by a law of the type $R \propto V^n$, and if so, find the values k and n in the formula $R = kSV^n$, in which S denotes wetted surface of plank. Find the probable value of R when V is 1000.

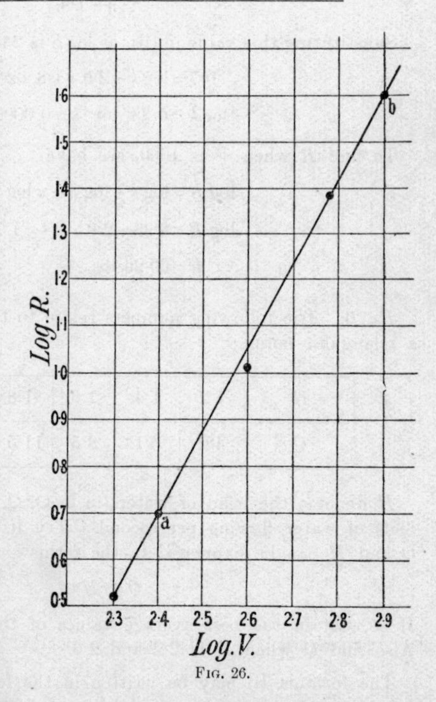

Fig. 26.

Plot $\log V$ and $\log R$ on squared paper as in Fig. 26, it will be found that a straight line can be drawn to lie evenly among the points, thus proving that the suggested formula is trustworthy. Now take a **strip of celluloid** on which a straight line is marked and draw a line such as ab, the intersection of the line with the axes will determine the numerical values of the constants, or they may be obtained by calculation. The equation may be written:

$$\log R = \log k + \log S + n \log V.$$

At point a, $\log R$ is 0·7 and $\log V$ is 2·4, and at b the values are 1·6 and 2·9 respectively.

Hence, substituting these values, we have

$$1{\cdot}6 = \log k + \log S + n \times 2{\cdot}9 \quad \text{(i)}$$

$$0{\cdot}7 = \log k + \log S + n \times 2{\cdot}4 \quad \text{(ii)}$$

Subtracting, $0{\cdot}9 = n \times 0{\cdot}5$;

$$\therefore\ n = 1{\cdot}8.$$

Substituting this value in (ii), as $\log S$ is 2·0, we get

$$0{\cdot}7 = \log k + 2{\cdot}0 + 1{\cdot}8 \times 2{\cdot}4;$$

$$\therefore\ \log k = \bar{6}{\cdot}38, \text{ or } k = 0{\cdot}000002399.$$

To find R when V is 1000, we have

$$\log R = \log k + \log S + n \log V;$$

$$\therefore\ \log R = \bar{6}{\cdot}38 + 2{\cdot}0 + 5{\cdot}4 = 1{\cdot}78;$$

$$\therefore\ R = 60{\cdot}26 \text{ lbs.}$$

Ex. 6. The following numbers relate to the flow of water over a triangular notch:

H	1·2	1·4	1·6	1·8	2·0	2·4
Q	4·2	6·1	8·5	11·5	14·9	23·5

H denotes the head of water (in feet), Q the quantity (in cubic feet) of water flowing per second. Try if the relation between Q and H can be expressed in the form

$$Q = cH^n. \quad \text{(i)}$$

If so, obtain the best average values of the constants c and n. Also find Q when H is 2·2 and 2·6.

The formula (i) may be written in the form

$$\log Q = \log c + n \log H. \quad \text{(ii)}$$

Hence, if the relation given by (i) is true, on plotting (ii) a straight line will be obtained.

The given data may be arranged as follows:

H	1·2	1·4	1·6	1·8	2·0	2·4
Q	4·2	6·1	8·5	11·5	14·9	23·5
$\log H$	0·0792	0·1461	0·2041	0·2553	0·3010	0·3802
$\log Q$	0·6232	0·7853	0·9294	1·0607	1·1732	1·3711

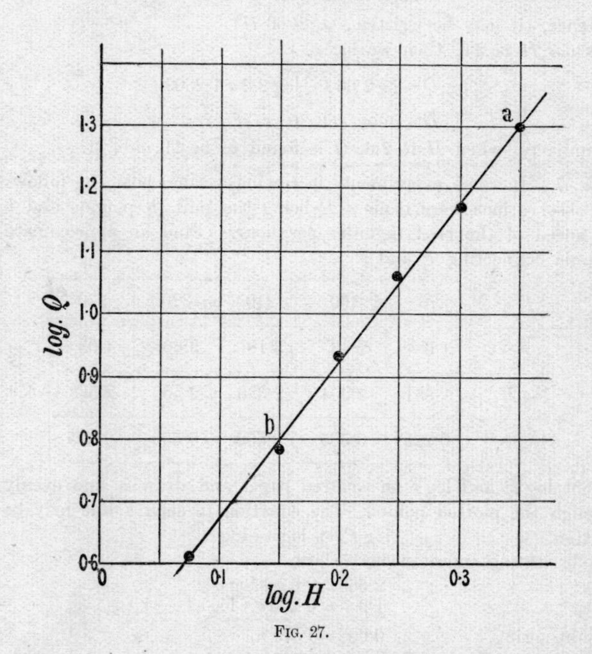

FIG. 27.

Plot the last two rows as in Fig. 27, and a straight line may be drawn through the plotted points.

By substituting in (ii) the values of $\log Q$ and $\log H$ from two points such as a and b, the values of c and n may be obtained as follows:

$$\begin{aligned} \log Q &= \log c + n \log H \\ 1{\cdot}3 &= \log c + n \times 0{\cdot}35 \\ 0{\cdot}8 &= \log c + n \times 0{\cdot}15 \\ \hline 0{\cdot}5 &= 0{\cdot}2n; \\ \therefore\ n &= \frac{5}{2}. \end{aligned}$$

Substituting this value, we have

$$1{\cdot}3 = \log c + \frac{5}{2} \times 0{\cdot}35;$$

$$\therefore\ \log c = 0{\cdot}425, \text{ or } c = 2{\cdot}66.$$

Hence, (i) may be written $Q = 2{\cdot}66\ H^{\frac{5}{2}}$.

When H is 2·2, then we have

$$\log Q = \log 2{\cdot}66 + \frac{5}{2} \log 2{\cdot}2 = 1{\cdot}2809;$$

$$\therefore\ Q = 19{\cdot}09 \text{ cub. ft.}$$

Similarly, when H is 2·6, Q is found to be 29 cub. ft.

Ex. 7. In some experiments in towing a canal boat the following observations were made; P being the pull in pounds and v the speed of the boat in miles per hour. Find an approximate formula connecting P and v.

P	76	160	240	320	370
v	1·68	2·43	3·18	3·60	4·03
$\log P$	1·881	2·204	2·380	2·505	2·568
$\log v$	0·225	0·386	0·502	0·556	0·605

Plot $\log P$ and $\log v$ on squared paper and draw a line evenly through the plotted points. The equation to such a line may be written $\log P = n \log v + \log c$.

Substituting simultaneous values,

$$\begin{aligned} 2{\cdot}568 &= 0{\cdot}6\,n + \log c \\ 1{\cdot}9\ \ &= 0{\cdot}225\,n + \log c \end{aligned}$$

Subtracting, $0{\cdot}668 = 0{\cdot}375\ n$,

or $$n = \frac{668}{375} = 1{\cdot}78.$$

Also, by substitution, $\log c = 2{\cdot}568 - 0{\cdot}6 \times 1{\cdot}78 = 1{\cdot}5 = \log 31{\cdot}6$.

Hence, the formula required is $P = 31{\cdot}6\ v^{1{\cdot}78}$.

Ex. 8. For the years 1896-1900, the following average numbers are taken from the accounts of the 34 most important electric companies of the United Kingdom.

U, means millions of units of electric energy sold to customers. C, means the total cost in millions of pence, and includes interest (7 per cent.) on capital, maintenance, rent, taxes, salaries, wages, coal, etc.

U	0·67	1·00	1·366	1·46	2·49
C	4·84	6·25	8·60	9·11	14·25

Is there any approximately correct simple law connecting U and C? If so, what is it? Assume that from the beginning there was the idea of, at some time, reaching a maximum output of 13·9, so that $U \div 13·9$ is called f, a certain kind of *load factor.* Let $C \div U$ be called c the total cost per unit; is there any law connecting c and f?

Using the given values of U and C we may proceed to find the values of $f = U \div 13·9$ and $C \div U = c$, and arrange as in the following table:

U	0·67	1·00	1·366	1·46	2·49
C	4·84	6·25	8·60	9·11	14·25
$f = U \div 13·9$	0·048	0·072	0·098	0·105	0·18
$c = C \div U$	7·22	6·25	6·29	6·24	5·72
$\frac{1}{f}$	20·7	13·9	10·2	9·52	5·58

Plotting the given values of U and C, a straight line may be drawn among the plotted points. Its equation may be written $U = aC + b$. Substituting simultaneous values of U and C obtained from the curve, we find

$$1 = a \times 6·4 + b$$
$$2 = a \times 12 + b$$

Subtracting, $1 = 5·6a$;

$$\therefore \ a = 0·18.$$

And, by substitution, $b = -0·16$.

Hence, the simple approximate law connecting U and C may be written $U=0{\cdot}18C-0{\cdot}16$.

In a similar manner plotting c and $\frac{1}{f}$, the relation $c=5{\cdot}56+\frac{0{\cdot}06}{f}$ is obtained.

Ex. 9. It is known that the relation connecting the pressure p and specific volume u of water-steam can be stated approximately as $pu^n=c$.

Test the accuracy of this rule for pressures ranging from 20 lbs. to 90 lbs. per sq. in.

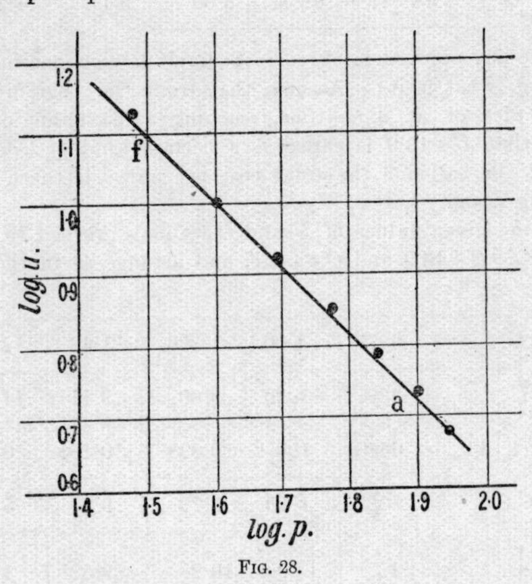

FIG. 28.

Find the best average values of the constants n and c for the range of values given.

p	20	30	40	50	60	70	80	90
u	19·75	13·49	10·3	8·35	7·04	6·09	5·37	4·81
$\log p$	1·301	1·477	1·602	1·699	1·778	1·845	1·903	1·954
$\log u$	1·296	1·130	1·013	0·922	0·848	0·785	0·730	0·682

Plotting the values of $\log p$ and $\log u$ as in Fig. 28, a straight line is obtained; its equation may be written $\log p + n \log u = \log c$. To find the constants it is only necessary to substitute simultaneous values of $\log u$ and $\log p$ from the curve. Thus at f, $\log p$ is 1·5, $\log u = 1{\cdot}1$, and at a, $\log p$ is 1·9, $\log u$ is 0·725. Substituting these values, we have

$$1{\cdot}5 + n \times 1{\cdot}1 \quad = \log c \ldots\ldots\ldots\ldots\ldots\ldots\ldots\ldots\text{(i)}$$

$$1{\cdot}9 + n \times 0{\cdot}725 = \log c \ldots\ldots\ldots\ldots\ldots\ldots\ldots\ldots\text{(ii)}$$

By subtraction, $0{\cdot}4 = 0{\cdot}375n$;

$$\therefore \ n = \frac{0{\cdot}4}{0{\cdot}375} = 1{\cdot}067.$$

Substituting this value for n in (i), we obtain the value of $\log c$;

$$\therefore \ 1{\cdot}5 + 1{\cdot}067 \times 1{\cdot}1 = 2{\cdot}6737;$$

$$\therefore \ c = 471{\cdot}8.$$

It will be noticed in the preceding example that the two varying quantities follow a somewhat complex law. In such

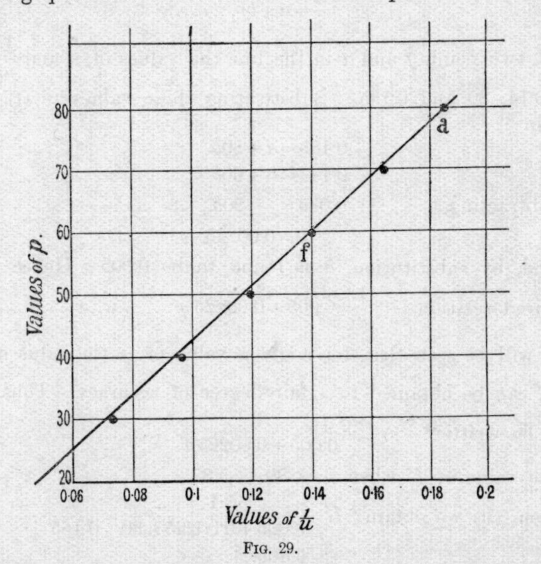

FIG. 29.

cases it is often possible to determine a simpler law, which between certain limits will give values closely approximating to the correct ones. And we may plot the reciprocals or squares, etc., of one instead of both the given quantities. Thus, in the preceding case, using the values of u, we may calculate values of the reciprocals $\frac{1}{u}$, and we obtain the following :

p	20	30	40	50	60	70	80	90
u	19·75	13·49	10·30	8·35	7·04	6·09	5·37	4·81
$\frac{1}{u}$	0·0506	0·0741	0·0971	0·120	0·142	0·164	0·186	0·208

Plotting p and $\frac{1}{u}$ as in Fig 29, a straight line may be drawn amongst the plotted points. Its equation may be written

$$\frac{1}{u}=a+bp. \qquad \text{(i)}$$

At two points f and a in the line the values of p and $\frac{1}{u}$ are 60, 0·14, 80 and 0·185. Substituting these values in (i), we obtain

$$0·185=a+80b$$
$$0·14\ =a+60b$$

Subtracting, $$0·045=\quad 20b\,;$$
$$\therefore\ b=0·00225.$$

And, by substitution, a is found to be 0·005. Hence, the required relation is $\frac{1}{u}=0·005+0·00225\,p$ ....(i)

It will be seen that, for a given value of p, the value of $\frac{1}{u}$ or U can be obtained to a fair degree of accuracy. Thus, (i) may be written

$$U=\frac{1}{0·005+0·00225p} \qquad \text{(ii)}$$

The value of U when p is 80 is 5·37.

From (ii) we obtain $U=\frac{1}{0·005+0·00225\times 80}=\frac{1}{0·185}$

$$=5·405.$$

Hence, percentage error $=\frac{5·405-5·37}{5·405}\times 100=0·65.$

Ex. 10. Given that

$$y = 5\log_{10}x + 6\sin\frac{1}{10}x + 0{\cdot}084\,(x - 3{\cdot}5)^2. \quad\text{(i)}$$

Find a simpler function of x the values of which will have a small percentage error between $x=3$ and $x=6$.

Since the angle $\frac{1}{10}x$ is in radians, and as the values between 3 and 6 are required, we may use, for ease in calculation, numbers such as π, $\frac{3}{2}\pi$ and 2π for x.

Thus, let $x=\pi$, then, by substituting in (i),

$$\begin{aligned} y &= 5\log\pi + 6\sin\frac{\pi}{10} + 0{\cdot}084\,(3{\cdot}1416 - 3{\cdot}5)^2 \\ &= 5\log\pi + 6\sin 18^\circ + 0{\cdot}084\,(-0{\cdot}3584)^2 \\ &= 5 \times 0{\cdot}4972 + 6 \times 0{\cdot}309 + 0{\cdot}0108 \\ &= 2{\cdot}486 + 1{\cdot}854 + 0{\cdot}0108 = 4{\cdot}351. \end{aligned}$$

In a similar manner, when x is $1{\cdot}5\pi$,

$$y = 5\,(\log 1{\cdot}5 + \log\pi) + 6\sin 27^\circ + 0{\cdot}084\,(1{\cdot}469);$$

$$\therefore\; y = 6{\cdot}214.$$

When $x=2\pi$,

$$y = 5\log 2\pi + 6\sin 36^\circ + 0{\cdot}084\,(7{\cdot}746) = 8{\cdot}168.$$

Plot these values and we find that a straight line can be drawn very evenly through the plotted points. Now, assume this simpler or linear function to replace the given one. Its equation may be written in the usual form,

$$y = ax + b \ldots.$$

By substituting two pairs of simultaneous values, we can obtain the numerical values of the two constants a and b.

Thus, $\quad 4{\cdot}15 = 3a + b$

$\quad\quad\quad 7{\cdot}5 = 5{\cdot}75a + b$

Subtracting, $\quad 3{\cdot}35 = 2{\cdot}75a;$

$$\therefore\; a = \frac{3{\cdot}35}{2{\cdot}75} = 1{\cdot}22.$$

Substituting this value,

$$4{\cdot}15 = 3 \times 1{\cdot}22 + b;$$

$$\therefore\; b = 4{\cdot}15 - 3{\cdot}66 = 0{\cdot}49.$$

Hence, the simpler function required is $y = 1{\cdot}22x + 0{\cdot}49$.

It will be found on substitution that the values obtained from the simpler function are, for any value between the limits referred to, not more than 2 per cent. in error.

Ex. 11. At the following draughts in sea water, a particular vessel has the following displacements:

Draught h (feet)	15	12	9	6·3
Displacement T (tons)	2098	1512	1018	586
$\log h$	1·1761	1·0792	0·9542	0·7993
$\log T$	3·3218	3·1796	3·0076	2·7679

(i) Plot $\log T$ and $\log h$ on squared paper, and obtain a simple relation connecting T and h between the given limits.

(ii) If one ton of sea water measures 35 cubic feet, find the rule connecting V and h if V is the displacement in cubic feet.

Plotting $\log T$ and $\log h$, a straight line may be drawn lying evenly among the points.

The relation may be expressed by

$$ch = T^n, \qquad \text{(i)}$$

where c and n are constants.

To determine the numerical values of c and n, we may write the equation in the form

$$n \log T = \log c + \log h. \qquad \text{(ii)}$$

From such a line we find that when $\log T$ is 3·0, $\log h$ is 0·95; and when $\log T$ is 3·3, $\log h$ is 1·153.

Substituting these values in (ii),

$$n \times 3{\cdot}3 = \log c + 1{\cdot}153 \qquad \text{(iii)}$$

$$n \times 3{\cdot}0 = \log c + 0{\cdot}95 \qquad \text{(iv)}$$

Subtracting, $$0{\cdot}3n = 0{\cdot}203;$$

$$\therefore\ n = \frac{0{\cdot}203}{0{\cdot}3} = 0{\cdot}6767.$$

Substituting this value in (iv),

$$0{\cdot}6767 \times 3{\cdot}0 - 0{\cdot}95 = \log c = 1{\cdot}08 = \log 12;$$

$$\therefore\ c = 12.$$

Hence, (i) may be written in the form

$$T^{0{\cdot}6767} = 12h,$$

or $$T = (12)^{\frac{1}{0{\cdot}6767}} \times h^{\frac{1}{0{\cdot}6767}}. \qquad \text{(v)}$$

This is not in a convenient form for calculation, hence we may write (v) in the form

$$T^2=(12)^{\frac{2}{0\cdot6767}}\times h^{\frac{2}{0\cdot6767}},$$

and as $2\div0\cdot6767=2\cdot955$ we may obtain a good approximation by using the nearest whole number 3 and adjusting the constant.

Thus, (v) may be written as

$$T^2=b^3h^3, \quad\text{.................................(vi)}$$

or $$\frac{2}{3}\log T=\log b+\log h.$$

Hence, draw a line having a slope of $\frac{2}{3}$ and passing as evenly as possible through the points. To obtain the constant b, we have from (vi)

$$\log b=\frac{2}{3}\log T-\log h;$$

at c, where $\log T$ is 3·4, $\log h$ is 1·227.

Substituting,

$$\log b=\frac{2}{3}\times3\cdot4-1\cdot227=1\cdot040;$$

$$\therefore\ 3\log b=3\cdot120=\log 1318.$$

Hence, the relation is

$$T^2=1318h^3.$$

Also, $$V\div35=T;$$

$$\therefore\ \left(\frac{V}{35}\right)^2=1318h^3,$$

or $$V^2=1615000h^3.$$

Ex. 12. In the following table some observed values of x and y are given:

x	0	1	2	3	4	5	6	7
y	0	0·7485	0·5988	0·5614	0·5444	0·5347	0·5284	0·5241

It will be noticed that as x increases, the corresponding values of y are decreasing. If the given points are plotted, a curve is obtained. To obtain the algebraic law connecting x and y—instead of $y=a+bx$, try

$$y=\frac{ax}{x-b},\ \text{or}\ x=a\frac{x}{y}+b. \quad\text{..........................(i)}$$

Values of x and calculated values of $\frac{x}{y}$ are as follows:

x	1	2	3	4	5	6	7
$\frac{x}{y}$	1·336	3·339	5·343	7·348	9·351	11·36	13·36

Values of x and $\frac{x}{y}$ are plotted in Fig. 30 and a line is drawn through the plotted points. To obtain the equation of the line, or to obtain the values of the constants, in (i), we may select two points f and a, and substitute in (i) the values of x and $\frac{x}{y}$. Thus,

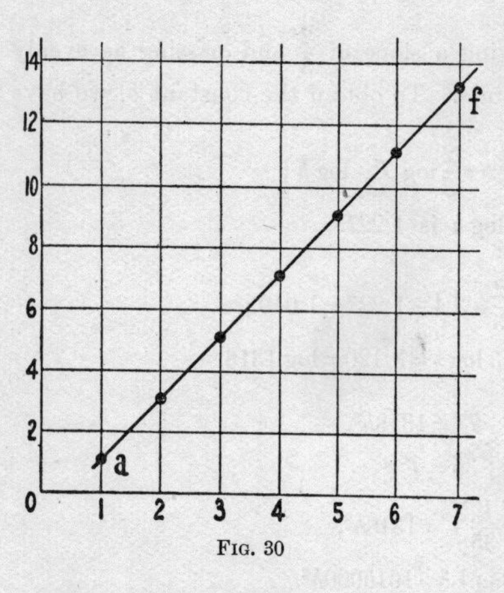

Fig. 30

$$7 = a \times 13{\cdot}36 + b \text{.......(i)}$$
$$1 = a \times 1{\cdot}336 + b \text{......(ii)}$$
$$6 = 12{\cdot}02a;$$
$$\therefore\ a = \frac{6}{12{\cdot}02} = 0{\cdot}5.$$

Substituting in (ii),

$$b = 0{\cdot}33.$$

Hence, the relation connecting x and y is given by

$$x = 0{\cdot}5\frac{x}{y} + 0{\cdot}33,$$

or $xy = 0{\cdot}5x + 0{\cdot}33y.$

Harmonic motion.—A simple harmonic motion may be defined as the motion of the projection, upon a diameter, of a point moving uniformly in a circle. Thus, let P be a point moving uniformly in a circle of radius a; the projections, M and N, of P on the axes move with simple harmonic motion.

Let ω denote the angular velocity of P (*i.e.* the angle in radians described by CP in one second). Then the angle ACP will be ωt; if x then denotes the displacement CM of the point M,

$$CM = x = a \cos \omega t. \text{ ....(i)}$$

The **amplitude** is the greatest displacement on either side of the mean position C; hence, the amplitude is a, or it is the value of x when P is at A.

The **period** or **periodic time** is the interval of time taken by the point M to pass from A to A' and back again. It is usually denoted by letter T.

The **frequency**, f, is the reciprocal of the periodic time, or is $\frac{1}{T}$.

It will be seen from Fig. 31 that the motion of N is precisely similar to that of M, the difference being that when the displacement of M is a maximum that of N is a minimum, or zero. The motion of points M or N is the simplest kind of vibrational motion, such as the up and down motion of a weight hanging from the end of a spiral spring, or the motion of the bob of a pendulum when the vibrations are small, or the motion of the prongs of a tuning fork, etc.

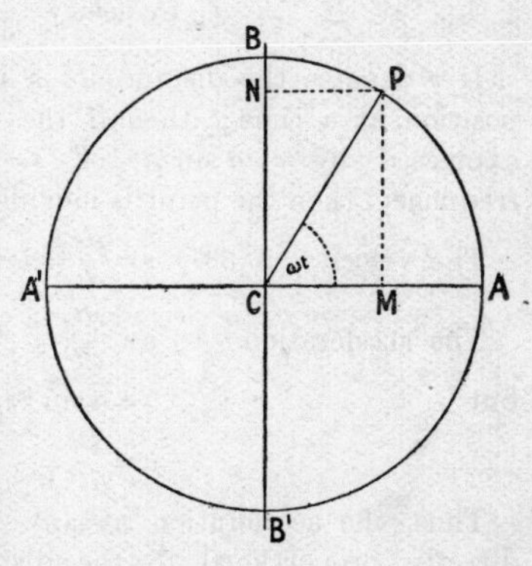

FIG. 31.

Similarly, the harmonic motion of point N may be expressed by

$$y = a \cos PCN = a \sin \omega t. \quad \text{....................(ii)}$$

It should be noticed that the coefficient a in (i) and (ii) gives in each case the amplitude, and ω the angular velocity of the corresponding circular motion.

The period (T) is the time required for one revolution $= \frac{2\pi}{\omega}$, and the frequency f is the reciprocal of the periodic time, or $\frac{\omega}{2\pi}$;

$$\therefore \ \omega = 2\pi f.$$

Ex. 1. $x = 7 \cos 3\omega t$.

This denotes a point moving with simple harmonic motion (usually denoted by the letters S.H.M.), the amplitude being 7, and angular velocity 3ω radians per second.

Ex. 2. Find the amplitude, angular velocity, period, and frequency of a point which has a simple harmonic motion given by the equation $x = 0{\cdot}15 \cos 1{\cdot}6t.$

Comparing the terms in this with Eq. (i), the amplitude is found to be 0·15. The angular velocity is the coefficient of t, and is 1·6. The period is the time required for 1 revolution, and is therefore

$$\frac{2\pi}{1{\cdot}6} = 3{\cdot}927.$$

The frequency is the reciprocal of the period;

$$\therefore\ f = \text{frequency} = \frac{1}{3{\cdot}927} = 0{\cdot}2546.$$

If s denotes the distance of a moving point from its mid-position, at a time t, then if the relation between s and t is expressed by $s = a \sin qt$, or $s = a \sin 2\pi ft$, where f is the frequency, then the point is moving with S.H.M. of amplitude a.

The velocity (p. 337) $v = \frac{ds}{dt} = 2a\pi f \cos 2\pi ft.$

The acceleration $\quad \alpha = \frac{d^2s}{dt^2} = -4a\pi^2 f^2 \sin 2\pi ft$;

but $\quad s = a \sin 2\pi ft,$

$$\therefore\ \alpha = \frac{d^2s}{dt^2} = -4\pi^2 f^2 s. \quad \text{.......................(iii)}$$

Thus, the acceleration at any instant varies with and is directly proportional to the distance of the moving point from its mid-position, but in the opposite direction.

If M is the mass of a body $= W \div 32{\cdot}2$, where W denotes the weight, then the force F acting towards the mid-position is given by

$$F = -4\pi^2 f^2 s \times M = -\frac{4\pi^2 f^2 s \times W}{32{\cdot}2}. \quad \text{..............(iv)}$$

Ex. 3. The relation between the distance s, from the middle point of the line of motion, being given by $s = A \sin (pt - e)$, where A, p and e are all constants. Find the velocity and acceleration at any instant.

$$v = \frac{ds}{dt} = Ap \cos (pt - e),$$

$$\alpha = \frac{d^2s}{dt^2} = -Ap^2 \sin (pt - e).$$

Hence, as in the preceding case, the acceleration is equal to p^2 times the distance from a fixed point, this is the characteristic property of harmonic motion.

It should be carefully noticed from (iv) that f (the frequency) is squared. Hence, when the frequency is doubled the force required is four times its former value, when the frequency is trebled the force is 9 times, etc.

The sinuous curve corresponding to (i) could be set out on a horizontal base, equal distances denoting equal intervals of time and the various values of CM, or x, as ordinates.

If the moving point starts at some point, say P_1 (Fig. 32), and t_0 is the interval of time required from A to P_1, then the angle P_1CA may be written ωt_0 or e.

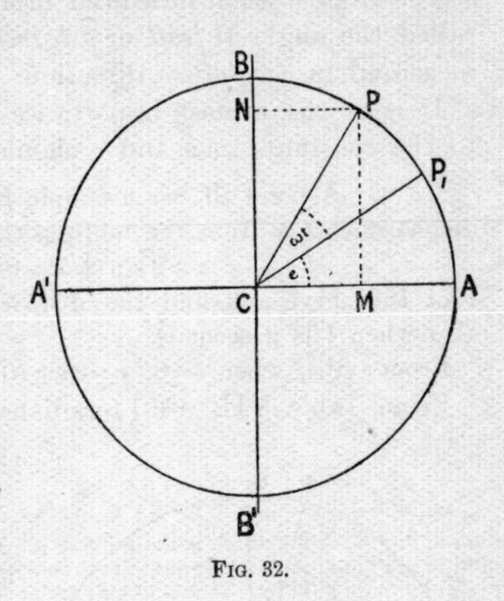

FIG. 32.

Thus, when the point is at P the angle described is $\omega t + e$;

$$\therefore\ x = a \cos(\omega t + e). \qquad \text{(v)}$$

The expression given by Eq. (v) is found not only in engineering, but also in mathematical physics, more frequently than any other. Every periodic function can be expressed in such terms, or a series of such terms. The most general form is expressed by Fourier's Theorem (p. 451).

It is more convenient in graphical work to project the various positions of point N (Fig. 32).

For this purpose angles are more conveniently measured from the line BB', or 90° behind the initial line AA', and Equation (v), defining the successive positions of point N, becomes

$$y = a \sin(\omega t + e). \qquad \text{(vi)}$$

Other letters may be used instead of x, ω, etc. Thus Eq. (vi) may be written $y = a \sin(bx + c)$* ....(vii)

Thus, when $x = 0$, from Eq. (vii)

$$y = a \sin c.$$

* See p. 583.

Or, when x is 0, the point P is ahead of the initial position B' by an angle $B'CP$ (Fig. 33).

The angle c when measured in a *positive* direction is usually called the angle of *lead* or *advance*; it is called the *lag* when measured in a *negative* direction.

It is of the utmost importance that the meanings attached to the constants a, b and c should be clearly made out.

Ex. 4. A point M has a simple harmonic motion in which the displacements x from the mid-position C is given in inches by

$$x=2\sin(1\cdot5t+0\cdot4014). \qquad \text{(viii)}$$

Plot the curve and find the displacement of M when $t=0$ and also when t is 2 seconds.

From (viii), when $t=0$, $x=2\sin(0\cdot4014)$.

From Table VII. 0·4014 radians$=23°$.

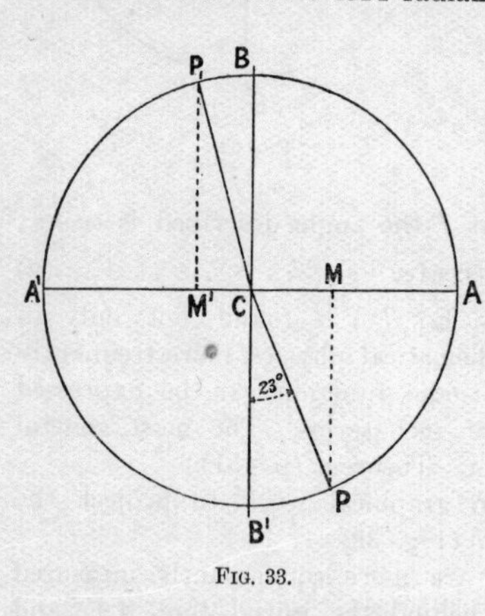

FIG. 33.

Hence, make the angle

$$B'CP=23°.$$

With C as centre describe a circle 2 inches radius, then P is the corresponding point in the auxiliary circle; and projecting on the diameter AA' the distance CM is the displacement required.

$\therefore\ CM=2\sin 23°=2\times0\cdot3907$;

$\therefore\ CM=x=0\cdot7814$ inches.

Similarly, when t is 2, we have, from (i),

$$\begin{aligned}x&=2\sin(3+0\cdot4014)\\&=2\sin(3\cdot4014)\\&=2\sin 194°\ 53';\end{aligned}$$

$\therefore\ CM'=x=0\cdot5$ inches.

The following important theorem may be shown either graphically or analytically:

A motion in a straight line which is compounded of two simple harmonic motions of equal periods and in the same straight line is itself a simple harmonic motion.

Thus, let two simple harmonic motions be expressed by the equations

$$a\sin(\omega t+e_1) \text{ and } b\sin(\omega t+e_2).$$

Now let

$$A \sin(\omega t + e) \equiv a \sin(\omega t + e_1) + b \sin(\omega t + e_2). \qquad \text{(ix)}$$

By expanding each side, we must have

$$A \cos e = a \cos e_1 + b \cos e_2$$

and

$$A \sin e = a \sin e_1 + b \sin e_2;$$

$\therefore$ By squaring and adding

$$A^2 = a^2 + b^2 + 2ab \cos(e_1 - e_2),$$

and by division,

$$\tan e = \frac{a \sin e_1 + b \sin e_2}{a \cos e_1 + b \cos e_2}.$$

Hence when a, b, e_1, e_2 are given, the resultant motion can be obtained from (ix).

Ex. 5. Given $a = 2$ inches, $b = 3$ inches, $e_1 = 0{\cdot}25$ radians, $e_2 = 1{\cdot}1$ radians. Determine graphically and measure the amplitude A and advance e of the resultant motion.

Also find and measure the displacement x when $t = 0$, and also when $t = 3$ seconds. The angular velocity ω is $\frac{1}{2}$ radian per second.

Substituting, the equation becomes

$$x = 2 \sin(\omega t + 0{\cdot}25) + 3 \sin(\omega t + 1{\cdot}1).$$

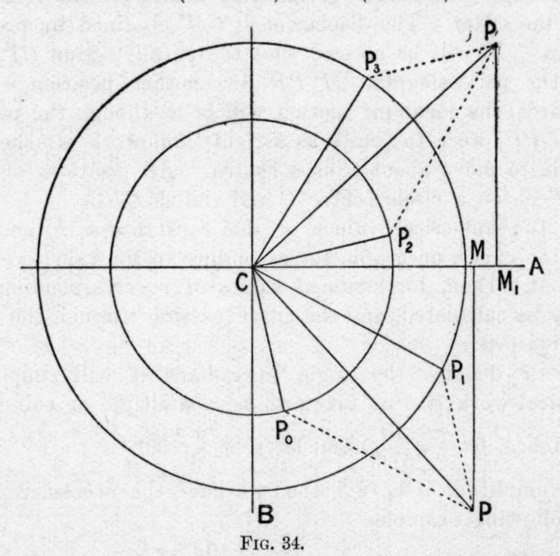

Fig. 34.

With centre C (Fig. 34) draw two circles of radii 2 and 3 inches respectively. When $t = 0$, the first component motion gives angular advance $= 0{\cdot}25$ radian $= 14° 19'$. The second component gives angular advance$=1\cdot1$ radian$=63^\circ\ 1'$. Hence, make the angle $BCP_0=14^\circ\ 19'$, and the angle $BCP_1=63^\circ\ 1'$, giving two points, P_0 on the smaller and P_1 on the larger circle respectively.

Complete the parallelogram of which P_0C and P_1C are adjacent sides; then CP, equal to 4·55 inches, is the amplitude and BCP is the angle of advance equal to $43^\circ\cdot5$. Projecting P on to CA the displacement CM is found to be 3·15 in.

Again, when t is 3 seconds.

Substituting the given angular velocity, the equation becomes

$$x=2\sin(0\cdot5t+0\cdot25)+3\sin(0\cdot5t+1\cdot1),$$

and this, when $t=3$, gives for the first component an angle of advance of

$$0\cdot5\times3+0\cdot25=1\cdot75 \text{ radians}=100^\circ\ 16' \text{ very nearly},$$

and for the second component

$$3\times0\cdot5+1\cdot1=2\cdot6 \text{ radians}=148^\circ\cdot98.$$

Set off the angle BCP_2 equal to $100^\circ\ 16'$, and the angle BCP_3 equal to $148^\circ\ 58'$, giving as before the two sides of a parallelogram. Completing the parallelogram, CP is the resultant amplitude and BCP the angle of advance, giving 4·55 inches for the former and 131° for the latter. The displacement CM' obtained by projection is 3·45 in. It will be noticed that the parallelogram CP_2PP_3 is merely the parallelogram CP_0PP_1 in another position. Or, in other words, the resultant motion will be as though the parallelogram CP_0PP_1 were to rotate as a rigid framework attached to C, and made to move about C as a centre. All positions of P will therefore lie on a circle centre C and radius CP.

When the numerical values of the constants a, b, and c are known, the curve, or graph, corresponding to $y=a\sin(bx+c)$ may be set out. Then, for assumed values of x corresponding values of y may be calculated, and the curve passing through the plotted points obtained.

As $bx+c$ denotes the angle in radians it will simplify the arithmetical work if b be taken to be a multiple or sub-multiple of π. Hence, let $b=\frac{10}{57\cdot3}$, and let c be $\frac{\pi}{6}=30^\circ$.

If the amplitude a be 2·5, then we have the necessary data, as in the following example:

Ex. 6. Plot the curve $y=2\cdot5\sin\left(\frac{10x}{57\cdot3}+\frac{\pi}{6}\right)$.

Values of y corresponding to various values of x may be found. Thus, when $x=4$, $\sin(40^\circ+30^\circ)=\sin 70^\circ$;

$$\therefore\ y=2\cdot5\sin 70^\circ=2\cdot5\times 0\cdot9397$$
$$=2\cdot349.$$

Other values of y may be tabulated as follows:

x	0	1	2	3	4	5	6	7	8	9
y	1·25	1·607	1·915	2·165	2·349	2·462	2·5	2·462	2·349	2·165

From these values the curve may be plotted. The sinuous line is much more easily obtained by graphical construction, as on p. 145.

The graph of $y=Ae^{kt}$, or $y=Ae^{kx}$—when the constants A and k are known and e is the base of Naperian logarithms $=2\cdot718$—can be obtained by assuming various values for x or t and calculating corresponding values of y.

Ex. 7. Plot the curve
$$y=Ae^{kx},$$
when $A=1$, $k=0\cdot3$.

Substituting the given values, the equation becomes
$$y=e^{0\cdot3x}.$$

Assuming values 0, 1, ... for x, values of y can be calculated.

Thus, let $x=4$, then
$$y=2\cdot718^{1\cdot2},$$
or
$$\log y=1\cdot2\log 2\cdot718$$
$$=1\cdot2\times0\cdot4343$$
$$=0\cdot52116;$$
$$\therefore\ y=3\cdot321.$$

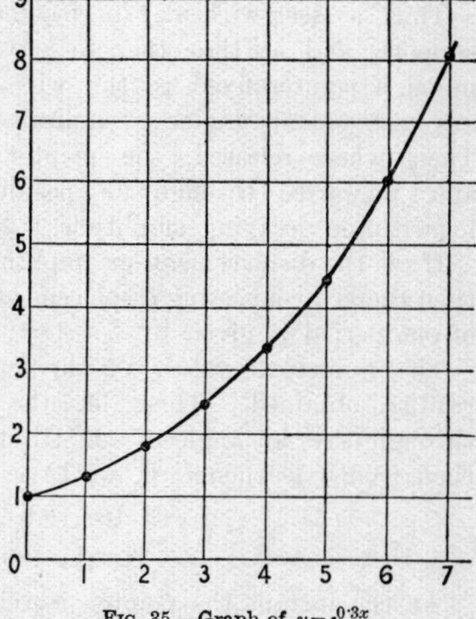

FIG. 35.—Graph of $y=e^{0\cdot3x}$

In a similar manner other values of y can be ascertained as follows:

x	0	1	2	3	4	5	6	7	8
y	1	1·35	1·822	2·460	3·321	4·481	6·049	8·166	11·03

A portion of the curve is drawn in Fig. 35.

Damped oscillations.—A simple experimental apparatus illustrating what is meant by damped oscillations may consist of a comparatively heavy cylindrical disc suspended at one end of a wire. The other end of the wire is fixed to a suitable support, and the disc may be made to oscillate in a liquid such as water, oil, glycerine, etc.

When displaced from its position of rest and allowed to oscillate freely the amplitude of the oscillation diminishes more or less rapidly, due to the viscosity of the liquid.

If on a base denoting intervals of time, ordinates of the curve denote amplitudes, then the maximum amplitude is obviously at a time $t=0$, and therefore equal to A, and the amplitudes in successive swings diminish according to the logarithmic law $s=Ae^{-kt}$.

Thus, a steel wire may be fastened at one end to a fixed support, and at the other to a comparatively heavy disc of metal, a pointer fixed to the wire can be displaced through any convenient angle as indicated on a graduated disc. Then when released, the pointer will oscillate backwards and forwards, through its position of equilibrium, with logarithmic decaying amplitude.

If s is the displacement, or amplitude, of point p at the time t, then the law connecting displacements separated by equal times of one period is given by $s=Ae^{-kt}$. ....(i)

The numerical values of the two constants A and k are readily obtained. Thus, let the pointer p be displaced through (say) an angle of 180° ; if this denotes the time $t=0$, then from (i), when $t=0$, we have

$$180^\circ = Ae^0,$$

or

$$A = 180^\circ.$$

At the instant the pointer is released, let a stop-watch be started. Then the time of successive oscillations and the amplitudes can be read off ; these may be tabulated. Similar observations should be made when different fluids, water, oil, glycerine, etc., are used.

Eq. (i) can be written $\log s = \log A - kt \log e$.

Plotting t and $\log s$ as co-ordinates of points, the points will be found to lie on a straight line, and the values of k, which will express the *relative viscosities* of the liquids, can be obtained.

The relation between s and t is given by the differential equation (see p. 480)

$$\frac{d^2s}{dt^2}+2k\frac{ds}{dt}+s=0,$$

The solution is $s=ae^{-kt}\sin\{(\sqrt{1-k^2})\,t+b\}$,

where a and b are constants to be determined (p. 480).

Values obtained from an experiment are given.

Water.			Oil.			Glycerine.		
s	log s	t	s	log s	t	s	log s	t
180°	2·255	0	180°	2·255	0	180°	2·255	0
164°	2·215	39	92°	1·964	41·4	24°	1·380	14·4
149°	2·173	79	46°	1·663	83·6	3°	0·477	28·4
137°	2·137	119	22°	1·342	126·2	0·7°	0·155	42·2
125°	2·097	159	10°	1·0	169·0			
115°	2·061	198	5°	0·699	210·6			

The values of the constants may be obtained by plotting, and the relations become:

For water, $s=180e^{-0\cdot0023t}$; for oil, $s=180e^{-0\cdot0162t}$; for glycerine, $s=180e^{-0\cdot14t}$.

These values should be verified. Thus, in the case of glycerine, let $t=14\cdot4$, and proceed to find the value of s.

$$\log_e s=\log_e A-k\times t\log_e e, \text{ or to base 10,}$$

$$\log_{10}s=\log_{10}180-0\cdot14\times14\cdot4\times0\cdot4343$$

$$=2\cdot2553-0\cdot14\times14\cdot4\times0\cdot4343.$$

The product can be obtained either by a slide rule or logarithms. Thus, if x denote the product,

$$\log x=\log 0\cdot14+\log 14\cdot4+\log 0\cdot4343=\bar{1}\cdot9423;$$

$$\therefore\ x=0\cdot8756;$$

$$\therefore\ \log s=2\cdot2553-0\cdot8756=1\cdot3797.$$

In a similar manner the remaining two values may be verified.

Graph of $y=Ae^{kx}\sin(bx+c)$.—One of the most important curves in engineering is given by the equation

$$y=Ae^{kx}\sin(bx+c).$$

When k is negative this equation indicates a damped vibration.

It will be noticed that this curve is a combination of the two preceding curves, *i.e.* $y=e^{kx}$ and $y=A\sin(bx+c)$, and, if plotted on the same sheet, it is only necessary to multiply together the ordinates, for the same value of x, of the two curves to obtain the ordinates of the new curve.

Ex. 8. In the equation $y=Ae^{kx}\sin(bx+c)$.

Let $A=2{\cdot}5$, $k=0{\cdot}3$, $b=\frac{10}{57{\cdot}3}$, $c=\frac{\pi}{6}$.

Calculate values of y for values 0, 2, ... 16 for x, and plot the curve. Find the slope of the curve at the point $x=4$.

Substituting the given values, the equation becomes

$$y=2{\cdot}5e^{0{\cdot}3x}\sin\left(\frac{10x}{57{\cdot}3}+\frac{\pi}{6}\right)\text{.......................(i)}$$

Substituting values 0, 2, 4 ... for x, then, from (i), corresponding values of y can be obtained, or values may be obtained from Exs. 5 and 6. Thus, when $x=4$ the ordinate of the curve $y=e^{0{\cdot}3x}$ is 3·321.

For the same value of x the ordinate of the curve

$$y=2{\cdot}5\sin\left(\frac{10}{57{\cdot}3}x+\frac{\pi}{6}\right) \text{ is } 2{\cdot}349.$$

The product will give the ordinate of the new curve;

$$i.e.\ 3{\cdot}321\times2{\cdot}349=7{\cdot}8.$$

By substituting values of x, corresponding values of y can be calculated. Thus, let $x=4$, then, substituting in (i),

$$y=2{\cdot}5e^{1{\cdot}2}\sin(70^\circ)$$
$$=2{\cdot}5e^{1{\cdot}2}\times0{\cdot}9397.$$
$$\log y=\log 2{\cdot}5+1{\cdot}2\log e+\log 0{\cdot}9397$$
$$=0{\cdot}3979+0{\cdot}5212+\bar{1}{\cdot}9730=0{\cdot}8921;$$
$$\therefore\ y=7{\cdot}8.$$

Other values of x can be assumed and values of y calculated as follows:

x	0	2	4	6	8	10	12	14	16
y	1·25	3·49	7·8	15·12	25·89	38·46	45·75	42·24	-52·72

The curve passing through the plotted points may be obtained as in Fig. 36.

To find the slope at $x=4$, we must find $\frac{dy}{dx}$ (p. 303).

When $y=Ae^{kx}\sin(bx+c)$,

$$\begin{aligned}\frac{dy}{dx}&=Ake^{kx}\sin(bx+c)+Abe^{kx}\cos(bx+c)\\&=2{\cdot}5\times0{\cdot}3e^{1{\cdot}2}\sin70^\circ+2{\cdot}5\times\frac{10}{57{\cdot}3}e^{1{\cdot}2}\cos70^\circ\\&=2{\cdot}8353.\end{aligned}$$

Ex. 9. Obtain the graphs of the following:

$$\text{(i) } y_1=2{\cdot}5\sin\left(\frac{10x}{57\,3}+\frac{\pi}{6}\right), \quad \text{.......................(i)}$$

$$\text{(ii) } y=2{\cdot}5e^{-0{\cdot}02x}\sin\left(\frac{10x}{57{\cdot}3}+\frac{\pi}{6}\right).$$

(i) This graph may be obtained, as in preceding cases, by calculation; but, more easily, by graphical construction, as follows:

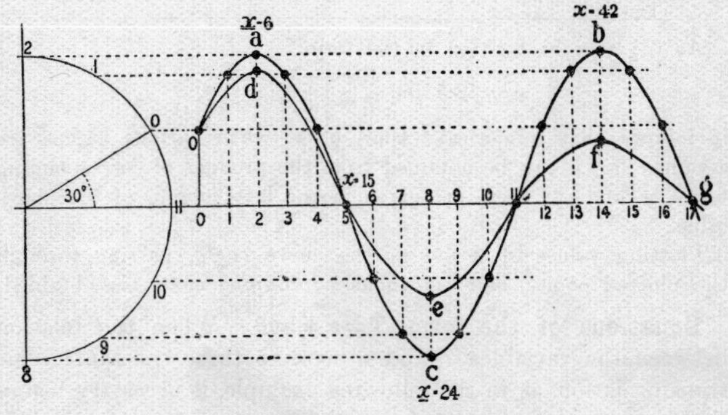

FIG. 36.—Graph of $y=2{\cdot}5e^{-0{\cdot}02x}\sin\left(\frac{10x}{57{\cdot}3}+\frac{\pi}{6}\right)$.

Draw a circle 2·5″ radius and divide its circumference into 12 equal parts. Now draw a straight line (Fig. 36) to denote the periodic time, or time taken by the point to move once round the circle. Divide the line into the same number of parts as the circle, *i.e.* into 12 equal parts, and at each point set up ordinates. Then points in the curve may be obtained by projection. In this manner, by drawing a curve through the points, a curve such as *oacbg* (Fig. 36) is obtained.

The sine of an angle has its maximum positive values when the angle is 90°, or of the form $(4n+1)90°$.... Similarly, the maximum negative values occur when the angle is 270°, *i.e.* of the form $(4n+3)90°$, the maximum positive values occurring at a and b, where $x=6$ and $x=42$, and maximum negative value at c, where $x=24$.

(ii) For various values of x, values of $y_2=e^{-0\cdot02x}$ may be calculated and tabulated. Thus, when $x=6$, $y_2=e^{-0\cdot12}=0\cdot8869$. Multiplying these by the corresponding values of y_1, we obtain the ordinate required as in the following table:

x	6	15	24	33	42
y_1	2·5	0	−2·5	0	2·5
y_2	0·8869	0·7408	0·6187	0·5169	0·4317
$y_1 \times y_2 = y$	2·2172	0	−1·5467	0	1·0792

As (ii) may be written in the form

$$y=2\cdot5\sin\left(\frac{10x}{57\cdot3}+\frac{\pi}{6}\right)\times e^{-0\cdot02x},$$

it follows that numerical values of y, when various values are assumed for x, can be obtained from the product of corresponding terms y_1 and y_2; these are given in the last column of the above table.

Plotting values of x and y, the curve *odefg*, passing through the plotted points, and known as a *damping curve*, is obtained.

Equations of the form $T=a+bv^n$.—When the relation between the variables T and v involves three constants some transformation, as in the following example, is necessary before the constants can be determined.

Ex. 10. Two variable quantities v and T are supposed to be connected by a relation of the form

$$T=a+bv^n. \qquad \text{(i)}$$

When v is 3, T is 48·97; when v is 4, $T=41·49$; and when v is 6, T is 34·74.

Determine the numerical values of the three constants a, b, and n. Also find T when v is 5.

We may denote the three given values of v by v_1, v_2, and v_3; and the corresponding values of T by T_1, T_2, and T_3, respectively.

As Eq. (i) is not adapted to logarithms, it may be written

$$T-a=bv^n.$$

Writing T_1 for T, and v_1 for v, and take logarithms of both sides,

$$\log(T_1-a)=\log b+n\log v_1. \quad \text{(ii)}$$

Similarly $$\log(T_2-a)=\log b+n\log v_2. \quad \text{(iii)}$$

Subtracting (iii) from (ii),

$$\log(T_1-a)-\log(T_2-a)=n(\log v_1-\log v_2). \quad \text{(iv)}$$

In a similar manner we obtain

$$\log(T_1-a)-\log(T_3-a)=n(\log v_1-\log v_3). \quad \text{(v)}$$

Dividing (iv) by (v),

$$\frac{\log(T_1-a)-\log(T_2-a)}{\log(T_1-a)-\log(T_3-a)}=\frac{\log v_1-\log v_2}{\log v_1-\log v_3}. \quad \text{(vi)}$$

Thus, we obtain an equation involving only the constant a, which has to be determined.

Eq. (vi) may be written

$$\therefore\ f(a)=\frac{\log(T_1-a)-\log(T_2-a)}{\log(T_1-a)-\log(T_3-a)}-\frac{\log v_1-\log v_2}{\log v_1-\log v_3}. \quad \text{(vii)}$$

The solution required being that for which $f(a)=0$.

Substituting various values for a in (vii), the value of a, which makes the expression zero, and therefore satisfies the given equation, can be obtained. Thus, let $a=20$.

$$\therefore\ f(a)=\frac{\log(48{\cdot}97-20)-\log(41{\cdot}49-20)}{\log(48{\cdot}97-20)-\log(34{\cdot}74-20)}-\frac{\log 3-\log 4}{\log 3-\log 6}$$

$$=\frac{\log 28{\cdot}97-\log 21{\cdot}49}{\log 28{\cdot}97-\log 14{\cdot}74}-\frac{\log 3-\log 4}{\log 3-\log 6}$$

$$=\frac{1{\cdot}4620-1{\cdot}3322}{1{\cdot}4620-1{\cdot}1685}-\frac{0{\cdot}4771-0{\cdot}6021}{0{\cdot}4771-0{\cdot}7782}$$

$$=\frac{0{\cdot}1298}{0\ 2935}-\frac{0{\cdot}1250}{0{\cdot}3011};$$

$$\therefore\ f(a)=0{\cdot}4424-0{\cdot}4152=0{\cdot}0273.$$

Substitute values 10, and 30, for a, then corresponding values of $f(a)$ may be obtained and tabulated as follows:

a	10	20	30
$f(a)$	0·0540	0·0273	−0·0536

As the value of $f(a)$ changes sign in passing from $a=20$ to $a=30$, it follows that the value of a which will make $f(a)$ equal to zero lies between the two values. By plotting, or by trial, a is found to be 25.

Hence, the given equation may be written

$$T=25+bv^n.$$

and substituting in Eq. (iv), we find

$$n=-1{\cdot}3,$$

again, from Eq. (ii) or Eq. (iii)

$$b=+100.$$

Hence, the required relation is

$$T=25+100v^{-1{\cdot}3}.$$

Substituting for v, the given value

$$T=25+100\times5^{-1{\cdot}3}=37{\cdot}34.$$

In some cases, by assuming a value for $n=2$, 3, etc., it is possible to obtain the law, as in the following example:

Ex. 11. A series of values of two variables (which may be denoted by x and y) are given in the following table. Find the relation between x and y.

x	0	1	2	3	4	5	6	7
y	2·35	2·77	4·03	6·13	9·1	12·85	17·5	22·9

When these values are plotted a curve passes through the plotted points; but, by plotting values of y and x^2, a straight line is obtained. Its equation may be written $y=a+bx^2$, and by substitution the constants a and b are found to be 2·35 and 0·42. Hence, the required relation is

$$y=2{\cdot}35+0{\cdot}42x^2.$$

It will be obvious that the same result would have been obtained by using the general formula

$$y=a+bx^n.$$

Instead of the preceding, a still more general formula may be used, viz.: $y=a+b\,.\,10^{cx}$, ...(i)

and from three given values of x and y the values of the three constants a, b, and c, may be found.

Thus, if three given values of x and y are denoted by x_1, x_2, and x_3, and the corresponding values of y by y_1, y_2, and y_3, respectively, then substituting in (i)

$$\log(y_1-a)=\log b+cx_1\log 10;$$

but as $\log_{10} 10 = 1$, we obtain using common logarithms

$$\log(y_1 - a) = \log b + cx. \quad \text{(ii)}$$

Hence, as in the preceding cases,

$$\log(y_1 - a) - \log(y_2 - a) = c(x_1 - x_2) \quad \text{(iii)}$$

and $$\log(y_1 - a) - \log(y_3 - a) = c(x_1 - x_3),$$

and by division

$$\frac{\log(y_1 - a) - \log(y_2 - a)}{\log(y_1 - a) - \log(y_3 - a)} = \frac{x_1 - x_2}{x_1 - x_3}.$$

From this result the value of the constant a can be obtained, and by substitution in (ii) and (iii) the values of the remaining two constants b and c are found.

Ex. 12. In how many years will a sum of money double itself at r per cent. per annum?

Let A denote the amount, P the sum of money, and n the number of years.

Then $$A = P\left(1 + \frac{r}{100}\right)^n. \quad \text{(i)}$$

When $A = 2P$, then from (i)

$$2P = P\left(1 + \frac{r}{100}\right)^n,$$

or $$n = \log 2 \div \log\left(1 + \frac{r}{100}\right). \quad \text{(ii)}$$

Taking various values 2, $2\frac{1}{2}$, 3, ..., etc., for r we may calculate n in each case from (ii).

If the values of r and n are plotted a curve can be drawn through the points; plotting n and $\frac{1}{r}$ the points are found to lie nearly on a straight line; and when r does not exceed 5, it will be found that the approximate relation

$$n = 70 \div r \quad \text{(iii)}$$

may be used.

Thus, if $r = 5$, then from (ii)

$$n = \log 2 \div \log\left(1 + \frac{5}{100}\right)$$
$$= \frac{\log 2}{\log 1{\cdot}05} = 14{\cdot}2.$$

Hence, a sum of money at 5 per cent. per annum will double itself in 14·2 years.

Using the approximate relation given by (iii), we have

$$n = \frac{70}{5} = 14 \text{ years.}$$

EXERCISES. XV.

1. The following observed values of E and R are supposed to be related by a linear law $R=a+bE$, but there are errors of observation. Find by plotting the values of R and E the most probable values of a and b.

(i)

E	2·5	3·5	4·4	5·8	7·5	9·6	12·0	15·1	18·3
R	13·6	17·6	22·2	28·0	35·5	47·4	56·1	74·6	84·9

(ii)

E	5	9·44	13·37	15·56	21·94	26·12	30·25
R	14	28	42	56	70	84	98

(iii)

E	1	1·84	2·75	3·62	4·56	5·4	6·18
R	14	28	42	56	70	84	98

(iv)

E	7	8·5	10	11·5	13·25	14·75	16·25	17·75
R	27·9	41·9	55·9	69·9	83·9	97·9	111·9	125·9

2. The relation between two variable quantities F and R is given by $F=cR+d$.

If when R is 20, F is 140, and when R is 50, F is 395. Find the numerical values of c and d.

3. The expression $ax^2+bx-30$ is equal to 240 when $x=5$, and equals 100 when $x=-2$. Find its value when $x=11$.

4. If $x=a(\phi-\sin\phi)$, $y=a(1-\cos\phi)$, and $a=5$; then taking various values of ϕ between 0 and, say 1·5, calculate x and y, and plot this part of the curve.

5. Plot the curve $y=\sin x$.

Give x values which are multiples and sub-multiples of $\frac{\pi}{2}$.

Notice that y is a maximum when $x=\frac{1}{2}\pi$, $\frac{5}{2}\pi$, etc., and y is a minimum when $x=-\frac{1}{2}\pi$, $\frac{3}{2}\pi$, etc.

6. The following values of p and u, the pressure of specific volume of steam, are taken from tables:

p	15	20	30	40	50	65	80	100
u	25·87	19·72	13·48	10·29	8·34	6·52	5·37	4·36

Find whether an equation of the form $pu^n = \text{const.}$ represents the law connecting p and u; and if so, find the best average value of the index n for the range of values given.

7. Values of p and u are given in the following table. Find the best average values of n and c in the equation $pu^n = c$ for the range of values given.

p	100	91·3	84·5	78·23	68·71	67·85	63·54	56·19
u	3·0	3·2	3·4	3·6	3·8	4·0	4·2	4·6

Also find the value of p when $u = 4·4$.

8. A series of values of x and y are given in the following table; assuming that the relation between x and y can be expressed by $y = a + bx^2$. Find the numerical values of the constants a and b.

x	0	1	2	3	4	5	6	7	8
y	3·25	3·45	3·65	5·0	6·45	8·25	10·45	12·0	16·0

9. A series of values of H and Q are given in the following table. Try if the relation between H and Q can be expressed in the form $Q = cH^n$. If so, obtain the best average values of the constants c and n.

H	1·0	1·5	2·0	2·5
Q	2·6	7·3	14·9	26·0

10. The following table gives the ordinates of a curve at various distances (x) measured from one end of the axis. Find the mean ordinate and area of the curve.

Ordinates	53	75	84	94·5	123	139	134	106	76	45
x inches	0	9	22	41	62	78	97	114	128	144

11. The following values of x and y are supposed to be related by an equation of the form $y=a+bx^2$. Plot on squared paper, and find numerical values of a and b.

x	0	1	2	3	4	5	6	7	8
y	2	2·05	2·2	2·45	2·8	3·25	3·8	4·45	5·2

12. Two variables x and y are connected by the relation $y=a+bx+cx^2$; the following simultaneous values of x and y are given. Find the numerical values of a, b and c.

x	0	1	2	3	4	5	6	7	8
y	2	1·85	1·8	1·85	2·0	2·25	2·6	3·04	3·6

13. Two variable quantities x and y are found to be related to one another for certain values of x as shown in the following table:

x	2	3	4	5	6
y	6·9	11·2	15·7	20·7	25·8

Try if the quantities are connected by a law of the form $y=ax^n$; and if so, find approximately the values of n and a.

14. The following quantities are thought to follow a law like $pv^n=\text{constant}$. Try if they do so; find the most probable value of n.

p	1	2	3	4	5
v	205	114	80	63	52

15. Taking $x=0, 1, \dots 5$, find values of y if

$$y=\frac{2{\cdot}5x}{3+0{\cdot}5x},$$

and draw the curve.

16. Plot the following observed values of A and B on squared paper, and determine the most probable law connecting A and B. Then assume this law to be correct and find the percentage error in the observed value of B when A is 150.

A	0	50	100	150	200	250	300	350	400
B	6·2	7·4	8·3	9·5	10·3	11·6	12·4	13·6	14·5

17. The following values of x and y are connected by a relation of the form $y=ax^2+b$. Find the numerical values of the constants a and b and the area of the curve from $x=0$ to $x=8$.

x	0	1	2	3	4	5	6	7	8
y	2·5	2·8	3·7	5·2	7·3	10	13·3	17·2	21·7

18. The following values of x and y are connected by a relation of the form $y=Ae^{bx}$. Find the numerical values of the constants A and b.

x	0·1	0·2	0·3	0·4	0·5	0·6	0·7	0·8	0·9	1·0
y	0·4524	0·4093	0·3704	0·3352	0·3032	0·2744	0·2483	0·2246	0·2033	0·1839

19. Work the following three exercises as if in each case one were alone given, taking in each case the simplest supposition which your information permits:

(*a*) The total yearly expense in keeping a school of 100 boys is £2100; what is the expense when the number of boys is 175?

(*b*) The expense is £2100 for 100 boys, £3050 for 200 boys; what is it for 175 boys?

(*c*) The expenses for three cases are known as follows:

£2100 for 100 boys,
£2650 for 150 boys,
£3050 for 200 boys.

What is the probable expense for 175 boys?

If you use a squared paper method, show all three solutions together.

20. A steam electric generator is found to use the following amounts of steam per hour for the following amounts of power:

Lbs. of steam per hour	4020	6650	10800
Indicated horse-power	210	480	706
Kilowatts produced	114	290	435

Find the indicated horse-power and the weight of steam used per hour when 330 kilowatts are being produced.

21. (i) Given $T_1=28{\cdot}689$, $T_2=28{\cdot}249$, $T_3=27{\cdot}546$, $v_1=2150$, $v_2=1900$, $v_3=1600$. The relation between T and v may be expressed by $T=a+bv^n$. Calculate the numerical values of a, b and n.

(ii) If the relation is $T=a+bv^{-1}$, find the values of a and b which will make the formula best represent the observations.

22. Experiments on the loss of head in a lead pipe of 0·4 inches diameter give, for a length of $3\frac{1}{2}$ feet, the following results:

Velocity of flow in feet per second $=v$	8·04	11·67	14·43	17·41	19·9
Observed difference of head in feet of water $=h$	3·03	6·11	9·07	12·21	15·62

Test whether the results can be expressed by a formula of the type $h \propto v^n$; and if so, obtain the value of n. If we assume that

$$h=f\frac{4l}{d}\frac{v^2}{2g},$$

in which the length l and diameter d of the pipe are in feet, what is the best value of the coefficient f? Take $g=32{\cdot}2$.

23. A is the horizontal sectional area of a vessel in square feet at the water level, h being the vertical draught in feet.

A	14850	14400	13780	13150
h	23·6	20·35	17·1	14·6

Plot; and read off values of A for values of $h=23$, 20, 16.

If the vessel changes in draught from 20·5 to 19·5, what is the diminution of its displacement in cubic feet?

24. A series of values of v and T are given in the following table. Assuming the relation between T and v to be given by $T=a+bv^n$, find the numerical values of the constants a, b and n.

T	2·867	2·876	2·884	2·891	2·899	2·906
v	3·0	3·2	3·4	3·6	3·8	4·0

25. Two variables S and v are assumed to be connected by a relation of the form $S=c+av^n$. Three values of v are 2·8, 3·4 and 4·0, and the corresponding values of S are 7·858, 7·88 and 7·9 respectively; find the numerical values of the constants c, a and n.

26. The slide valve of a horizontal steam-engine derives its motion from a point P in a link A_1A_2, where $A_1P=\frac{1}{3}A_1A_2$.

The horizontal displacements of A_1 and A_2 for any crank position θ are given by the equations

$$x_1=2\cdot5''\sin(\theta+27^\circ),\quad x_2=2\cdot6''\sin(\theta+150^\circ).$$

The resulting motion of the valve being defined by the equation

$$x=a''\sin(\theta+\alpha),$$

find the half travel a'' and the advance α.

27. A series of soundings taken across a river channel is given by the following table, x being the distance in feet from one shore and y the corresponding depth in feet:

x	0	10	16	23	30	38	43	50	55	60	70	75	80
y	10	20	26	28	30	31	28	23	15	12	8	6	0

Find the area of the cross-section.

28. If $x=a\sin pt+b\cos pt$ where a, b and p are constants. Show that this is the same as $x=A\sin(pt+e)$ if A and e are properly evaluated, and find the values of A and e.

29. The relation between s, the space described by a moving body, and t, the time in seconds, is given by

$$s=Ae^{-kt}\cos 2\pi\left(\frac{t}{t_1}+e\right).$$

Show that its velocity at time t is (p. 337):

$$\frac{ds}{dt}=-Ae^{-kt}\left\{\frac{2\pi}{t_1}\sin 2\pi\left(\frac{t}{t_1}+e\right)+k\cos 2\pi\left(\frac{t}{t_1}+e\right)\right\}.$$

30. Given $y=2\cdot45e^{0\cdot4x}$ calculate y for each of the following values of x, and plot the curve.

x	0	1	2	3	4	5	6	7	8
y									

Find the slope of the curve at the point $x=4$, also the average value of y from $x=0$ to $x=8$.

31. Plot the curve $y=3\sin x+4\cos x$, and from your curve see that the figure obtained is really a sine curve with different constants.

32. Plot the curve $y=25e^{-0\cdot3x}\sin(bx+c)$, where $b=\frac{10}{57\cdot3}$, $c=\frac{\pi}{6}$.

33. A body weighs 1610 lbs., the force F in lbs. necessary to raise it a distance x feet is automatically recorded, and is as follows:

x	0	11	20	34	45	55	66	76
F	4010	3915	3763	3532	3366	3208	3100	3007

Find the work done on the body when it has risen 70 feet? What is then the velocity of the body?

34. A car weighs 10 tons; what is its mass in engineers' units? It is drawn by the pull P lbs., varying in the following way, t being seconds from the time of starting:

P	1020	980	882	720	702	650	713	722	805
t	0	2	5	8	10	13	16	19	22

The retarding force of friction is constant and equal to 410 lbs. Plot $P-410$ and the time t, and find the *time average* of this excess force. What does this represent when it is multiplied by 22 seconds? What is the speed of the car at the time 22 seconds from rest?

35. Plot on the same sheet of paper and to the same scales, the curves $pv^n=c$, from $v=1$ to $v=10$, for values of n, 0·8, 0·9, 1, 1·13, 1·3, 1·414. Given that $p=100$ when $v=1$.

36. Plot the curves $\frac{x^2}{a^2}+\frac{y^2}{b^2}=1$, $\frac{x^2}{a^2}-\frac{y^2}{b^2}=1$.

$$\text{(i) } a=4,\ b=3, \quad \text{(ii) } a=2,\ b=2.$$

37. On the same axes and to the same scales plot the curves $y=\sin x$, $y=e^{-x}$. Hence, at the points of intersection of the curves find the values of x, between 0 and π, which satisfy the equation

$$e^x \sin x=1.$$

38. The coefficient of friction μ, in a certain bearing running at a velocity of V feet per minute, was found to be in Beauchamp-Towers' experiments on friction as follows:

V	105	157	209	262	314	366	419
μ	0·0018	0·0021	0·0025	0·0028	0·003	0·0033	0·0036

If the law connecting μ and V is of the form $\mu=kV^n$, find the values of k and n.

CHAPTER VIII.

SOLUTION OF TRIANGLES.

Solution of triangles.—In every triangle there are **six elements,** viz.: the **three angles** and the **three sides.** To solve a triangle, three of these elements must be known—one at least of these being a side. The angles are denoted by the letters A, B, C, (Fig. 37), at each angular point. The angle ACB, for example, is simply referred to as the angle C. The side AB opposite the angle C is denoted by the letter c, and similarly the other two sides of the triangle by a and b.

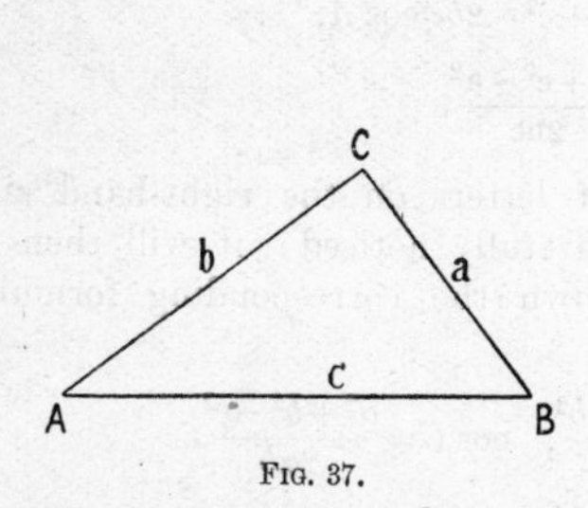

FIG. 37.

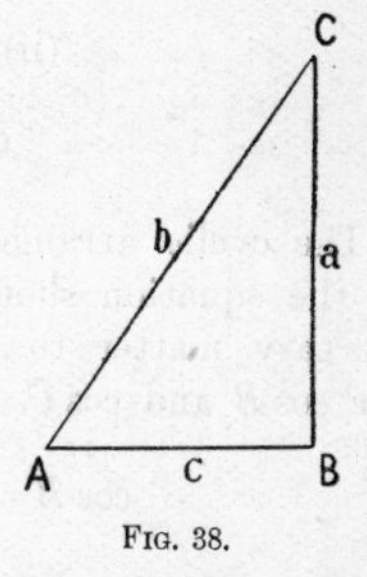

FIG. 38.

When the angle B (Fig. 38) is a right angle, the three sides are connected by the relation $b^2=a^2+c^2$.

It is advisable in the solution of triangles to have some convenient method of checking the results obtained. This check is furnished by drawing the triangle on *squared paper*, using the sides of the squares as suitable units of length, and setting out angles by means of (*a*) chords of angles (Table VIII.); (*b*) a table of tangents (Table VI.); or (*c*) a protractor.

It may be difficult to measure with sufficient accuracy by graphical methods; hence, the magnitudes of lines, or angles, are most conveniently obtained by calculation. Various formulae adapted to logarithmic computation, together with the tables of ratios of angles (IV., V. and VI.), are used for the purpose.

The remaining elements of a triangle may be obtained either by construction or by calculation when the data include :—

(*a*) **Two sides and an angle.**

(*b*) **The three sides.**

(*c*) **Two angles and one side.**

The following formulae may be used:

$$\text{(i)} \quad \frac{a}{\sin A} = \frac{b}{\sin B} = \frac{c}{\sin C},$$

or

$$\frac{\mathbf{a}}{\mathbf{b}} = \frac{\mathbf{\sin A}}{\mathbf{\sin B}}.$$

The sum of the three angles of a triangle is equal to 180°, so that when A and B are known, C is also known.

$$\text{(ii)} \quad a^2 = b^2 + c^2 - 2bc \cos A,$$

or,

$$\mathbf{\cos A = \frac{b^2 + c^2 - a^2}{2bc}}.$$

The cyclic arrangement of letters on the right-hand side of the equation should be carefully noticed; it will then be an easy matter to write down the corresponding formulae for $\cos B$ and $\cos C$. Thus,

$$\cos B = \frac{c^2 + a^2 - b^2}{2ca}, \quad \cos C = \frac{a^2 + b^2 - c^2}{2ab}.$$

The preceding formulae, except in the case of comparatively simple numbers, involve somewhat tedious and troublesome calculations; hence, other formulae better adapted for the application of logarithms are generally used.

Sine rule.—In a triangle ABC, the sines of the angles are proportional to the lengths of the opposite sides.

$$\therefore \frac{\sin A}{a} = \frac{\sin B}{b} = \frac{\sin C}{c}.$$

From B, (Fig. 39) draw a line perpendicular to and meeting the side AC, in D. Then

$$\sin A=\frac{BD}{AB}=\frac{BD}{c},$$

$$\sin C=\frac{BD}{BC}=\frac{BD}{a}.$$

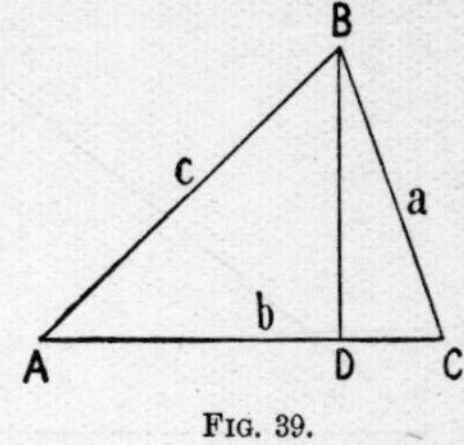

FIG. 39.

Hence, $$\frac{\sin A}{\sin C}=\frac{a}{c},$$

or $$\frac{\sin A}{a}=\frac{\sin C}{c}.$$

In a similar manner, if a line is drawn from C perpendicular to AB, we can prove

$$\frac{\sin A}{a}=\frac{\sin B}{b}.$$

Hence, $$\frac{\sin A}{a}=\frac{\sin B}{b}=\frac{\sin C}{c}.$$

The result shows that the greatest side subtends the greatest angle, and conversely.

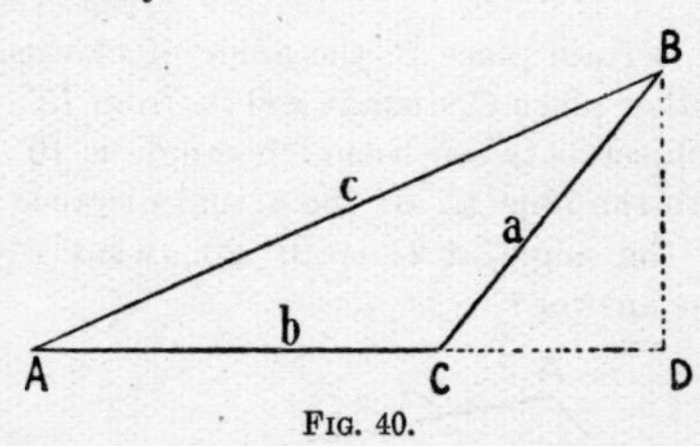

FIG. 40.

The results are also true when the given triangle is obtuse (Fig. 40).

Thus, $$\frac{BD}{c}=\sin A, \text{ or } BD=c\sin A.$$

Also, $$\frac{BD}{a}=\sin(180^\circ-C)=\sin C;$$

$$\therefore\ BD=a\sin C,$$

giving $$a\sin C=c\sin A;$$

$$\therefore\ \frac{a}{c}=\frac{\sin A}{\sin C} \text{ as before.}$$

Ex. 1. In a triangle ABC, given $A=38°$, $B=72°$, $c=2''\cdot 66$ (Fig. 41), find the remaining sides of the triangle.

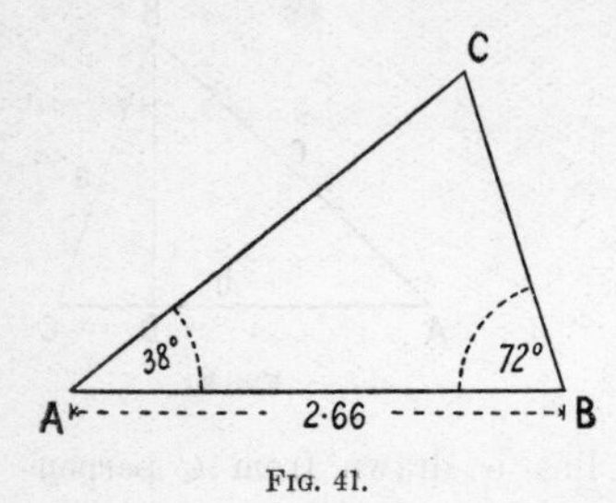

Fig. 41.

Here

$$C=180° - (38° + 72°) = 70°,$$

$$\frac{b}{c}=\frac{\sin B}{\sin C};$$

$$\therefore\ b=\frac{c \sin B}{\sin C}$$

$$=\frac{2\cdot 66 \times \sin 72°}{\sin 70°}$$

$$=\frac{2\cdot 66 \times 0\cdot 9511}{0\cdot 9397}.$$

$$\log b = \log 2\cdot 66 + \log 0\cdot 9511 - \log 0\cdot 9397$$

$$= 0\cdot 4249 + \bar{1}\cdot 9782 - \bar{1}\cdot 9730 = 0\cdot 4301 = \log 2\cdot 693;$$

$$\therefore\ b = 2\cdot 693.$$

Similarly, $$a=\frac{c \sin A}{\sin C}=\frac{2\cdot 66 \sin 38°}{\sin 70°}$$

$$=1\cdot 743.$$

Ex. 2. At a certain place B, the angle of elevation of an object is 45°. At another place C, distant 200 ft. from B, and in a straight line with the object between them, the angle is 10°. Find the distance from C to the object. If the actual distance from B to C is 199·7 ft., and the angle at C is 10° 20′, what is the percentage difference in the answer?

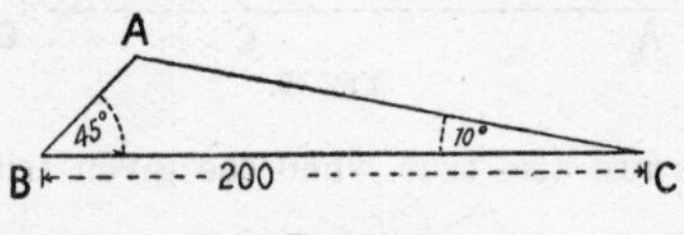

Fig. 42.

In Fig. 42 BC is 200 ft., and the angles at B and C are 45° and 10° respectively, A is the object, and the distance AC or b in the triangle ABC is required.

$$A = 180° - (B + C) = 180° - 55° = 125°$$

and $$\frac{b}{a}=\frac{\sin B}{\sin A}=\frac{\sin 45°}{\sin 125°};$$

$$\therefore\ b=\frac{200 \sin 45°}{\sin 55°}=172\cdot 6 \text{ ft.}$$

When the angle at C is 10° 20′, the angle at A

$$=(180-45°-10°\ 20')=124°\ 40',$$

and $\sin 124°\ 40' = \sin 55°\ 20'$;

$$\therefore\ b=\frac{199{\cdot}7\times\sin 45°}{\sin 55°\ 20'}=171{\cdot}9\text{ ft.}$$

Hence, by comparison of lengths 172·6 and 171·9

$$\text{Difference}=\frac{0{\cdot}7\times 100}{171{\cdot}9}=0{\cdot}407\ \%\text{ in excess.}$$

Ex. 3. In a triangle ABC, the base AB is 1000 feet long, and the angles at A and B are 31° 20′ and 125° 19′ respectively; find the length of the perpendicular let fall from C on AB produced, and the distance from A to the foot of the perpendicular.

Let D (Fig. 43) be the foot of the perpendicular.

$$b=\frac{1000\sin 54°\ 41'}{\sin 23°\ 21'}$$

$$=\frac{1000\times 0{\cdot}8160}{0{\cdot}3964}$$

$$=2059.$$

$$CD=2059\sin 31°\ 20'$$

$$=2059\times 0{\cdot}5200=1071.$$

$$AD=2059\sin 58°\ 40'$$

$$=2059\times 0{\cdot}8542$$

$$=1759.$$

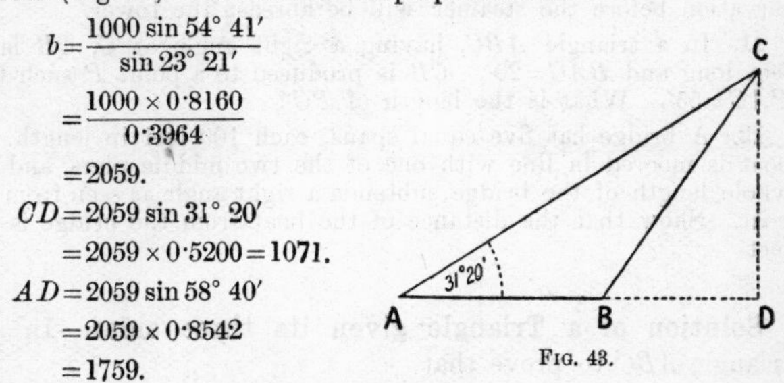

Fig. 43.

EXERCISES. XVI.

1. Two sides of a triangle are 2·5 and 3·75 respectively, the angle subtended by the longer side is 85°; find the remaining side and angles.

2. The angles at the base of a triangle measure 43° and 67° respectively; the base is 2″·5 long. Find the remaining sides.

3. If $A=55°$, $B=65°$ and $c=270$, find a.

4. Given $b=105$, $c=55$, $A=51°$, find B and C.

5. In a triangle ABC, the base AB is 1000 feet long, and the angles at A and B are 31° 20′ and 125° 19′ respectively; find the length of the perpendicular let fall from B on AC, and the distance from A to the foot of the perpendicular.

6. Two angles of a triangle being 150° and 11° 40′, and the longest side being 100 feet long; find the length of the shortest side.

7. In the triangle ABC, $A=60° \; 15'$, $B=54° \; 30'$ and $AB=100$ yards; find AC.

8. A station B is due north of a station A. Two cyclists leave A and B at the same time and ride along straight roads—AC, BC, to a station C, which bears 35° N. of E. from A and 10° S. of E. from B. Compare their average speeds if they reach C at the same time.

9. If the angles adjacent to the base of a triangle are $22°{\cdot}5$ and $112°{\cdot}5$, show that the perpendicular altitude will be one-half the base.

10. A passenger on a steamer moving due north along a straight reach of a lake, at a uniform speed of 10 miles an hour, observed at a certain instant that the bearing of a tower on shore made an angle of 28° with the direction of the steamer, and 3 minutes later an angle of 54°. Find the distance of the tower from the track of the steamer. Find, also, the time from the second observation before the steamer will be abreast the tower.

11. In a triangle ABC, having a right angle at C, CB is 30 feet long and $BAC=20°$. CB is produced to a point P such that $PAC=55°$. What is the length of PC?

12. A bridge has five equal spans, each 100 feet in length. A boat is moored in line with one of the two middle piers, and the whole length of the bridge subtends a right angle as seen from the boat. Show that the distance of the boat from the bridge is 245 feet.

Solution of a Triangle given its three sides.—In any triangle ABC to prove that

$$a^2=b^2+c^2-2bc\cos A. \qquad \text{(i)}$$

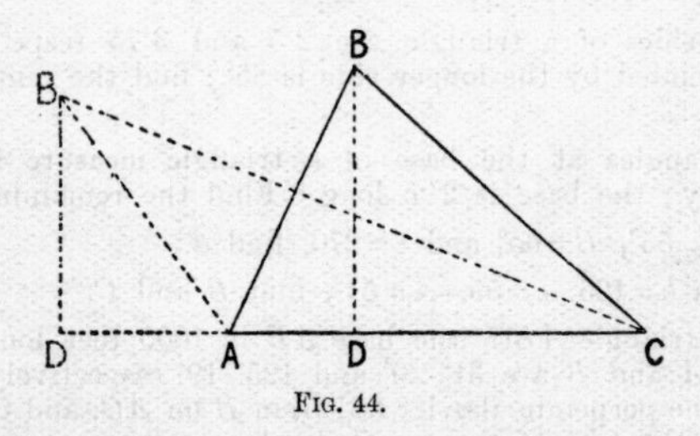

FIG. 44.

From B (Fig. 44) draw BD perpendicular to the base AC and meeting it in D. If the length AD be denoted by x, then $DC=b-x$ (see p. 592).

Let $y = BD$. Then, from the right-angled triangle ABD,

$$AB^2 = AD^2 + DB^2,$$

or

$$c^2 = x^2 + y^2. \quad \text{..............................(ii)}$$

Similarly, from the right-angled triangle BDC,

$$a^2 = (b-x)^2 + y^2 = b^2 - 2bx + x^2 + y^2.$$

Substituting from (ii),

$$a^2 = b^2 + c^2 - 2bx.$$

Also, $x = c \cos A$ because AD is the projection of AB on the base ;

$$\therefore\ a^2 = b^2 + c^2 - 2bc \cos A.$$

When the angle at A is an obtuse angle, then, with the same notation as before,

$$a^2 = y^2 + (b+x)^2 = y^2 + b^2 + 2bx + x^2.$$

Also, $\quad c^2 = x^2 + y^2.$

Substituting this value,

$$a^2 = b^2 + c^2 + 2bx.$$

Also, $\quad x = c \cos DAB.$

But $\quad \cos DAB = -\cos A.$

Substituting, we obtain $a^2 = b^2 + c^2 - 2bc \cos A.$

When the angle at A is 90° the triangle is right-angled.

But $\quad \cos 90^\circ = 0$;

hence, $\quad a^2 = b^2 + c^2.$

Eq. (i) may be written, $\quad \cos A = \dfrac{b^2 + c^2 - a^2}{2bc}.$

In a similar manner, if perpendiculars are let fall from A and C upon the opposite sides, the corresponding expressions for $\cos B$ and $\cos C$ may be obtained. Or, their values may be written down by noticing the cyclic arrangement of the letters. Thus,

$$\cos B = \frac{a^2 + c^2 - b^2}{2ac}, \text{ and } \cos C = \frac{a^2 + b^2 - c^2}{2ab}.$$

From the three formulae for $\cos A$, $\cos B$, and $\cos C$, the angles of a triangle can be obtained when the three sides are given. These expressions are chiefly useful for those cases where the given numbers are such that the operations indicated can be readily carried out. When the numbers indicating the lengths of the sides consist of three or more figures, formulae adapted to logarithms should be used.

Ex. 1. The sides of a triangle are 5, 6 and 7 respectively. Find the three angles.

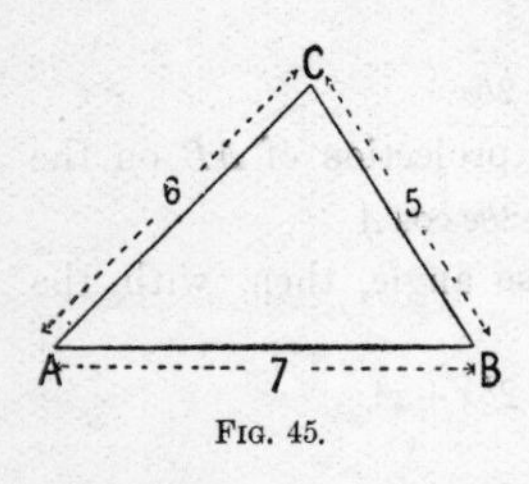

FIG. 45.

Using squared paper, set out AB as base and equal to 7 units (Fig. 45). Then, from A and B as centres, with radii 6 and 5 units respectively, describe arcs intersecting in C. The angles can now be measured. Or, using the formula

$$\cos A=\frac{b^2+c^2-a^2}{2bc}=\frac{6^2+7^2-5^2}{2\times6\times7}=\frac{60}{84}$$

$$=0{\cdot}7143.$$

From Table V., $A=44°\ 25'$.

$$\cos B=\frac{a^2+c^2-b^2}{2ac}=\frac{5^2+7^2-6^2}{2\times5\times7}=\frac{38}{70}=\frac{19}{35}=0{\cdot}5429;$$

$$\therefore\ B=57°\ 7'.$$

$$\cos C=\frac{a^2+b^2-c^2}{2ab}=\frac{5^2+6^2-7^2}{60}=\frac{1}{5}=0{\cdot}2;$$

$$\therefore\ C=78°\ 28'.$$

Ex. 2. Find the cosine of the largest angle of the triangle whose sides are 8 feet, 11 feet and 14 feet long respectively, and find the angle itself.

Let the three sides 14, 11 and 8 be denoted by a, b and c respectively. The largest angle A is opposite the largest side a.

Then $\cos A=\frac{b^2+c^2-a^2}{2bc}=\frac{121+64-196}{2\times11\times8}=-\frac{1}{16}=-0{\cdot}0625.$

From Table V., $A=93°\ 35'$.

Formulae adapted to logarithmic computation.

To prove that $$\sin\frac{A}{2}=\sqrt{\frac{(s-b)(s-c)}{bc}}$$

and $$\cos\frac{A}{2}=\sqrt{\frac{s(s-a)}{bc}},$$

where s denotes half the sum of the sides.

$$\cos A = 1 - 2\sin^2\frac{A}{2}, \ \dots \text{ (p. 32)};$$

$$\therefore\ 2\sin^2\frac{A}{2} = 1 - \cos A = 1 - \frac{b^2+c^2-a^2}{2bc} = \frac{2bc+a^2-b^2-c^2}{2bc}$$

$$= \frac{a^2-(b-c)^2}{2bc} = \frac{(a-b+c)(a+b-c)}{2bc}.$$

But $$s = \frac{1}{2}(a+b+c).$$

Then $$a-b+c = 2(s-b)$$

and $$a+b-c = 2(s-c).$$

Hence, $$\sin^2\frac{A}{2} = \frac{4(s-b)(s-c)}{4bc};$$

$$\therefore\ \mathbf{\sin\frac{A}{2} = \sqrt{\frac{(s-b)(s-c)}{bc}}}. \ \dots\dots\dots\dots\dots\dots\text{(i)}$$

Again, $$\cos A = 2\cos^2\frac{A}{2} - 1;$$

$$\therefore\ 2\cos^2\frac{A}{2} = 1 + \cos A = 1 + \frac{b^2+c^2-a^2}{2bc} = \frac{2bc+b^2+c^2-a^2}{2bc}$$

$$= \frac{(b+c)^2-a^2}{2bc} = \frac{(b+c+a)(b+c-a)}{2bc};$$

$$\therefore\ \cos^2\frac{A}{2} = \frac{4s(s-a)}{4bc};$$

$$\therefore\ \mathbf{\cos\frac{A}{2} = \sqrt{\frac{s(s-a)}{bc}}}. \ \dots\dots\dots\dots\dots\dots\text{(ii)}$$

Dividing (i) by (ii), $$\tan\frac{A}{2} = \sqrt{\frac{(s-b)(s-c)}{s(s-a)}}.$$

Also, $$\sin A = 2\sin\frac{A}{2}\cos\frac{A}{2};$$

$$\therefore\ \sin A = \frac{2}{bc}\sqrt{s(s-a)(s-b)(s-c)}.$$

Area of a triangle.—The area of a triangle can be found in any case when the triangle can be solved.

Let ABC (Fig. 46) be a triangle. The two sides, b and c, and angle A being known, the area of the triangle is $\frac{1}{2}p \times b$, where p is the length of the perpendicular BD.

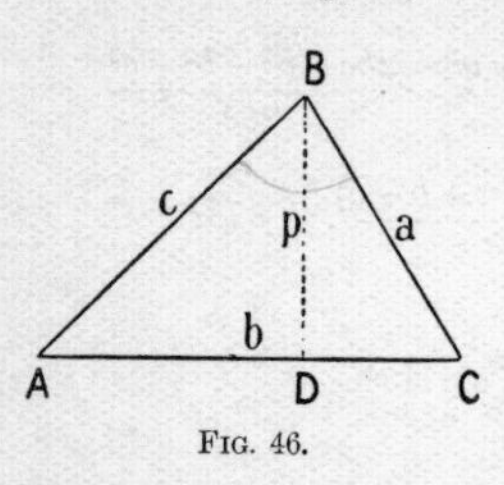

Fig. 46.

Also, $p = c \sin A$. Hence,

$$\textbf{Area of triangle} = \tfrac{1}{2}\mathbf{bc \sin A}, \ldots\ldots \text{(i)}$$

or one-half of the product of two sides and sine of included angle.

When the included angle is a right angle or 90°, then $\sin 90° = 1$, and Eq. (i) reduces to half the product of the sides which contain the right angle.

When the three sides of a triangle are given, it is only necessary to substitute in (i) the value of $\sin A$ (p. 165).

$$\therefore \text{ area of triangle} = \tfrac{1}{2}bc \times \frac{2}{bc}\sqrt{s(s-a)(s-b)(s-c)}$$

$$= \sqrt{s(s-a)(s-b)(s-c)}.$$

It is always advisable to check the results obtained from the above formulae by graphical methods.

When only one angle is required, we may use the formula for $\sin\frac{A}{2}$, or $\cos\frac{A}{2}$; but if all the angles are required, the most suitable formula is $\mathbf{\tan\frac{A}{2} = \sqrt{\frac{(s-b)(s-c)}{s(s-a)}}}$, *

because it will only be necessary to look out the logarithms for the four terms s, $(s-a)$, $(s-b)$ and $(s-c)$.

One method which may be used will be seen from the following example:

Ex. 3. The sides a, b, c are 1·2, 1·6 and 2 feet respectively; find the angles of the triangle and its area.

$$\left.\begin{aligned} a &= 1\cdot2, \\ b &= 1\cdot6, \\ c &= 2\cdot0, \end{aligned}\right\} \begin{aligned} s &= 2\cdot4, \\ s-a &= 1\cdot2, \\ s-b &= 0\cdot8, \\ s-c &= 0\cdot4. \end{aligned}$$

*See p. 592.

$$\tan\frac{A}{2}=\sqrt{\frac{0{\cdot}8\times0{\cdot}4}{2{\cdot}4\times1{\cdot}2}}=\sqrt{\frac{0{\cdot}32}{2{\cdot}88}}.$$

$$\log\tan\frac{A}{2}=\frac{1}{2}(\log 0{\cdot}32-\log 2{\cdot}88)=\bar{1}{\cdot}5228\,;$$

$$\therefore\ \tan\frac{A}{2}=0{\cdot}3333.$$

From Table VI., $\frac{A}{2}=18°\ 26'$;

$$\therefore\ A=36°\ 52'.$$

$$\tan\frac{B}{2}=\sqrt{\frac{(s-a)(s-c)}{s(s-b)}}=\sqrt{\frac{1{\cdot}2\times0{\cdot}4}{2{\cdot}4\times0{\cdot}8}}$$

$$=\sqrt{\frac{0{\cdot}48}{1{\cdot}92}}=\sqrt{\frac{1}{4}}=0{\cdot}5\,;$$

$$\therefore\ \tan\frac{B}{2}=0{\cdot}5,$$

$$\frac{B}{2}=26°\ 34'\,;$$

$$\therefore\ B=53°\ 8'.$$

Having found A and B, then C is known from the relation,

$$A+B+C=180°\,;$$

$$\therefore\ C=180°-(A+B)=90°.$$

$$\text{Area}=\sqrt{s(s-a)(s-b)(s-c)}=\sqrt{2{\cdot}4\times1{\cdot}2\times0{\cdot}8\times0{\cdot}4}$$

$$=0{\cdot}96 \text{ square feet.}$$

Ex. 4. The sides a, b, c of a triangle are 5, 6, and 7 inches respectively. Find the smallest angle.

The smallest angle will be the angle opposite the side a.

$$s=\frac{1}{2}(5+6+7)=9,\quad s-b=3,\quad s-c=2\,;$$

$$\therefore\ \sin\frac{A}{2}=\sqrt{\frac{(s-b)(s-c)}{bc}}=\sqrt{\frac{3\times2}{6\times7}}=\sqrt{\frac{1}{7}}\,;$$

$$\therefore\ \frac{A}{2}=22°\ 12',$$

$$A=44°\ 24'.$$

Ex. 5. The three sides of a triangle are 3745 ft., 5762 ft. and 7593 ft. respectively. Find the largest angle.

$$\tan^2 \frac{1}{2} A = \frac{(s-b)(s-c)}{s(s-a)} = \frac{4805 \times 2788}{8550 \times 957};$$

$$\therefore \frac{1}{2} A = 52° \text{ nearly},$$

$$A = 104°.$$

EXERCISES. XVII.

1. The three sides a, b, c of a triangle are $\sqrt{6}$, 2 and $\sqrt{3}+1$ respectively; find the angles A, B and C.

2. The sides of a triangle are 242, 1212 and 1450 yards respectively; show that the area is 6 acres.

3. The sides a, b, c of a triangle are 0·9, 1·2 and 1·5 respectively; find the angle B and the area of the triangle.

4. The sides of a triangle are as 4 : 5 : 6; find the angle opposite to the side 5.

5. The sides of a triangle are 35, 40 and 45 feet respectively; find the largest angle.

6. The sides a, b, c of a triangle are 12·5, 12·3 and 6·2 respectively; find $\sin \frac{1}{2} B$ and also B.

7. The sides of a triangle are 1·8, 1·2 and 1 ft. respectively; find the angles.

8. The sides of a triangle being 20 ft., 21 ft. and 29 ft., find the angle subtended by the side 29; also find the area of the triangle. Prove the formulae you use.

9. Given $a=13$, $b=9$, $c=12$; find the numerical value of $\tan \frac{A}{2}$, and then the angle A.

10. The sides of a triangle are 5·25 feet, 6·50 feet and 7·77 feet respectively; determine the smallest angle.

11. Find the smallest angle of the triangle whose three sides are 200, 250, 300 feet respectively.

12. Find the smallest angle of the triangle whose sides are 8, 9 and 13 units respectively.

13. In a triangle ABC, $a=17$, $b=20$, $c=27$; find $\tan \frac{1}{2} A$; also find A.

14. Determine the smallest angle in the triangle whose sides are in the ratio of 9 : 10 : 11.

15. Determine the smallest angle and the area of the triangle whose sides are 72·7 ft., 129 ft. and 113·7 ft. Prove any formula you may use in the calculation.

16. Prove the formula $\tan\frac{A}{2}=\left\{\frac{(s-b)(s-c)}{s(s-a)}\right\}^{\frac{1}{2}}$, and use it to find the angles of a triangle whose sides are 4002, 9760 and 7942 feet respectively.

17. In a triangle ABC, $a=\sqrt{5}$, $b=2$, $c=\sqrt{3}$; show that $8\cos A\cos C=3\cos B$.

18. The sides of a triangle are 36, 48 and 60 feet respectively; find the values of the angles opposite to them.

19. In a triangle ABC, given $a=3$, $b=2·75$, $c=1·75$ ft., find the angle B; also find the length of the side of a square the area of which is equal to the given triangle.

20. The sides of a triangle are 1·3 ft., 1·4 ft. and 1·5 ft.; a rectangle equal in area to the given triangle has one side 1·4 ft. long; find the remaining side.

21. The diagonals of a parallelogram make an angle of 35° with one another, and are severally 117·72 and 157·41 feet long. What is the area of the parallelogram?

22. (*a*) Find a formula for the area of a rectangle, having given a diagonal and an angle contained by the diagonals. (*b*) If the diagonal is 63·86 ft. long, and the angle 106° 9′, calculate the area.

23. Find a formula for the area of a parallelogram, having given the diagonals and the angle between them. If the diagonals are 30 ft. and 55·44 feet long, and the angle 146° 54′, calculate the area.

24. If the sides of a triangle be 7·152 inches, 8·263 inches, 9·375 inches, find its area.

25. The sides of a triangle are 1·3, 1·4 and 1·5 feet respectively; find the angles.

Show that the area of this triangle is 0·84 square feet. What is the area of a triangle whose sides are 13, 14 and 15 feet respectively?

26. The three sides of a triangle are 524, 566 and 938 feet respectively. Determine the three angles.

Solution of a triangle given two sides and the included angle.—When the data include two sides and included angle, we may use the formula

$$\tan\tfrac{1}{2}(\mathbf{B}-\mathbf{C})=\frac{\mathbf{b}-\mathbf{c}}{\mathbf{b}+\mathbf{c}}\cot\frac{\mathbf{A}}{2},$$

which may be obtained as follows:

From the sine rule (p. 159)

$$\frac{\sin B}{\sin C}=\frac{b}{c};$$

$$\therefore \frac{\sin B-\sin C}{\sin B+\sin C}=\frac{b-c}{b+c}.$$

Using the results given (p. 28), we obtain

$$\frac{2\sin\frac{B-C}{2}\cos\frac{B+C}{2}}{2\cos\frac{B-C}{2}\sin\frac{B+C}{2}}=\frac{b-c}{b+c};$$

$$\therefore \frac{\tan\frac{1}{2}(B-C)}{\tan\frac{1}{2}(B+C)}=\frac{b-c}{b+c},$$

or $\tan\frac{1}{2}(B-C)=\frac{b-c}{b+c}\cot\frac{A}{2}, \ldots \left(\text{since } \frac{B+C}{2}=90-\frac{A}{2}\right).$

This determines $(B-C)$, and since $B+C=180-A$, it follows that B and C can be obtained.

The remaining parts of a triangle may be obtained more easily as follows:

In Fig. 46 let x and y denote the segments of the base AD and DC respectively.

Then $x=c\cos A,\ y=b-x,\ p=c\sin A,$

$\tan C=p\div y,$ and $a=p\div\sin C.$

Ex. 1. If the sides b, c of a triangle ABC (Fig. 46), are 5·35 ft. and 4·65 ft., included angle 51° 20′. Find the remaining parts.

$$x=4\cdot65\cos 51°\ 20'=2\cdot905 \text{ ft.};$$
$$y=5\cdot35-2\cdot905=2\cdot445 \text{ ft.};$$
$$p=4\cdot65\sin 51°\ 20'=3\cdot631 \text{ ft.}$$

$$\tan C=\frac{3\cdot631}{2\cdot445};$$

$$\therefore C=56°\ 3'.$$

$B=180°-(51°\ 20'+56°\ 3')=72°\ 37'$; $a=3\cdot631\div\sin 56°\ 3'=4\cdot376$ ft

Ex. 2. Given the two sides of a triangle b and c equal to 3·45 and 1·74 ft. respectively, and angle $A=37°\ 20'$; find the angles B and C, the remaining side a, and the area of the triangle.

$$\tan\tfrac{1}{2}(B-C)=\frac{b-c}{b+c}\cot\frac{A}{2}*$$

$$=\frac{3·45-1·74}{3·45+1·74}\cot 18°\ 40'$$

$$=\frac{1·71}{5·19}\times 2·9600=0·9752;$$

$$\therefore\ \tfrac{1}{2}(B-C)=44°\ 17',$$

$$\tfrac{1}{2}(B+C)=71°\ 20',\ i.e.\ \tfrac{1}{2}(180°-37°\ 20'),$$

$$\therefore\ B=115°\ 37',\text{ and }C=27°\ 3'.$$

The side a may be found from the relation

$$\frac{a}{c}=\frac{\sin A}{\sin C};$$

$$\therefore\ a=\frac{1·74\sin 37°\ 20'}{\sin 27°\ 3'}=\frac{1·74\times 0·6065}{0·4548}=2·32\text{ ft.}$$

$$A=\text{area of triangle}=\tfrac{1}{2}bc\sin A$$

$$=\tfrac{1}{2}\times 3·45\times 1·74\sin 37°\ 20'$$

$$=1·725\times 1·74\times 0·6065;$$

$$\therefore\ \log(A)=\log 1·725+\log 1·74+\log 0·6065=0·2601;$$

$$\therefore\ A=1·82\text{ sq. ft.}$$

Ex. 3. Two sides of a triangle are measured and found to be 32·5 and 24·2 inches, the included angle being 57°; find the area of the triangle. If the true lengths of the sides are 32·6 and 24·1, what is the percentage error in the answer?

$$\text{Area}=\tfrac{1}{2}\times 32·5\times 24·2\times\sin 57°=329·8\text{ sq. in.}$$

$$,,\ =\tfrac{1}{2}\times 32·6\times 24·1\times\sin 57°=329·5\quad ,,$$

$$\text{Error}=0·3\text{ sq. in.; percentage error}=\frac{0·3\times 100}{329·5}$$

$$=0·09\ \%.$$

* Tables of Cotangents. Pp. 592B, 592C.

Ex. 4. Two sides of a triangle are 385 feet and 231 feet respectively, and the included angle is 50°.

Find the other two angles and the remaining side.

$$\tan \tfrac{1}{2}(B-C)=\frac{b-c}{b+c}\tan \tfrac{1}{2}(B+C)$$

$$=\frac{385-231}{385+231}\tan 65^\circ$$

$$=\frac{154}{616}\times 2{\cdot}1445=0{\cdot}5361.$$

From Table VI.,

$$\tfrac{1}{2}(B-C)=28^\circ\ 12'.$$

Also, $\tfrac{1}{2}(B+C)=65^\circ$;

$$\therefore\ B=93^\circ\ 12',\ \ C=36^\circ\ 48'.$$

Ex. 5. ABC is a triangle in which a and b are together twice c; show that the area equals $3c^2\tan\frac{1}{2}C\div 4$.

What is the greatest value of C consistent with the given conditions?

$$a+b=2c;$$

$$\therefore\ s=\frac{1}{2}(a+b+c)=\frac{3c}{2}.$$

Let A denote the area of the triangle.

$$A=\sqrt{s(s-a)(s-b)(s-c)}$$

$$=s(s-c)\sqrt{\frac{(s-b)(s-a)}{s(s-c)}},\ \text{but}\ \sqrt{\frac{(s-b)(s-a)}{s(s-c)}}=\tan\tfrac{1}{2}C$$

$$=\frac{3c}{2}\times\frac{c}{2}\tan\tfrac{1}{2}C$$

$$=3c^2\tan\tfrac{1}{2}C\div 4.$$

If $a+b=2c$, $\sin A+\sin B=2\sin C$;

$$\therefore\ 2\sin\frac{A+B}{2}\cos\frac{A-B}{2}=4\sin\frac{C}{2}\cos\frac{C}{2}.\ \ldots\ldots\ldots\ldots\ldots\ldots\text{(i)}$$

But since $A+B+C=180$,

$$\sin\frac{A+B}{2}=\cos\frac{C}{2};$$

$$\therefore\ \sin\frac{C}{2}=\frac{1}{2}\cos\frac{A-B}{2}\ \text{from (i)}.$$

Obviously, $\frac{C}{2}$ is greatest when $A=B$.

In which case $$\sin\frac{C}{2}=\frac{1}{2}=\sin 30^\circ;$$

$$\therefore\ C=60^\circ.$$

EXERCISES. XVIII.

1. The sides of a triangle are 535 feet and 465 feet, and the angle between them is 51° 29′; find the other angles to the nearest minute.

2. In a triangle ABC, given $b=400$ feet, $c=100$ feet and $A=64^\circ\ 20'$; find B and C.

3. In a triangle ABC, given $a=3$, $b=5$ and $C=120^\circ$; find $\tan\frac{1}{2}(B-A)$.

4. In a triangle $A=60^\circ$, $b=9$, $c=6$; find the other angles.

5. In a triangle ABC, $b=14$, $c=11$, $A=60^\circ$; find the other angles.

6. In a triangle ABC, $\frac{b}{c}=\frac{3}{7}$ and $A=6^\circ\ 37'$; find the other angles.

7. Two of the sides of a triangle are 11 and 5 respectively, and the included angle is 60°; find the other angles. Also find the length of the other side of the triangle.

8. Two sides of a triangle are 1·5 and 13·5 respectively, and the included angle is 65°; find the remaining angles.

9. Two sides of a triangle are 4 feet and 6 feet in length respectively, and the included angle is 30°; find the area of the triangle.

10. Two sides of a triangle are 9 and 7 feet respectively, and the angle between them is 60°; find the other angles.

11. The two sides AB and BC of a triangle are 44·7 and 69·8 respectively, the angle ABC is 32°. (*a*) Find the length of the perpendicular from A to BC, (*b*) the area of the triangle ABC, (*c*) the angles A and C.

12. Two sides of a triangle are 729 and 353 feet respectively, and the included angle is 54°; find the other angles, and the remaining side.

13. Two sides of a triangle are 3747 and 1528 feet respectively, the included angle is 33°; find the other two angles.

14. Prove that the area of a triangle $ABC=\frac{a^2\sin B\sin C}{2\sin A}$. If $A=75^\circ$, $C=60^\circ$ and $a=2(1+\sqrt{3})$, show that the area is equal to $6+2\sqrt{3}$.

Solution of a triangle given two of its sides and the angle opposite one of these sides.—When the given data include two sides and the angle opposite one of these, we may use the sine rule. Thus, let a and b (Fig. 47) be the two sides and A the given angle.

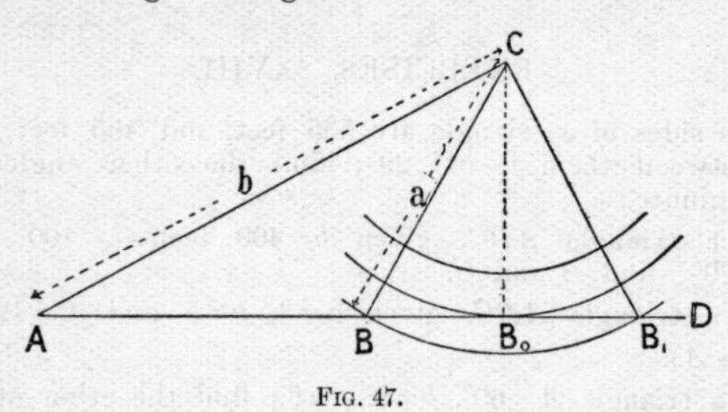

FIG. 47.

The angle B may be obtained from the relation

$$\sin B = \frac{b}{a} \sin A.$$

The angle B is obtained from its sine, but, as two angles less than 180° may have the same sine, this case is usually known as the **ambiguous case.**

This may be shown graphically as follows:

Draw two lines, AC and AD, at an angle A (Fig. 47). Along one side measure a length $AC=b$. From C as centre and radius a, describe an arc of a circle.

(i) If this cuts the base AD in two points B and B_1, then, on joining B and B_1 to C, we obtain two triangles ABC or AB_1C, either of which satisfies the given conditions.

But if a is greater than b there is only one triangle.

(ii) If the circle touches AD at B_0, then the triangle is right-angled.

(iii) If the circle does not cut AD (as indicated), then there is no solution.

It will be seen that the three conditions just referred to are obtainable from Eq. (i) as follows:

(i) Thus, if $b \sin A < a$, $\sin B$ is <1, and there may be two solutions.

(ii) When $b \sin A = a$, then $\frac{b \sin A}{a} = 1$;

$$\therefore \sin B = 1 \text{ and } B = 90^\circ.$$

Hence, the triangle is a right-angled triangle.

(iii) If $b \sin A > a$, then $\frac{b \sin A}{a}$ is greater than unity, and there is no triangle with the given parts.

Algebraic solution.—It will be obvious from the preceding paragraph that from the data given we may obtain two values, one value, or an imaginary or impossible value of the remaining side c.

Thus, from the equation

$$a^2 = b^2 + c^2 - 2bc \cos A,$$
$$c^2 - 2bc \cos A = a^2 - b^2.$$

This is a quadratic equation from which to find c;

$$\begin{aligned} \therefore\ c^2 - 2bc \cos A + (b \cos A)^2 &= a^2 - b^2 + b^2 \cos^2 A \\ &= a^2 - b^2(1 - \cos^2 A) \\ &= a^2 - b^2 \sin^2 A; \end{aligned}$$

$$\therefore\ c = b \cos A \pm \sqrt{a^2 - b^2 \sin^2 A}.$$

(i) If $b \sin A < a$, there are two values of c.

(ii) If $b \sin A = a$, the two roots are equal.

(iii) If $b \sin A > a$, the quantity under the root sign is negative, and the values, or roots, are imaginary.

EXERCISES. XIX.

1. Find the angle A of the triangle ABC, having given that $AC = 257$ feet, $BC = 650$ feet and $C = 90^\circ$. Find also the length of the line AD which meets BC in D, so that the angle ADC is $40^\circ\ 32'$.

2. Find the value or values of c, having given $A = 35^\circ\ 36'$, $a = 1770$, $b = 2164$.

3. Find all the parts of the triangles which have one side 90 feet long, another side 60 feet long, and the angle opposite to the shorter side equal to $18^\circ\ 37'$.

4. Given $b = 8{\cdot}4$ inches, $c = 12$ inches, $B = 37^\circ\ 36'$; find A.

5. In any triangle, if $A = 47^\circ$, $a = 180$, $b = 215$; find B.

6. In a triangle ABC, given $AC = 166 \cdot 5$ feet, $BC = 162 \cdot 5$ feet, the angle $A = 52^\circ\ 19'$. Solve either of the triangles to which the data belong.

7. Given $A = 40^\circ$, $a = 140 \cdot 5$, $b = 170 \cdot 6$; find B.

8. In the triangle ABC, $A = 26^\circ\ 26'$, $b = 127$ and $a = 85$; find B.

9. Two angles of a triangular field are $22\frac{1}{2}^\circ$ and 45° respectively, and the length of the side opposite to the latter is a furlong. Show that the field contains exactly two acres and a half.

10. The lengths of two sides of a triangle are $537 \cdot 4$ feet and $158 \cdot 7$ feet, the angle opposite the shorter side is $15^\circ\ 11'$. Calculate the other angles of the triangle, or of the triangles, if there are two.

11. Having given $A = 30^\circ$, $a = \sqrt{2}$, $c = 2$, solve the triangle.

12. In a given triangle $a = 145$, $b = 178$, $B = 41^\circ\ 10'$; find A.

13. Given $B = 30^\circ$, $c = 150$, $b = 50\sqrt{3}$; show that of the two triangles that satisfy the data, one will be isosceles and the other right-angled. (i) Find the third side in the greatest of these triangles; (ii) would the solution be ambiguous if the data had been $B = 30^\circ$, $c = 150$, $b = 75$?

Measurement of heights and distances.—The angle made with the horizontal plane by a straight line joining a point of observation to a distant point, when the point is above the point of observation, is called the **angle of elevation.** The angle is called the **angle of depression** when the distant point is below the horizontal line through the point of observation. These angles are measured by an instrument called a **Theodolite.**

The angle subtended by a line joining two distant objects may be measured by a **Sextant.**

Fig. 48.

Thus, if A (Fig. 48) denotes the place of observation, and C a distant point above A, then the angle, between the line joining A to C and a horizontal line AB, is the angle of elevation of C.

If CB be drawn perpendicular to AB and meeting AB in B (Fig. 48), then the height of the object C can be obtained when AB and the angle at A are given.

Since $$\frac{BC}{AB}=\tan A;$$

$$\therefore\ BC=AB\tan A. \qquad \text{(i)}$$

The plan adopted is to write the fraction so that the unknown quantity is the numerator and the known quantity the denominator.

When it is either impossible or inconvenient to obtain the distance AB, a distance such as DA in the line BA produced (Fig. 48) may be measured and the angles of elevation ADC and BAC obtained. Denoting the known length DA by l, and the distance AB by x, then if h denotes the height BC, $h=x\tan BAC$ (i).

Also, $$h=(l+x)\tan BDC. \qquad \text{(ii)}$$

If we substitute the value of h from (i) in (ii), we obtain a simple equation in x, and finally h may be found from (i).

Angles of depression.—If a horizontal line be drawn through C, then the angles at C subtended by two objects D and A, are called angles of depression, and the solution is effected as in the preceding case.

Ex. 1. At a distance of 99 ft. from the foot of a tower the angular elevation is 60°. Find the height of the tower.

If h denote the height, then

$$h=99\tan 60^\circ=99\times\sqrt{3}.$$

$$\log h=\log 99+\tfrac{1}{2}\log 3=2{\cdot}2341;$$

$$\therefore\ h=171{\cdot}4\text{ ft.}$$

This result may be verified by construction, as in Fig. 48. Draw a right-angled triangle having the angle at $A=60^\circ$ and $AB=99$. Then $BC=171{\cdot}4$.

Ex. 2. The elevation of an object on a hill is observed, from a certain place in the horizontal plane through its base, to be 15°. After walking 120 feet towards it on level ground the elevation is found to be 18°. Find the height of the object and its distance from the second place of observation.

Draw a line DAB and from D set off DA (Fig. 49) to represent 120 feet, and make the angles BAC and BDC equal to 18° and 15° respectively. From C, the point of intersection, draw BC perpendicular to DA and meeting DA produced in B. Then BC is the height and BA is the distance required.

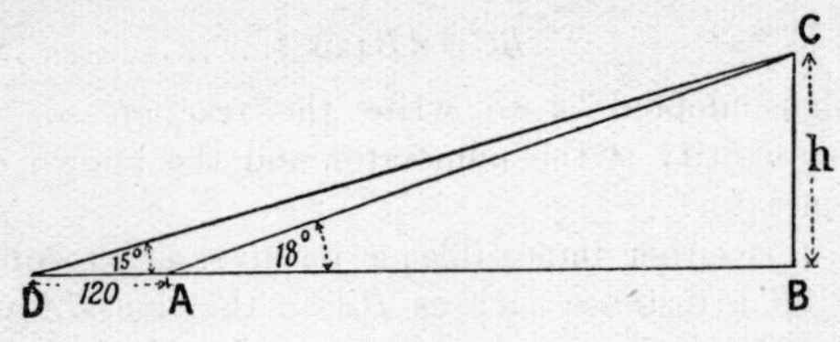

FIG. 49.

Let $BA=x$ and $BC=h$. By calculation, two or more methods may be used to find x and h. If necessary, one method may be used to check another.

First method. As the angle $BAC=ADC+ACD$, the angle $ACD=3°$;

$$\therefore \quad \frac{AC}{AD}=\frac{\sin 15°}{\sin 3°},$$

or
$$AC=\frac{AD\sin 15°}{\sin 3°}.$$

Again,
$$BC=AC\sin 18°;$$

$$\therefore \quad h=\frac{AD\sin 15°\sin 18°}{\sin 3°}=\frac{120\times 0{\cdot}2588\times 0{\cdot}3090}{0{\cdot}0523}$$

$$=183{\cdot}5 \text{ ft.}$$

Also,
$$x=h\cot 18°$$
$$=183{\cdot}5\times 3{\cdot}0777=564{\cdot}76 \text{ ft.}$$

Second method. Using the same notation,

$$h=x\tan 18°. \quad \text{.......................(i)}$$

Also,
$$h=(120+x)\tan 15°. \quad \text{.......................(ii)}$$

Substitute in (ii) the value of h from (i);

$$\therefore \quad x\tan 18°=120\tan 15°+x\tan 15°,$$

or
$$x(\tan 18°-\tan 15°)=120\tan 15°;$$

$$\therefore \quad x=\frac{120\tan 15°}{\tan 18°-\tan 15°}=\frac{120\times 0{\cdot}2679}{0{\cdot}057};$$

$$\therefore \quad x=564{\cdot}76 \text{ ft.}$$

Substituting this value for x in (i), h is obtained.

In the preceding example the angle of elevation has been used. A similar method is employed when the angles of depression are given.

Ex. 3. From the top of a hill, the angles of depression of two objects on a horizontal plane through the base of a hill are found to be 15° and 18° respectively. Find the height of the hill, the distance between the objects being 120 feet.

Draw a horizontal line passing through C (Fig. 49). Make the angles of depression equal to 15° and 18° respectively. Draw a horizontal line DA equal to 120 ft. Produce DA to meet a line CB perpendicular to DA in B. Then BC is the height required.

As a good exercise in manipulation of symbols it is interesting to solve the preceding question, assuming that the data consist of letters instead of numerical quantities.

Let the angles BAC and BDC be denoted by α and β respectively, the distance AD by l, the remaining quantities as in the preceding.

Then
$$\frac{DC}{l}=\frac{\sin DAC}{\sin DCA}$$

$$=\frac{\sin(180°-\alpha)}{\sin(\alpha-\beta)}=\frac{\sin\alpha}{\sin(\alpha-\beta)};$$

$$\therefore\ DC=\frac{l\sin\alpha}{\sin(\alpha-\beta)},$$

$$h=DC\sin\beta=\frac{l\sin\alpha\sin\beta}{\sin(\alpha-\beta)},$$

and substituting numerical values for l, α and β it will be seen that the result agrees with the preceding result.

Ex. 4. From a station h feet above the water the angular depression from the horizontal of the light of a passing vessel and of its reflection in the water was observed to be D_1 and D_2 minutes; prove that the horizontal distance of the vessel was

$$2h\ \text{cosec}\,(D_1+D_2)\cos D_1\cos D_2 \text{ feet.}$$

If the angle D_1 and D_2 are small, prove that the distance is practically

$$\frac{3438h}{\frac{1}{2}(D_1+D_2)} \text{ feet, or } \frac{1146h}{\frac{1}{2}(D_1+D_2)} \text{ yards.}$$

Let P denote the station at a height h feet above the surface of the water AS (Fig. 50), L the light and R its reflection, then $RS=SL$, $\angle MPL=D_1$, and $\angle MPR=D_2$, where M is vertically over L.

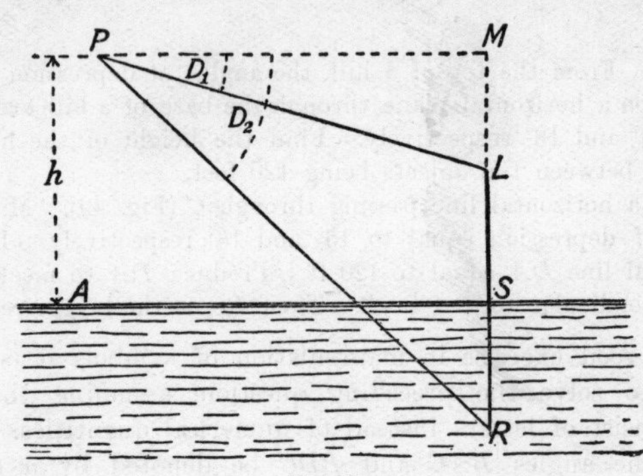

FIG. 50.

Let distance $MP=s$, then

$$LM=s\tan D_1 \quad \text{and} \quad RM=s\tan D_2;$$

$$\therefore\ LM+RM=s(\tan D_1+\tan D_2)$$

$$=s\left(\frac{\sin D_1}{\cos D_1}+\frac{\sin D_2}{\cos D_2}\right)$$

$$=\frac{s\sin(D_1+D_2)}{\cos D_1 \,.\, \cos D_2}.$$

But $LM+RM=LM+RL+LM=2LM+2SL=2SM=2h$;

$$\therefore\ 2h=\frac{s\sin(D_1+D_2)}{\cos D_1 \,.\, \cos D_2},$$

or

$$s=\frac{2h\cos D_1\cos D_2}{\sin(D_1+D_2)}$$

$$=2h\cos D_1\cos D_2\operatorname{cosec}(D_1+D_2).$$

When D_1 and D_2 are small angles, $\cos D_1$ and $\cos D_2$ may each be taken to be unity.

Hence, from (i), $$S=\frac{2h}{\sin(D_1+D_2)}. \quad \text{(ii)}$$

Also, when an angle is small the sine of an angle is approximately equal to the radian measure of the angle, substituting in (ii);

$$\therefore\ S=\frac{2h}{\frac{3{\cdot}1416}{180\times 60}(D_1+D_2)}=\frac{3438h}{\frac{1}{2}(D_1+D_2)}\text{ ft.}=\frac{1146h}{\frac{1}{2}(D_1+D_2)}\text{ yds.}$$

When in problems concerned with heights and distances the data include the points of the compass, it is desirable to draw a perspective view; for even if such a sketch is only a rough approximation, it tends to clearness.

Ex. 5. The angle of elevation of a steeple at a place due south of it is 45°, and at another place due west of the former the angle is 16°. If the distance between the two places is 100 feet, find the height of the steeple.

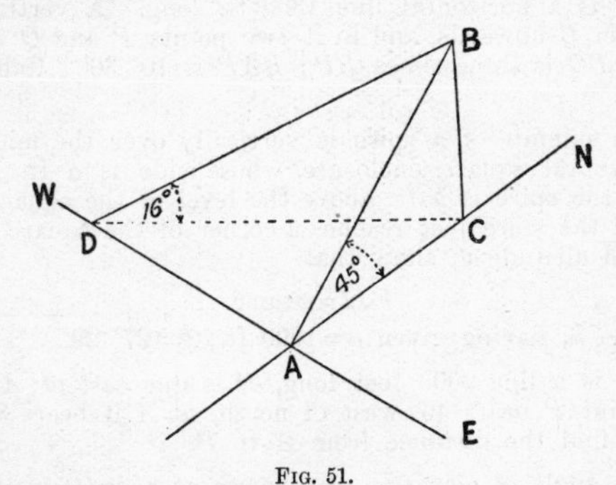

FIG. 51.

Let BC (Fig. 51) denote the steeple, A the first place and D the second place of observation.

$$BC = h = CD \tan 16°, \quad \text{or} \quad h^2 = (CD)^2 \tan^2 16° \quad \ldots\ldots\ldots\ldots\ldots \text{(i)}$$

Also, as BAC is 45°, AC is equal to h.

$$CD^2 = 100^2 + h^2.$$

Substituting this value in (i),

$$h^2 = (100^2 + h^2)\tan^2 16° = 100^2 \tan^2 16° + h^2 \tan^2 16°;$$

$$\therefore\ h^2(1 - \tan^2 16°) = 100^2 \tan^2 16°,$$

$$h^2 = \frac{100^2 \times 0{\cdot}2867^2}{1 - 0{\cdot}2867^2} = \frac{100^2 \times 0{\cdot}2867^2}{1{\cdot}2867 \times 0{\cdot}7133}.$$

$$2 \log h = 2(\log 100 + \log 0{\cdot}2867) - \log 1{\cdot}2867 - \log 0{\cdot}7133,$$

$$\text{or } \log h = 1{\cdot}4760 = \log 29{\cdot}92;$$

$$\therefore\ h = 29{\cdot}92 \text{ feet.}$$

EXERCISES. XX.

1. A person standing on one bank of a river observes the altitude of the top of a tower on the edge of the opposite side to be 55°; after receding 30 feet, he finds it to be 48°. Determine the breadth of the river.

2. Calculate the height of a tower from the following data: angles 20° and 55°; distance between points of observation 1000 feet in a direct line from the foot of the tower.

3. AB is a horizontal line 1300 ft. long. A vertical line is drawn from B upwards, and in it two points P and Q are taken, such that BQ is three times BP; BAP is 10° 30′. Calculate BP and BAQ.

4. The summit of a spire is vertically over the middle point of a horizontal square enclosure, whose side is a ft. long; the height of the spire is h ft. above the level of the square. If the shadow of the spire just reaches a corner of the square when the sun has an altitude θ, show that

$$h\sqrt{2}=a\tan\theta.$$

Calculate h, having given $a=1000$ ft., $\theta=27°\ 29'$.

5. AB is a line 2000 feet long, B is due east of A; at B a distant point P bears 46° west of north, at A it bears 8° 45′ east of north; find the distance from A to P.

6. The angle of elevation of a tower at a distance of 20 yards from its foot is three times as great as the angle of elevation 100 yds. from the same point. Show that the height of the tower is $\frac{300}{\sqrt{7}}$ ft.

7. (*a*) The angular elevation of a tower from a certain station is A; at another station, in the same horizontal plane, and a feet nearer the tower, the angular elevation is $(90°-A)$; if h be the height of the tower above the horizontal plane, show that

$$h(1-\tan^2 A)=a\tan A.$$

(*b*) Calculate h, when $A=30°$ and $a=100$ feet.

8. ABC is a triangle in a horizontal plane, with a right angle at C, and P is the middle point of AB; a flagstaff is set up at C, and it is found that its angles of vertical elevation at A, B and P are α, β, θ; show that $\tan^2\theta=2\tan\alpha\tan\beta\sin 2A$.

9. The foot, C, of a tower and two stations, A and B, are in the same horizontal plane. The angular elevation of the tower at A is 60° and at B it is 45°, the distance from A to B is 100 feet and the angle ACB is 60°; show that the height of the tower is approximately 115 feet.

10. P and Q are two stations 1000 yards apart on a straight stretch of sea shore, which bears East and West. At P a rock bears 42° West of South, at Q it bears 35° East of South. Show that the distance of the rock from the shore is

$$1000 \sin 48° \sin 55° \div \sin 77° \text{ yards},$$

and calculate this distance to the nearest yard.

11. Find the length of an arc on the sea which subtends an angle of one minute at the centre of the earth, supposing the earth a sphere of diameter 7920 miles. Give the answer in miles to three places of decimals.

12 A person standing due south of a lighthouse observes that his shadow, cast by the light at the top, is 24 feet long; on walking 100 yards due east he finds his shadow to be 30 feet. Supposing that he is 6 feet high, find the height of the light from the ground.

13. The angle of elevation of a cliff at a certain place is 12° 30′, and at a second place of observation, distant 950 yards from the first and in a direct line towards the base, the second altitude is found to be 69° 30′. Find the height of the cliff.

14. A tower stands at the foot of a hill whose inclination to the horizon is 9°, at a point 100 feet up the hill the tower subtends an angle of 54°; find its height.

15. The angles of elevation of a tower from the two ends of a measured line of length l, in the same horizontal plane and in the same straight line as the base of the tower are 30° and 18° respectively. Find the height of the tower in terms of l.

16. The angle of elevation of a balloon from a station due south of it is 47° 20′, and from another station due west of the former on the same horizontal plane, and distant 671·3 feet from it, the elevation is 41° 15′. Find the height of the balloon.

17. The angular elevation of a steeple at a place due south of it is 45°, and at another place due west of the former station and 100 yards from it the elevation is 15°. Find the height of the steeple.

18. From the top of a tower, whose height is 100 feet, the angles of depression of two small objects on the plain below, which are in the same vertical plane with the tower, are observed, and found to be 45° and 30°; find to one decimal place the distance between them.

19. A person observes that two objects A and B bear due N. and 30° W. of N., respectively. On walking a mile in the direction N.W., he finds that the bearings of A and B are N.E. and due E. respectively; find the distance between A and B.

20. The altitude of a certain rock is observed to be 47°, and after walking 1000 feet towards the rock, up a slope inclined at an angle of 32° to the horizon, the observer finds that the altitude is 77°. Find the vertical height of the rock above the first point of observation.

21. From two stations A and B on shore, 3742 yards apart, a ship C is observed at sea. The angles BAC, ABC are simultaneously observed to be 73° and 82°, respectively. Find the distance from A to the ship.

22. A tower, whose height is known to be 100 feet, stands on a vertical cliff; the angle subtended by the tower at the eye of an observer in a boat at sea level is found to be 28°, and at the same station the cliff subtends an angle of 31°. Find the height of the cliff above sea level and the distance of the boat from the foot of the cliff.

23. ABC is a triangle in a horizontal plane, and D is a point vertically above C; if $AB=600$ feet, $ACB=117°\ 16'$, $CAD=28°\ 28'$, and $CBD=13°\ 32'$, show that

$$\tan\tfrac{1}{2}(BAC-ABC)=\sin 14°\ 56' \tan 31°\ 22' \div \sin 42°,$$

and calculate the length of CD.

24. A man standing due south of a spire finds the angular elevation of its summit to be α. He then walks to a point a yards due west of his former position and finds the elevation to be β. Show that the height of the spire in yards is

$$\frac{a \sin\alpha \sin\beta}{\sqrt{\sin(\alpha-\beta)\sin(\alpha+\beta)}}.$$

25. A flagstaff is fixed on the top of a tower standing on a horizontal plane. An observer finds that the angles subtended at a point in the horizontal plane by the tower and the flagstaff are respectively α and β. He then walks a distance c directly towards the tower, and finds that the flagstaff subtends the same angle β as before. Prove that the heights of the tower and the flagstaff are respectively

$$\frac{c\sin\alpha\cos(\alpha+\beta)}{\cos(2\alpha+\beta)} \text{ and } \frac{c\sin\beta}{\cos(2\alpha+\beta)}.$$

26. A flagstaff a feet high is on a tower $3a$ feet high; prove that, if the observer's eye is on a level with the top of the staff and the staff and tower subtend equal angles, the observer is at a distance $a\sqrt{2}$ from the top of the staff.

27. The plane of a rectangular target is vertical and lies east and west; compare the area of the shadow on the ground with the area of the target when the sun is 10° from the south at an altitude of 64°.

CHAPTER IX.

AREA.

Area.—The reader has already studied the areas and volumes of simple solids in an elementary course, and it is therefore only necessary here to collect the results for reference.

Parallelogram.—The area of a parallelogram is the product of the number of units of length in the base AB (Fig. 52) and in the width BC.

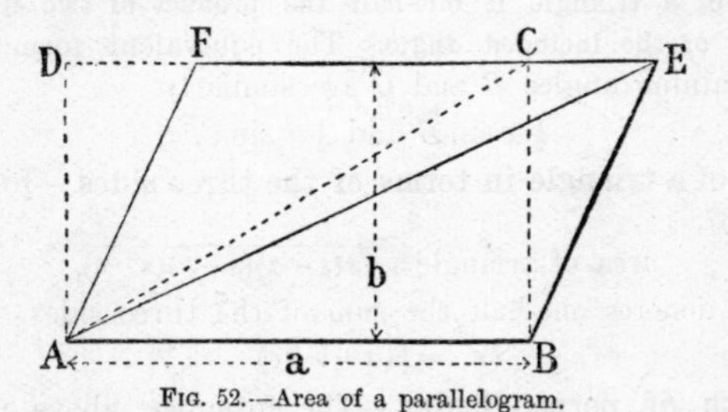

FIG. 52.—Area of a parallelogram.

If a denotes the length of the base AB and b the width or height of BC, then

$$A = a \times b,$$

where A denotes the area of the parallelogram.

The **rectangle**, as shown by the dotted lines (Fig. 52), is a particular case of the parallelogram in which all the angles are right angles. When, in addition, the four sides of a rectangle are equal; the four-sided figure is called a **square**, and $A = a^2$. The area of a parallelogram is also one-half the product of the two diagonals and the sine of the angle of inclination.

Rhombus.—When the four sides of a parallelogram are equal, but the angles are *not* right angles, the figure is called a rhombus, and its **area is one-half the product of the two diagonals.**

Triangle.—Any parallelogram is divided into two equal parts by a diagonal (Fig. 52). Hence, when the base and height of a triangle are given, the **area of a triangle is one-half the product of the base and the height.** As any side may be considered as the base of a triangle, the rule may be stated thus: the **area of a triangle is equal to one-half the product of any side of a triangle and the length of the perpendicular let fall on that side from the opposite angle.**

If p denote the length of the perpendicular BD (Fig. 46, p. 166),

$$\text{area} = \tfrac{1}{2} \times bp,$$

but $p = c \sin A$;

$$\therefore \text{ area of triangle} = \tfrac{1}{2}bc \sin A, \quad \text{.................(i)}$$

or **area of a triangle is one-half the product of two sides and the sine of the included angle.** The equivalent formulae for the remaining angles B and C are similarly

$$\tfrac{1}{2}ac \sin B \text{ and } \tfrac{1}{2}ab \sin C.$$

Area of a triangle in terms of the three sides.—Referring to p. 167,

$$\text{area of triangle} = \sqrt{s(s-a)(s-b)(s-c)},$$

where s denotes one-half the sum of the three sides

$$i.e. \ = \tfrac{1}{2}(a+b+c).$$

Length of perpendicular.—The formulae above may be used to obtain the length of the perpendicular from any angle on to the opposite side.

Ex. 1. The sides of a triangle are 5, 6 and 7 inches respectively. Find the length of the perpendicular on the shortest side from the opposite angle.

If p denote the length, then

$$\text{area of triangle} = \tfrac{1}{2}p \times 5 = \sqrt{s(s-a)(s-b)(s-c)},$$

where $$s = \tfrac{1}{2}(5+6+7) = 9;$$

$$\therefore p = \frac{2\sqrt{9 \times 4 \times 3 \times 2}}{5} = \frac{12}{5}\sqrt{6}$$

$$= 5{\cdot}879 \text{ inches.}$$

Right-angled triangle.—When the included angle is a right angle, $B=90°$ and $\sin 90°=1$;

$$\therefore \text{ area}=\tfrac{1}{2}ab.$$

Ex. 2. The sides of a right-angled triangle are 4·3 inches and 5·4 inches. Find the length of the perpendicular from the right angle on the hypotenuse.

$$\text{Hypotenuse}=\sqrt{4{\cdot}3^2+5{\cdot}4^2}=\sqrt{47{\cdot}65}.$$

$$\text{Area}=\tfrac{1}{2}\times 4{\cdot}3\times 5{\cdot}4=\tfrac{1}{2}p\sqrt{47{\cdot}65};$$

$$\therefore\ p=\frac{4{\cdot}3\times 5{\cdot}4}{\sqrt{47{\cdot}65}}$$

$$=3{\cdot}36 \text{ inches.}$$

Equilateral triangle.—In an equilateral triangle $a=b=c$ and each angle is 60°.

$$\therefore\ \text{Area}=\tfrac{1}{2}ac\sin B=\tfrac{1}{2}a^2\sin 60°=\tfrac{1}{4}a^2\sqrt{3}.$$

Ex. 3. Find the area of an equilateral triangle each side of which is 10 ft. long.

$$\text{Area}=\frac{10^2\sqrt{3}}{4}=\frac{173{\cdot}2}{4}$$

$$=43{\cdot}3 \text{ sq. ft.}$$

Area of a regular polygon.—If AB (Fig. 53) is one side of a regular polygon of n sides, the circle passing through the angular points is called the **circumscribed circle.** The circle touching all the sides of the figure is called the **inscribed circle.**

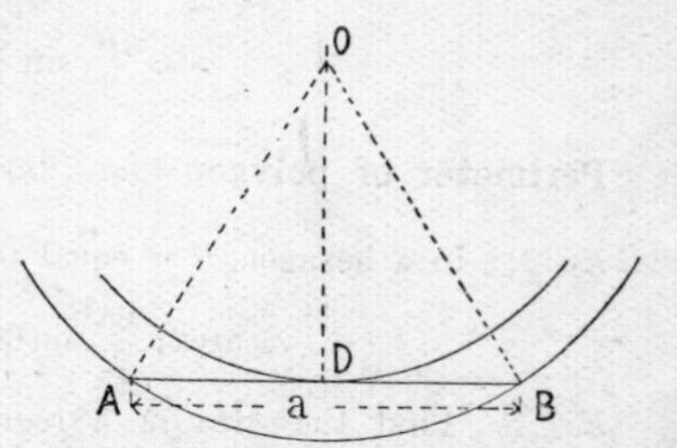

FIG. 53.—Area of a regular polygon.

The angle AOB is $\dfrac{360°}{n}$, and if a perpendicular OD be drawn to side AB, then angle $AOD=\dfrac{180°}{n}$. Denoting the length of the side AB by a,

$$\text{area of triangle } AOB=\tfrac{1}{2}AB\times OD$$

$$=\frac{a}{2}\times OD. \qquad \text{(i)}$$

If r denote the radius of the inscribed circle,

$$\text{area of triangle } AOB = \frac{a}{2} r.$$

As $$r = \frac{a}{2} \cot \frac{180^\circ}{n}; \text{ ....(ii)}$$

$$\therefore \text{ area of triangle } AOB = \frac{a^2}{4} \cot \frac{180^\circ}{n}, \text{ ....(iii)}$$

and $$\text{area of polygon} = \frac{na^2}{4} \cot \frac{180^\circ}{n}. \text{ ....(iv)}$$

From (iv), the area of a polygon can be obtained when the length of one side is given.

To obtain the area when the radius r is given, we may eliminate a from (iv) by means of (ii).

$$\text{Area of polygon} = nr^2 \tan \frac{180^\circ}{n}.$$

To obtain the area of the polygon in terms of R, the radius of the circumscribed circle, we have from Fig. 53,

$$OD = R \cos \frac{180^\circ}{n}. \quad \text{Also, } \frac{a}{2} = R \sin \frac{180^\circ}{n};$$

$$\therefore \text{ area of polygon} = nR^2 \sin \frac{180^\circ}{n} \cos \frac{180^\circ}{n}$$

$$= \frac{nR^2}{2} \sin \frac{360^\circ}{n} \text{ (p. 32).}$$

Perimeter of polygon $= na = 2nr \tan \frac{180^\circ}{n} = 2nR \sin \frac{180^\circ}{n}.$

Ex. 4. In a hexagon R is equal to the length of the side a;

$$\therefore \text{ area} = \frac{6a^2}{2} \sin 60^\circ = \frac{3\sqrt{3}a^2}{2}.$$

Ex. 5. Find the area of a regular pentagon in a circle of 4 inches radius.

Here $n=5$, $R=4$;

$$\therefore \text{ area} = \frac{5 \times 16}{2} \sin 72^\circ = 40 \sin 72^\circ$$

$$= 40 \times 0{\cdot}9511 = 38{\cdot}044 \text{ sq. in.}$$

* In a triangle ABC, $R = \frac{a}{2 \sin A} = \frac{abc}{4\Delta}$, $r = \frac{\Delta}{s}$, where Δ denotes the area of the triangle.

Trapezium.—A four-sided figure such as $ABCD$ (Fig. 54), in which two sides AD and BC are parallel, is called a **trapezium.**

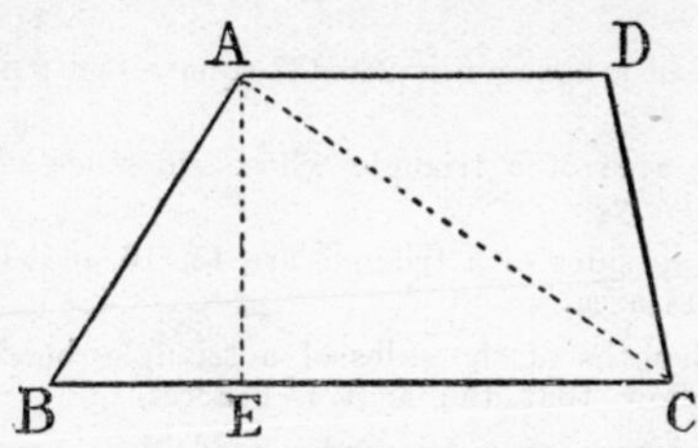

FIG. 54.—Area of a trapezium.

If a and b denote the lengths of AD and BC, and h the perpendicular distance AE between them, then, joining the points A and C by the line AC, the figure is divided into the two triangles ABC and ACD.

$$\text{Area of triangle } ACD = \frac{1}{2}ah,$$

$$\text{,, ,, ,, } ABC = \frac{1}{2}bh;$$

$$\therefore \text{ area of } ABCD = \frac{1}{2}(a+b)h, \text{ or in words,}$$

area of a trapezium is one-half the sum of two parallel sides multiplied by the perpendicular distance between them.

EXERCISES. XXI.

1. The area of a rectangular field is 462 square yards, its length is 25 yards 2 feet; find its width.

2. Find the cost of enclosing a square field, area two acres, with a fence costing 3s. 6d. per yard.

3. A public garden occupies two acres, and is in the form of a square. If a pathway goes completely round its inner edge, and occupies one-eighth of an acre, what is its width? [Acre=4840 square yards.]

4. The area of a rectangular field is $\frac{2}{5}$ of an acre, and its length is double its breadth; determine the length of its sides.

5. In a quadrilateral the diagonal is 84 feet, and the two perpendiculars on it from the other two angles are 16 feet and 18 feet respectively; find the area.

6. Find the area of a triangle, base 625 links, height 1040 links [100 links = 22 yds.].

7. The length of each side of a hexagon is 12 feet; find its area.

8. The area of a hexagon is 286·437 square feet; find the length of a side.

9. Find the area of a triangle whose sides are 21, 20 and 29 inches respectively.

10. The three sides of a triangle are 15, 16 and 17 feet respectively; find its area.

11. If the lengths of the sides of a triangle be 242, 1212 and 1450 yards, show that the area is 6 acres.

12. Find the area of a triangular field ABC from the following measurements on the Ordnance Survey of 25 inches to the mile: AC 4·1 inches, perpendicular from B on AC 1·59 inches. Calculate the area of the triangle ABC from the three sides, AB measuring 3·3 inches and BC 2 inches. Express the mean of the two in acres.

13. The diagonal of a rectangular field is $6\frac{1}{2}$ chains. What is the length and width if the area is $1\frac{1}{2}$ acres? [1 chain = 22 yds.]

14. Find the area of a quadrilateral of which the diagonal is 1274 feet and the perpendiculars upon it from the opposite angles 550 and 583 feet respectively.

15. The perimeter of a square field is 588 yards and of another 672 yards. Find the perimeter of a third equal in area to the other two together.

16. Find the area of a quadrilateral $ABCD$ in which the sides AB, BC, CD, DA, and diagonal AC are 25, 60, 52, 39 and 65 respectively.

17. Each side of a rhombus is 120 yards and two of its opposite angles are each 60°; find the area.

18. A field in the form of a trapezium has its parallel sides 10 chains 30 links and 7 chains 70 links. If the area be 6 acres 3 roods, find the length of the shortest way across the field.

19. The parallel sides of a trapezium are 5 chains 15 links and 3 chains 85 links respectively, the perpendicular distance between them is 15 chains; find the area.

20. The side of an equilateral triangle is 20 feet; find the numerical value of the radius of the circle circumscribing the triangle.

21. Regular polygons of 15 sides are inscribed in and circumscribed about a circle whose radius is one foot; show that the difference of their areas is nearly 20 square inches.

Circle.—The following rules are important:

$$\textbf{Circumference} = 2\pi r, \text{ or } \pi d.$$

$$\textbf{Area} = \pi r^2, \text{ or } \frac{\pi}{4} d^2,$$

where r denotes the radius and d the diameter of the given circle.

Annulus or circular ring.—If the external radius is R and internal radius r

$$\textbf{Area of annulus} = \pi(R^2 - r^2) = \pi(R + r)(R - r),$$

or
$$\frac{\pi}{4}(D^2 - d^2) = \frac{\pi}{4}(D + d)(D - d),$$

where D and d denote the external and internal diameters respectively.

Ellipse.—If $2a$ and $2b$ denote the lengths of the major and minor axes respectively, then

$$\textbf{circumference} = \pi(a + b), \textbf{ approx.}; \quad \textbf{area} = \pi ab.$$

Ex. 1. Find the radius of a circle equal in area to that of an ellipse whose axes are 21 ft. and 14 ft.

Let r denote the radius of the circle.

Then, area of circle $= \pi r^2 = \pi\left(\frac{21}{2} \times \frac{14}{2}\right)$;

$$\therefore r = \sqrt{\left(\frac{21}{2} \times 7\right)} = \sqrt{\frac{147}{2}}.$$

$$\log r = \tfrac{1}{2}(\log 147 - \log 2) = 0{\cdot}9331 = \log 8{\cdot}572;$$
$$\therefore r = 8{\cdot}572 \text{ ft.}$$

Area of sector of a circle.—**The area of the sector of a circle AOE is one-half the product of the angle in radians and the square of the radius.**

Let A denote the area;

$$\therefore A = \frac{\theta r^2}{2}.$$

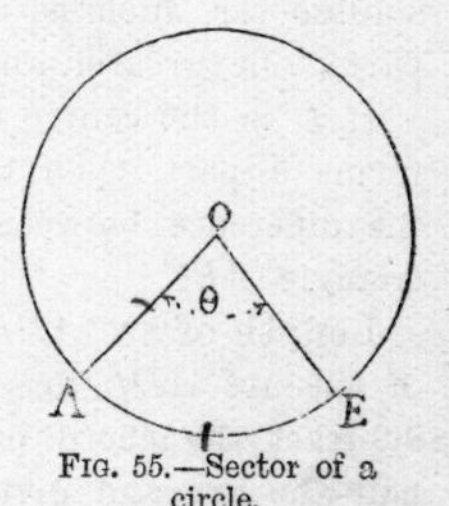

FIG. 55.—Sector of a circle.

If N denotes the number of degrees in the angle AOE, then, as the sector is simply a fractional part of the circle,

$$\text{Length of arc } AE = \frac{N}{360^\circ} \times 2\pi r.$$

$$\text{Area of sector} = \frac{N}{360^\circ} \times \pi r^2.$$

The two following theorems are important and may be verified by drawing the figures to scale:

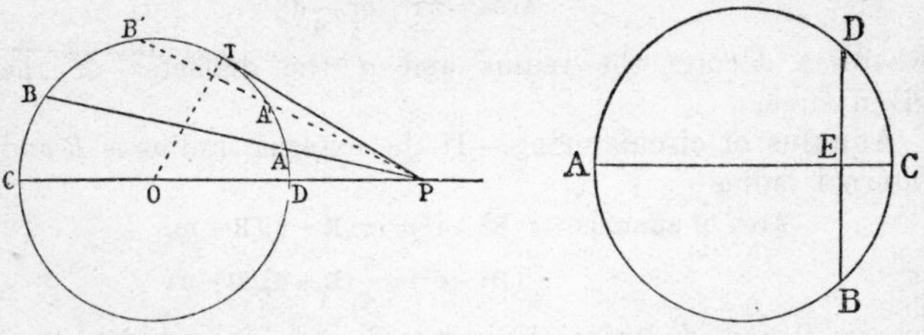

FIG. 56.—$PT^2 = PA \times PB$.

FIG. 57.—$AE \cdot EC = DE^2$.

(i) From any point P outside a circle draw two lines—one which touches, or is a tangent to, the circle; the other cutting it in two points A and B. Then $PT^2 = PA \times PB$.

(ii) If two straight lines within a circle, such as AC and BD, cut one another at a point E, the rectangle contained by the segments of one is equal to the rectangle contained by the segments of the other, i.e. $AE \cdot EC = DE \cdot EB$.

If one line such as AC passes through the centre of the circle and the other is perpendicular to AC, then $DE = EB$;

$$\therefore\ AE \cdot EC = DE^2.$$

Segment of a circle.—Any chord of a circle, which is not a diameter, such as AB (Fig. 58), divides the circle into two parts, one greater and one less than a semicircle.

If C is the centre of the circle of which the given arc ADB forms a part, then **the area of the segment ADB is equal to the difference between the area of the sector $CADB$ and the triangle ABC.**

Length of arc ADB (Huygens' Approximation).—The length of the arc ADB may be found approximately by the rule:—**Subtract the chord of the arc from eight times the chord of half the arc and divide the result by 3.**

$$\text{Length of arc } ADB = \frac{8AD - AB}{3} = \frac{8a - c}{3},$$

where a denotes the length of the chord AD (of half the arc) and c the length of AB (chord of the whole arc).

It will be found that results may be obtained by this rule to a fair degree of accuracy, but the angle must not be too large, *i.e.* the rule should not be used for angles greater than 90°. Thus, for 80°, the rule gives 1·3953, the accurate value is 1·3953. For an angle of 167° the length obtained by the rule is in error by 1%.

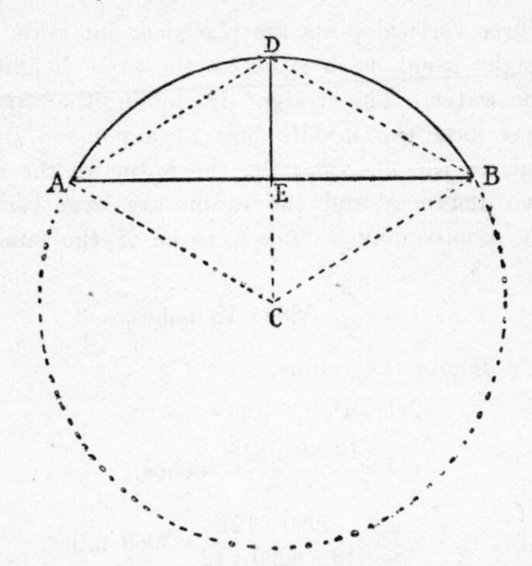

FIG. 58.—Segment of a circle.

Area of segment.—If h denote the height ED (Fig. 58), the area of the segment is approximately

$$\frac{h^3}{2c}+\frac{2}{3}ch, \text{ or } \frac{h}{6c}(3h^2+4c^2).$$

Chord of a circle.—The chord of an arc, c, and the chord of half the arc, a, may be expressed in terms of the height, h; thus, produce DE to cut the circumference of the circle in a point F.

Since $$AE \times EB = FE \times ED;$$

$$\therefore \left(\frac{c}{2}\right)^2 = h(2r-h);$$

$$\therefore c^2 = 4h(2r-h). \quad \text{.........................(i)}$$

Also, $$a^2 = \frac{c^2}{4} + h^2;$$

$$\therefore\ c^2 = 4(a^2 - h^2).$$

Substitute this value in (i);

$$\therefore\ a^2 = 2hr. \qquad \text{(ii)}$$

Ex. 2. Three vertical posts are placed at intervals of one mile along a straight canal, each rising to the same height above the surface of the water. The straight line joining the tops of the two extreme posts cuts the middle post at a point 8 inches below the top; find, to the nearest mile, the radius of the earth.

As the two distances and the radius are large compared with 8 inches, the chord may be taken to be of the same length as the arc;

$$\therefore\ a = \frac{c}{2} = 5280 \times 12 \text{ inches.}$$

Hence, if r denote the radius,

$$2rh = a^2,$$

$$\text{or } r = \frac{(5280 \times 12)^2}{2 \times 8} \text{ inches}$$

$$= \frac{(5280 \times 12)^2}{16 \times 5280 \times 12} = 3960 \text{ miles.}$$

Area of a segment of a parabola.—The area of a portion of a parabola such as ABC (Fig. 59) is two-thirds the product of the base and the height;

$$\therefore \text{ area of parabola} = \tfrac{2}{3}ab.$$

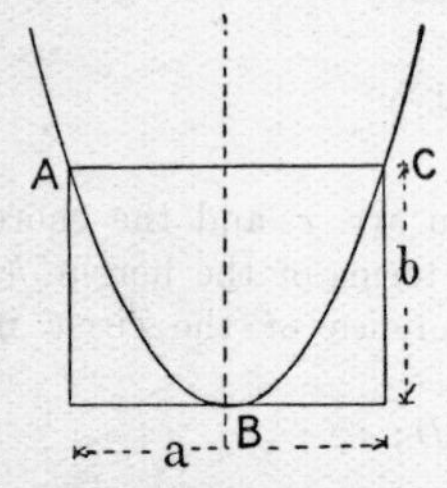

Fig. 59.—Area of segment of a parabola.

Ex. 3. Find the area of the segment of a circle, chord 40 in., height 6 in. What would be the area of a parabolic segment having the same dimensions?

$$\text{Area} = \frac{h^3}{2c} + \frac{2}{3}ch$$

$$= \frac{6^3}{80} + \frac{2}{3} \times 40 \times 6 = 2{\cdot}7 + 160$$

$$= 162{\cdot}7 \text{ sq. in.}$$

The area of a parabolic segment is $\frac{2}{3}$ (product of chord and height)

$$= \tfrac{2}{3} \times 40 \times 6 = 160 \text{ sq. in.}$$

Area of an irregular figure.—When the boundaries of an irregular figure consist of straight lines, the area may be obtained by dividing the figure into a number of triangles, rectangles, etc. The sum of the areas of all the simple figures, into which the given figure has been divided, will be the area required. When one or more of the boundaries of a given figure consist of curved lines, the area may be found by one of the following methods explained in the elementary course the student is already supposed to have taken: (*a*) by using a planimeter, (*b*) using squared paper, (*c*) by weighing, (*d*) by mid-ordinate rule.

In addition to the above methods there are, amongst others, the trapezoidal rule, and the two important rules of Simpson and Weddle (p. 405).

Planimeter.—The planimeter is an instrument adapted for estimating rapidly and accurately the area of any figure. There are many forms in general use to which various names—Hatchet, Amsler, etc.—are given Of these the more accurate forms are mostly modifications of the Amsler planimeter.

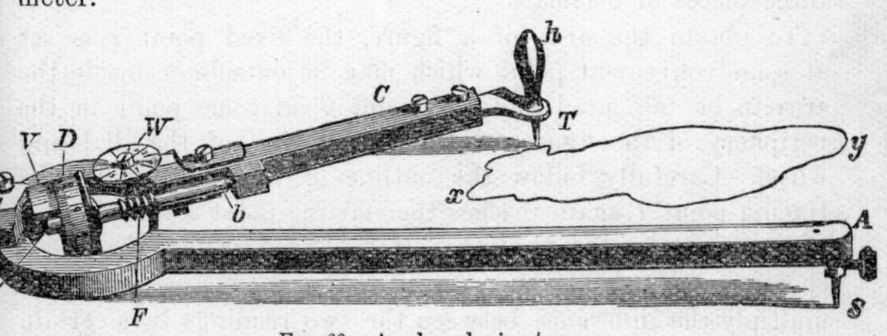

FIG. 60.—Amsler planimeter.

Amsler planimeter.—One form of the instrument is shown in Fig. 60, and consists of two arms *AB* and *BC*, pivoted together at a point *B*. The arm *BA* is fixed at some convenient point *s*. The other arm *BC* carries a tracing point *T*. This tracing point is passed round the outline of the figure, the area of which is required. The arm *BC* carries a wheel *D*, the rim of which is usually divided into 100 equal parts, about which it turns as an axis and records by its revolution the area of the figure traced out by *T*. From its construction it is obvious that the revolving wheel registers only the motion which is perpendicular to the moving arm on which it revolves.

When the instrument is in use, the rim of the wheel rests on the paper, and, as the point *T* is carried round the outline of the figure, the wheel, by means of a spindle rotating on pivots at *a* and *b*, gives motion to a small worm *F*, which in turn rotates the dial *W*.

One rotation of the wheel corresponds to one-tenth of a revolution of the dial. A vernier, *V*, is fixed to the frame of the instrument, and a distance equal to 9 scale divisions on the rim of the wheel is divided into ten on this vernier. The readings on the dial are indicated by means of a small finger, or pointer, shown in Fig. 60. If the figures on the dial indicate units those on the wheel will be $\frac{1}{10}$ths; as each of these is subdivided into 10, the subdivisions indicate $\frac{1}{100}$ths. Finally, the vernier, *V*, in which $\frac{9}{100}$ of the wheel is divided into 10 parts, enables a reading to be made to three places of decimals.

To obtain the area of a figure, the fixed point *s* is set at some convenient point which may be outside or inside the area to be measured and the point *T* at some point in the periphery of the figure. Note the reading of the dial and wheel. Carefully follow the outline of the figure until the tracing point *T* again reaches the starting-point a second time, and again take the reading. If the fixed point *s* has been chosen *outside* the given area, all that is now necessary is to multiply the difference between the two readings by a certain constant to obtain the area of the figure; the value of the constant may be found by using the instrument to obtain a known area, such as a square, or circle of known radius. If the fixed point *s* had been chosen inside the figure it is possible to clamp the joint *B* of the instrument so that whilst *T* describes a circle, the indicating wheel shall always move on the paper perpendicular to the plane of its rim, and consequently register no rotation in any part of its course. The circle which *T* thus describes is called the zero circle, and its area (marked on the instrument) must be added to the indication of the instrument in order to obtain the measure of a given area.

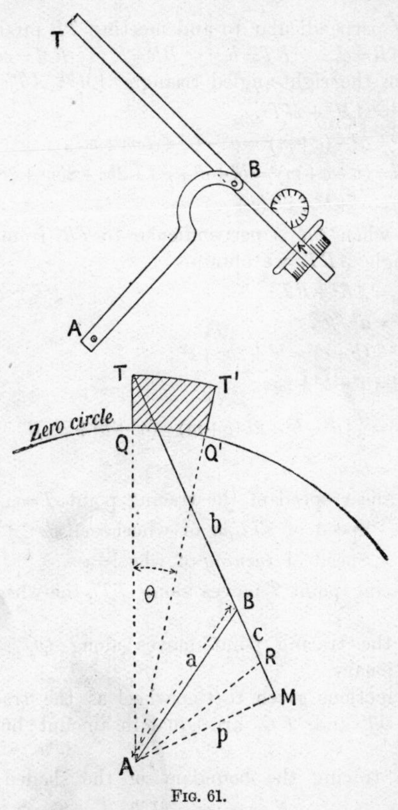

FIG. 61.

T is the tracing point (Fig. 61) and A the fixed point. When AR is perpendicular to TM and the joint at B is locked (*i.e.* does not turn), the point T describes a circle, called the **zero circle**, about A as centre. The indicating wheel under these conditions remains stationary.

Let $AT = r$ and $AQ = r_0$.

The shaded area $QTT'Q' = \frac{\theta}{2}(r^2 - r_0^2)$.

Draw AM perpendicular to and meeting TB produced in M.

Let $AB = a$, $BT = b$, $BR = c$, $RM = m$.

Then, from the right-angled triangle AMT, AT^2 or

$$r^2 = AM^2 + MT^2.$$

But $AM^2 = a^2 - (c+m)^2 = a^2 - (c^2 + 2cm + m^2)$,

and $MT^2 = (b+c+m)^2 = b^2 + c^2 + m^2 + 2bc + 2bm + 2cm$;

$$\therefore r^2 = a^2 + b^2 + 2b(c+m).$$

Similarly, when AR is perpendicular to TR, from the right-angled triangle ART, we obtain

AQ^2 or $r^2_0 = AR^2 + RT^2$

$$AR^2 = a^2 - c^2.$$

Also $RT^2 = (b+c)^2 = b^2 + 2bc + c^2$;

$$\therefore r_0^2 = a^2 + b^2 + 2bc;$$

$$\therefore \frac{\theta}{2}(r^2 - r_0^2) = \frac{\theta}{2}\{a^2 + b^2 + 2b(c+m) - (a^2 + b^2 + 2bc)\}$$

$$= \theta bm.$$

Now the linear speed of the tracing point $T = \omega AT = \omega r$.

Speed of *sliding* of wheel $= \omega AM$.

Speed of *turning* of wheel $= \omega m$.

As the tracing point T moves along TT', the wheel registers $\theta \times m$.

And, as the tracing point moves along QQ', the wheel remains stationary.

Also, the motions given to the wheel as the tracing point moves over QT and $T'Q$, are equal in amount but opposite in direction.

Hence, in tracing the boundary of the shaded area, the wheel records a motion of $\theta \times m = \frac{\text{area}}{b}$;

$$\therefore \text{area} = b\theta m = b \times \text{motion of wheel}.$$

The tracing point T is usually carried by a bar which can slide in a sleeve carrying the point B, and the adjustment is made by altering the position of B.

Simpson's Rule.—When an odd number of ordinates is given, except in the special case of 7 ordinates, probably the most acccurate rule that can be used is **Simpson's First Rule.** As this rule is so important it is usually referred to simply as Simpson's Rule. Except where otherwise expressed the following exercises are supposed to be solved, as in the following example, by using Simpson's Rule:

Ex. 4. An irregular figure has the following ordinates (in feet):

3·5, 4·75, 5·25, 7·5, 8·25, 14·75, 6, 9·5, 4.

The common interval being 2·5 ft., find the area.

$$\text{Area} = \frac{S}{3}(A + 4B + 2C),$$

where S denotes the common interval, A the sum of extreme ordinates, B the sum of the even ordinates, C the sum of the odd ordinates;

$\therefore$ sum of extreme ordinates $= 3{\cdot}5 + 4 = 7{\cdot}5$;

$\therefore$ sum of even ordinates $= 4{\cdot}75 + 7{\cdot}5 + 14{\cdot}75 + 9{\cdot}5 = 36{\cdot}5$;

$\therefore$ sum of odd ordinates $= 5{\cdot}25 + 8{\cdot}25 + 6 = 19{\cdot}5$.

$$\text{Area of figure} = \frac{2{\cdot}5}{3}(7{\cdot}5 + 4 \times 36{\cdot}5 + 2 \times 19{\cdot}5) = 160{\cdot}41.$$

Mean ordinate.—The product of the mean ordinate and the length of the line assumed as the base of an irregular figure gives its area. Hence, in order to obtain the mean ordinate in any of the preceding cases, it is only necessary to divide the calculated area by the length. Thus, in the preceding example, as the line EF is 20 feet;

$$\therefore \text{ mean ordinate} = \frac{160{\cdot}41}{20}$$

$$= 8{\cdot}02 \text{ feet.}$$

EXERCISES. XXII.

1. Find the perimeter and the radius of a circle the area of which is 5·3093 square feet.

2. The area of a semicircle is 13013 square feet; find its total perimeter.

3. One circle is described *about* and a second is inscribed *within* a regular hexagon length of side 1 foot; find the area between the two circles.

4. The side of a regular hexagon is 2 feet; find the radius of a circle equal to it in area.

5. The radius of a circle is 33·5 feet; find the area of a sector enclosed by two radii and an arc 133·74 feet in length.

6. Find the length of an arc which subtends an angle of 60° in a circle whose radius is 100 feet.

7. The length of an arc subtending an angle of 60° is 11 feet; find the radius of the circle.

8. The area of a trapezium-shaped field is $4\frac{1}{2}$ acres, the perpendicular distance between the parallel sides is 120 yards, and one of the sides is 10 chains; find the other.

9. The minute hand of a clock is 10 inches long; find the area which it describes on the clock face between 9 a.m. and 9.35 a.m.

10. The radius of circle is 8 feet; find the area of a sector of the circle, the angle of which is 36°.

11. Find the radius of a circle such that the area of a sector corresponding to an angle of 90° may be 181·16 square feet.

12. Find the radius of a circle in which an arc 15 inches long subtends at the centre an angle containing 71° 36′.

13. The side of an equilateral triangle is 20 feet; find the radius of the circle circumscribing the triangle.

14. The interior diameter of a circular building is 51 feet and the thickness of wall 2 feet. What is the area occupied by the wall?

15. A road 10 feet wide has to be made round a circular plot of ground 75 yards diameter; find the cost of the road at 4s. per square yard.

16. The diameters of the piston and air-pump of an engine are as 2 : 1·2; find the diameter of the air-pump when the area of the piston is 1134·1 square inches.

17. Find the length of an arc of a circle of radius 20 feet subtending a certain angle at the centre, when the length of an arc of a circle of radius 4 feet, subtending three times the former angle at the centre, is 9 feet.

18. If three equal circles whose common radius is 12 inches touch each other, what is the area enclosed between them?

19. A circular grass plot is surrounded by a ring of gravel b feet wide; if the radius of the circle, including the ring, be a

feet, find the relation between a and b, so that the areas of grass and gravel may be equal.

20. Find the expense of paving a circular court 80 feet in diameter, at 3s. 4d. per square foot, leaving in the centre a space for a fountain in the shape of a hexagon, each side of which is a yard.

21. The area of an equilateral triangle is 17320·5 square feet. About each angular point as centre, a circle is described with radius equal to half the length of a side of the triangle. Find the area of the space included between the three circles.

22. The semi-ordinates of the load water plane of a vessel in feet are respectively: 0·1, 5, 11·6, 15·4, 16·8, 17, 16·9, 16·4, 14·5, 9·4 and 0·1; the common interval is 11 feet. Find the area of the plane in square feet.

23. The half-ordinates of a water plane are 15 feet apart, and their lengths are respectively: 1·9, 6·6, 11, 14·5, 17·4, 19·4, 20·5, 20·8, 20·3, 18·8, 15·8, 10·6 and 2·6 feet. Find the area of the plane.

24. The semi-ordinates of the load water plane of a vessel are 0·2, 3·6, 7·4, 10, 11, 10·7, 9·3, 6·5 and ·2 feet respectively, and they are 15 feet apart. What is the area?

25. The half-ordinates of the load water plane of a vessel are spaced 18 feet apart, and their lengths are 0·6, 3·4, 7·1, 11·4, 16·0, 20·3, 24·0, 26·8, 28·8, 30·0, 30·5, 30·5, 30·0, 28·9, 27·0, 24·3, 21·1, 17·2, 12·7, 7·7 and 3·0 feet respectively. Calculate the total area of the plane in square feet.

26. The ordinates of a curved figure in inches are, 2·6, 3·5, 3·66, 3·63, 3·37, 2·85, 2·4, 2·1, 1·89, 1·74, 1·6, 1·38, 0·49; common interval $\frac{1}{2}$ inch. Find the area.

27. The length of an indicator diagram is 4 inches, the end ordinates are 1, 0·22, and the other ordinates are 1, 0·82, 0·71, 0·55, 0·45, 0·38, 0·33, 0·29 and 0·26 inches respectively. The scale of pressure is 60 lbs. per square inch to one inch. Find the mean pressure (i) by the common rule, (ii) by Simpson's rule.

28. The half-ordinates of the midship section of a vessel are 22·3, 22·2, 21·7, 20·6, 17·2, 13·2 and 8 feet in length respectively. The common interval between consecutive ordinates is 3′ between the 1st and 5th ordinates and 1′ 6″ between the 5th and 7th ordinates. Calculate the total area.

29. The half-ordinates of the midship section of a vessel are 12·8, 12·9, 13, 13, 13, 12·9, 12·6, 12, 10·5, 6 and 1·5 feet respectively; the common distance between the ordinates is 18 inches. Find the area.

CHAPTER X.

MENSURATION OF SOLIDS.

Prism.—The base of the right prism (Fig. 62) is the rectangle $ABCD$. If l denote the length AB, and b the width BC, then the area of the base is $b \times l$. If the thickness, or height, BE, be denoted by h, then, if V denote the volume of the prism,

$$V = bl \times h,$$

or **volume**

$$= \textbf{(area of base)} \times \textbf{(height)}.$$

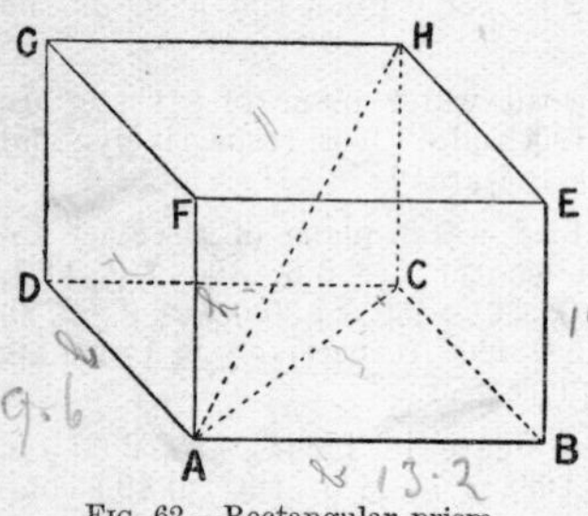

Fig. 62.—Rectangular prism.

The surface of the solid consists of six rectangles. If S denote the total surface, then

$$S = 2(bl + hl + bh)$$

If A be joined to C, the triangle ACB is a right-angled triangle and

$$AC^2 = AB^2 + BC^2;$$

$$\therefore\ AC = \sqrt{b^2 + l^2}.$$

The line AH joining two opposite corners A and H is called a *diagonal of the solid.*

And
$$AH^2 = AC^2 + CH^2 = b^2 + l^2 + h^2;$$

$$\therefore\ AH = \sqrt{b^2 + h^2 + l^2}.$$

Ex. 1. The length, width, and height, of a rectangular prism are 5, 3, and 2 feet respectively. Find the volume, the surface, and the length of a diagonal, of the solid.

$$V = 5 \times 3 \times 2 = 30 \text{ cubic feet.}$$
$$S = 2(5 \times 3 + 2 \times 5 + 2 \times 3)$$
$$= 62 \text{ square feet.}$$
$$\text{Length of diagonal} = \sqrt{5^2 + 3^2 + 2^2}$$
$$= 6{\cdot}164 \text{ feet.}$$

Oblique prism.—The volumes of all prisms, so long as they have the same, or equal, bases and the same altitude, are equal. Thus, in Fig. 63, an oblique prism $ADCGFBE$ is shown. By drawing CN and DH perpendicular to DC, and NP and HM parallel to BF, wedge-shaped pieces are obtained. Assuming the wedge-shaped piece $GCNPFB$ transferred to the left as indicated, the oblique prism becomes a right prism, and thus, as before, the volume of the prism is equal to the area of the base multiplied by the altitude.

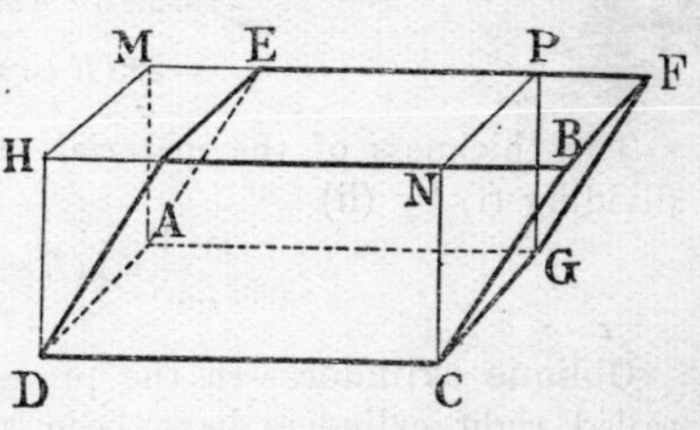

FIG. 63.—Oblique prism.

Cube.—When the three dimensions of length, breadth, and height, are all equal and all the angles right-angles, the solid is called a **cube**, or a cube may be defined as contained by six plane faces all of which are squares. If a denote the length of the edge of the solid, then

$$V = a^3, \quad S = 6a^2.$$
$$\text{Diagonal of solid} = \sqrt{3a^2} = a\sqrt{3}.$$

Cylinder.—The base of a prism may consist of any plane closed curve, and it has been seen that the **volume is the product of area of base and height.** When the base is a circle of radius r, and the height (or length) of the cylinder is denoted by h, the volume V and curved surface S are obtained by using the rules,

$$V = \pi r^2 h, \qquad \text{(i)}$$
$$S = 2\pi rh. \qquad \text{(ii)}$$

Total surface.—To obtain the total surface, the areas of the two ends must be added to (ii). This gives

$$\text{Total surface} = 2\pi rh + 2\pi r^2 = 2\pi r(h + r).$$

Weight.—The weight of the solid is the volume multiplied by weight of unit volume. This may be written $W = Vw$, where w is the weight of unit volume.

Hollow circular cylinder.—If V is the volume, S the curved surface of a hollow cylinder, external radius R, internal radius r, and height h, then

$$V = \pi(R^2 - r^2)h, \quad \text{(i)}$$

$$S = 2\pi Rh + 2\pi rh$$

$$= 2\pi(R + r)h. \quad \text{(ii)}$$

The thickness of the material of a cylinder is $R - r$, and dividing (i) by (ii)

$$\frac{V}{S} = \frac{1}{2}(R - r).$$

Oblique cylinder.—In the preceding paragraphs what are called right cylinders have been assumed, viz., the sides of the prism are at right angles to the plane of the base, but the preceding rules apply equally to oblique prisms, when S and A are as follows:

S = area of curved surface together with the sum of the areas of the two ends.

V = (area of base) × (altitude).

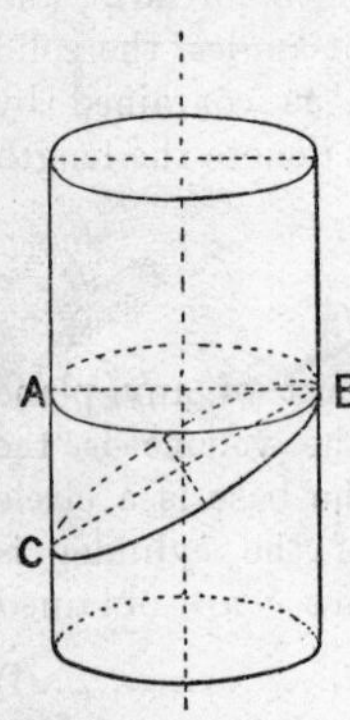

Fig. 64.—Cylinder.

Cross section.—The term *cross section* is generally used to denote the section of a right cylinder, or a right prism, by a plane perpendicular to its axis. Thus, the term *radius of a cylinder* is simply a shortened expression for the radius of a perpendicular cross section. If AB (Fig 64) indicates the cross section of a circular cylinder (which is a circle), any oblique section, such as BC will be an ellipse. Also the area of an oblique section BC multiplied by the cosine of the included angle will give the area of the cross section, *i.e.*

$$AB = BC \cos ABC.$$

Ex. 2. The diameter of a right circular cylinder is 3 inches. There is a section making an angle of 20° with the cross section. What is its area?

$$\text{Area of cross section} = \pi\left(\tfrac{3}{2}\right)^2.$$

As $$AB = BC \cos ABC,$$

$$\therefore \text{ area of } BC = \frac{\text{area of } AB}{\cos 20°} = \frac{\pi \times \left(\frac{3}{2}\right)^2}{0{\cdot}9397}$$

$$= \frac{9\pi}{4 \times 0{\cdot}9397} = 7{\cdot}523 \text{ sq. in.}$$

Ex. 3. A prism has a cross section of 50·32 square inches. There is a section making an angle of 70° with the cross section. What is its area?

$$\text{Area} = \frac{50{\cdot}32}{\cos 70°} = \frac{50{\cdot}32}{{\cdot}3420}$$

$$= 147{\cdot}2.$$

EXERCISES. XXIII.

1. In a circular cylinder, volume V, curved surface S, height h, and radius of base r, weight of unit volume w.

(i) If $r = 8$ ft., $h = 8$ ft., find S and V.

(ii) If $S = 66{\cdot}759$ sq. ft., and $V = 70{\cdot}93$ cub. ft., find r.

(iii) Find W if $r = 6$ in., $h = 20$ in., $w = 0{\cdot}3$ lbs. per cub. in.

(iv) $V = 5497{\cdot}8$ cub. ft., $r = 2\frac{1}{2}$ ft.; find h.

2. The length, width and thickness of a rectangular block are 9·6, 13·2 and 14·3 inches respectively. Find the volume, the surface, and the length of a diagonal of the solid.

3. If V is the volume, S the curved surface of a hollow cylinder, external radius R, internal radius r, height or length h and w is the weight of unit volume—

(i) If $R = 5$ in., $r = 3$ in., $h = 8$ in., find S and V; also find W if $w = 0{\cdot}26$ lbs. per cub. in.

(ii) If $V = 36{\cdot}67$ cub. ft., $S = 220$ sq. ft., find $R - r$.

(iii) If $W = 8{\cdot}2$ tons, $R = 9$ in., $r = 5$ in., $w = 0{\cdot}29$ lbs. per cub. in., find h.

4. Find the total surface, also the volume, of a hexagonal prism, height = 8 ft., base a regular hexagon, with a side of length = 3 ft.

5. The volume of a square bar of copper 40 feet in length is 1 cubic foot. If the greatest exact cube is cut from the bar, what will be its weight? (1 cub. in. copper = 0·3192 lbs.)

6. Find the weight of a wrought iron cylinder, outer circumference 10 ft. 7·3 in., height 3 ft. 6 in., thickness of metal $\frac{1}{2}$ inch. (1 cub. in. weighs 0·28 lbs.)

7. What weight of water will fill a hose pipe 2 in. bore and 90 ft. long? (1 cubic foot of water weighs 62·3 lbs.)

8. Find the volume and weight of 6 ft. length of a cast-iron pipe, outer diameter 12·5 in. and thickness of metal $\frac{7}{8}$ in. (1 cubic in. weighs 0·26 lbs.)

9. Find the surface and volume of hollow cylinder, height 12 in., internal and external radii of base 4 in. and 6 in. respectively.

10. The base of a prism is a triangle, sides 17, 25 and 28 ft. respectively. The volume of the prism is 4200 cub. ft. What is its height?

11. Find the internal width of a square bottle to hold a quart of water when the depth is 6 inches. (1 gallon of water weighs 10 lbs.)

12. A section of a stream is 10 ft. wide and 10 inches deep; the mean flow of the water through the section is 3 miles an hour; find how many gallons of water flow through the section in 24 hours.

13. Determine the number of cubic yards in a bank of earth on a horizontal rectangular base 60 ft. long and 20 ft. broad, the four sides of the bank sloping up to a ridge at an angle of 40° to the horizon.

14. The water in a rectangular reservoir is $9\frac{1}{2}$ ft. deep and covers an area of 5390 square yards. In what time can the water be emptied by a pipe 5 inches in diameter, through which the water runs at the rate of 17 miles per hour?

15. A cylindrical vessel 16 feet diameter, 20 feet long, is filled with water at 210° C.; what is the weight of water in tons? [Water is 17·2 per cent. greater in volume at 210° C. than when cold.]

16. A prism has a cross-section of 50·32 square inches. There is a section making an angle of 20° with the cross-section; what is its area?

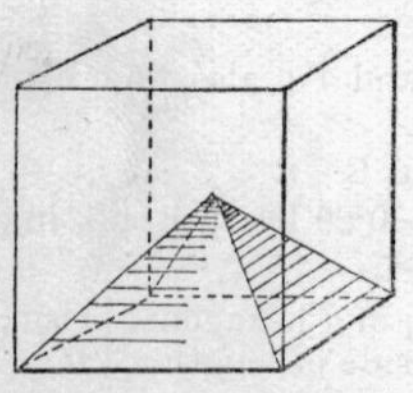

FIG. 65.—Volume of a pyramid.

Pyramid.—The volume of a pyramid is

$$\tfrac{1}{3}(\text{area of base}) \times \text{height}.$$

This important result may be easily derived from the known volume of a cube. By joining each angular point of a cube to the centre (Fig. 65) six equal pyramids are formed. The base of each pyramid is one of the faces of the cube. Hence, the volume of each pyramid is one-sixth of the cube.

If a denote the length of each side of the cube, then h the height of the pyramid is $\frac{a}{2}$.

$$\therefore \text{ Volume of pyramid} = \tfrac{1}{6}a^3$$
$$= \tfrac{1}{3}a^2 \times \frac{a}{2}.$$

Hence, **volume of pyramid $= \frac{1}{3}$(area of base) $\times$ height,**

or volume of a pyramid is one-third that of a prism on the same base and the same altitude.

If A denote area of base, then volume is given by

$$V = \tfrac{1}{3}Ah,$$

a result which applies both to right and oblique pyramids.

Surface of a pyramid.—The surface, or area, of a pyramid consists of the **lateral surface**, this is the area of a number of triangles which form the faces, or sides, of the figure, together with the **area of the base** (which may be any polygon). In a right pyramid, if the polygon forming the base be regular, each of the faces ABO, BCO, etc., of the solid (Fig. 66) consist of equal isosceles triangles. If a denote the length of the edge AB, h the height OP, and l the slant height OQ, the slant height is the same for each triangle only when a circle can be described touching *each* side of the polygonal base. If the radius of such a circle be r and if h be the height of the pyramid, then

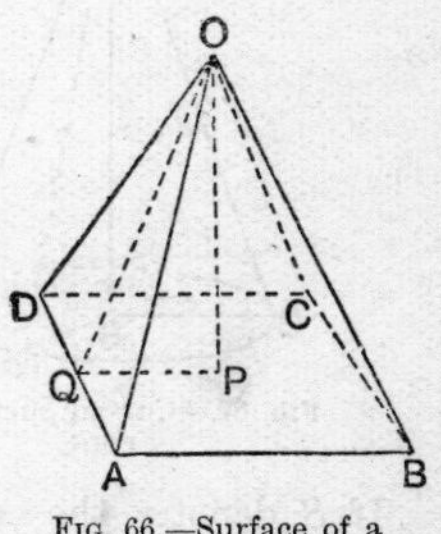

FIG. 66.—Surface of a pyramid.

$$\text{slant height, } l = \sqrt{r^2 + h^2},$$
$$\text{area of each triangle} = \tfrac{1}{2}(a \times l).$$

The slant surface of a right pyramid whose base is a regular polygon of n sides each equal to a is $\frac{1}{2}nal$.

$\therefore$ **the lateral surface of a pyramid equals half the perimeter of the base multiplied by the slant height.**

When a and h are given, $\quad l = \sqrt{h^2 + \left(\frac{a}{2}\right)^2}.$

Cone.—A cone is the solid bounded by an area, and by lines passing through the successive points of the boundary of that area and a fixed point outside the plane of the given area. The area usually consists of a circle, or an ellipse, and the preceding rules for volume and surface of a pyramid are used. When the area is circular and the given point is perpendicularly above the centre and at a distance h from it, if l (Fig. 67) denote the length AC, then

$$\text{the curved surface} = \tfrac{1}{2}(2\pi r)l = \pi rl.$$

When the altitude h and the radius of the base are given, from the right-angled triangle CBA,

$$l = \sqrt{h^2 + r^2}.$$

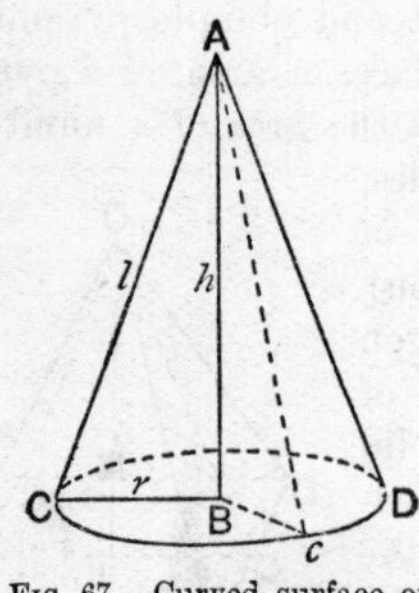

FIG. 67.—Curved surface of cone.

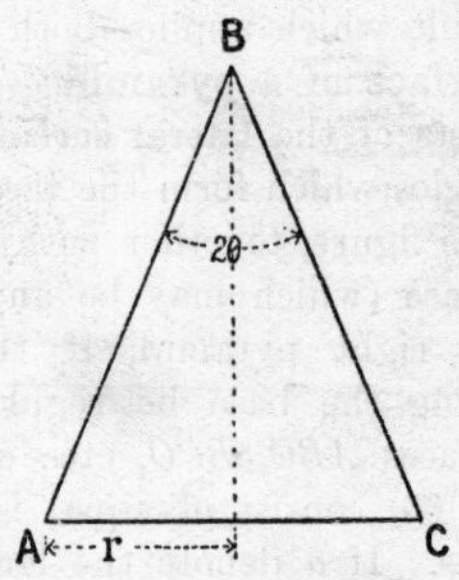

FIG. 68.—Vertical angle of cone.

If S denotes the curved surface and V the volume of the cone, then

$$S = \pi rl,$$

$$\text{total surface} = \pi rl + \pi r^2 = \pi r(l + r),$$

$$V = \tfrac{1}{3}\pi r^2 h.$$

Generally, the volume of a cone, whether right or oblique, is $\frac{1}{3}$ (area of base × height).

Vertical angle.—If the vertical angle of a cone (Fig. 68) be denoted by 2θ, then

$$r = h \tan\theta, \quad l = h \sec\theta.$$

Ex. 1. Find the curved and the whole surface, the volume and vertical angle of a cone, when $r = 45$ in., $h = 48$ in.

Here $\quad l = \sqrt{48^2 + 45^2} = \sqrt{4329}$

$$= 65{\cdot}8 \text{ in.};$$

$$\therefore S = \pi \times 45 \times 65{\cdot}8 = 9302 \text{ sq. in.},$$

$$\text{total surface} = \pi \times 45(65{\cdot}8 + 45) \text{ sq. in.}$$

$$= 108{\cdot}8 \text{ sq. ft.},$$

$$V = \frac{\pi}{3} \times 45^2 \times 48 \div 1728 = 58{\cdot}91 \text{ cub. ft.}$$

Vertical angle.—We have

$$\tan\theta = \frac{r}{h} = \frac{45}{48} = 0{\cdot}9376;$$

$$\therefore\ \theta = 43^\circ\ 9';$$

$$\therefore\ \text{vertical angle} = 86^\circ\ 18'.$$

The curved surface of a right circular cone may also be obtained as follows:—Let a piece of thin paper be made to cover the surface of a cone exactly; then, when opened out, it will form a sector of a circle of radius equal to l. The length (Fig. 69) of the arc $CD = 2\pi r$, the area of sector is one-half the product of the arc and the radius;

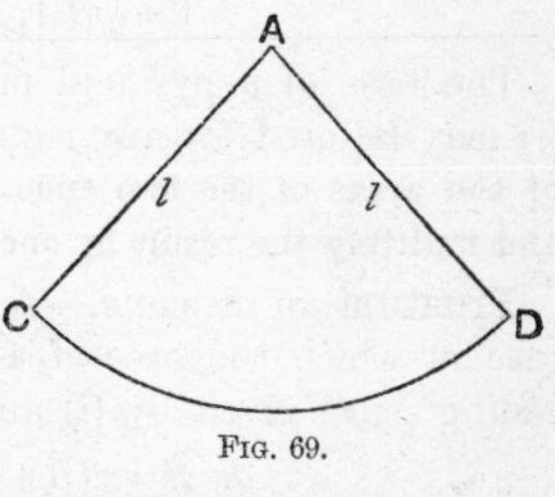

Fig. 69.

$$\therefore\ \text{area of sector} = \tfrac{1}{2}\times 2\pi r\times l = \pi r l.$$

Frustum of a right pyramid on a regular base.—Each of the faces such as $ABCD$ of the frustum of a pyramid (Fig. 70) is a trapezium, and the area of each trapezium will be half the sum of the parallel sides, AB and CD, multiplied by the slant distance between them, and by the number of faces.

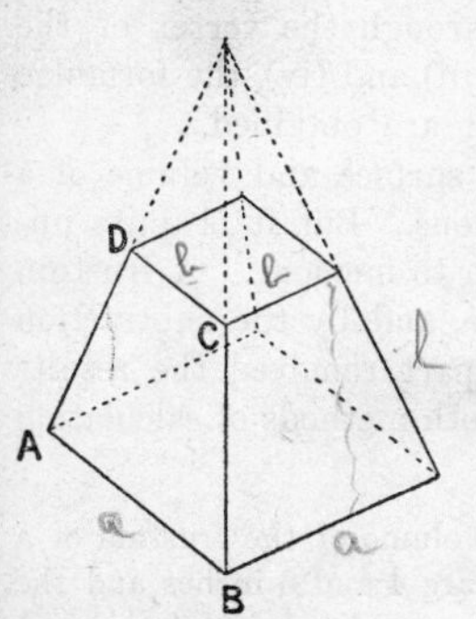

Fig. 70.—Frustum of a pyramid.

In the frustum of a pyramid on a square base (Fig. 70) let a denote the length of each side of the base, b the length of each side of the other end, l the slant height of the frustum.

Each face $ABCD$ is a trapezium, the lengths of the parallel sides a and b.

$$\text{Area } ABCD = \tfrac{1}{2}(a+b)l.$$

As there are four such trapeziums in the lateral surface S, we have $S = 2(a+b)l$, or

slant surface = ½(sum of perimeters of ends) × (slant height). ...(i)

The **total surface** would obviously be the **lateral surface together with the areas of the two ends.**

If h denote the altitude of the frustum, then the volume is given by

$$V=\tfrac{1}{3}h(a^2+b^2+ab);$$

or we may denote by A_1 the area of the base and by A_2 the area of the face parallel to it; then

$$V=\tfrac{1}{3}h(A_1+A_2+\sqrt{A_1A_2}). \qquad \text{(ii)}$$

The base of a pyramid may be any polygon, and the rule (i) may be used for any right regular frustum; *i.e.* **to the sum of the areas of the two ends add the square root of their product and multiply the result by one-third the altitude.** *

Frustum of a cone.—A circular cone is merely a special case in which the base of a pyramid is a circle, and the preceding rules given by (i) and (ii) apply.

$$\therefore\ S=\pi(R+r)l, \qquad \text{(iii)}$$

$$V=\frac{h}{3}(\pi R^2+\pi r^2+\sqrt{\pi^2R^2r^2})$$

$$=\frac{\pi h}{3}(R^2+r^2+Rr). \qquad \text{(iv)}$$

When the cutting plane passes through the vertex of the cone, r is zero, and putting $r=0$ in (iii) and (iv), the formulae for the surface and volume of a cone are obtained.

The expressions dealing with the surface and volume of a frustum are of great use in calculations. But it is quite unnecessary to attempt to commit them to memory. A frustum may be considered as part of a whole, and by the subtraction of the surface and volume of the part removed the results for the frustum may be obtained. Both methods of calculation are shown in the following example.

Ex. 2. Find the curved surface and volume of the frustum of a cone whose top and bottom diameters are 4 and 6 inches and the slant height 8 inches. What is the surface and volume of the cone of which this frustum forms a part?

Here $R=3$, $r=2$, $l=8$;

$$\therefore\ S=\pi(3+2)8=40\pi$$

$$=125{\cdot}71 \text{ sq. in.}$$

* Another method is shown on p. 582.

First obtain the height, h, of the frustum;

$$\therefore\ h=\sqrt{8^2-(3-2)^2}=\sqrt{8^2-1^2}=\sqrt{9\times 7}=7{\cdot}936 \text{ in.},$$

Then $V=\dfrac{7{\cdot}936\pi}{3}(3^2+2^2+3\times 2)=\dfrac{7{\cdot}936\times\pi\times 19}{3}=158$ cubic in.

Let ABC (Fig. 71) be a section through the axis of the cone, then if the length AC be denoted by l, EC is $l-8$. From the similar triangles EFC and ADC,

$$\frac{l}{l-8}=\frac{3}{2};\quad \therefore\ l=24 \text{ in.};$$

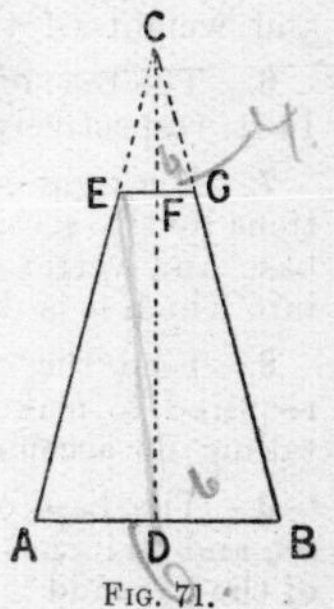

FIG. 71.

whence the curved surface of the whole cone

$$=\pi\times 3\times 24=72\pi=226{\cdot}2 \text{ sq. in.}$$

The height CD can be obtained from the right-angled triangle ADC, where $AC=24$ and $AD=3$.

$$\therefore\ CD=\sqrt{24^2-3^2}=\sqrt{27\times 21}=23{\cdot}81 \text{ in.},$$

volume of cone $ABC=\frac{1}{3}\pi\times 3^2\times 23{\cdot}81$

$$=224{\cdot}5 \text{ cub. in.}$$

Having obtained the surface and volume of the cone ABC, it is only necessary to subtract the surface and volume respectively of the smaller cone CEG to obtain the results for the frustum.

As $EC=16$ in.,

lateral surface of cone $CEG=\pi\times 2\times 16=32\pi$;

$\therefore$ surface of frustum $=(72-32)\pi=40\pi$ as before.

Also $CF=23{\cdot}81-7{\cdot}936=15{\cdot}87$ in.,

volume of smaller cone $=\dfrac{15{\cdot}87}{3}\times\pi\times 4=66{\cdot}5$ sq. in.;

$\therefore$ volume of frustum $=224{\cdot}5-66{\cdot}5=158$ cub. in.

EXERCISES. XXIV.

In the following exercises the axis of the solid is assumed to be at right angles to the base unless otherwise expressed:

1. Let V denote the volume and S the surface of a pyramid on a square base; given $V=645{\cdot}3$ cub. ft., and the height $h=19{\cdot}36$ ft., find the length of the side of the base and the lateral surface S.

2. The diameter of the base of a cone is 6 inches, altitude 5 inches; find the volume and curved surface.

3. The volume of a hexagonal pyramid is 249·4 cub. ft.; if the altitude is 8 ft., what is the length of each side of the base?

4. The radii of the circular ends of the frustum of a lead cone are 4 in. and 6 in. respectively. The height of the frustum is 3·5 in.; find the volume and the weight. (1 cubic in. of lead weighs 0·4121 lbs.)

5. A piece of wood is in the form of a square pyramid; the side of the base is 6 inches, and height 8 in. Find the surface, volume and weight (if the specific gravity of the material be 0·53).

6. The base of a right cone is an ellipse whose axes are 21 ft. and 14 ft. respectively. The altitude is 12 ft.; find the volume.

7. If a right cone on a circular base be divided into three portions by two sections parallel to the base at equal distances from the base and vertex and from one another, compare the three volumes into which it is divided.

8. Find the cost of the canvas, 2 ft. wide at 3s. 6d. a yard, required to make a conical tent, 12 feet diameter and 8 ft. high, taking no account of waste.

9. The base of a pyramid is a triangle whose sides measure 72, 58, and 50 inches; if the volume is 48 cubic feet, what is the height of the pyramid?

10. What is the volume and the total surface of a frustum of a cone, 42 ft. diameter at the base, 21 ft. diam. at the top, and 14 ft. high.

11. The base of a pyramid is an equilateral triangle, length of side 10 inches, height 12 inches. Find the volume.

12. Find the curved surface of the frustum of a cone, top and bottom diameters 4 and 6 ft. respectively, slant side = 8 ft.

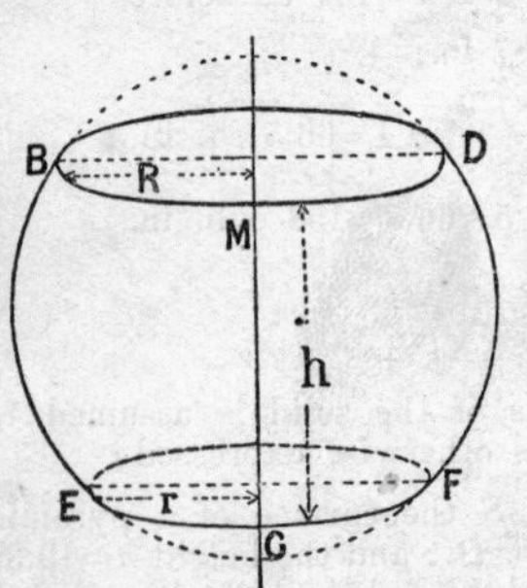

Fig. 72.—Zone of a sphere.

Sphere.—If S denote the surface, and V the volume of a sphere of radius, r, or diameter d,

$$S = 4\pi r^2 = \pi d^2,$$

$$V = \tfrac{4}{3}\pi r^3 = 0{\cdot}5236 d^3.$$

For proof of these rules see p. 411.

The ratio of V to S is $\tfrac{1}{3}r$, hence $3V \div S = r$.

Zone of a sphere.—Any plane cuts a sphere in a circle. Let two parallel planes cut a sphere in two circles BMD, EGF (Fig. 72), and let R and r denote the radii of the two circles. The distance between the planes, usually known as the *thickness of the zone*, may be denoted by h, radius of sphere $=r_1$.

$$S=2\pi r_1 h, \quad \text{(i)}$$

$$V=\frac{\pi h}{2}(R^2+r^2)+\frac{\pi h^3}{6}. \quad \text{(ii)}$$

The result for the convex surface may be stated as follows :

Convex surface of zone = (circumference of a great circle of the sphere) × (thickness of zone), showing that the surface of a zone depends only on the radius of the sphere and the thickness of the zone. Hence, all zones cut from the same, or equal, spheres and having the same thickness, have equal convex surfaces. It follows that if a cylinder be circumscribed to a sphere, then, if d_1 denote the diameter,

curved surface of cylinder $=\pi d_1 \times d_1 = \pi d_1^2 =$ surface of sphere.

Segment of a sphere.—As the plane EGF approaches C, the radius r diminishes, and when the plane touches the sphere, r is zero. The zone then becomes a segment of a sphere BCD.

If S denote the convex surface and h the height of the segment,

$$S=2\pi r_1 h,$$

the same as in Eq. (i).

The volume may be obtained by putting $r=0$, in Eq. (ii) and we obtain

$$V=\frac{\pi h}{2}R^2+\frac{\pi h^3}{6}$$

$$=\frac{\pi h}{6}(3R^2+h^2). \quad \text{(iii)}$$

It should be noticed that the surface and volume of a sphere may be obtained from Eq. (i) and Eq. (ii). Thus, if both the planes touch the sphere, then h, the distance between them, is $2r_1$, and Eq. (i) becomes

$$S=2\pi r_1 \times 2r_1 = 4\pi r_1^2.$$

Also, when the planes touch the sphere, R and r are both zero. Hence, from Eq. (ii) we obtain,

$$V=\frac{\pi h^3}{6}=\frac{4}{3}\pi r^3.$$

From (i) we find that to obtain the convex surface of a zone or segment of a sphere it is necessary to ascertain the radius of the sphere.

Ex. 1. The diameter of a sphere is 22·48 inches; find its surface and volume. Let d denote the diameter.

$$S=\pi d^2=\pi\times(22{\cdot}48)^2;$$

$$\therefore\ \log S=2\log 22{\cdot}48+\log\pi=3{\cdot}2006=\log 1587;$$

$$\therefore\ S=1587 \text{ sq. in.}$$

$$V=0{\cdot}5236d^3,$$

$$\log V=\log 0{\cdot}5236+3\log 22{\cdot}48=3{\cdot}7741=\log 5944;$$

$$\therefore\ V=5944 \text{ cub. in.}$$

Ex. 2. The inside diameter of a hollow sphere of cast iron is the fraction 0·57 of its outside diameter. Find these diameters if the weight is 60 lb. Take one cubic inch of cast iron as weighing 0·26 lb.

Let r denote the external radius, then the inside radius will be $0{\cdot}57r$, and volume of sphere is

$$\frac{4}{3}\pi r^3-\frac{4}{3}\pi(0{\cdot}57r)^3.$$

As 1 cubic inch weighs 0·26 lb., the volume of the sphere is $\dfrac{6000}{26}$;

$$\therefore\ \frac{4}{3}\pi r^3\{1-(0{\cdot}57)^3\}=\frac{6000}{26};$$

$$\therefore\ {\cdot}8148r^3=\frac{4500}{26\pi},$$

or

$$r^3=\frac{4500}{26\pi\times 0{\cdot}8148};$$

$$\therefore\ r=4{\cdot}074;$$

$\therefore$ external diameter $=2\times 4{\cdot}074=8{\cdot}148$ inches,

internal ,, $=8{\cdot}148\times 0{\cdot}57=4{\cdot}644$ inches.

When the outside diameter alone is made 1 per cent. smaller, then percentage diminution of weight is

$$\frac{\{1^3-(1-0{\cdot}01)^3\}}{1-(0{\cdot}57)^3}\times 100=3{\cdot}6\%.$$

Ex. 3. What is the area of the convex surface of the segment of a sphere, the height being 8 inches and diameter of sphere $10\frac{1}{2}$ inches?

$$S=\pi\times 10{\cdot}5\times 8$$

$$=263{\cdot}9 \text{ sq. in.}$$

Ex. 4. Find the convex surface and the volume of the zone of a sphere, radii of the two ends 10 inches and 2 inches, and thickness of zone 6 inches.

Let $ABFE$ be the zone and C the centre of the sphere.

Join C to A and E, and draw a line through C perpendicular to AB and EF.

If r denote the radius of the sphere, and x the perpendicular distance from C to AB, then

$$r^2=10^2+x^2,$$

and similarly,

$$r^2=2^2+(6+x)^2.$$

Hence,

$$100+x^2=4+36+12x+x^2,$$

or $\quad 12x=60, \quad x=5;$

$$\therefore\ r=\sqrt{10^2+5^2}=\sqrt{125}$$
$$=11{\cdot}18 \text{ in.}$$

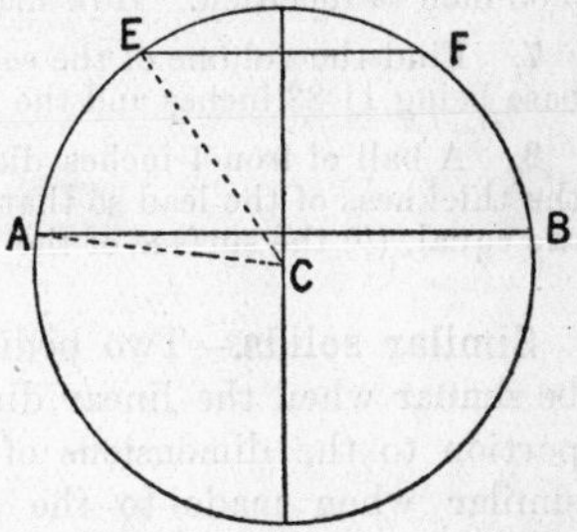

Fig. 73.

$$\text{Convex surface}=2\pi\times 11{\cdot}18\times 6$$
$$=421{\cdot}5 \text{ sq. in.}$$

$$\text{Volume of zone}=\frac{6\pi}{2}(10^2+2^2)+\frac{\pi\times 6^3}{6}$$
$$=348\pi \text{ cub. in.}$$
$$=1093 \text{ cub. in.}$$

EXERCISES. XXV.

1. In a sphere of radius r the surface S and volume V may be obtained from $S=4\pi r^2$ (i) $V=\frac{4}{3}\pi r^3$ (ii).
   (i) Given $r=6{\cdot}25$ in., find S and V.
   (ii) Find r when V is 1 cub. ft.
   (iii) Find r when S is 1 sq. ft.

2. In a spherical zone the height is 4 in., the radii of the two ends being 8 in. and 5 in. respectively. Find the convex surface and the volume.

3. If the radii of the two circles of a spherical zone are 12·5 in. and 4·25 in. and the thickness of the zone 6 in., what is its volume, its convex surface, and its total surface?

4. The radii of the internal and external surfaces of a hollow spherical shell are 3 ft. and 5 ft. respectively. If the same amount of material were formed into a cube what would be the length of an edge?

5. A cubical box, 5 feet deep, is filled with layers of spherical balls, whose diameters, where they touch, are in vertical and horizontal lines. Find what portion of the space in the box would be left vacant if the diameter of a ball is half-an-inch.

6. A circular disc of lead, 3 inches in thickness and 12 inches diameter, is wholly converted into shot of the same density, and of 0·05 inch radius each. How many shot does it make?

7. Find the volume of the segment of a sphere, the radius of the base being 11·83 inches and the radius of the sphere 12 inches.

8. A ball of iron 4 inches diameter is covered with lead. Find the thickness of the lead so that (*a*) the volumes of the iron and lead are equal, (*b*) the surface of the lead is twice that of the iron.

Similar solids.—Two bodies of the same shape are said to be **similar** when the linear dimensions of one are each in proportion to the dimensions of the other. Or, two figures are similar when made to the same drawings but to different scales.

If the linear dimensions of one solid are n times that of another, then the areas of any similar faces are in ratio of n^2 to 1, and the volumes are in the ratio of n^3 to 1.

Thus, if the radius of a sphere is twice those of another, the area, or surface, of the first is 2^2 or 4 times that of the second, and the volume is 2^3 or 8 times that of the second. Thus, if the first weighs 16 lbs., the second will weigh 2 lbs.

Ex. 1. Compare the surfaces of a cube, cylinder, and sphere, the volume in each case being one cubic foot. The altitude of the cylinder is equal to the diameter of its base.

Let a denote, in inches, one side of the cube.

Then
$$a=\sqrt[3]{1728}=12,$$
$$S=6a^2=864 \text{ sq. in.}$$

For the cylinder
$$\pi r^2\times 2r=1728\,; \qquad \therefore\ r=\sqrt[3]{\frac{864}{\pi}}.$$

Surface of cylinder $=2\pi r(h+r)=2\pi r(2r+r)$
$$=6\pi r^2=6\pi\times\left(\frac{864}{\pi}\right)^{\frac{2}{3}}$$
$$=797{\cdot}3 \text{ sq. in.}$$

For the sphere we have $\frac{4}{3}\pi r_1^3 = 1728$,

$$r_1^3 = \frac{1728 \times 3}{4\pi} = \frac{1296}{\pi}. \quad \therefore r_1 = 7{\cdot}444.$$

$$\text{Surface} = 4\pi r_1^2 = 4\pi\left(\frac{1296}{\pi}\right)^{\frac{2}{3}}$$

$$= 696{\cdot}5 \text{ sq. in.}$$

Similarly, if the altitude of a cone is equal to the diameter of the base and the volume is one cubic foot, then

$$\text{volume of cone} = \tfrac{1}{3}\pi r_2^2 \times 2r_2 = 1728\,;$$

$$\therefore r_2^3 = \frac{2592}{\pi}. \quad \therefore r_2 = 9{\cdot}378.$$

If l denotes length of slant side, then

$$l = \sqrt{2^2r^2 + r^2} = r\sqrt{5}.$$

$$\text{Surface of cone} = \pi r(l + r)$$

$$= \pi \times \sqrt[3]{\frac{2592}{\pi}}\left\{\left(\frac{2592}{\pi}\right)^{\frac{1}{3}} \times \sqrt{5} + \left(\frac{2592}{\pi}\right)^{\frac{1}{3}}\right\}$$

$$= 894{\cdot}1 \text{ square inches.}$$

Guldinus' Theorems.—We have already found that surfaces may be generated by the revolution of a line (straight or curved) about an axis, and a solid by the revolution of an area. Familiar examples are cylinders, cones, spheres, etc. In general, any line, straight or curved, will, when rotating about a given axis, generate a surface called a **surface of revolution.** In like manner an area will generate a **solid of revolution.** The area of the surface, or the volume of the solid, may be obtained by means of two theorems, known as Guldinus' theorems. These are as follows:

(i) The area of a surface, traced out by the revolution of a curve about an axis in its own plane, is equal to the product of the perimeter of the curve and the distance moved through by its centre of gravity.

(ii) The volume, generated by the revolution of such a curve, is the product of the area enclosed by the curve and the distance moved through by the centre of area or centre of gravity.

For proofs of these rules see page 425.

Solid ring.—If a circular disc, whose centre is C, rotates about an axis AD, the solid described is called a **solid circular ring.** The circle C would be the cross-section of the ring. Such a ring may be considered as a cylinder bent into a circular form. Familiar examples of solid rings are found in anchor rings, umbrella rings, curtain rings, etc. If r is the radius of cross-section and R the mean radius or length DC,

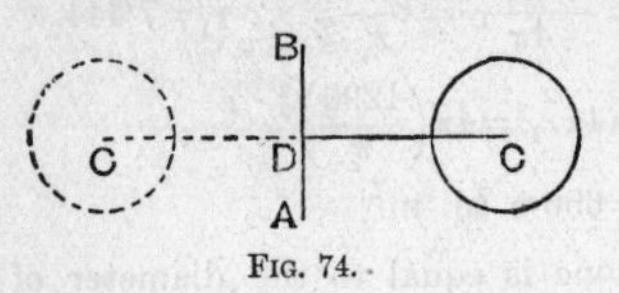

FIG. 74.

$$\textbf{area of ring} = 2\pi r \times 2\pi R$$
$$= 4\pi^2 Rr,$$

i.e. **curved surface of a ring is equal to the perimeter or circumference of a cross-section multiplied by the circumference of the circle passed through by the centre of gravity of the boundary.**

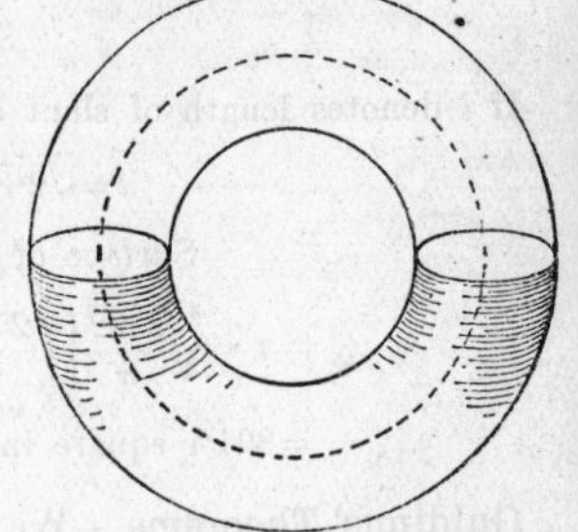
FIG. 75.—Solid ring.

$$\textbf{Volume} = \pi r^2 \times 2\pi R$$
$$= 2\pi^2 Rr^2,$$

i.e. **volume of a ring is the area of a cross-section multiplied by the circumference of the circle described by the centre of area.**

A similar formula may be used when the cross-section of the ring is a rectangle.

Cylinder.—If a line CD (Fig. 76) rotates about an axis AB, and at a distance r from it, it will trace out the curved surface of a cylinder. The rectangle $ABCD$ will, in a similar manner, trace out the volume of a cylinder.

If h denote the distance of CD, then as the centre of gravity of CD is at a distance r from AB, the surface is given by

$$S = h \times 2\pi r = 2\pi rh.$$

The area of the rectangle is rh,

Distance moved through by centre of area

$$= 2\pi \times \frac{r}{2} = \pi r;$$

$$\therefore \; V = rh \times \pi r = \pi r^2 h.$$

Other cases may be treated in like manner.

A rectangle $ABCD$, when made to rotate about an axis EF parallel to AB, and at a distance r from it, will generate a **hollow cylinder.** Then, if R denote the distance from CD to EF, and h the height of the rectangle, AD will be $R-r$, also distance of centre of area from EF will be $\frac{1}{2}(R+r)$.

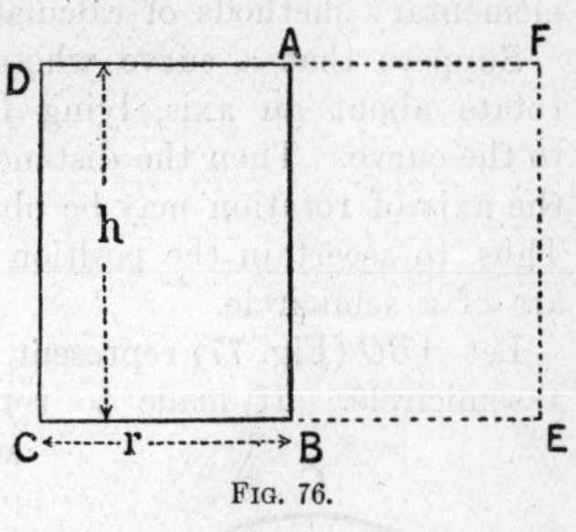

FIG. 76.

Area of $ABCD=(R-r)h$;

$\therefore$ volume

$$=(R-r)h\times\frac{2\pi(R+r)}{2}$$

$$=\pi(R^2-r^2)h.$$

When h is small compared with R, the short cylinder so formed is usually called a flat ring.

Ex. 1. The cross-section of a ring is an ellipse whose principal diameters are 2 inches and $1\frac{1}{2}$ inches; the middle of this section is at 3 inches from the axis of the ring; what is the volume of the ring?

$$\text{Area of cross-section}=\left(2\times 1\tfrac{1}{2}\right)\frac{\pi}{4}.$$

Distance moved through by centre of area in one revolution

$$=2\pi\times 3,$$

$$\therefore \text{ volume of ring}=\left(2\times 1\tfrac{1}{2}\right)\frac{\pi}{4}\times 2\pi\times 3;$$

$$=\frac{9\pi^2}{2}=44\cdot 42 \text{ cub. in.}$$

Any irregular area.—In the case of an irregular area, Simpson's Parabolic Rules, the Trapezoidal, Mid-ordinate, or any of the methods usually adopted, may be used to find the area of the figure. The position of the centre of area may be found graphically, experimentally, or by calculation. Then, the volume traced out can be obtained by application of the rule.

Centre of gravity.—The centre of gravity, or centre of area, of a plane figure may be obtained graphically, experimentally, or by calculation. To obtain accurately the position of the point, it is in many cases necessary to apply the methods of the Integral Calculus (p. 424). In some few cases, however, and especially where the surface is one of revolution, more elementary methods of calculation may be adopted.

Suppose that a curve whose length is known, is made to rotate about an axis, lying in the same plane but exterior to the curve. Then the distance of the centre of gravity from the axis of rotation may be obtained from Guldinus' Theorem. Thus, to ascertain the position of the centre of gravity of the arc of a semicircle.

Let ABC (Fig. 77) represent a piece of wire in the form of a semicircle. If made to rotate about a diameter AB, the surface of a sphere will be traced out.

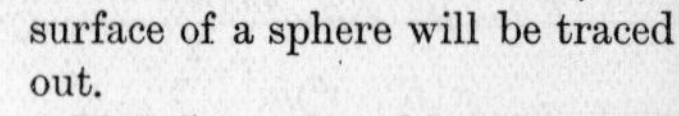

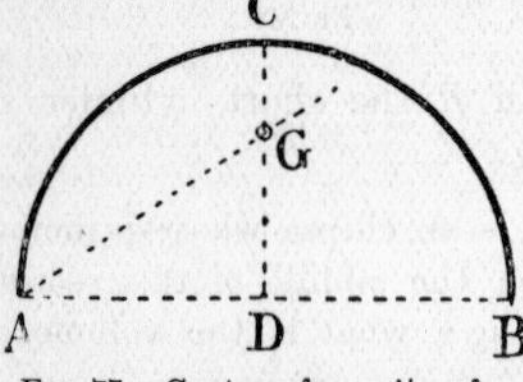

FIG. 77.—Centre of gravity of a semicircle.

If DC is a line bisecting, and at right angles to, AB, G the position of the centre of gravity, which is from the symmetry of the figure at some point in the line DC, let x denote its distance from AB, and r the radius AD or BD, then the position of G, in terms of r, can be obtained from the first theorem of Guldinus' (p. 217) as follows: *

Perimeter of curve $= \pi r$.

Distance moved through by G in one revolution $= 2\pi x$.

Surface traced out is the surface of a sphere $= 4\pi r^2$;

$$\therefore \pi r \times 2\pi x = 4\pi r^2;$$

$$\therefore x = \frac{2r}{\pi}. \quad \text{.............................(i)}$$

Ex. 1. A piece of wire is bent into the form of a semicircle of 3 feet radius; find the distance of its centre of gravity from the diameter AB.

From (i) $$x = \frac{6}{\pi} = 1{\cdot}91 \text{ feet.}$$

In like manner, the centre of gravity of a plane area can be obtained when the volume traced out by it is known. Thus, when it is required to find the centre of area of a semicircle

* See pp. 425, 428.

the volume described is that of a sphere. Let x denote the distance of G from AB.

Then area $=\frac{\pi r^2}{2}$.

Distance moved through by $G=2\pi x$;

$$\therefore \frac{\pi r^2}{2}\times 2\pi x=\tfrac{4}{3}\pi r^3;$$

$$\therefore x=\frac{4r}{3\pi}. \quad \text{.............................(ii)}$$

Ex. 2. The radius of semicircle is 3 feet; find the distance of its centre of area from the diameter AB.

Here, from (ii), we have

$$x=\frac{4}{\pi}=1\cdot274 \text{ feet.}$$

Addition and subtraction of solids.—In many cases, to obtain the volume of a solid or a hollow vessel, it may be necessary to add or subtract the volumes of two or more simple solids. In other cases a good approximation to the actual volume is obtained by assuming the volume to be represented by that of one or more simple solids, the volume of which can be readily determined

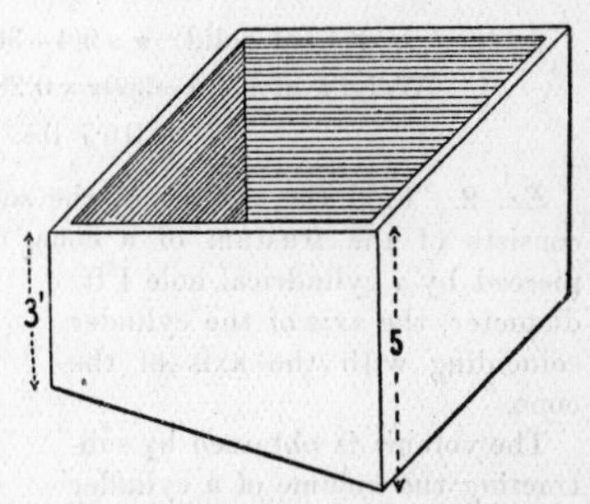

FIG. 78.—Rectangular and triangular prism.

As a simple example, find the weight of water which a tank of the form in Fig. 78 can contain. The tank is rectangular in plan, its dimensions 6 ft. × 4 ft., depth at one end 3 ft., at the other 5 ft.

The volume is obviously the sum of a rectangular, together with a triangular, prism;

$$\therefore \text{volume}=(6\times 4\times 3)+\tfrac{1}{2}(2\times 6\times 4),$$

$$72+24=96 \text{ cub. ft.};$$

$$\therefore \text{weight of water}=96\times 62\cdot 3=5980\cdot 8 \text{ lbs.}$$

Or, the volume may be obtained as follows:

$$\text{Average depth} = \frac{3+5}{2} = 4 \text{ ft.},$$

$$\text{volume} = 6 \times 4 \times 4 = 96 \text{ cub. ft.},$$

$$\text{and weight} = 96 \times 62{\cdot}3 = 5980{\cdot}8 \text{ lbs.}$$

Cylinder and cone.—An example of a combination of a cylinder and cone is furnished by an ordinary sharpened lead pencil.

Ex. 1. A solid consists of a cylinder 6 in. diameter and 3 ft. long, and a cone base 6 in., length 12 in. (Fig. 79). If one cub. in. of the material weighs 0·28 lbs., find the weight of the solid.

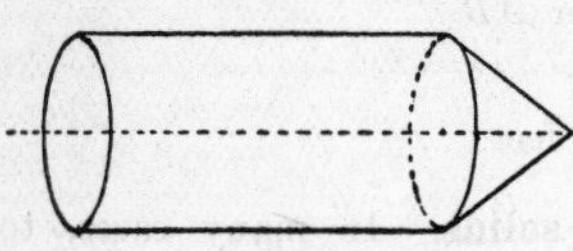

FIG. 79.—Cylinder and cone.

$$\text{Vol. of cylinder} = \pi \times 3^2 \times 36,$$

$$\text{vol. of cone} = \frac{\pi \times 3^2 \times 12}{3} = \pi \times 3^2 \times 4;$$

$$\therefore \text{vol. of solid} = \pi \times 9(4+36) = 360\pi \text{ cub. in.}$$

$$\text{Weight of solid} = 360\pi \times 0{\cdot}28 \text{ lbs.}$$

$$= 316{\cdot}7 \text{ lbs.}$$

Ex. 2. Find the volume of the solid shown in Fig. 80, which consists of the frustum of a cone, 6 ft. high, base 6 ft. diam., pierced by a cylindrical hole 1 ft. diameter, the axis of the cylinder coinciding with the axis of the cone.

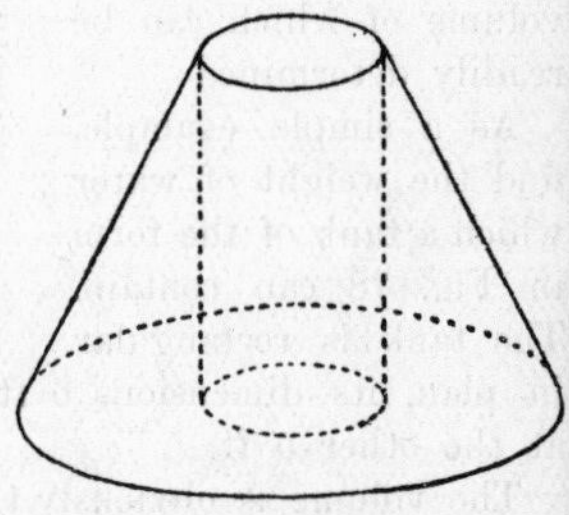

FIG. 80.—Frustum of a cone and a cylinder.

The volume is obtained by subtracting the volume of a cylinder from that of the frustum of a cone.

Volume of frustum

$$= \frac{\pi \times 6}{3}(3^2 + \tfrac{1}{2}^2 + 3 \times \tfrac{1}{2})$$

$$= 2\pi \times 10{\cdot}75 \text{ cub. ft.}$$

$$\text{Volume of cylinder} = \frac{\pi}{4} \times 1^2 \times 6 = \frac{3\pi}{2} \text{ cub. ft.};$$

$$\therefore \text{volume of solid} = 21{\cdot}5\pi - 1{\cdot}5\pi = 20\pi \text{ cub. ft.} = 62{\cdot}84 \text{ cub. ft.}$$

Cylinder and sphere.—When a sphere is pierced by a cylindrical hole we obtain a solid, usually known as a bead. If the axis of the hole is coincident with the axis of the sphere, take the formula for the volume of the zone of a sphere (p. 212), write $R_2=r_2$, and we obtain

$$\text{volume of zone}=\frac{\pi h}{2}\left(2r_2{}^2+\frac{h^2}{3}\right).$$

To obtain the volume of the bead, we must subtract the volume of the cylinder;

$$\therefore \text{ volume of bead}=\frac{\pi h}{2}\left(2r_2{}^2+\frac{h^2}{3}\right)-(\pi r_2{}^2\times h)$$

$$=\frac{\pi h^3}{6}.$$

Ex. 3. A cast-iron sphere 12 inches diameter has a cylindrical hole 4 inches diameter bored through it. Find the weight of the solid. (1 cub. in. weighs 0·26 lb.)

Let x denote the half-height, or thickness OE.

Then $$x=\sqrt{6^2-2^2}=\sqrt{32},$$

$$h=2x=2\sqrt{32}=8\sqrt{2}\text{ in.},$$

$$\text{volume of solid}=\frac{\pi(8\sqrt{2})^3}{6}=758{\cdot}2\text{ cub. in.},$$

$$\text{weight}=758{\cdot}2\times 0{\cdot}26=197{\cdot}2\text{ lbs.}$$

MISCELLANEOUS EXERCISES. XXVI.

1. A piece of paper in the form of a circular sector, of which the radius is 7 inches and the curved side 11 inches, is formed into a conical cup. Find the area of the conical surface, and also of the base of the cone.

2. The interior of a building is in the form of a cylinder of 15 feet radius and 12 feet altitude, surmounted by a cone of equal base and whose vertical angle is a right angle. Find the area of surface and the cubical content of the building.

3. What weight of lead weighing 6 lb. per square foot is required to cover a cone 1 ft. in diameter and 2 ft. high? If the covering is to be made with one soldered joint, to what shape should the lead be cut?

4. The slant side of a cone is 25 ft., and the area of its curved surface is 550 sq. ft. Find its volume.

5. Find the lateral surface and volume of the frustum of a cone, slant height of frustum 25 ft. and the diameters of the two ends 5 ft. and 27 ft. respectively.

6. The vertical ends of a hollow trough are equilateral triangles of 12 in. side, the bases of the triangles are horizontal; if the length of the trough is 6 ft., find the number of gallons of water it will contain.

7. Find the surface of the six equal faces of a hexagonal pyramid, each side of the base being 6 ft., and altitude of pyramid 8 ft.; find also the volume of the pyramid.

8. A cone and a hemisphere have a common base diameter 10 centimetres; find the weight of the solid so formed if the material is steel and the height of the cone is equal to the diameter of the base. (1 cubic in. steel weighs 0·29 lbs.)

9. A cylindrical boiler 4 ft. internal diameter and 15 feet long is traversed by 50 tubes, each 3 inches diameter; determine the volume of water the boiler will hold.

10. Two thin vessels without lids each contain a cubic foot; the one is a prism on a square base, height equal to half the length of each side of base, the other a cylinder, height equal to radius of base. Compare the amounts of material it would require to make them, the thickness being the same for both.

11. A pipe supplying 6 gallons of water per minute will fill a hemispherical tank in 4 hours 32 min.; find the diameter of the tank.

12. Find the volume of a hexagonal room, each side of which is 20 ft. and height 30 ft., which also is finished above with a roof in the form of a hexagonal pyramid 15 ft. high.

13. A lead bar, length 10 cms., width 5 cms., and thickness 4 cms., is melted down and made into 5 equal spherical bullets; find the diameter of each.

14. A sphere of radius r fits closely into the inside of a closed cylindrical box, the height of which is equal to the diameter of the cylinder. Write down the expressions for the volume of the empty space between the sphere and the cylinder. If the volume of this empty space is 134 cub. in., what is the radius of the sphere?

15. A cast-iron ball of 8 in. diameter is coated with a layer of lead 7 in. thick. Find the total weight.

16. Two spheres of the same material weigh 512 lbs. and 729 lbs. respectively, and the cost of gilding the second at $1\frac{3}{4}$d. per sq. in. is £29 13s. $7\frac{1}{2}$d. Find the radius of the first sphere.

17. A sphere, whose diameter is one foot is cut out of a cubic foot of lead, and the remainder is melted down into the form of another sphere; find its diameter.

18. A spherical shell of iron, whose diameter is one foot, is filled with lead; find the thickness of the iron, when the weights of the iron and lead are equal. (Relative densities are as 1 : 1·58.)

19. What is the diameter of a sphere which contains 716 cub. in.?

20. The weights of two spheres are as 9 : 25, and the weights of equal volumes of the substances are as 15 : 9. Compare the diameters.

21. A solid consisting of a right cone standing on a hemisphere is placed in a bath full of water; if the solid is completely immersed, find the weight of water displaced; radius of hemisphere 2 ft., and height of cone 4 ft.

22. The diameters of a spherical shell are 6 in. and 5 in. respectively, and its weight is 13·4 lbs.; if the ratio of the weights of equal volumes of lead and iron be as 1·58 to 1, what will be the weight of 12 in. length of lead tubing, external diameter 7 in., internal 5 in.

23. Find the radius of a circle whose area is equal to the sum of the areas of two triangles whose sides are 35, 53, 66 ft. and 33, 56, 65 ft.

24. Find the area of the segment of a circle of which the arc is one-third the circumference, the radius being $7\frac{1}{2}$ inches.

25. A piece of copper (specific gravity 8·9) 1 ft. long, 4 inches wide, and $\frac{1}{2}$ inch thick is drawn out into wire of uniform diameter $\frac{1}{16}$ inch. Find the length and the weight of the wire.

26. What is the area of a triangle whose sides are 18·40, 13·36, and 15·20 feet?

27. A cubical tank 6 feet edge is half full of water. Find the height to which the surface of the water is raised when an iron cube of 2 ft. edge and an iron sphere 2 ft. diameter are placed in the tank.

28. A sphere, radius R is pierced by a cylindrical hole whose axis passes through the centre of the sphere. If r is the radius of the cylinder, express in terms of r and the radius of the sphere the volume of the bead thus formed. If the length of the cylindrical hole be 0·75 in., find the volume of the bead.

29. What is the weight of a cast-iron spherical shell, external diameter 6 in., thickness $\frac{1}{2}$ in.?

30. Find the weight of a cast-iron water pipe, 30 inches external diameter, thickness of metal 1 in., length 12 ft.

31. The radii of the two ends of the frustum of a cone are 12 feet and 8 feet respectively; the area of its curved surface is 975·4 square feet. Find the slant height, and volume of the frustum.

32. A frustum of a pyramid has rectangular ends, the sides of the base being 25 and 36 feet; if the area of the top face be 784 sq. ft. and the height of the frustum 60 ft., find its volume. Find the radius of a sphere whose volume is equal to the volume of the frustum.

33. Two spheres, each 10 ft. diameter, are melted down and recast into a cone whose height is equal to the radius of its base. Find the height.

CHAPTER XI.

POSITION OF A POINT IN SPACE.

Projections of a line.—To obtain the projections of a line AB on the plane MN (Fig. 81) we may proceed as follows: From B and A draw lines Bb, Aa, perpendicular to the plane and meeting the plane in points b and a; then the line joining a to b is the projection required. The angle BHb is the angle between the line and the plane; or if a line AC be drawn through A parallel to ab, then CAB is the angle, θ, of inclination of the line to the plane and

$$ab = AB \cos \theta.$$

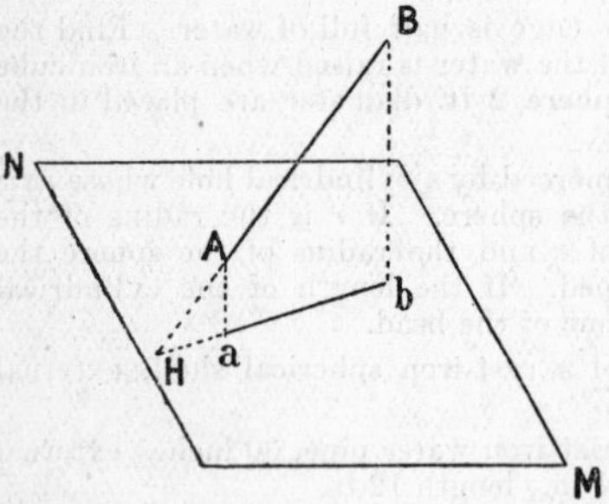

Fig. 81.—Angle between a line and a plane.

The angle between a line and plane, or the inclination of a line to a plane, is the angle between the line and its projection on the plane. Thus, if BA produced meets the plane NM (Fig. 81) in H, the inclination of the line to the plane is the angle between the line and its projection on the plane. Or, the angle may be obtained by drawing from A a line parallel to ab.

Rabattement.—The graphical method of rabattement is to assume that the line AB rotates about its projection, or plan, ab as an axis until AB lies in the horizontal plane. That is, from a and b lines perpendicular to ab and equal in length to aA, bB, are drawn, and the angle can be measured. Such a process is called *rabatting* the line.

Three co-ordinate planes of projections.—Very little reflection will convince the student that it is impossible to give measurements which will define the position of a point in space *absolutely*. The most that can be done is to choose some point as *origin of co-ordinates*, and take three lines passing through this point (only two of which lie in any one plane) as axes of co-ordinates. The three planes which each contain two of these axes are called the co-ordinate planes. A point in space may be represented by means of the projections on the three planes; these projections determine the distances of the point from the three planes, and hence the position of the point is known. Usually the planes are chosen mutually at right angles to each other, such as those at one corner of a cube or, roughly, the corner of a room.

In the latter case the floor may represent the horizontal plane, sometimes spoken of as the plane xy; one vertical wall the plane xz, and the other vertical wall—at right angles to xz—the plane zy.

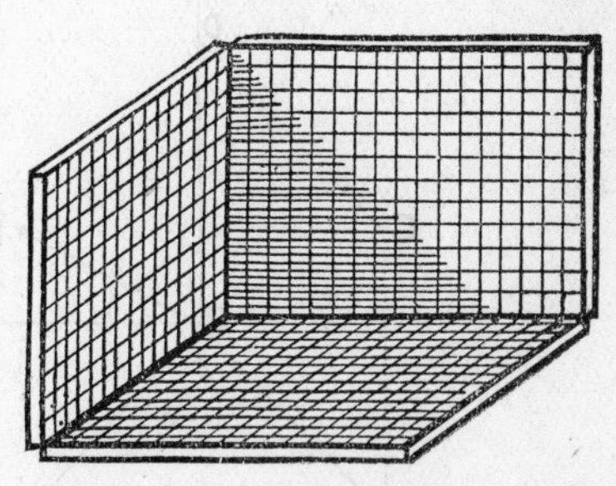

FIG. 82.—Model of the three co-ordinate planes of projection.

A model to illustrate these reference planes may be constructed of a piece of flat board (Fig. 82) and two other pieces mutually at right angles to each other. It is advisable to have the latter two boards hinged. This arrangement enables the two sides to be rotated until all three planes lie in one plane. The planes may be ruled into squares; or squared paper may be fastened on them. Then by means of hat pins many problems can be effectively illustrated with the assistance of the model planes.

A model can be more easily made from drawing paper, or cardboard. Draw a square of 9 or 10 inches side (Fig. 83).

Along two of its sides mark off distances of 4″ and 6″ and use letters as shown in the illustration. Cut through one of the lines OZ, and fold the paper so that the two points, marked Z, coincide.

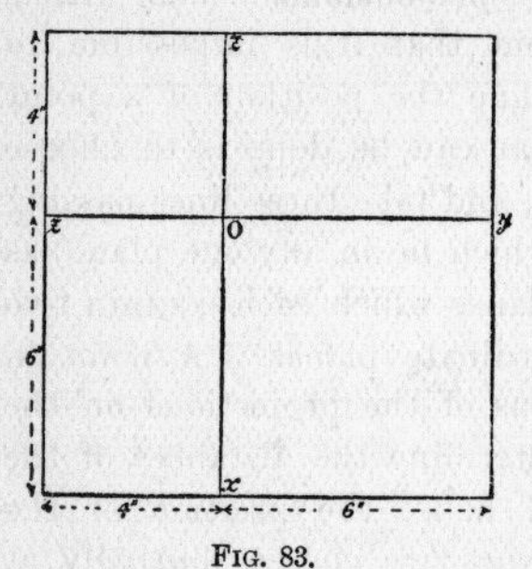

FIG. 83.

To fix the position of a point in space, imagine such a point P (Fig. 84). From P draw a perpendicular PA to the horizontal plane and meeting it in A. AP is the distance of the point P from the plane xy; or, is the z-co-ordinate of P.

In a similar manner a perpendicular to the plane yz, meeting it in B, will give the distance of the point from the plane yz; or, the x-co-ordinate of P. Finally, the distance PC, the

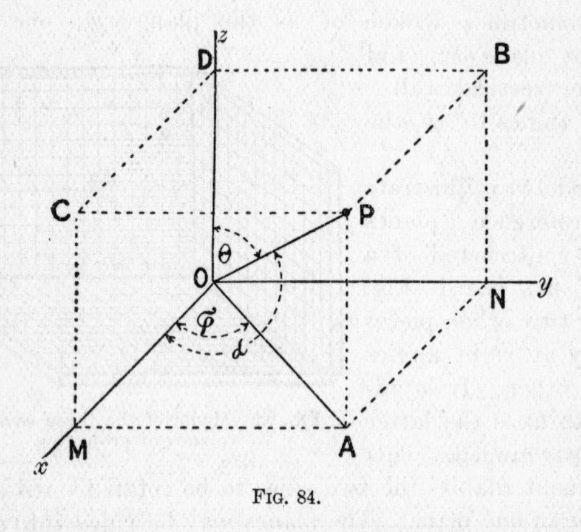

FIG. 84.

y-co-ordinate of the point, is the distance of the point from the plane zx.

Conversely, given the x-, y-, and z-co-ordinates of a point P, set off $OM=x$, $ON=y$, then the point A is obtained by drawing lines MA, and NA, parallel to the two axes Ox and Oy. AP, drawn perpendicular to the xy plane equal to z, determines the position of the point P.

From the right-angled triangles, AMO, PAO (Fig. 84),

$$OA^2 = OM^2 + MA^2 = x^2 + y^2.$$

and
$$OP^2 = OA^2 + AP^2 = x^2 + y^2 + z^2;$$

$$\therefore\ OP = \sqrt{x^2 + y^2 + z^2}.$$

Thus, the three projections of a point on three intersecting planes definitely determine the distance of a point from these planes.

Negative values of the co-ordinates indicate that the lines affected must be drawn in the opposite direction to that shown in Fig. 84.

It will be found that problems dealing with the projections of a point, line, or plane, may be solved either by graphical methods, using a fairly accurate scale and protractor, or by calculation. One method should be used as a check on the other.

Ex. 1. Given the x-, y-, and z-co-ordinates of a point as 2″, 1·5″, and 2″, respectively. Draw the three projections of the line OP on the three planes xy, yz, and zx, and in each case measure the length of the projection. Find the distance of P from the origin O, and the angles made by the line OP with the three axes.

Let P (Fig. 84) be the given point and O the origin of co-ordinates. Join OP.

The projection on the axis of x is the line OM; on the axis of y is the line ON; and on the axis of z is the line OD.

$$OM = 2'',\ ON = 1{\cdot}5'',\ \text{and}\ OD = 2''.$$

Graphical construction.—The arrangement of the lines and angles can be seen from Fig. 84. To measure the lengths of the lines and the magnitudes of the angles, proceed as follows:

Draw the three axes intersecting at O (Fig. 85), and letter as shown. Set off along the axis of z a distance $OD = 2''$, along the axis of y a distance $ON = 1{\cdot}5''$, and along the axis of x a distance $OM = 2''$. Draw through these points, M and N, lines parallel to the axes to meet in A, and join A to O. Then OA is the projection of OP, on the plane xy its length is $\sqrt{2^2 + (1{\cdot}5)^2} = 2{\cdot}5''$. In a similar manner, the projection OB

on the plane yz, and OC on the plane xz, are obtained; $OB=2{\cdot}5''$ and $OC=2{\cdot}83''$.

The distance of P from the origin, or the length of the line OP, is the hypotenuse of a right-angled triangle, of which the base is OA, and the perpendicular AP the height of P above the plane of xy, or simply the z-coordinate of the point. Hence, as in Fig. 85, draw AP perpendicular to OA and make $AP=OD=2''$. Join O to P; then $OP=3{\cdot}2''$ is the distance required.

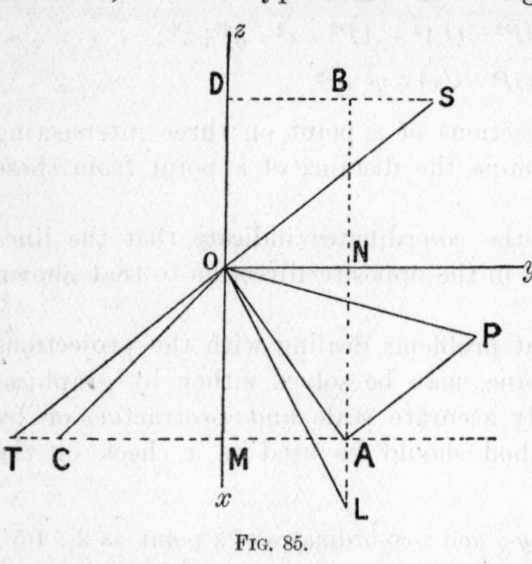

FIG. 85.

To obtain graphically the angles which the line makes with the three axes it is necessary to **rabat** the line into each of the three planes. Produce NA to L making $NL=OC$. Join O to L. Then the angle NOL is the inclination of the line to the axis of $y=62^\circ\,3'$. Similarly, make $DS=OA$ and $MT=OB$. Join S and T to O. Then DOS is the angle made by the line with the axis of $z=51^\circ\,19'$, and MOT is the angle made by the line with the axis of $x=51^\circ\,19'$.

A line which passes through two given points may be reduced to the preceding case by taking one of the given points as origin.

Ex. 2. Find the distance between the two points (3, 4, 5·3) (1, 2·5, 3·3) and the angles which the line joining the two given points makes with the axes.

The solution of this problem can be made to depend on the preceding rules by taking as origin the point (1, 2·5, 3·3). The coordinates of the remaining points will be $(3-1)$ $(4-2{\cdot}5)$ and $(5{\cdot}3-3{\cdot}3)$ or (2, 1·5, 2). Hence the true length, the projections, and the angles may be obtained as in the preceding example.

The manner in which the three axes are lettered should be noticed. It would appear at first sight to be more convenient to use the horizontal line, drawn from the origin O to the right, as the axis of x instead of y as in the diagram. But when it becomes necessary to apply mathematics to mechanical, or physical, problems, the notation adopted in Fig. 84 is more useful, and therefore it is advisable to use it from the commencement.

Calculation.—The preceding results are readily and accurately obtained by calculation.

Thus, as in Fig 86, let θ denote the angle which the line OP makes with the axis of z, and ϕ the angle which the projection OA makes with the axis of x. Then, the position of P is fixed either when its **Cartesian co-ordinates**, x, y, and z, or its **polar co-ordinates**, r, θ, ϕ, are known; r denoting the length of OP.

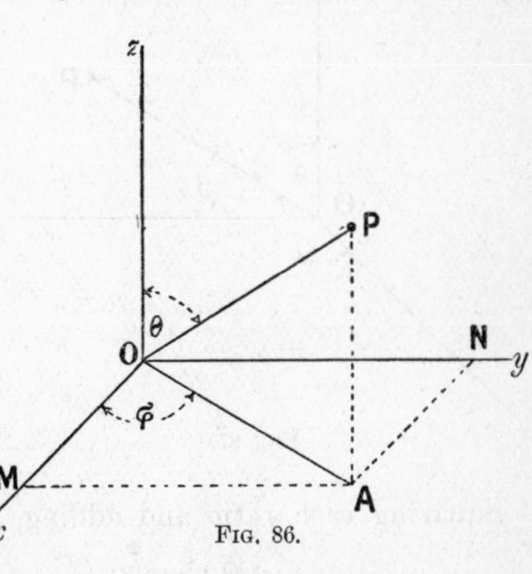

Fig. 86.

The conversion from Cartesian to polar co-ordinates may be effected as follows:

From Fig. 86, OA is the projection of OP on the plane xy;

$$\therefore \ OA = OP \cos POA = r \sin \theta.$$

Also $\quad OM = x = OA \cos \phi = r \sin \theta \cos \phi$;

$$\therefore \ \cos \phi = \frac{x}{r \sin \theta}. \quad \text{(i)}$$

Or, as $NA = OM$,

$$\tan \phi = \frac{y}{x}. \quad \text{(ii)}$$

Thus, ϕ may be found either from (i) or (ii), and when the numerical values of x, y, z, are given, the numerical values of r, θ, and ϕ can be obtained.

Direction-cosines of a line.—As already indicated, when the numerical values of x, y, z, are given, the distance of the point from the origin may be obtained from the relation $r^2=x^2+y^2+z^2$. Hence, we can proceed to find the ratios $\frac{x}{r}, \frac{y}{r}, \frac{z}{r}$. These are called the **direction-cosines** of the line.

Thus, if OP (Fig. 87) is the line joining the point (x, y, z) to the origin, and α, β and θ, denote the angles made by the line with the axes of x, y, and z respectively, then

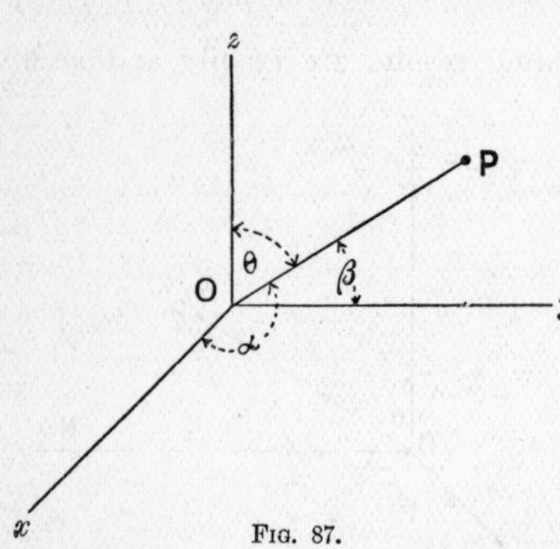

FIG. 87.

$$\cos\alpha=\frac{x}{OP}=\frac{x}{r},$$

$$\cos\beta=\frac{y}{r},$$

and $$\cos\theta=\frac{z}{r}.$$

In this manner the angles made by the line with the three axes can be obtained.

Squaring each ratio and adding,

$$\cos^2\alpha+\cos^2\beta+\cos^2\theta=\frac{x^2}{r^2}+\frac{y^2}{r^2}+\frac{z^2}{r^2}=\frac{x^2+y^2+z^2}{r^2}=1.$$

The letter l is often used instead of $\cos\alpha$; and similarly m and n replace $\cos\beta$ and $\cos\theta$ respectively.

From the relation $\cos^2\alpha+\cos^2\beta+\cos^2\theta=1$, or its equivalent $l^2+m^2+n^2=1$, it will be obvious that, if two of the angles which a given line OP makes with the axes are known, then the remaining angle can be found. As indicated on page 230 the angles α, β, and θ, can be obtained by construction, but by calculation more accurate results can be obtained.

Ex. 3. *A* line makes an angle of 60° with one axis and 45° with another. What angle does it make with the third?

Let θ denote the required angle.

Then $$\cos^2\theta+\cos^2 60^\circ+\cos^2 45^\circ=1;$$

$$\therefore\ \cos^2\theta=1-\cos^2 60^\circ-\cos^2 45^\circ=\tfrac{1}{4},$$

or $$\cos\theta=\tfrac{1}{2};\quad\therefore\ \theta=60^\circ.$$

We may repeat Ex. 1 as follows:

Ex. 4. The co-ordinates of a point P are 2, 1·5, 2. Find the distance of the point from the origin, and the angles made by the line OP with the three axes.

$$OP=\sqrt{2^2+1\cdot5^2+2^2}=3\cdot2,$$

$$x=OM=OP\cos\alpha=r\cos\alpha,$$

whence $$\cos\alpha=\frac{x}{r}=\frac{2}{3\cdot2}=0\cdot6250, \quad \therefore\ \alpha=51°\ 19';$$

$$y=r\cos\beta,$$

or $$\cos\beta=\frac{1\cdot5}{3\cdot2}=0\cdot4688, \quad \therefore\ \beta=62°\ 3';$$

$$z=r\cos\theta,$$

or $$\cos\theta=\frac{2}{3\cdot2}=0\cdot6250, \quad \therefore\ \theta=51°\ 19'.$$

Ex. 5. If $x=3$, $y=4$, $z=5$, find r, l, m, and n.

$$r^2=x^2+y^2+z^2=3^2+4^2+5^2=50,$$

$$\therefore\ r=\sqrt{50}=7\cdot071;$$

$$l=\frac{x}{r}=\frac{3}{7\cdot071}=0\cdot4242,$$

$$m=\frac{y}{r}=\frac{4}{7\cdot071}=0\cdot5657,$$

$$n=\frac{z}{r}=\frac{5}{7\cdot071}=0\cdot7071.$$

Ex. 6. The co-ordinates of a point P are (2, 3, 4); find its polar co-ordinates.

$$r=OP=\sqrt{2^2+3^2+4^2}=\sqrt{29}=5\cdot385,$$

$$OD=r\cos\theta,$$

$$\therefore\ \cos\theta=\frac{4}{5\cdot385}=0\cdot7428, \quad \theta=42°\ 2';$$

$$x=OA\cos\phi, \text{ and } OA=r\sin\theta,$$

$$\therefore\ x=r\sin\theta\cos\phi, \ldots\ldots\ldots\ldots\ldots\ldots\text{(i)}$$

or $$y=r\sin\theta\sin\phi, \ldots\ldots\ldots\ldots\ldots\ldots\text{(ii)}$$

The value of ϕ may be obtained either from (i) or (ii):

Thus $$\sin\phi=\frac{3}{5\cdot385\times\sin 42°\ 2'}=\frac{3}{5\cdot385\times0\cdot6695},$$

$$\log(\sin\phi)=\log 3-\log 5\cdot385-\log 0\cdot6695=\bar{1}\cdot9202,$$

$$\therefore\ \sin\phi=0\cdot8322, \quad \therefore\ \phi=56°\ 20';$$

again, dividing (ii) by (i), $$\tan\phi=\frac{y}{x},$$

$$\tan\phi=\tfrac{3}{2}=1\cdot5, \quad \therefore\ \phi=56°\ 20'.$$

Angles between a line and the three co-ordinate planes—Since the angle between a line and a plane is the angle between the line and its projection on the plane, the angle between a line OP (Fig. 84) and the plane xy is the angle between the line and its projection OA on that plane.

From the right-angled triangle ONA,

$$OA^2=ON^2+NA^2=y^2+x^2\,;\ \therefore\ OA=\sqrt{x^2+y^2}.$$

Similarly, the projection on the plane $xz=\sqrt{x^2+z^2}$ and on the plane $yz=\sqrt{y^2+z^2}$.

Thus, if the three angles made by a line OP with the three co-ordinate planes xy, yz, and zx, be denoted by F, G, and H respectively, then we have the relations:

$$\cos F=\frac{\sqrt{x^2+y^2}}{r},\ \cos G=\frac{\sqrt{y^2+z^2}}{r},\ \cos H=\frac{\sqrt{x^2+z^2}}{r}.$$

Also $$\cos^2 F+\cos^2 G+\cos^2 H=2.$$

Ex. 7. The three rectangular co-ordinates of a point P are 3, 4, and 2, respectively.

Find

(i) the length of the line OP joining P to the origin O;

(ii) the angles made by the line OP with the three co-ordinate planes xy, yz, and zx;

(iii) the angles which the line OP makes with the three axes.

(i) Length $OP=\sqrt{3^2+4^2+2^2}=\sqrt{29}$
$=5{\cdot}385.$

(ii) The length of the line and the angles may be obtained by graphical methods or by calculation, as follows, F, G, H denoting the angles as above:

The projection of OP on the plane xy is given by $\sqrt{3^2+4^2}=5.$

$$\therefore\ \cos F=\frac{5}{5{\cdot}385}=0{\cdot}9285\,;\ \ \therefore\ F=21^\circ\ 48'.$$

The projection on the plane zy is

$$\sqrt{4^2+2^2}=\sqrt{20}=4{\cdot}472.$$

Let G denote the angle between the line and plane.

$$\therefore\ \cos G=\frac{4{\cdot}472}{5{\cdot}385}=0{\cdot}8305\,;\ \ \therefore\ G=33^\circ\ 52'.$$

The projection on the plane xz is $\sqrt{3^2+2^2}=\sqrt{13}$.

$$\cos H=\frac{\sqrt{13}}{5{\cdot}385}=0{\cdot}6696\,; \quad \therefore\ H=47^\circ\ 58'.$$

(iii) Let α, β, and θ, denote the angles made by the line with the axes of x, y, and z, respectively, then $x=r\cos\alpha$, $y=r\cos\beta$, $z=r\cos\theta$,

$$\cos\alpha=\frac{3}{5{\cdot}385}=0{\cdot}5571, \quad \therefore\ \alpha=56^\circ\ 9';$$

$$\cos\beta=\frac{4}{5{\cdot}385}=0{\cdot}7429, \quad \therefore\ \beta=42^\circ\ 2';$$

$$\cos\theta=\frac{2}{5{\cdot}385}=0{\cdot}3714, \quad \therefore\ \theta=68^\circ\ 12'.$$

Ex. 8. There is a point P whose x-, y-, and z-co-ordinates are 2, 1·5, and 3. Find its r-, θ-, and ϕ-co-ordinates. If O is the origin, find the angles made by OP with the axes of co-ordinates.

$$r=\sqrt{x^2+y^2+z^2}=\sqrt{15{\cdot}25}, \quad \therefore\ r=3{\cdot}905\,;$$

$$\tan\phi=\frac{y}{x}=\frac{1{\cdot}5}{2}=0{\cdot}75, \quad \therefore\ \phi=36^\circ\ 52';$$

$$\cos\theta=\frac{z}{r}=\frac{3}{3{\cdot}905}=0{\cdot}7683, \quad \therefore\ \theta=39^\circ\ 48';$$

$$\cos\alpha=\frac{x}{r}=\frac{2}{3{\cdot}905}=0{\cdot}5122, \quad \therefore\ \alpha=59^\circ\ 12';$$

$$\cos\beta=\frac{y}{r}=\frac{1{\cdot}5}{3{\cdot}905}=0{\cdot}3841, \quad \therefore\ \beta=67^\circ\ 25'.$$

Ex. 9. The polar co-ordinates of a point are $r=5$ feet, $\theta=52^\circ$, and $\phi=70^\circ$, find the x-, y-, and z-co-ordinates. Also find the angles made by the line joining the point to the origin, with the axes of co-ordinates.

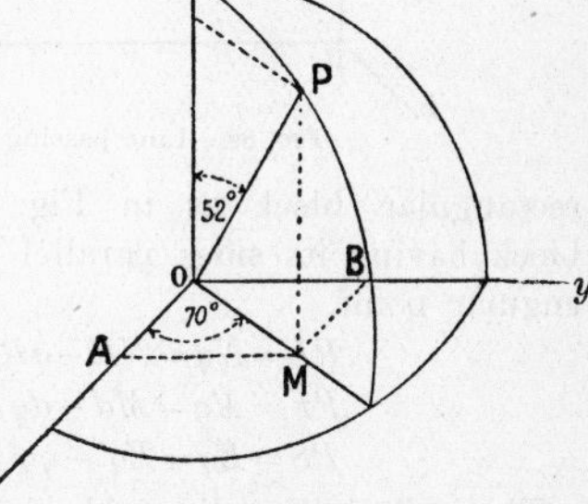

FIG. 88.

Let P be the given point (Fig. 88). Join O to P. Then, by projecting on the three axes, OA is the x-co-ordinate; similarly, OB and OC are the y- and z-co-ordinates respectively.

$$z=5\cos 52^\circ=5\times 0{\cdot}6157=3{\cdot}078,$$

$$OM=5\sin 52^\circ=5\times 0{\cdot}7880=3{\cdot}940,$$

$$x=OM\cos 70^\circ=3{\cdot}94\times 0{\cdot}342=1{\cdot}348,$$

$$y=OM\sin 70^\circ=3{\cdot}94\times 0{\cdot}9397=3{\cdot}702.$$

Let α, β, and θ, be the three angles made with the three axes.

$$\cos\alpha = \frac{x}{r} = \frac{1\cdot348}{5} = 0\cdot2696, \quad \therefore\ \alpha = 74^\circ\ 22';$$

$$\cos\beta = \frac{y}{r} = \frac{3\cdot702}{5} = 0\cdot7404, \quad \therefore\ \beta = 42^\circ\ 14'.$$

Line passing through two given points.—If the co-ordinates of two points P and q be denoted by (x, y, z), and (x', y', z'), the equation of the line passing through the two points is

$$\frac{x-x'}{l} = \frac{y-y'}{m} = \frac{z-z'}{n}.$$

Through P, draw three lines Pp, Pp', Pp'', parallel to the three axes respectively, and draw the remaining sides of the

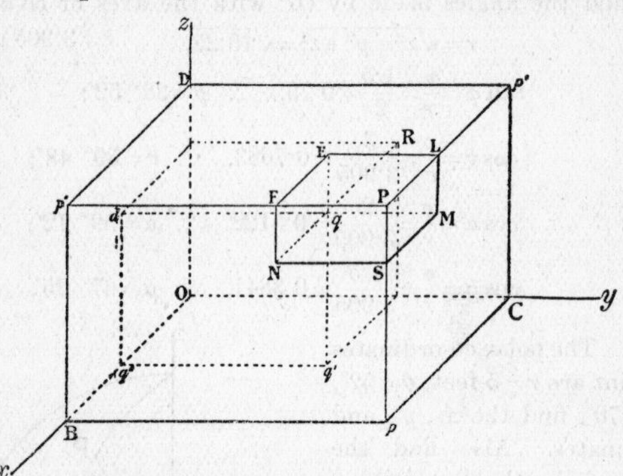

FIG. 89.—Line passing through two points.

rectangular block as in Fig. 89. Complete a rectangular block having its sides parallel to the former, and q for an angular point.

$$PL = Nq = NR - qR = Pp' - Lp' = x - x',$$
$$PF = Mq = Md - dq = y - y',$$
$$PS = Eq = Eq' - qq' = z - z'.$$

Thus, Pq is the diagonal of a rectangular block, the edges of which are $x-x'$, $y-y'$, $z-z'$. Therefore, to find the length of Pq the line joining P and q,

$$Pq = \sqrt{(x-x')^2 + (y-y')^2 + (z-z')^2}.$$

The angle between the line Pq and the axis of z is equal to the angle between Pq and a line qE parallel to the axis of z.

Hence, denoting the angle by θ,

$$n = \cos\theta = \frac{z-z'}{Pq} = \frac{z-z'}{\sqrt{(x-x')^2+(y-y')^2+(z-z')^2}}.$$

Similarly, $$l = \frac{x-x'}{Pq}, \quad m = \frac{y-y'}{Pq}.$$

When the second point is the origin O, x', y', and z', are each zero, and the equation

$$\frac{x-x'}{l} = \frac{y-y'}{m} = \frac{z-z'}{n}$$

becomes $$\frac{x}{l} = \frac{y}{m} = \frac{z}{n}.$$

Ex. 10. Find the length of the line joining the two points (7, 9, 11), (3, 4, 5). Find the polar co-ordinates of the line and the angles which the line makes with the three axes of co-ordinates.

$$r = \sqrt{(7-3)^2+(9-4)^2+(11-5)^2} = \sqrt{77}$$
$$= 8{\cdot}774;$$

$$z - z' = r\cos\theta, \quad \therefore \cos\theta = \frac{6}{8{\cdot}774} = 0{\cdot}6839;$$
$$\theta = 46^\circ\ 51';$$

$$\tan\phi = \frac{y-y'}{x-x'} = \frac{5}{4} = 1{\cdot}25, \quad \therefore \phi = 51^\circ\ 20';$$

$$\cos\alpha = \frac{x-x'}{r} = \frac{4}{8{\cdot}774} = 0{\cdot}4559, \quad \therefore \alpha = 62^\circ\ 53';$$

$$\cos\beta = \frac{y-y'}{r} = \frac{5}{8{\cdot}774} = 0{\cdot}5699, \quad \therefore \beta = 55^\circ\ 16'.$$

The method is equivalent to shifting the origin to the point (3, 4, 5).

A practical application.—Some of the data we have considered in this chapter may perhaps be better explained by the terms **latitude** and **longitude** of a place on the earth's surface. At regular distances from the two poles a series of parallel circles are drawn (Fig. 90) and are called *Parallel of Latitude.* The parallel of latitude midway between the poles is called the **Equator**. These parallels are crossed perpendicularly by circles passing through the poles and called **meridians of longitude.** Selecting one meridian as a standard (the meridian passing through Greenwich), the position of any object *on the earth's surface* can be specified. This information together with the depth below the surface, or the height above it, determines any point or place *on or near* the earth.

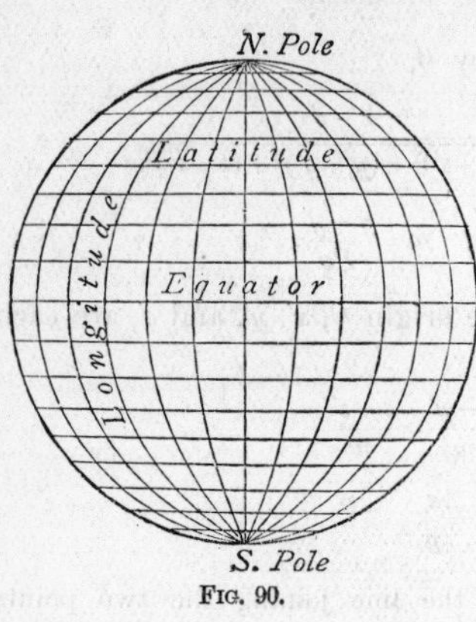

FIG. 90.

The plane xoy may be taken to represent the equatorial plane of the earth, and OZ the earth's axis. Then the position of a point P (Fig. 91) on the surface of the earth, or that of a point outside the surface moving with the earth, is known when we are given its distance OP (or r) from the centre, its latitude θ, or co-latitude $(90-\theta)$, and its ϕ or east longitude, from some standard meridian plane, such as the plane passing through Greenwich.

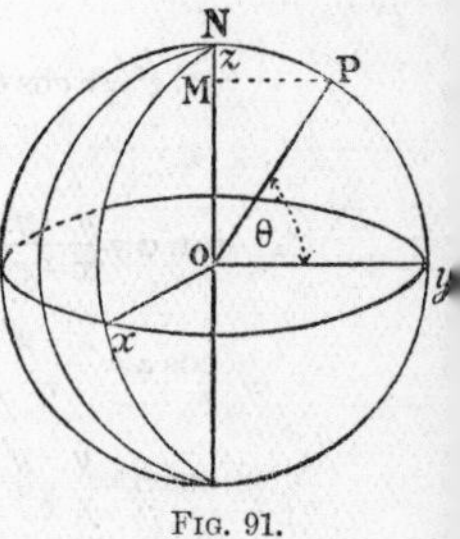

FIG. 91.

Assuming the earth to be a sphere of radius r, then the distance of a point on the surface can be obtained. If P be a point on the surface, the distance of P from the axis is the distance PM, and

$$PM = r \sin POM = r \cos \theta.$$

Ex. 11. **A point on the earth's surface is in latitude 40°. Find its distance from the axis, assuming the earth to be a sphere of 4000 miles radius.**

Required distance $= 4000 \times \cos 40°$

$= 4000 \times 0·766 = 3064$ miles.

Having found the distance PM, the speed at which such a point is moving due to the rotation of the earth can be found.

Ex. 12. Assuming the earth to be a sphere of 4000 miles radius, what is the linear velocity of a place in 40° north latitude? The earth makes one revolution in 23·93 hours.

Radius of circle of latitude $= 4000 \times \cos 40°$.

Let s denote the speed.

Then
$$s = \frac{4000 \times \cos 40° \times 2\pi}{23·93}$$
$$= \frac{4000 \times 0·766 \times 2\pi}{23·93} = 804·4 \text{ miles per hour.}$$

Ex. 13. Find the distance between the two points (3, 4, 5·3) 1, 2·5, 3) and the angles made by the line with the three axes.

$$\text{Distance} = \sqrt{(3-1)^2 + (4-2·5)^2 + (5·3-3)^2}$$
$$= \sqrt{2^2 + 1·5^2 + 2·3^2} = 3·397.$$
$$l = \cos \alpha = \frac{3-1}{3·397} = 0·5887; \quad \therefore \alpha = 53° \ 56'.$$
$$m = \cos \beta = \frac{4-2·5}{3·397} = 0·4416; \quad \therefore \beta = 63° \ 48'.$$
$$n = \cos \theta = \frac{5·3-3}{3·397} = 0·6770; \quad \therefore \theta = 47° \ 24'.$$

Cartesian Co-ordinates (two dimensions).—When the given point or points are in the plane of x, y, a resulting simplification occurs. Thus, denoting the co-ordinates of two points P and Q by (x, y) and (a, b), respectively, and the angles made by the line PQ with the axes of x and y by α and β.

Then, if r be the distance between the points,

$$r = \sqrt{(x-a)^2 + (y-b)^2}.$$

Also
$$\frac{x-a}{\cos \alpha} = \frac{y-b}{\cos \beta};$$
$$\therefore \ y - b = \frac{\cos \beta}{\cos \alpha}(x-a);$$

but β is the complement of α;

$$\therefore \ \cos \beta = \sin \alpha.$$

Hence, $$y-b=\tan\alpha(x-a),$$

and the equation of the line joining the two points may be written

$$y-b=m'(x-a),$$

where m' is the tangent of the angle made by the line with the axis of x.

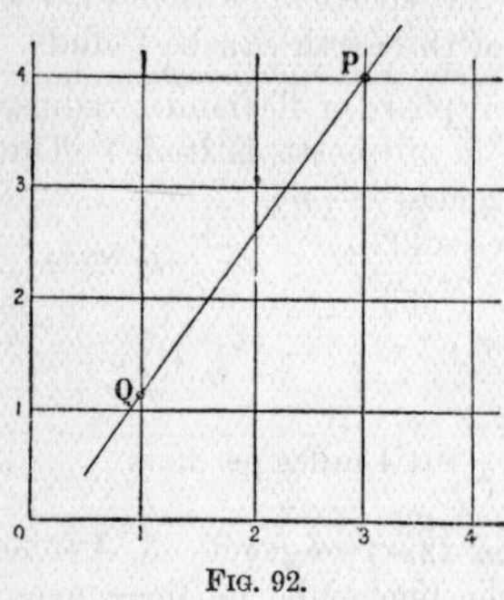

FIG. 92.

Thus, given $x=3$, $y=4$, the point P (Fig. 92) is obtained by marking the points of intersection of the lines $x=3$, $y=4$.

In a similar manner, the point Q (1, 1·134) is obtained. Join P to Q, then PQ is the line through the points (3, 4), (1, 1·134), and

$$PQ=\sqrt{(3-1)^2+(4-1{\cdot}134)^2}=3{\cdot}495,$$

and the equation of the line is

$$y-1{\cdot}134=\frac{2{\cdot}87}{2}(x-1);$$

$$\therefore\ y=1{\cdot}435x-0{\cdot}3.$$

Polar co-ordinates in two dimensions.—If from a point P a line be drawn to the origin, then if the length of OP be denoted by r, and the angle made by OP with the axis of x be θ, when r and θ are known, the position of the point is determined. Also $x=r\cos\theta$, $y=r\sin\theta$, and the rectangular co-ordinates can be found.

Conversely, $r=\sqrt{x^2+y^2}$, $\tan\theta=\dfrac{y}{x}$.

Ex. 14. Let $r=20$, $\theta=35°$; find the co-ordinates x and y.

Here $$x=r\cos 35°=20\times 0{\cdot}8192=16{\cdot}384;$$

$$y=r\sin 35°=20\times 0{\cdot}5736=11{\cdot}472.$$

Ex. 15. Given the co-ordinates of a point P (4, 3); find the length of the line joining P to the origin and the angle θ.

$$r^2=4^2+3^2=25;\quad \therefore\ r=5;$$

$$\tan\theta=\tfrac{3}{4}=0{\cdot}75,\quad \theta=36°\ 52'.$$

EXERCISES. XXVII.

1. The x- and y-co ordinates of a point A measure $2''$ and $3''$ and he point is $4''$ from the origin. Determine the z-co-ordinate and raw the three projections of A.

2. Obtain the length of the line joining two opposite corners of a ectangular prism $3'' \times 5'' \times 4''$; and find the angles which this line nakes with the edges of the solid.

3. The co-ordinates of two points P and Q are (3, 1, 2) (4, 2, 4); nd the distance PQ.

4. The three rectangular co-ordinates of a point P are 3, 4, and ; determine the polar co-ordinates of the line; the cosines of the ngles which the line makes with the three axes.

5. The polar co-ordinates of a line joining a point to the origin re $r=3$, $\theta=65°$, $\phi=50°$. Determine its rectangular co-ordinates.

6. The co-ordinates of the two points are (3, 4, 5·3) (1, 2·5, 3); ind the length of the line joining the two points and the direction-osines of the line.

7. The co-ordinates of two points are (7, 9, 11) and (3, 4, 5); find he length of line joining the points and the direction-cosines of the ne.

8. The polar co-ordinates of a point are $r=5$, $\theta=52°$, $\phi=70°$; nd the x-, y-, and z-co-ordinates.

9. The co-ordinates of two points A and B are as follows:

Point:	x	y	z
A	0·5″	0·8″	3·5″
B	2·4″	3·1″	1·2″

ind the length of the line AB and the cosines of the angles made y the line with the three axes.

10. Given $r=100$, $\theta=25°$, $\phi=70°$, find x, y, z.

11. The three rectangular co-ordinates of a point P are $x=1·5$, $=2·3$, $z=1·8$. Find the length of the line joining P to the origin nd the cosines of the angles which OP makes with the three axes.

12. The polar co-ordinates of a point are $r=20$, $\theta=32°$, $\phi=70°$. ind the rectangular co-ordinates.

13. A point P is 50 inches from the origin, the angles θ and ϕ ar 30° and 70° respectively; find the rectangular co-ordinates x, y, an z, and the angles made by the line joining P to the origin with th three axes.

In co-ordinate geometry on a plane:

14. Given $r=10$, $\theta=25°$, find x and y.

15. Given $x=3''$, $y=4''$, find r and θ.

16. Given $x=5$, $y=8$, find r and θ.

17. Given $r=100$, $\theta=15°$, find x and y.

18. Given $r=50$, $\theta=20°$, find x and y.

19. Show that $(x''-x')(y-y')=(y''-y')(x-x')$ is the equation o a straight line passing through two given points whose co-ordinate are (x', y'), (x'', y'').

20. Draw, on squared paper, the straight lines which pas through the following pairs of points:

(i) (2, 3) and (2, 4). (ii) (3, 4) and (5, 6). (iii) (3, 4) and (3, 5).
(iv) (1, 1) and $(-2, -2)$. (v) (a, b) and $(-a, -b)$.
(vi) (0, 1) and $(1, -1)$. (vii) (0, 1), (3, 8).

Show that the equations of the lines are:

(i) $x-2=0$. (ii) $y-x=1$. (iii) $x-3=0$. (iv) $y-x=0$.
(v) $bx-ay=0$. (vi) $y+2x=1$. (vii) $3y-7x=3$.

21. Show that double the area of the triangle formed by th lines joining the points (x', y'), (x'', y'') to the origin is given b $y'x''-y''x'$.

22. The rectangular co-ordinates of the two points P and Q ar (2, 3) and (6, 1) respectively. Prove that the area of the triangl POQ (O being the origin) is 8 sq. units.

23. Draw the following curves, given $a=4$ and $b=3$:

$$\frac{x^2}{a^2}+\frac{y^2}{b^2}=1\ ;\quad \frac{x^2}{a^2}+\frac{y^2}{a^2}=1\ ;$$

$$\frac{x^2}{a^2}-\frac{y^2}{b^2}=1\ ;\quad y^2=4a(x-a).$$

CHAPTER XII.

VECTORS.

Scalar quantities.—There are many quantities which can be fully represented by a number. Thus; time, mass, moment of inertia, area, volume, density, temperature, etc., are all examples of so-called **scalar quantities**, or, more shortly, **scalars**, to distinguish them from others called **vectors**, which involve direction as well as magnitude, such as forces, displacements, velocities, accelerations, etc.

In specifying a force, its direction, or sense, and point of application, must be given. The direction may be indicated by using the points of the compass E., W., N., or S., or some intermediate direction. To say that a vector acts in a vertical direction is not sufficiently definite; it must also be stated whether it acts in an upward or a downward direction.

In dealing with vectors in one plane and acting at a point, addition or subtraction may be carried out by calculation or graphically by using a parallelogram or triangle. By resolving a single vector horizontally and vertically two sides of a right-angled triangle are obtained, the hypotenuse giving the sum, or resultant, in magnitude and direction as in Fig 93.

When the given vectors are all in one plane, but do not act at a point, in addition to the polygon necessary to obtain the magnitude of the resultant, another polygon, called a **funicular** or **link-polygon**, is required to determine its position. In the general case three scalars are necessary. Thus, a vector may be represented in Cartesian co-ordinates by $x-x'$, $y-y'$, $z-z'$ (when one point is the origin this becomes the point x, y, z); or, in polar co-ordinates, by $r, \theta. \phi$.

Resolution of vectors.—Two vectors acting at a point can be replaced by a single vector which will produce the same effect. Thus, in Fig. 93, the two vectors A and B may be replaced by the vector C.

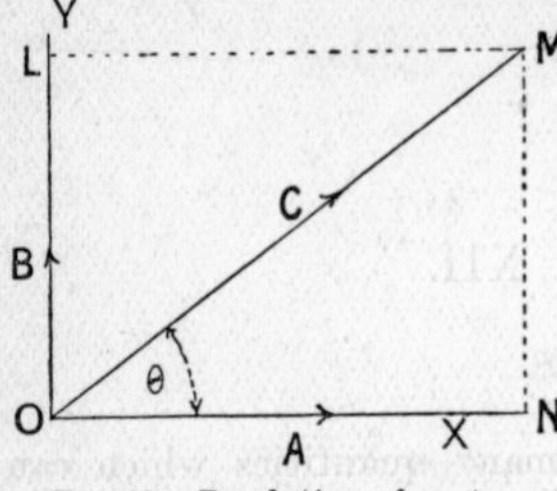

Fig. 93.—Resolution of vectors.

Conversely, we may replace a single vector by two vectors acting in different directions. The two directions usually taken are at right angles to each other.

Let OM (Fig. 93) represent in direction and magnitude a vector acting at the point O. Two lines OX, OY, at right angles to each other are drawn through O. From M, draw MN perpendicular to OX. Then ON is the resolved part of the vector C, in the direction OX.

If θ is the inclination of the vector C, then

$$ON = OM \cos \theta.$$

Similarly, if ML be drawn perpendicular to the axis Oy,

$$OL = OM \cos LOM$$
$$= OM \sin \theta.$$

Thus, we obtain two vectors $ON = A$, and $OL = B$, which, acting simultaneously, produce the same effect on the point O as the single vector OM.

This important relation may be stated as follows: **The resolved part of a vector in any given direction is equal to the magnitude of the vector multiplied by the cosine of the angle made by the vector with the given direction.**

The two vectors ON and OL are called the **rectangular components** of OM.

The process of replacing a vector by its **rectangular components** is called **resolving a vector.** The magnitudes of the components may be obtained by drawing the vector C to a convenient scale and measuring the components to the same scale. Or, the magnitudes may be readily obtained by calculation, using either a slide-rule or logarithms for the purpose.

Addition of vectors.—Let A and B (Fig. 94) be two vectors. Then, on the two vectors as sides, complete the parallelogram. The diagonal OD denotes the vector sum $A+B$.

Vector subtraction.—What is called vector subtraction may be performed in a manner similar to that adopted in addition; thus, the diagonal lm will represent $A-B$. This may be seen from Fig. 94, in which on is equal to ol, but in the reverse direction; hence, if $ol=B$, $on=-B$. op is the sum of om and on;

$$\therefore\ op=lm=A-B.$$

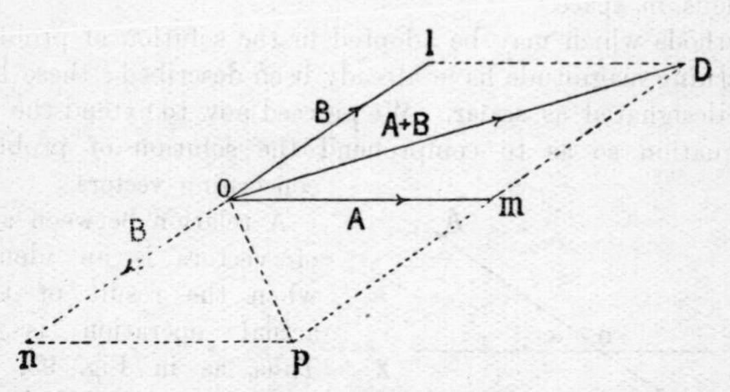

FIG. 94.—Addition of vectors.

In the preceding example $A-B$ may be written $A+(-B)$, or the vector B is added to A after a reversal of direction.

When several vectors act at a point, the sum, or resultant, of the first two can be combined with the third, etc. Or, better, set off a line denoting the magnitude and direction of the first; from the end of this line set off a line equal in magnitude and parallel in direction to the second. Proceeding in this manner, as many different sides of a polygon as there are given vectors are obtained. The magnitude and direction of the line joining the initial position to the final is the resultant in direction and magnitude. A vector equal in magnitude but reversed in sense will balance the given vectors; or, is the **equilibrant** of the given system of vectors. If the lines, drawn in the manner indicated, form a closed polygon, it follows that the given vectors have no resultant; or, in other words, the vector sum is zero. Thus, if the vectors denote displacements, the effect of carrying out the series of displacements is zero; or, the point having been displaced through the distances indicated by the sides of the polygon is brought back to the starting point. Similarly, if the vectors denote forces, the resultant force is zero, or the given vectors form a system of forces in equilibrium.

Vector equations.—So-called vector equations are for many purposes of the utmost importance, and it is necessary to become familiar with the notation usually adopted to specify a number of vectors acting either in one plane or in various positions in space.

Methods which may be adopted in the solution of problems concerning magnitude have already been described; these have been designated as **scalar.** We proceed now to extend the idea of equation so as to comprehend the solution of problems concerning **vectors.**

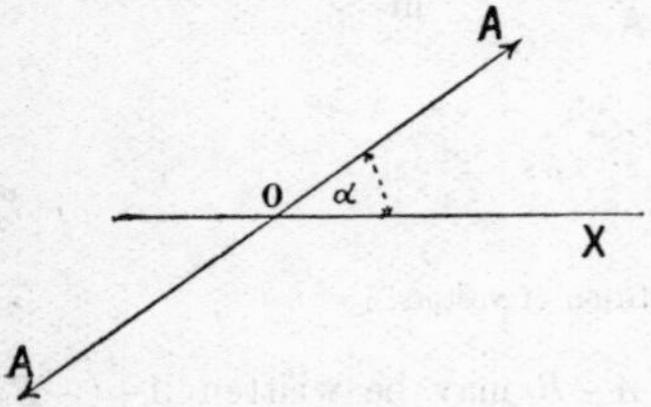

Fig. 95.

A relation between a set of vectors is an identity when the result of their actual operation is *nil.* Thus, as in Fig. 95, two equal forces acting in the same straight line at an angle α to the line OX may be written as $A_\alpha - A_\alpha = 0$,

$$\text{or} \quad A_\alpha + A_{180^\circ+\alpha} = 0.$$

Similarly, the sum of a vector A in a direction due E., and an equal vector in a direction due W., is zero; or,

$$A_0 + A_{180^\circ} = 0.$$

In like manner, the following results follow:

$$A_{0^\circ} + A_{120^\circ} + A_{240^\circ} = 0, \quad A_{90^\circ} + A_{180^\circ} + A_{270^\circ} = A_{180^\circ}.$$

The solution of a vector equation is therefore the process of finding a suitable value of R_θ (magnitude and direction). It is necessary to assume an initial line OX from which all angles are measured, the positive direction being anti-clockwise.

In many cases the solution of a given vector equation may be obtained by two or more methods, and one may be used as a check on the other.

Ex. 1. Solve the vector equation

$$R_\theta = A_0 + A_{60^\circ} - A_{240^\circ}.$$

The given vectors may be set out as in Fig. 96, in which $oa = A_0$, and ob denotes A_{60°. Also $-A_{240^\circ}$ denotes a vector such as $-bo = ob$, and as this is the same as A_{60°, the given system reduces to

$$R_\theta = A_0 + 2A_{60^\circ}.$$

If the parallelogram $oadb$ be completed on oa and ob as sides, then the resultant, R, is given in magnitude and direction by the diagonal od.

By calculation,

$$(od)^2 = A^2 + (2A)^2 - 4A^2 \cos 120^\circ$$
$$= 7A^2;$$
$$\therefore \; od = A\sqrt{7} = 2{\cdot}645A.$$

Let θ denote the angle aod.

Then

$$\frac{\sin\theta}{\sin 120^\circ} = \frac{2A}{A\sqrt{7}} = \frac{2}{\sqrt{7}};$$

$$\therefore \; \sin\theta = \frac{2}{\sqrt{7}} \times \frac{\sqrt{3}}{2} = \frac{\sqrt{21}}{7}$$
$$= 0{\cdot}6546;$$
$$\therefore \; \theta = 40^\circ \, 53'.$$

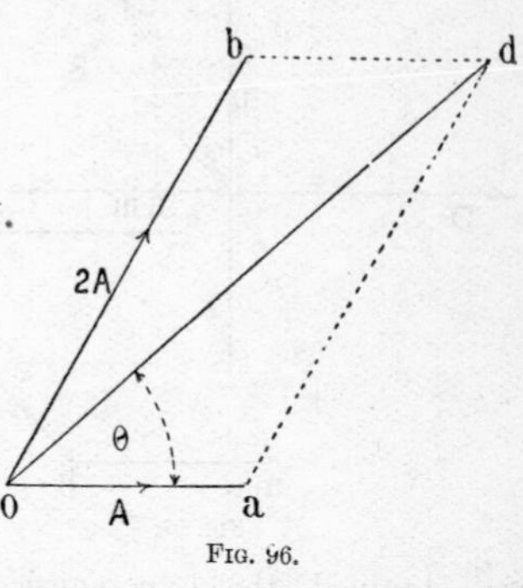

FIG. 96.

The result may also be obtained by the process of resolution of vectors, thus:

$$X = A + 2A \cos 60^\circ = 2A,$$
$$Y = 2A \sin 60^\circ = A\sqrt{3},$$
$$R = \sqrt{X^2 + Y^2} = A\sqrt{7} = 2{\cdot}645A,$$
$$\tan\theta = \frac{A\sqrt{3}}{2A} = \frac{\sqrt{3}}{2}; \quad \therefore \; \theta = 40^\circ \; 53'.$$

As already indicated, when several vectors are given acting at a point, the sum may be obtained by repeated applications of the parallelogram, or better by means of a polygon. Let A, B, C, D (Fig. 97) denote, in magnitude and direction, four vectors acting at a point O. To find the sum we may use the two given vectors as two adjacent sides of a parallelogram, the diagonal of which will give the sum $A + B$. Next, we may use the diagonal and the vector C as two sides of a new parallelogram; and obviously the sum of the given vectors can be obtained by successive applications. But a better method is to form a polygon as follows:—From a point *a* make *ab* on any convenient scale equal in magnitude and parallel in direction to vector *A*. Similarly, *bc* is made to represent the vector *B*, *cd* to represent vector *C*, and *de* to represent vector *D*. Then, the line *ae* to the same scale denotes the magnitude and direction of the sum of the four given vectors.

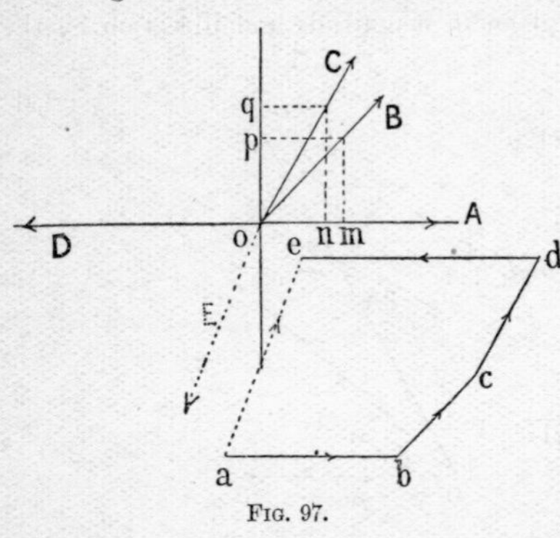

FIG. 97.

If a vector equal and parallel to *ea* were to act at *O*, then the sum of the five vectors

$$A+B+C+D+E$$

would be zero.

The sum may also be obtained by resolving the given vectors along and perpendicular to the line *OA*. In this manner two sides of a right-angled triangle are obtained, the hypotenuse of which is the resultant in direction and magnitude. Thus, let *om* and *on* be the resolved parts of the magnitudes of *B* and *C* in the direction *OA*, then by adding, $OA+om+on-OD$ gives the resolved part of the sum in a horizontal direction; this may be used as the base of a right-angled triangle, the perpendicular being the sum of the distances *op* and *oq*. The hypotenuse is the value of *R*, and the angle θ is the inclination of the hypotenuse to the base.

Ex. 2. The magnitudes of four given vectors acting at a point are $A=24$, $B=10$, $C=16$, $D=16$; the angle $AOB=30°$, $AOC=60°$. Find the sum.

If *R* denotes the sum, and θ its inclination to the horizon, the vector equation may be written

$$R_\theta = 24_{0°} + 10_{30°} + 16_{60°} + 16_{180°}.$$

As already described in Fig. 97, make *ab* equal to 24 on any convenient scale, also *bc*, *cd* and *de* equal to 10, 16 and 16 respectively.

Then R is numerically equal to the length ae, and θ is the angle eab. R is found to be 31, and $\theta=37^\circ\ 25'$.

The result is also readily obtained by calculation.

Sum of horizontal components

$$=24+10\cos 30^\circ+16\cos 60^\circ+16\cos 180^\circ$$

$$=24+8{\cdot}66+8-16=24{\cdot}66.$$

Sum of vertical components

$$=24\times 0+10\sin 30^\circ+16\sin 60^\circ+16\times 0$$

$$=5+13{\cdot}86=18{\cdot}86.$$

$$R=\sqrt{(24{\cdot}66)^2+(18{\cdot}86)^2}=31{\cdot}04,$$

$$\tan\theta=\frac{18{\cdot}86}{24{\cdot}66}=0{\cdot}7649;$$

$$\therefore\ \theta=37^\circ\ 25'.$$

Ex. 3. Three forces of 27, 52 and 49 lbs. respectively act at a point O; the angle $AOB=32^\circ$, the angle $AOC=58^\circ$. Find the resultant in direction or magnitude.

The equation may be written in the form

$$R_\theta=A_0+B_{32^\circ}+C_{58^\circ}.$$

Substituting the magnitudes of A, B, and C,

$$R_\theta=27_{0^\circ}+52_{32^\circ}+49_{58^\circ}.$$

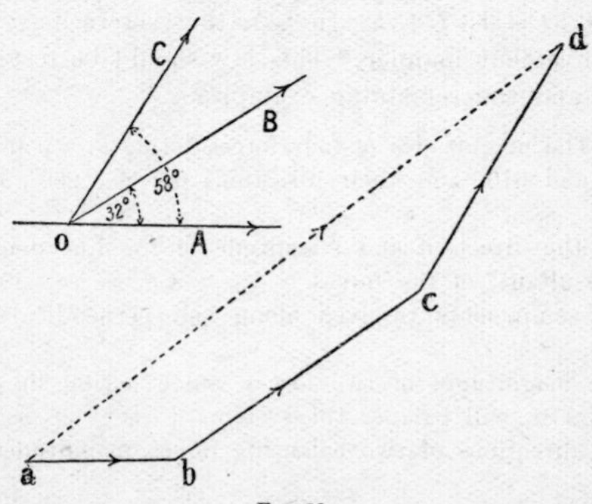

Fig. 98.

Draw ab (Fig. 98) equal and parallel to vector A, bc equal and parallel to B, and cd equal and parallel to vector C. Then, ad denotes the sum, or resultant, in direction and magnitude.

The magnitude and direction of the resultant may be obtained by calculation. The work may be arranged as follows:

Force.	Angle.	Horizontal Component.	Vertical Component.
27	0°	27	0
52	32°	$52 \cos 32° = 44{\cdot}096$	$52 \sin 32° = 27{\cdot}55$
49	58°	$49 \cos 58° = 25{\cdot}96$	$49 \sin 58° = 41{\cdot}55$
By addition,		97·06	69·10

$$R = \sqrt{(97{\cdot}06)^2 + (69{\cdot}10)^2} = \sqrt{14196}$$
$$= 119{\cdot}1,$$

$$\tan\theta = \frac{69{\cdot}10}{97{\cdot}06} = 0{\cdot}7119;$$
$$\therefore \theta = 35° \ 27'.$$

One of the most important theorems with regard to vectors is—**that a vector sum is the same in whatever sequence the vectors are added.** Thus, if A, B, and C, are three vectors, then it is easy to show either analytically or by graphical construction that $A+B+C=A+C+B$. In fact, the vectors may be added in any convenient manner. This law should be tested in the preceding and the remaining examples.

Ex. 4. The magnitudes of four forces acting at a point are 835, 400, 650, and 610, and their directions 0°, 58°, 260°, and -23° (Fig. 99).

Find (i) the direction and magnitude of the line denoting the sum, or resultant, of the forces.

(ii) The components resolved along and perpendicular to the initial line.

(iii) The magnitudes of two forces which acting in directions at 70° and 170° will balance the system.

(iv) The directions of two balancing forces, magnitudes 500 and 700.

(i) The vector equation may be written

$$R_\theta = 835_{0°} + 400_{58°} + 650_{260°} + 610_{-23°}.$$

Graphically, make ab on a convenient scale equal to vector A, *i.e.* equal to 835 and horizontal; make bc parallel to vector B

(Fig. 99), and equal to 400. Similarly, *cd* is made equal and parallel to vector C, and *de* equal and parallel to vector D. Then, the resultant is the line joining *a* the initial, to *e* the final point; the inclination of the line *ae* to the horizon is the required inclination of the line denoting the sum.

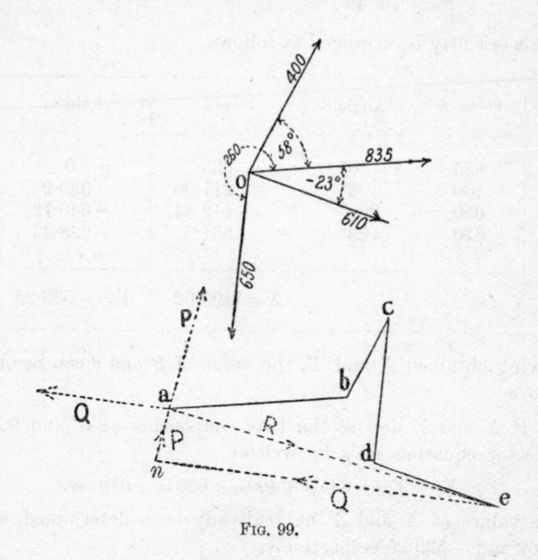

Fig. 99.

Or, the sum of the projections on the axes of x and y could be obtained and made to form two sides of a right-angled triangle; the sum of the given vectors is the hypotenuse of the triangle.

Let X denote the sum of the projections on the axis of x.

Then, $X = 835 \cos 0° + 400 \cos 58° - 650 \cos 80° + 610 \cos 23°$

$= 835 + 400 \times 0{\cdot}5299 - 650 \times 0{\cdot}1736 + 610 \times 0{\cdot}9205$

$= 835 + 211{\cdot}96 - 112{\cdot}84 + 561{\cdot}5$

$= 1495{\cdot}62.$

Similarly, $Y = 400 \sin 58° - 650 \sin 80° - 610 \sin 23°$

$= 400 \times 0{\cdot}848 - 650 \times 0{\cdot}9848 - 610 \times 0{\cdot}3907$

$= 339{\cdot}2 - 640{\cdot}12 - 238{\cdot}33$

$= -539{\cdot}25;$

$$\therefore\ R=\sqrt{(1495{\cdot}62)^2+(-539{\cdot}25)^2}=\sqrt{2527679{\cdot}7469}$$
$$=1589{\cdot}87,$$
$$\tan\theta=\frac{Y}{X}=\frac{-539{\cdot}25}{1495{\cdot}62}=-0{\cdot}3602,$$
$$\theta=-19^\circ\ 49'.$$

The work may be arranged as follows:

Force P.	Angle.	$P\cos a$.	$P\sin a$.
835	0°	835	0
400	58°	211·96	339·2
650	260°	−112·84	−640·12
610	−23°	561·5	−238·33
		$X=1495{\cdot}62$	$Y=-539{\cdot}25$

Having obtained X and Y, the value of R and θ can be obtained as above.

(ii) If X and Y denote the two components at 0° and 90°, then the vector equation may be written

$$X_{0^\circ}+Y_{90^\circ}=835^\circ{}_{0^\circ}+400_{58^\circ}+650_{260^\circ}+610_{-23^\circ}.$$

The values of X and Y have already been determined, and are 1495·62 and −539·25 respectively.

(iii) The inclination of the resultant may be stated as −19° 49′, or 360° − 19° 49′ = 340° 11′. The three forces keeping equilibrium are as indicated in Fig. 99. Hence, set off ae equal and parallel to R. Draw a line en parallel to Q, and a line an parallel to P, intersecting the former in n; then, aen is the triangle of forces required, and the magnitudes of P and Q can be measured to the scale on which ae is equal to R.

It will be seen that the triangle aen in Fig. 99 which is used to determine the magnitudes of P and Q, could be drawn as a separate diagram.

(iv) The directions are obtained by using a triangle of forces; *i.e.* from a and e as centres, and with radii 500, and 700, respectively, describe arcs of circles; then the triangle of forces is obtained, and from this the inclinations may be found.

Some vectors, such as displacements, velocities, accelerations, etc., may be represented by a line, or any parallel line may be used. Such vectors may be called **free vectors**, to distinguish them from other vectors such as **forces**, in which the vectors are localised in a line, and are only free to move in the direction of the length of the line.

Link polygon.—In the preceding example the given vectors have been assumed to act at a point, when this is not the case, it is necessary to obtain the *position* of the resultant, in addition to its magnitude and direction. For this purpose what is called a **funicular** or **link polygon** is used.

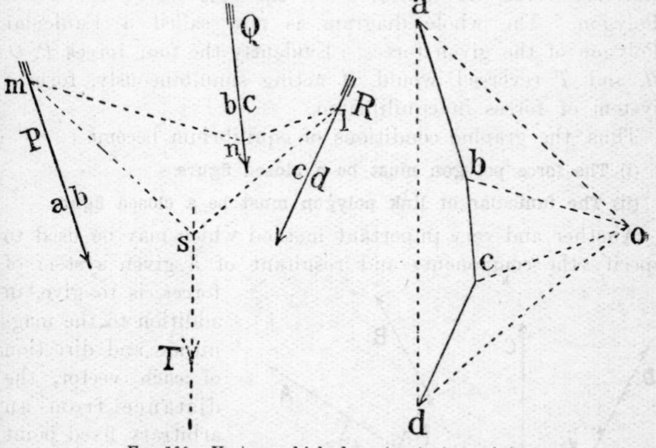

FIG. 100.—Vectors which do not act at a point.

Given three forces P, Q, and R, which, acting at different points on a rigid body, do not meet at the same point when produced, to find the *resultant* and also its *point of application*.

Instead of denoting a force by a single letter, a very convenient and simple notation is to put a letter on each side of a force, the second letter b for any force P being carried to the first side of the next force Q, thus, in Fig. 100, the force P may be denoted by the letters ab, Q by bc, and R by cd.

In Fig. 100, called the **force polygon**, ab, bc, and cd, are drawn parallel to, and containing as many units of length as there are units of force in P, Q, R, respectively; the resultant is given in direction and magnitude by the line joining a to d. But this *does not* determine its position. To find the *position* or *point of its application*, we choose any point o and draw radiating lines from o to a, b, c, d.

In the space b of the original diagram of forces, at any point m of P draw a line mn parallel to ob intersecting the line of action of the force Q at n. In the space c draw a line nl parallel to oc intersecting the force R at l. Finally, draw lines ls, ms parallel to od and oa respectively, intersecting at s. This determines a point on the resultant whose direction and magnitude are indicated by the side ad of the Force Polygon. The whole diagram is now called a Funicular Polygon of the given forces. Evidently the four forces P, Q, R, and T reversed, would, if acting simultaneously, form a system of forces in equilibrium.

Thus, the graphic conditions of equilibrium become

(i) The force polygon must be a closed figure.

(ii) The funicular or link polygon must be a closed figure.

Another and very important method which may be used to specify the components and resultant of a given system of forces, is to give, in addition to the magnitude and direction of each vector, the distance from an arbitrary fixed point to the point of intersection of the line denoting a given vector with a horizontal line passing through the point. This is called the **intercept** of the vector.

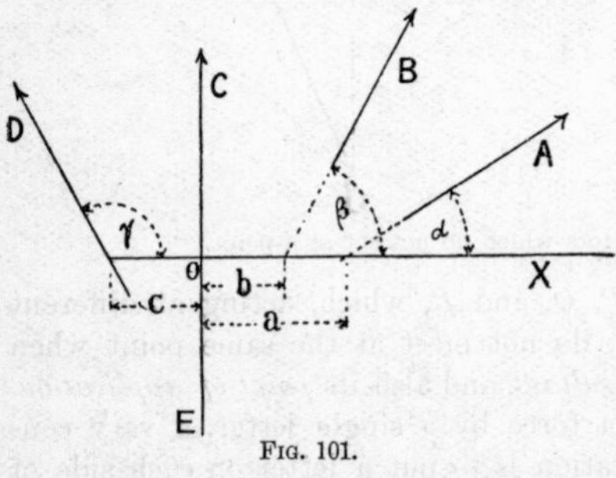

Fig. 101.

Thus, let $ABCDE$ (Fig. 101) be five given vectors in one plane. O is any convenient arbitrary point, and OX a horizontal line passing through O. The distances, a, b, c, of the points, where the lines denoting the vectors intersect the line OX, are called the *intercepts* of A, B, and D. Thus, the vector A is completely specified by its intercept a, its inclination α, and its sense, indicated by an arrow-head on the line denoting the vector.

In a similar manner, the vector B is specified by its inclination β, its intercept b, and its sense. The vectors C and E pass through the origin and the intercept is zero. In the case of the vector D the intercept is negative or $-d$.

Hence, if R, r, and θ, denote the resultant, its intercept and inclination to OX respectively, then the vector equation may be written

$$_rR_\theta = {}_aA_\alpha + {}_bB_\beta + {}_0C_{90^\circ} + {}_{-c}D_\gamma + {}_0E_{270^\circ}.$$

If all the given vectors act at a point the preceding equation becomes:
$$R_\theta = A_\alpha + B_\beta + C_\gamma + \ldots.$$

Ex. 5. Five vertical forces A, B, C, D, E, are as follows:

	A	B	C	D	E
Magnitude in tons,	1·85	3·2	3·2	2·7	3·8
Angle, - - -	270°	90°	270°	270°	90°
Intercept (feet), -	0	4·2	8·2	11·5	16·2

(i) Find the sum of $A+B+C+D+E={}_rR_\theta$.
(ii) " " $C+D+E={}_sS_\phi$.

R is found to be 0·75 tons, $\theta=270^\circ$, $r=23{\cdot}6$ ft.

The vector equation is

$$_rR_\theta = {}_01{\cdot}85_{270^\circ} + {}_{4\cdot2}3{\cdot}2_{90^\circ} + {}_{8\cdot2}3{\cdot}2_{270^\circ} + {}_{11\cdot5}2{\cdot}7_{270^\circ} + {}_{16\cdot2}3{\cdot}8_{90^\circ}.$$

The given vectors form a system of parallel forces, the sum of the upward components is $3{\cdot}2+3{\cdot}8=7{\cdot}0$, and of the downward components is $1{\cdot}85+3{\cdot}2+2{\cdot}7=7{\cdot}75$; hence the resultant is $-0{\cdot}75$, and its direction 270°.

To find the position of the resultant it is only necessary to take moments about any convenient point such as O. Then, if $\bar{x}$ denote the distance of R from O,

$$\bar{x}\times(-0{\cdot}75) = -3{\cdot}2\times4{\cdot}2+3{\cdot}2\times8{\cdot}2+2{\cdot}7\times11{\cdot}5-3{\cdot}8\times16{\cdot}2$$
$$= -17{\cdot}71;$$
$$\therefore\ x = \frac{17{\cdot}71}{0{\cdot}75} = 23{\cdot}61.$$

Ex. 6. In the preceding example, if M and N are two points, such that M is -4 and N is 6 feet, respectively, show that the vertical forces, which acting through M and N will balance the given forces, are 2·071 and 1·321, the former at 90°, the latter at 270°.

Ex. 7. Eight gallons of water per second flow through a pipe 6 inches diam. in which there is a right-angled bend; what is the resultant force exerted by the water on the pipe at the bend, neglecting friction?

What is the change in the velocity of the water (that is the *vector* change)? Find the change in the momentum of the water and the resultant force exerted at the bend (1 gallon of water $=0·1605$ cub. ft.).

Volume which passes in a second is $8 \times 0·1605 \times 1728$ cub. in.

$$\text{Speed} = \frac{8 \times 0·1605 \times 1728}{\pi \times 3^2 \times 12} = 6·539 \text{ ft. per sec.}$$

Eight gallons $= 10 \times 8 = 80$ lb.

$$\text{Mass} = \frac{80}{32·2} \text{ lb.}$$

The resultant of two equal forces each equal to $A = A\sqrt{2}$.

$$\therefore \text{ change of momentum per sec.} = \frac{80 \times \sqrt{2}}{32·2} \times 6·539 = 22·97;$$

$$\therefore \text{ resultant force at bend} = 22·97 \text{ lb.}$$

Product of two vectors.—The **scalar product** of two vectors is **the product of the scalars of the vectors multiplied by the cosine of the angle between them.** The **vector product** may be defined as **the product of the scalars of the vectors multiplied by the sine of the angle between them. Its direction is perpendicular to the plane of the vectors.** The simplest example of the former occurs in the case of the product of a force and a displacement. If, as in Fig. 102, the force F is inclined at an angle θ to the direction in which displacement occurs, then the effective part of F, so far as translation is concerned, is the resolved part of F. Thus, set off OL to represent the force, and draw LN perpendicular to OM; then ON is the resolved part of F in the direction OM; but $ON = OL \cos \theta = F \cos \theta$.

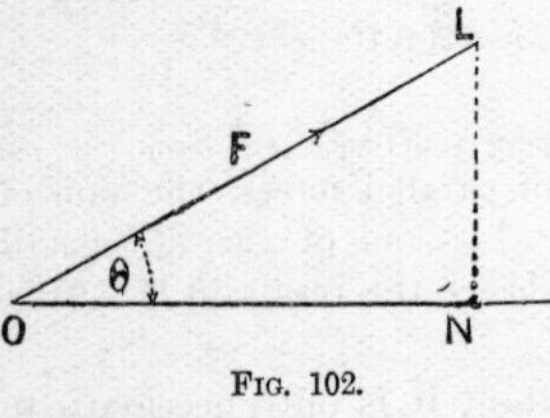

FIG. 102.

Hence, the product of the two vectors, or work done by the force, is $Fd\cos\theta$, ...(i)
where d denotes the displacement.

When the angle is 0°, *i.e.* when the direction of the force and the displacement are coincident, since $\cos 0°=1$, the product is $F\times d$.

When $\theta=90°$ the force F has no component in the direction of motion, and the work done by F is zero. For any inclination 90° to 180°, the resolved part of F acts in a negative direction, and the work done by F would be in the nature of a resistance or retardation. This would obviously have its maximum value when $\theta=180°$.

Eq. (i) may be expressed in words as follows:

Project one vector on the other, the product of the vector and the projection is the scalar product required. Or, multiply the numerical magnitudes of the two vectors by the cosine of the angle between them.

From Eq. (i) it follows that the product of two unit vectors such as unit force and unit displacement, is $\cos\theta$. In any diagram, when two vectors are shown acting at a point, care must be taken that the arrow-heads denoting the *sense* of each vector are made to go in a direction outwards from the point. When this is done, θ is the angle between the vectors.

Ex. 8. The direction of the rails of a tramway is due N., and a force A of 300 lbs. in a direction 60° N. of E. acts on the car. Find the work done by the force during a displacement of 100 ft.

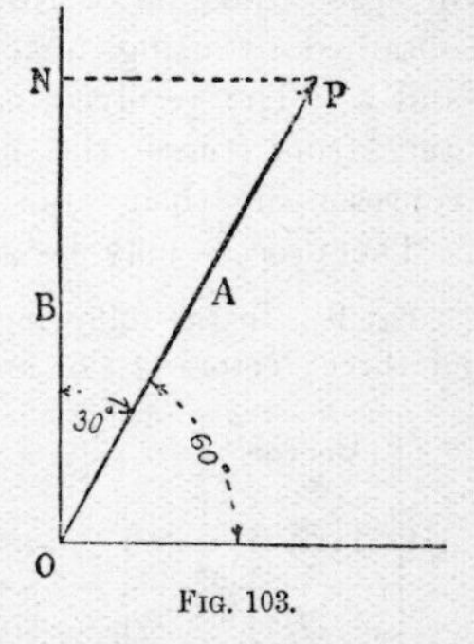

Fig. 103.

If θ denote the angle between the direction of the force A and the direction of the displacement ON, then the resolved part of A in the direction ON is $A\cos\theta$.

The product of a force, or the resolved part of a force, and its displacement, or distance moved through, is the work done by the force. Thus, in Fig. 103, if B denote the displacement of the car, then the work done is $AB\cos\theta$. ....(i)

As A is 300, $B=100$, and $\theta=30°$,

$$AB\cos 30° = 300 \times 100 \times 0\cdot866 = 25980 \text{ ft.-lbs.}$$

Observe by way of verification that if θ be 0°, then $\cos 0°=1$; the force A is acting in the direction ON, and hence

$$\text{work done} = 300 \times 100 = 30{,}000 \text{ ft.-lbs.}$$

When θ is 90°, then $\cos 90°=0$;

$$\therefore \text{ work done} = 0.$$

This latter result is obvious from the fact that, when the angle is 90°, the force is in a direction at right angles to the direction of motion, and hence no work is done by the force. Again, if the direction of the force were South, then negative work equal to $-300 \times 100 = -30000$ ft.-lbs. would be done.

The vector product is the product of the magnitudes of the two vectors and the sine of the included angle; thus, if θ denote the angle between the two vectors,

$$\text{vector product} = AB\sin\theta. \quad \text{.....................(i)}$$

If the two vectors are at right angles

$$\sin 90° = 1 \text{ and Eq. (i) gives } AB.$$

Vector products are of importance in "couples," etc.

The general case.—In the preceding examples the given vectors have been taken to act in one plane. In the general case, in which the vectors may act in any specified directions in space, the sum or resultant of a number of vectors may be obtained by using, instead of two, the three co-ordinates, x, y, and z. The resolved parts of each vector may be obtained, and from these the magnitude and direction of the line representing their sum.

The process may be seen from the following example:

Ex. 9. In the following table r denotes the magnitudes of each of three vectors A, B, and C, and α and β the angles made by

Vector.	r.	α.	β.	θ.	x.	y.	z.
A	50	45°	60°	60°	35·35	25	25
B	20	30°	100°	62° 2′	17·31	−3·472	9·38
C	10	120°	45°	60°	−5	7·071	5

each vector with the axes of x and y respectively. Find for each vector the values of θ (where θ denotes the inclination to the axis of z), x, y, and z, and tabulate as shown.

From the given values of α and β the value of θ can be calculated from the relation

$$\cos^2\alpha + \cos^2\beta + \cos^2\theta = 1.$$

Thus, for vector A, we have

$$\cos^2\theta = 1 - \cos^2\alpha - \cos^2\beta = 1 - \tfrac{1}{2} - \tfrac{1}{4} = \tfrac{1}{4};$$

$$\therefore \cos\theta = \tfrac{1}{2} \text{ and } \theta = 60°.$$

Similarly, for B,

$$\cos^2\theta = 1 - (0·866)^2 - (0·1736)^2 = 0·22; \quad \therefore \theta = 62°\ 2'.$$

And, for C,

$$\cos^2\theta = 1 - \tfrac{1}{4} - \tfrac{1}{2} = \tfrac{1}{4}; \quad \therefore \theta = 60°.$$

To obtain the projections x, y, and z of each vector, we use the relations $x = r\cos\alpha,\quad y = r\cos\beta,\quad z = r\cos\theta.$

Thus, for vector A,

$$r = 50°,\quad \alpha = 45°,\ \beta \text{ and } \theta \text{ are each } 60°;$$

$$\therefore x = 50\cos 45° = 50 \times 0·7071 = 35·35,$$

$$y = 50\cos 60° = 50 \times 0·50 = 25,$$

$$z = 50\cos 60° = 25.$$

For vector B,

$$x = 20\cos 30° = 17·32,\quad y = -20\cos 80° = -3·472,$$

$$z = 20\cos 62°\ 2' = 9·38.$$

For C, $\quad x = -10\cos 60° = -5,\quad y = 10\cos 45° = 7·071,$

$$z = 10\cos 60° = 5.$$

Adding all the terms in column x and denoting the sum by Σx,

$$\Sigma x = 35·35 + 17·32 - 5 = 47·67.$$

Similarly, $\quad \Sigma y = 25 - 3·472 + 7·071 = 28·6,$

and $\quad \Sigma z = 25 + 9·38 + 5 = 39·38.$

Hence the resultant of the three vectors is

$$A + B + C = \sqrt{(47·67)^2 + (28·6)^2 + (39·38)^2} = 68·1.$$

To find the angles made by the resultant vector with the three axes we have

$$\cos\alpha = \frac{47·67}{68·1} = 0·7000; \quad \therefore \alpha = 45°\ 35'.$$

$$\cos\beta = \frac{28·6}{68·1} = 0·4201; \quad \therefore \beta = 65°\ 10'.$$

$$\cos\theta = \frac{39·38}{68·1} = 0·5784; \quad \therefore \theta = 54°\ 40'.$$

Vector algebra.—Many algebraical and trigonometrical relations may be obtained by using vector notation.

Let A and B (Fig. 104) denote two vectors acting at a point O, and let θ denote the angle between A and B.

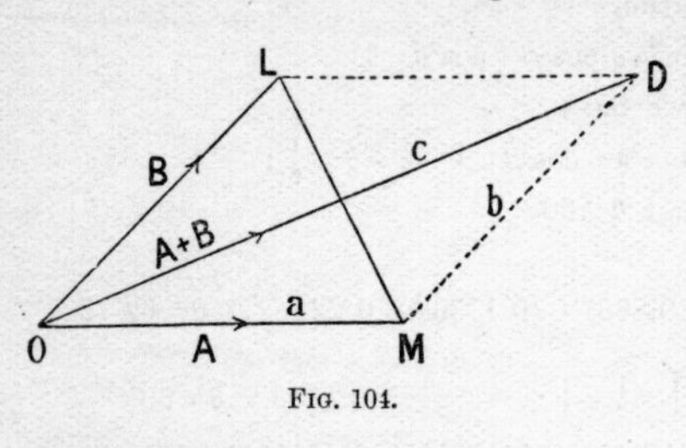

FIG. 104.

The diagonal of the parallelogram, on the two vectors as sides, is denoted by the sum $A+B$. Let the sides OM, MD, be denoted by a and b respectively, and the diagonal OD by c, and LM by d.

Then $(A+B)^2=A^2+2AB+B^2$.

$A^2=A\times A$ because the included angle is 0°.

Similarly, $B\times B=B^2$.

But, if a and b denote the magnitudes of A and B respectively, then $2AB=2ab\cos\theta$.

$$\therefore\ c^2=(A+B)^2=A^2+2AB+B^2=a^2+2ab\cos\theta+b^2.$$

Similarly,

$$\therefore\ d^2=(A-B)^2=A^2-2AB+B^2=a^2-2ab\cos\theta+b^2.$$

In a similar manner we obtain

$$(A+B)(A-B)=A^2-B^2,\quad\text{or}\quad cd\cos\alpha=a^2-b^2\ ;$$

$$(A+B)^2+(A-B)^2=2(A^2+B^2),\ \text{or}\ c^2+d^2=2(a^2+b^2)\ ;$$

$$(A+B)^2-(A-B)^2=4AB,\qquad\text{or}\qquad c^2-d^2=4ab\cos\theta.$$

Again, if the vectors A, B, C represent the sides of a triangle taken in order, $\therefore\ A+B+C=0.$

Let a, b, c, denote the three sides, and α, β, γ, the opposite angles, then,

$$(-A)^2=(B+C)^2,\ \text{or}\ a^2=b^2+c^2-2bc\cos\gamma;$$

$$(A+B+C)^2=0,\ \text{or}\ a^2+b^2+c^2-2(ab\cos\gamma+bc\cos\alpha+ca\cos\beta)=0.$$

The notation may easily be extended to the case of a plane quadrilateral figure, or a rectangular prism.

Ex. 10. Expand and interpret the following vector equation,

$$D^2=(A+B+C)^2,$$

(*a*) when applied to a plane quadrilateral,

(*b*) when applied to a parallelepiped.

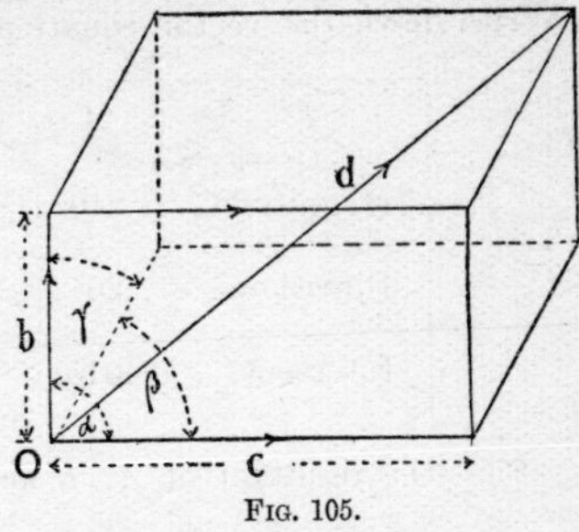

Fig. 105.

Let a, b, c respectively denote the magnitudes of three edges of a parallelopiped meeting at O (Fig. 105), and α, β, γ signify the internal angles between the sides bc, ca, ab.

In (*a*) we obtain

$$d^2=a^2+b^2+c^2-2ab\cos\gamma-2ac\cos\beta-2bc\cos\alpha,$$

or the square on the diagonal of a quadrilateral is given in terms of the three edges which it meets and their inclination to one another.

(*b*) $$d^2=a^2+b^2+c^2+2ab\cos\gamma+2bc\cos\beta+2ac\cos\alpha,$$

or, the square of a diagonal is given in terms of the lengths of the sides and the magnitudes of the included angles.

EXERCISES. XXVIII.

1. The following four forces act in one plane. Determine the resultant, and measure its magnitude, direction and intercept.

	A	B	C	D
Magnitude,	29	18	27	19
Direction,	32°	105°	172°	258°
Intercept,	2·5	1·8	0·5	−0·4

2. The following three vectors A, B, C act at a point; determine the vector sums $A+B+C$ and $A-B+C$, also the direction in each case.

	A	B	C
Magnitude,	37·2	59·5	88·0
Direction,	23°·6	115°·5	238°·0

Verify by construction that $A-(B-C)=A-B+C$. Use a scale of ½ inch to 10 units.

3. Given the following system of coplanar forces, by means of vector and link polygon determine the resultant of the system. Write down the vector equation.

	A	B	C	D	E
Magnitude,	210	185	313	125	167
Direction,	20°	71°	123°	190°	260°
Intercept,	2·15	1·3	4·6	0	5·5

Find the resultant of A, B and D.

4. Three vectors A, B, C, acting in a horizontal plane, are defined in the following table.

Find the vector sum $A+B+C$; show that $A+B+C=A+C+B$.

	A	B	C
Magnitude,	1·23	1·95	2·60
Direction,	E	33°·2 N. of E.	112° N. of E.

5. A ship A is sailing at 8·7 knots to the east, and a second ship B at 3·4 knots to the south-west. Find the velocity of B relatively to A.

6. Suppose the wind to be blowing at 5 knots from the north. Find the directions which wind vanes would take if carried by the two ships in the preceding exercise.

7. A ship is sailing eastwards at 10 miles an hour. It carries an instrument for recording the apparent velocity of the wind, in both magnitude and direction.

(*a*) If the wind registered by the instrument is apparently one of 20 miles per hour from the north-east, what is the actual wind? Give the answer in miles per hour and degrees north of east of the quarter from which the wind comes.

(*b*) If a wind of 15 miles per hour from the north-east were actually blowing, what apparent wind would the instrument on the vessel register? State this answer in miles per hour and degrees north of east as before.

Use a scale of $\frac{1}{4}$ inch to 1 mile per hour.

8. If three vectors A, B, C are represented by the sides of a triangle taken in order and sense $\therefore (A+B+C)^2=0$ obtain trigonometrical formulae by expanding the following equations:

$$(-A)^2=(B+C)^2,\ (A+B+C)^2.$$

Use a, b, c for the three sides, and α, β, γ for the opposite angles.

9. A ship is sailing at 8·7 knots through water apparently to the east, but there is an ocean current of 3·4 knots to the south-west. Find the actual velocity of the ship as regards the ocean bed.

10. A cyclist rides at 10 miles per hour in a direction due north. Find the apparent direction of the wind which the rider experiences when the actual velocity and direction of the wind is as follows:

(*a*) 10 miles from E. (*b*) 10 miles from N.E.
(*c*) 10 ,, ,, N. (*d*) 10 ,, ,, N.W.
(*e*) 10 ,, ,, S.

11. Show that $A_{0^\circ}+A_{120^\circ}+A_{240^\circ}=0$.

12. $A_{90^\circ}+A_{180^\circ}+A_{270^\circ}=A_{180^\circ}$.

13. $A_{0^\circ}+A_{60^\circ}+A_{60^\circ}=2{\cdot}645A_{40^\circ\ 53'}$.

Solve the vector equations:

14. $R_\theta=10_{0^\circ}-14_{30^\circ}+30_{160^\circ}$. Find R and θ.

15. $A_{60^\circ}+B_{310^\circ}+10_{0^\circ}-14_{30^\circ}+30_{160^\circ}=0$. Find A and B.

16. $16_\alpha+25_\beta+10_{0^\circ}-14_{30^\circ}+30_{160^\circ}=0$. Find α and β.

17. $C_{140^\circ}+27_\gamma+10_{0^\circ}-14_{30^\circ}+30_{160^\circ}=0$. Find C and γ.

18. Given the following five vectors:

	A	B	C	D	E
Magnitude, -	20	12	6·8	3·3	15·5
Direction, -	0°	75°	310°	225°	120°

Determine, by constructions, the following vector sums and differences:

(*a*) $A+B+C+D+E$, (*b*) $A+B+E+D+C$,

(*c*) $A+B-C+D-E$, (*d*) $A+B-E+D-C$.

19. If a vessel steams due N. against a N.E. wind, show in a diagram the direction in which the smoke leaves the funnel.

20. Find A and α in the following vector equation, that is, add the three given vectors, which are all in the plane of the paper.

$$A_{\alpha}=3{\cdot}7_{30^\circ}+1{\cdot}4_{82^\circ}+2{\cdot}6_{157^\circ}.$$

21. Find B and β from the equation

$$B_{\beta}=3{\cdot}7_{30^\circ}-1{\cdot}4_{82^\circ}+2{\cdot}6_{157^\circ}.$$

Use a scale 1 inch to 1 unit.

22. Find the resultant or vector sum, that is, find A and α from the vector equation

$$A_{\alpha}=26_{35^\circ}+37_{115^\circ}+41_{230^\circ}.$$

Use a scale of 1 inch to 10 lbs.

23. Verify by construction that

$$26_{35^\circ}+37_{115^\circ}+41_{230^\circ}=26_{35^\circ}+41_{230^\circ}+37_{115^\circ}.$$

24. A mass of 10 lbs. has a velocity of $1{\cdot}3_{15^\circ}$ ft. per sec. It receives a blow which changes its velocity into one of $0{\cdot}8_{100^\circ}$ ft. per sec. What change in the velocity and in the momentum is produced?

25. A point G moves in a straight line. Successive positions of G, measured from a point O in the line at interval of $\frac{1}{40}$ second, are given in the following table:

Distance of G (feet), -	0·038	0·302	0·515	0·600	0·515
Time t (seconds), - -	0·0	0·025	0·05	0·075	0·1

Determine successive values of the velocity and acceleration of G. Draw curves showing velocity and time, and acceleration and time. Read off the velocity and acceleration when $t=0{\cdot}05$ second.

Find R and θ in the following equation:

26. $R_{\theta}=20_{0^\circ}+12_{75^\circ}-15{\cdot}5_{120^\circ}+3{\cdot}3_{225^\circ}-6{\cdot}8_{310^\circ}$.

27. A force acts on a tram-car moving with velocity B. Find $A\times B$ the activity or power in the following cases:

	A	B
(a)	300 lbs. E.	20 ft. per sec. E.
(b)	250 lbs. N.E.	15 ,, ,, ,,
(c)	200 lbs. N.	20 ,, ,, ,,
(d)	150 lbs. S.W.	10 ,, ,, ,,

28. Solve the vector equation

$$A_{60^\circ}+B_{310^\circ}+10_{0^\circ}-15_{30^\circ}+30_{160^\circ}=0.$$

29. There are three vectors in a horizontal plane:

A of amount 1·5 towards the south-east.

B of amount 3·9 in the direction towards 20° west of south.

C of amount 2·7 towards the north.

(*a*) Find the vector sums $A+B+C$, (*b*) $A-B+C$, (*c*) $B-C$, (*d*) find the scalar products $A \cdot B$ and $A \cdot C$.

30. Values of three vectors acting at a point are given in the following table. Find in each case the value of θ, the magnitudes the angles made with the three axes of the line representing the sum of the three vectors.

	r	a	β
A	60	70°	37°
B	50	150°	84°
C	30	85°	170°

31. Water is flowing at 10 feet per second along a pipe having a right-angled bend. What is the vector change of velocity at the bend?

32. A boat is moving at the rate of 10 miles per hour in a direction 35° E of N. At what rate is it moving east and north.

33. Show from the definition of a vector product (p. 256) that the vector product $5_{40^\circ} \times 7_{120^\circ}$ is $5 \times 7 \sin(120^\circ - 40^\circ) = 35 \sin 80^\circ = 34{\cdot}47$, in a direction perpendicular to the plane of the vectors.

34. The magnitude and direction of the force F per unit length experienced by a straight wire placed in a magnetic field, of intensity M lines per square centimetre, is given by $F = \frac{1}{10} CM \sin\theta$, where C denotes the magnitude of the current (in amperes) in the wire, and θ the angle its direction makes with the magnetic field.

Given $C=4$ amperes, $M=6000$ lines per square centimetre, $\theta=55^\circ$, find F.

CHAPTER XIII.

PROGRESSIONS. BINOMIAL THEOREM. ZERO AND INFINITY.

Series.—The term **series** is applied to any expression in which every term is formed according to some common law.

Thus, in the series 1, 3, 5, 7 ... each term is formed by *adding* 2 to the preceding term. In 1, 2, 4, 8 ... each term is formed by *multiplying* the preceding term by 2.

Usually a few terms only are given, these being sufficient to indicate the law which will produce the given terms.

The first series is called an **arithmetical progression,** the constant quantity which is added to each term to produce the next is called the **common difference.** The letters A.P. are usually used to designate such a series.

The second series is called a **geometrical progression,** the constant quotient obtained by dividing any term by the preceding term is called the **common ratio** or *constant factor* of the series. The letters G.P. are used to denote a geometrical progression.

Arithmetical Progression.—A series is said to be an arithmetical progression when any term is formed by adding the same quantity (which may be positive or negative), to the preceding term.

Thus, the series 1, 2, 3, 4 ... is an arithmetical series, the constant difference, obtained by subtracting from any term the preceding term, is unity.

In a series 21, 18, 15, ... the constant difference is -3.

Again in a, $a+d$, $a+2d$, ... and a, $a-d$, $a-2d$, ... the first increases and the second diminishes by a common difference d.

In writing such a series, it will be obvious that if a is the first term, $a+d$ the second, $a+2d$ the third, etc., any term such as the seventh is the first term a together with the addition of d repeated $(7-1)$ times, or is $a+6d$.

If l denotes the last term, and n the number of terms, then

$$l=a+(n-1)d \qquad \text{(i)}$$

Let S denote the sum of n terms, then

$$S=a+(a+d)+(a+2d)+\ldots+(l-2d)+(l-d)+l.$$

Writing the series in the reverse order we obtain

$$S=l+(l-d)+(l-2d)+\ldots(a+2d)+(a+d)+a.$$

Adding we obtain

$$2S=(a+l)+(a+l)+\ldots \text{ to } n \text{ terms}$$

$$=n(a+l);$$

$$\therefore\ S=\frac{n}{2}(a+l) \qquad \text{(ii)}$$

From this equation, when a and l are known, the sum of n terms can be obtained.

Again, substituting in (ii) the value of l from Eq. (i), we obtain

$$S=\frac{n}{2}\{2a+(n-1)d\} \qquad \text{(iii)}$$

Giving the sum of n terms when the first term and the common differences are known.

Arithmetical Mean.—If a, A, and b form three quantities in arithmetical progression, then

$$A-a=b-A;$$

$$\therefore\ A=\frac{a+b}{2};$$

or, *the arithmetical mean of two quantities is one-half their sum.*

Ex. 1. The first term of an arithmetical progression is 3, the third term is 9. What is the sum of 20 terms?

From (i) above, $9=3+2d;$

$$\therefore\ d=3.$$

$$S=\tfrac{20}{2}\{6+(20-1)3\}$$

$$=630.$$

Ex. 2. The sum of three numbers in arithmetical progression is 21, and their product is 315. Find the three numbers.

Let $a-d$, a, and $a+d$ denote the three numbers.

$$\therefore\ (a-d)+a+(a+d)=21;$$
$$\therefore\ 3a=21,$$
$$a=7.$$

The product of the three terms is

$$a(a^2-d^2)=315;$$
$$\therefore\ 7(7^2-d^2)=315,$$

or

$$49-d^2=45;$$
$$\therefore\ d=\pm 2.$$

Hence, the numbers are 5, 7, 9.

Ex. 3. The fifth term of an arithmetical progression is 81, and the second term is 24. Find the series.

$$a+4d=81$$
$$a+\ d=24$$

Subtracting,

$$3d=57;$$
$$\therefore\ d=19 \text{ and } a=5.$$

Hence, the series is 5, 24, 43, ...

Ex. 4. Show that if unity be added to the sum of any number of terms of the series 8, 16, 24, etc., the result is the square of an odd number.

$$s=\frac{n}{2}\{16+(n-1)8\}$$
$$=4n^2+4n.$$
$$\therefore\ s+1=4n^2+4n+1=(2n+1)^2,$$

and $(2n+1)^2$ is the square of an odd number.

Ex. 5. Find the sum of the first n natural numbers.

Here $a=1$, $d=1$;

$$\therefore\ s=\frac{n}{2}\{2+(n-1)1\}=\frac{n(n+1)}{2}.$$

Sum of squares.—The sum of the squares of the first n natural numbers is often required; if this sum is denoted by Σn^2, then

$$\Sigma n^2=1^2+2^2+3^2+\dots n^2.$$

From the result already obtained (Ex. 5) for the sum of the first n natural numbers we may infer that the result will contain n^3. In fact, we find

$$n^3-(n-1)^3=n^3-(n^3-3n^2+3n-1)=3n^2-3n+1.$$

As this is true for all values of n, we may write $n-1$ for n, and we obtain

$$(n-1)^3-(n-2)^3=3(n-1)^2-3(n-1)+1.$$

In a similar manner, again writing $n-1$ for n,

$$(n-2)^3-(n-3)^3=3(n-2)^2-3(n-2)+1,$$

$$\dots\dots\dots\dots = \dots\dots\dots\dots\dots ,$$

$$\therefore\ 3^3-2^3=3\times 3^2-3\times 3+1,$$

$$2^3-1^3=3\times 2^2-3\times 2+1,$$

$$1^3-0^3=3\times 1^2-3\times 1+1.$$

By addition we obtain

$$n^3=3(1^2+2^2+3^2+\dots n^2)-3(1+2+3+\dots n)+n, \quad \dots\dots\text{(i)}$$

but

$$1+2+3+\dots n=\frac{n(n+1)}{2};$$

$$\therefore\ n^3=3\Sigma n^2-\frac{3n(n+1)}{2}+n;$$

or

$$3\Sigma n^2=n^3+\frac{3n(n+1)}{2}-n;$$

$$\therefore\ \Sigma n^2=\frac{n(n+1)(2n+1)}{6}.$$

EXERCISES. XXIX.

Find the sum of the following series:

1. 4, $3\frac{1}{4}$, $2\frac{1}{2}$, ... to 20 terms.

2. $11\frac{2}{3}+10\frac{1}{2}+9\frac{1}{3}+\dots$ to 21 terms.

3. 14·2, 12·3, 10·4, etc., to 15 terms.

4. $1\frac{2}{3}$, 2, $2\frac{1}{3}$, to 8 terms.

5. The third term of an A.P. is 7 and the seventh is 3. What is the series?

6. The sum of three numbers in A.P. is 24, and their product is 480. Find the numbers.

7. The sum of n terms of an A.P., whose first two terms are 43, 45, is equal to the sum of $2n$ terms of another progression whose first two terms are 45, 43. Find the value of n.

8. The sum of n terms of the series 3, 6, 9 ... is 975; find n.

9. The sum of 20 terms of an A.P., the first term being 4, is $-62\frac{1}{2}$. Find the common difference.

10. An A.P. consists of 21 terms, the sum of the three last is 117, and of the three middle is 88. Find the first term and common difference.

11. Find the sum of 14 terms of an arithmetical progression whose first term is 11, and common difference 9.

12. If the common difference is $-d$, and the sum of n terms $\frac{(2a+d)^2}{9d}$; find n.

13. The first term of an A.P. is 5 and the seventh is 23; find the twentieth term.

14. The sum of the first seven terms of an A.P. is 49, the sum of the next eight is 176. Find the series.

15. Find the sum of n terms of the progression

$$(p+1)+(p+3)+(p+5)+\ \dots .$$

If three successive positive terms be taken of any arithmetical progression, show that the ratio of the first to the second is less than the ratio of the second to the third.

16. The first term is 2, the fifth is 18. How many terms must be taken to make the sum 800?

17. The sum of 29 terms is 145, and common difference $\frac{1}{4}$. Find the middle term.

18. Find the first term and common difference of an arithmetical progression in which the fifth term from the beginning is 2 and the third from the end -2, the number of terms being 9.

19. If the nth term of an arithmetical series be a given number (A), show that the sum of $2n-1$ terms will be the same, whatever be the first term. Find the sum of 7 terms when the 4th term is 11, and verify the preceding statement by writing down and then adding up the seven terms when the first is -4.

Geometrical progression.—A series of terms are said to be in geometrical progression when the quotient obtained by dividing any term by the preceding term is always the same.

The constant quotient is called the **common ratio** of the series.

Let r denote the common ratio and a the first term.

The series of terms a, ar, ar^2, etc., form a geometrical progression, and any term, such as the third, is equal to a multiplied by r raised to the power $(3-1)$ or ar^2.

Thus, if l denote the last term and n the number of terms, then $$l=ar^{n-1}. \qquad \text{(i)}$$

Let S denote the sum of n terms, then

$$S = a + ar + ar^2 + \dots ar^{n-2} + ar^{n-1}. \dots\dots\dots\dots (ii)$$

Multiplying every term by r,

$$Sr = ar + ar^2 + ar^3 + \dots ar^{n-1} + ar^n. \dots\dots\dots\dots (iii)$$

Subtract (ii) from (iii).

$$\therefore\ rS - S = ar^n - a,$$

or

$$S(r-1) = a(r^n - 1);$$

$$\therefore\ S = \frac{a(r^n - 1)}{r - 1}. \dots\dots\dots\dots (iv)$$

Ex. 1. The first term of a geometrical progression is 3, and the third term 12. Find the sum of 8 terms.

From (i), $12 = 3r^2$; $\therefore\ r = \pm 2$.

From (iv), $S = 3\left(\frac{2^8 - 1}{2 - 1}\right) = 765.$

Or, using the minus value for r,

$$S = 3\left(\frac{(-2)^8 - 1}{-2 - 1}\right) = -255.$$

Ex. 2. Find the sum of 20 terms of the series

$$3 - 4 + \tfrac{16}{3} - \tfrac{64}{9} + \dots.$$

Here $r = -\frac{4}{3}$, $a = 3$, and $n = 20$;

$$S = 3\left\{\frac{(-\frac{4}{3})^{20} - 1}{-\frac{4}{3} - 1}\right\} = -\frac{9}{7}\left\{(\tfrac{4}{3})^{20} - 1\right\}.$$

The value of $(\frac{4}{3})^{20}$ is readily obtained by using logarithms.

Sum of an infinite number of terms.—By changing signs in both numerator and denominator, Eq. (iv) above becomes

$$S = \frac{a(1 - r^n)}{1 - r}. \dots\dots\dots\dots (v)$$

When r is a *proper fraction* it is evident that r^n decreases as n increases, so that, as n tends to infinity, r^n tends to zero, provided $-1 < r < 1$. Hence the sum to infinity is

$$S = \frac{a}{1 - r}. \dots\dots\dots\dots (vi)$$

Hence Eq. (vi) may be used to find the sum of an infinite number of terms; or, as it is called, the sum of a series of terms to infinity.

Ex. 3. Find the sum of the series $\frac{1}{2}+\frac{1}{3}+\frac{2}{9}+\frac{4}{27}+\ldots$ to infinity.

Here $a=\frac{1}{2}$, $r=\frac{2}{3}$;

$$\therefore\ S=\frac{\frac{1}{2}}{1-\frac{2}{3}}=\frac{3}{2}.$$

Ex. 4. Find the sum of the series $0{\cdot}9+0{\cdot}81+\ldots$ to infinity.

Here $a=0{\cdot}9$, $r=0{\cdot}9$;

$$\therefore\ S=\frac{0{\cdot}9}{1-{\cdot}9}=\frac{0{\cdot}9}{0{\cdot}1}=9.$$

Value of a recurring decimal.—The arithmetical rules for finding the value of a recurring decimal depend on the formula for the sum of an infinite series in G.P.

Ex. 5. Find the value of $3{\cdot}\dot{6}$.

$$3{\cdot}\dot{6}=3{\cdot}666\ldots=3+\frac{6}{10}+\frac{6}{10^2}+\frac{6}{10^3}+\ldots=3+S;$$

$$\therefore\ r=0{\cdot}1 \text{ and } a=0{\cdot}6;$$

$$\therefore\ S=\frac{0{\cdot}6}{1-0{\cdot}1}=\frac{6}{9}=\frac{2}{3};$$

$$\therefore\ 3{\cdot}\dot{6}=3\tfrac{2}{3}.$$

Geometrical mean.—The positive value of the square root of the product of any two quantities is said to be a *geometric mean* between the other two. The two initial letters G.M. may be used to denote the geometric mean. Thus, if x and y denote two numbers, the A.M. is $\frac{x+y}{2}$ the G.M. is $\sqrt{xy}$.

In the progression 2, 4, 8... the middle term 4 is the G.M. of 2 and 8. In like manner in a, ar, ar^2,... ar is the G.M. of a and ar^2.

To insert (n − 2) geometric means between two given quantities.

From $$l=ar^{n-1}$$

we obtain $$r^{n-1}=\frac{l}{a},$$

and from this equation when l and a are given r can be obtained.

Ex. 6 Insert four geometric means between 2 and 64.

Including the two given terms the number of terms will be 6, the first term will be 2, and the last 64.

$$\therefore\ r^{6-1}=\frac{64}{2};$$

$$\therefore\quad r^5=32, \text{ or } r=2.$$

Hence the means are 4, 8, 16, 32.

Ex. 7. The arithmetical mean of two numbers is 10, and the geometrical mean is 8. Find the numbers.

Let x and y denote the two numbers.

Then $$\frac{x+y}{2}=10;\quad \therefore\ x+y=20;\ \ldots\ldots\text{(i)}$$

$$\sqrt{xy}=8;\quad \therefore\quad xy=64.\ \ldots\ldots\text{(ii)}$$

Multiply (ii) by 4 and subtract from (i) squared.

$$\therefore\ x^2-2xy+y^2=144;$$

$$\therefore\ x-y=\pm 12.\ \ldots\ldots\text{(iii)}$$

Thus, from (iii) and (i),

$$2x=32 \text{ or } 8;\quad \therefore\ x=16 \text{ or } 4;$$

$$2y=8 \text{ or } 32;\quad \therefore\ y=4 \text{ or } 16.$$

Hence the numbers are 16 and 4.

MISCELLANEOUS EXERCISES. XXX.

Sum the following series:

1. $3+4\frac{1}{4}+5\frac{1}{2}+\ldots$ to 10 terms.

2. $12+4+1\frac{1}{3}+\ldots$ to 10 terms.

3. $1{\cdot}48-2{\cdot}22+3{\cdot}33-\ldots$ to 10 terms.

4. $1{\cdot}3-3{\cdot}1-7{\cdot}5-\ldots$ to 10 terms.

5. $14+64+114+\ldots$ to 20 terms.

6. $14+42+126\ldots$ to 8 terms.

7. $2+3\frac{1}{3}+4\frac{2}{3}+\ldots$ to 10 terms.

8. $12+3+\frac{3}{4}+\ldots$ to 10 terms.

9. $0{\cdot}74-1{\cdot}11+1{\cdot}665-\ldots$

10. $1{\cdot}2-2{\cdot}1+5{\cdot}4-\ldots$

11. Find the G.P. whose fifth and ninth terms are 1458 and 118098.

12. Find five numbers in G.P. such that their sum is 124 and the quotient of the sum of the first and last by the middle term shall be $4\frac{1}{4}$.

13. The continued product of three numbers in G.P. is 64, and the sum of the products of them in pairs is 84. Find the numbers.

14. Sum the series $2\sqrt{2}-2\sqrt{3}+3\sqrt{2}-\ldots$ to 10 terms.

15. Show that $5, \frac{5}{3}, \frac{5}{9},\ldots$ to infinity is equal to $3, \frac{9}{5}, \frac{27}{25},\ldots$ to infinity.

Sum where possible the following series to infinity:

16. $1, -\frac{3}{2}, +\frac{9}{4}-\ldots.$ **17.** $1-\frac{2}{3}+\frac{4}{9}-\ldots.$

18. $0{\cdot}9+0{\cdot}81+0{\cdot}729\ldots.$ **19.** $56+14+3\frac{1}{2}+\ldots.$

20. $\frac{1}{2}+\frac{1}{3}+\frac{2}{9}+\frac{4}{27}+\ldots.$

21. The fifth term is 81, and the second term 24. Find the series.

22. Find the sum of n terms of the geometrical series

$$1-\tfrac{3}{2}+\ldots.$$

What is the condition that the sum may be negative?

23. The first four terms of a G.P. are together equal to 45, and the first six to 189. Find the common ratio and the first term.

24. If the $(p+q)^{\text{th}}$ term of a G.P. be m and the $(p-q)^{\text{th}}$ term be n, show that the pth term is $\sqrt{mn}$.

25. Show that the arithmetic mean between two positive quantities is greater than the geometric mean. There is an exceptional case; state it.

Harmonical progression.—A series of terms are said to be in Harmonical Progression when the reciprocals of the terms are in Arithmetical Progression.

Thus, since 1, 2, 3, etc., $\frac{1}{4}$, $-\frac{1}{4}$, $-\frac{3}{4}$, etc., are in A.P., their reciprocals, 1, $\frac{1}{2}$, $\frac{1}{3}$, etc., and 4, -4, $-\frac{4}{3}$, etc., are in H.P.

The preceding rule may be expressed in a more general manner as follows:

Let the three quantities a, b, c be in H.P., then $\frac{1}{a}, \frac{1}{b}, \frac{1}{c}$ are in A.P.

As $$\frac{1}{b}-\frac{1}{a}=\frac{1}{c}-\frac{1}{b}, \qquad \text{(i)}$$

we obtain the relation $a:c=a-b:b-c$, or **three quantities are in H.P. when the ratio of the first to the third is equal to the ratio of the first minus the second, to the second minus the third.**

Again from (i) the harmonical mean between two quantities ; and c is $b=\dfrac{2ac}{a+c}$.

Ex. 1. Find a harmonical mean between 42 and 7.

We may use the formula H.M. $=\dfrac{2ac}{a+c}=\dfrac{2\times 42\times 7}{42+7}=12$, or as $\dfrac{1}{42}$ nd $\dfrac{1}{7}$ are in A.P.,

$$\therefore \text{ mean}=\frac{\frac{1}{42}+\frac{1}{7}}{2}=\frac{1}{12}.$$

Hence, the required mean is 12, and 42, 12 and 7 are three terms n H.P.

Ex. 2. Insert two harmonical means between 3 and 12.

Inverting the given terms we find that $\frac{1}{3}$ and $\frac{1}{12}$ are the first nd last terms of an A.P. of four terms; therefore from

$$l=a+(n-1)d$$

ve have
$$\tfrac{1}{12}=\tfrac{1}{3}+(4-1)d;$$
$$\therefore\ 3d=-\tfrac{1}{4}, \text{ or } d=-\tfrac{1}{12}.$$

Hence the common difference is $-\frac{1}{12}$; therefore the terms are

$$\tfrac{1}{3}-\tfrac{1}{12}=\tfrac{1}{4} \text{ and } \tfrac{1}{3}-\tfrac{2}{12}=\tfrac{1}{6},$$

r the arithmetical means are $\frac{1}{4}$ and $\frac{1}{6}$.

Hence the harmonic means are 4 and 6.

Let A, G, and H denote the arithmetical, geometrical, and harnonical means respectively between two quantities a and c.

Then $\quad A=\dfrac{a+c}{2},\quad G=\sqrt{ac},\quad H=\dfrac{2ac}{a+c}$; hence $G^2=AH$.

EXERCISES. XXXI.

1. Define harmonic progression; insert 4 harmonic means beween 2 and 12.

2. Find the arithmetic, geometric, and harmonic means between 2 and 8.

3. Find a third term to 42 and 12 in H.P.

4. Find a first term to 8 and 20 in H.P.

5. The sum of three terms in H.P. is $1\frac{1}{12}$; if the first term is $\frac{1}{2}$, what is the series?

6. The arithmetical mean between two numbers exceeds the geometric by 2, and the geometrical exceeds the harmonical by 1·6. Find the numbers.

7. A H.P. consists of six terms; the last three terms are 2, 3 and 6; find the first three.

8. Find in H.P. the fourth term to 6, 8 and 12.

9. Insert three harmonic means between 2 and 3.

10. Find the arithmetic, geometric, and harmonic means between 2 and $\frac{9}{2}$, and write down three terms of each series.

11. If x, y, z be the pth, q^{th} and r^{th} terms of a H.P., show that

$$(r-q)yz+(p-r)xz+(q-p)xy=0.$$

Miscellaneous Series.—The preceding methods may sometimes be adopted to obtain the summation of given series neither in A.P. nor in G.P. The processes employed may be seen from the following examples:

Ex. 1. (*a*) Find the sum of the series

$$a+(a+b)x+(a+2b)x^2+\ldots+\{a+(n-1)b\}x^{n-1}.$$

(*b*) Show that the sum of the first n even numbers is equal to $\left(1+\frac{1}{n}\right)$ times the sum of the first n odd numbers.

(*a*) Let $S=a+(a+b)x+(a+2b)x^2+\ldots\{a+(n-1)b\}x^{n-1}$.

Multiplying all through by x,

$$Sx=ax+(a+b)x^2+\ldots\{a+(n-2)b\}x^{n-1}+\{a+(n-1)b\}x^n.$$

By subtraction,

$$S(1-x)=a+b(x+x^2+\ldots x^{n-1})-\{a+(n-1)b\}x^n$$

$$=a+\frac{bx(1-x^{n-1})}{1-x}-\{a+(n-1)b\}x^n,$$

or

$$S=\frac{a(1-x^n)}{1-x}+\frac{bx(1-x^{n-1})}{(1-x)^2}-\frac{(n-1)bx^n}{1-x}.$$

(*b*) The sum of the first n even numbers is an A.P. Common difference and first term 2.

$$\therefore\ S=2+4+6\ldots+2n$$

$$=\frac{n}{2}(2+2n)=n(n+1).\ \ldots\ldots\ldots\ldots\text{(i)}$$

Similarly, for the sum of the first n odd numbers,

$$S'=1+3+5\ldots+(2n-1)$$

$$=\frac{n}{2}(2n-1+1)=n^2.\ \ldots\ldots\ldots\ldots\text{(ii)}$$

Hence, comparing (i) and (ii),

$$n(n+1)=n^2\left(1+\frac{1}{n}\right);$$

$\therefore$ sum of first n even numbers $=\left(1+\frac{1}{n}\right)$ times the sum of the irst n odd numbers.

MISCELLANEOUS EXERCISES. XXXII.

Sum to infinity the following series in G.P.:

1. 9·6, 7·2, 5·4, etc.
2. 14·8, 10·8, 8·1, etc.
3. $\frac{1}{2}+\frac{1}{3}+\frac{2}{9}$, etc.
4. $4-3+\frac{9}{4}$, etc.
5. $84+14+2\frac{1}{3}$, etc.
6. $56+14+3\frac{1}{2}$, etc.
7. $0·8-0·64+$etc.
8. $7-\frac{7}{4}+\frac{7}{4}$, etc.
9. $2+\frac{8}{7}+\frac{32}{49}$, etc.

10. What is meant by the sum of a geometrical series to infinity? iven that r is positive and that

$$(1+r+r^2+\dots \text{ to infinity})(1+p+p^2+\dots \text{ to infinity})$$
$$=1+rp+r^2p^2+\dots,$$

how that p must be negative and r less than $\frac{1}{3}$.

11. The first and second terms of a progression are $5\frac{1}{3}$ and $2\frac{1}{2}$ ind the 4th term on the supposition that the progression is a) A.P., (b) G.P., (c) H.P.

12. Find the A.P. in which the tenth term is -100 and forty-ighth term is 128.

13. Find the sum of 8 terms of the series $1\frac{2}{3}$, 2, $2\frac{1}{3}$, ..., and he sum of 17 terms of $-1\frac{1}{3}$, -1, $-\frac{2}{3}$, ...

14. Insert 8 arithmetical means between -250 and 1370. If ne arithmetical mean, A, and two geometrical means, p and q, e inserted between two given quantities, show that $p^3+q^3=2Apq$.

15. Insert 8 geometrical means between 512 and 19683. If one eometrical mean, G, and two arithmetical means, p and q, be in-erted between two given quantities, show that $G^2=(2p-q)(2q-p)$.

16. Find the sum of n terms of the series 8, 16, 24, .. and show hat if unity be added to the sum the result is the square of an dd number.

17. Find the sum of the series

(a) $1+x+x^2+x^3+\dots+x^{n-1}$,

(b) $1+2x+4x^2+8x^3+\dots+2^{n-1}x^{n-1}+2^nx^n$,

(c) $1+2x+3x^2+4x^3+\dots+nx^{n-1}$.

18. If a and b are any two numbers, and A, G, H three other numbers, such that a, b, A are in arithmetical progression, a, b, G in geometrical progression, and a, b, H in harmonical progression show that $4H(A-G)(G-H)=G(A-H)^2$.

19. Find the sum of y^2+2b, y^4+4b, y^6+6b, etc., to n terms.

Binomial Theorem.—By the binomial theorem—one of the most useful theorems in mathematics—any binomial expression i.e. an expression consisting of two terms, can be raised to any required power. The theorem may be stated as follows

$$(\mathbf{a}+\mathbf{b})^n=\mathbf{a}^n+\mathbf{n}\mathbf{a}^{n-1}\mathbf{b}+\frac{\mathbf{n}(\mathbf{n}-1)}{2}\mathbf{a}^{n-2}\mathbf{b}^2+\frac{\mathbf{n}(\mathbf{n}-1)(\mathbf{n}-2)}{2\times 3}\mathbf{a}^{n-3}\mathbf{b}^3+\ldots.\text{ (i}$$

The terms on the right-hand side of the equation form what is called the expansion of $(a+b)^n$.

The series on the right terminates only when n is a positive whole number. Thus, when n is 2,

$$(a+b)^2=a^2+2ab+\frac{2\times 1}{2}b^2$$
$$=a^2+2ab+b^2.$$

When n is 3,

$$(a+b)^3=a^3+3a^2b+\frac{3\times 2}{2}ab^2+\frac{3\times 2\times 1}{2\times 3}b^3$$
$$=a^3+3a^2b+3ab^2+b^3.$$

The expansions of $(a+b)^4$, $(a+b)^5$, etc., can be obtained in like manner. In each of the preceding results, where n is a positive integer, the following rules hold:

(1) The index of the highest power is n and its coefficient is 1.

(2) Indices of a *decrease* by 1 in each succeeding term whilst those of b *increase* by one in each term.

(3) Number of terms is equal to index $+1$.

(4) The coefficients of the terms equally distant from the beginning and the end of the series are the same.

When the preceding rules have been carefully studied it will be possible for the student to write down the second third, or any other term, such as the rth or $r+1$th term, of an expansion. The general or $(r+1)$th term is

$$\frac{\mathbf{n}(\mathbf{n}-1)(\mathbf{n}-2)\ldots(\mathbf{n}-\mathbf{r}+1)}{\underline{|\mathbf{r}}}\mathbf{a}^{n-r}\mathbf{b}^r.$$

where $\lfloor r$, which is also written $r\,!$, signifies

$$1 \times 2 \times 3 \times \ldots \times r.$$

Note that when $r=0$ the value of $\lfloor r$ is called $=1$.

Now it may be proved that the binomial expansion for $(a+b)^n$ is valid for all values of n, provided $-1 < b/a < 1$, this condition being essential since when n is not a positive integer, the resulting series has an infinite number of terms. Thus assuming the condition to be fulfilled,

$$(\mathbf{a}+\mathbf{b})^{-n} = \mathbf{a}^{-n} - \mathbf{n}\mathbf{a}^{-n-1}\mathbf{b} + \frac{\mathbf{n}(\mathbf{n}+\mathbf{1})}{\lfloor 2}\mathbf{a}^{-n-2}\mathbf{b}^2 -, \text{ etc.,}$$

and the general, or $(r+1)^{\text{th}}$, term will be

$$(-1)^r \frac{\mathbf{n}(\mathbf{n}+\mathbf{1})\ldots(\mathbf{n}+\mathbf{r}-\mathbf{1})}{\lfloor \mathbf{r}} \mathbf{a}^{-n-r}\mathbf{b}^r.$$

Ex. 1. Find the 9th term of $(a+b)^{11}$.

Here $\qquad r+1=9; \qquad \therefore\ r=8;$

$$\therefore \text{ required term} = \frac{11\,.\,10\ldots(11-8+1)a^3b^8}{\lfloor 8}$$

$$=165a^3b^8.$$

The theorem may be applied to expand an expression of more than two terms, thus:

$$(a+b+c)^4 = (a+b)^4 + 4(a+b)^3c + 6(a+b)^2c^2 + 4(a+b)c^3 + c^4,$$

and each binomial may be expanded in the usual manner.

As n may be an integer, positive or negative, or a fractional number, it follows that a binomial expression may be raised to a given power, provided the condition stated above is fulfilled. In numerical cases it is advisable, before expanding $(a+b)^n$, to make the first term of the binomial expression unity; thus

$$(a+b)^n = a^n\,(1+b/a)^n.$$

Ex. 2. $(17)^{\frac{1}{2}} = (4^2+1)^{\frac{1}{2}} = (4^2)^{\frac{1}{2}}(1+\frac{1}{16})^{\frac{1}{2}}$

$$=4\left\{1+\tfrac{1}{32}+\frac{\frac{1}{2}(\frac{1}{2}-1)}{\lfloor 2}(\tfrac{1}{16})^2 +, \text{ etc.}\right\}$$

$$=4(1+\tfrac{1}{32}-\tfrac{1}{2048}+\text{etc.}) = 4{\cdot}1231 \text{ approx.}$$

Ex. 3. Find the value of $0{\cdot}9^{\frac{4}{5}}$ by the binomial theorem. Compare the result with that obtained by using logarithms.

$$\left(\tfrac{9}{10}\right)^{\frac{4}{5}}=\left(1-\tfrac{1}{10}\right)^{\frac{4}{5}}.$$

Expanding by the binomial theorem, this becomes

$$1-\tfrac{4}{5}\left(\tfrac{1}{10}\right)+\frac{\frac{4}{5}\left(\frac{4}{5}-1\right)}{\lfloor 2}\left(\tfrac{1}{10}\right)^2-\frac{\frac{4}{5}\left(\frac{4}{5}-1\right)\left(\frac{4}{5}-2\right)}{\lfloor 3}\left(\tfrac{1}{10}\right)^3+\dots$$

$$=1-0{\cdot}08+\frac{4(-1)2^2}{2\times 10^4}-\frac{4(-1)(-6)2^3}{\lfloor 3\times 10^6}+\frac{4(-1)(-6)(-11)2^4}{\lfloor 4\times 10^8}-\dots$$

$$=1-0{\cdot}08-0{\cdot}0008-0{\cdot}000032-\frac{11\times 16}{10^8}+\dots$$

$$=1-0{\cdot}08083376=0{\cdot}91916624.$$

Using four-figure logarithms we have

$$\log(0{\cdot}9)^{\frac{4}{5}}=\tfrac{4}{5}\log 0{\cdot}9=\tfrac{4}{5}\times\bar{1}{\cdot}9542=\bar{1}{\cdot}9633$$
$$=0{\cdot}9189.$$

Approximations.—The binomial theorem gives the expansion of $(1+a)^n$ thus:

$$(1+a)^n=1+na+\frac{n(n-1)}{1\times 2}a^2+\frac{n(n-1)(n-2)}{1\times 2\times 3}a^3+\dots.$$

When a is small compared with 1, then a^2 will be very small, and the first two terms of the expansion are sufficiently accurate for many practical purposes. Thus

$$\mathbf{(1+a)^n=1+na,}$$

when a is small compared with 1.

Ex. 4. Find the value of $1{\cdot}05^3$.

$$1{\cdot}05^3=(1+0{\cdot}05)^3=1+3\times 0{\cdot}05+3(0{\cdot}05)^2+(0{\cdot}05)^3$$
$$=1+0{\cdot}15+0{\cdot}0075 \text{ approx.}$$

Using only the first two terms,

$$1{\cdot}05^3=1{\cdot}15.$$

It will be noticed that the error introduced only affects the third decimal place, and the numerical magnitude of the error decreases as the term a diminishes.

Again, if $a=0{\cdot}005$, then

$$1{\cdot}005^3=(1+0{\cdot}005)^3=1+3\times 0{\cdot}005+\frac{3\times 2}{2}(0{\cdot}005)^2+(0{\cdot}005)^3$$
$$=1+0{\cdot}015+0{\cdot}000075=1{\cdot}015075 \text{ approx.}$$

The first two terms give $(1{\cdot}005)^3=1+0{\cdot}005\times 3=1{\cdot}015$, which is quite accurate enough for most practical purposes.

We may, of course, use the same rule when n is fractional.

Ex. 5. $\sqrt[3]{1 \cdot 05} = (1 + 0 \cdot 05)^{\frac{1}{3}}$

$$= 1 + \tfrac{1}{3} \times 0 \cdot 05 = 1 \cdot 0167.$$

Ex. 6. $\dfrac{1}{\sqrt[3]{1 \cdot 05}} = (1 + 0 \cdot 05)^{-\frac{1}{3}}$

$$= 1 - \tfrac{1}{3} \times 0 \cdot 05 = 1 - 0 \cdot 0167 = 0 \cdot 9833.$$

Ex. 7. Find the superficial and cubical expansion of iron, taking a, the coefficient of linear expansion, as $0 \cdot 000012$ or $1 \cdot 2 \times 10^{-5}$.

If the side of a square be of unit length, then when the temperature is increased by 1° C., the length of each side becomes $1 + a$, and the area of the square is $(1 + a)^2 = 1 + 2a + a^2$;

$$\therefore \; (1 + a)^2 = 1 + 2 \times 0 \cdot 000012 + (0 \cdot 000012)^2.$$

Subtracting the value of the original area from this, we find the coefficient of superficial expansion to be $2 \times 0 \cdot 000012 + (0 \cdot 000012)^2$.

As a is a small quantity its square will be very small, even if an exact determination of it were made it would have no appreciable effect on the larger quantity;

$\therefore$ coefficient of superficial expansion is $2a = 0 \cdot 000024$ or $2 \cdot 4 \times 10^{-5}$.

In a similar manner $(1 + a)^3$ (when a is a small quantity compared with unity) may be written as $1 + 3a$;

$\therefore$ coefficient of cubical expansion for the same material

$$= 3a = 0 \cdot 000036 = 3 \cdot 6 \times 10^{-5}.$$

Again, by multiplication,

$$(1 + a)(1 + b) = 1 + a + b + ab;$$

when a and b are both small compared with unity, we may write

$$\mathbf{(1 + a)(1 + b) = 1 + a + b.}$$

Ex. 8. Find the approximate value of $1 \cdot 05 \times 1 \cdot 07$.

Here we have

$$(1 + 0 \cdot 05)(1 + 0 \cdot 07) = 1 + 0 \cdot 05 + 0 \cdot 07 = 1 \cdot 12.$$

More accurately $(1 \cdot 05)(1 \cdot 07) = 1 + 0 \cdot 05 + 0 \cdot 07 + 0 \cdot 0035 = 1 \cdot 1235.$

Hence, the result obtained by the approximate method is true to the third significant figure.

Similarly, when a and b are small compared with 1,

$$\mathbf{(1 + a)^n (1 + b)^m = 1 + na + mb.}$$

We collect the preceding approximation formulae for reference and add others which may be proved in a similar manner.

$$(1 \pm a)^n = 1 \pm na$$

$$(1 \pm a)(1 \pm b) = 1 \pm a \pm b$$

$$(1 \pm a)(1 \pm b)(1 \pm c) \ldots = 1 \pm a \pm b \pm c \ldots .$$

$$\frac{1}{(1 \pm a)} = 1 \mp a.$$

$$\frac{1}{(1 \pm a)^n} = 1 \mp na.$$

On degree of accuracy.—In the various arithmetical processes of multiplication, division, involution, and evolution the numbers which are dealt with are usually known to be "correct" to a certain number of significant figures, and it is frequently necessary to ascertain to what number of significant figures a result such as a product or quotient is accurate.

Thus, for example, to find the product of 3·54 and 2·36, it being given that the decimals are correct to the second place. It follows that the four decimal places which are obtained in the product are not necessarily correct. Thus, 3·54 means that the number lies between 3·535 and 3·545; and 2·36 lies between 2·355 and 2·365. Hence, the product will lie between $3{\cdot}535 \times 2{\cdot}355$ and $3{\cdot}545 \times 2{\cdot}365$, *i.e.* between 8·324925 and 8·383925. The product of the given numbers is $3{\cdot}54 \times 2{\cdot}36 = 8{\cdot}3544$, but in the two extreme cases the result may be expressed as 8·32 or 8·38. Hence the four decimal figures cannot be retained. The result is correct only so far as the whole number is concerned, and at the most we can only retain one decimal place in the result.

Hence, in calculating the area of a given figure from two measured lengths, say in inches, it follows that if the measurement be such that an error of 0·01 of an inch is possible then care is necessary to avoid giving a result which is apparently far more accurate than the given data will supply.

So, too, in dealing with the square, cube, or higher power of a number, the result must not indicate greater accuracy han is obtainable from the given data. As an example, the area of a circle is given by $\frac{\pi}{4}d^2$, where d is the diameter. If the diameter is 0·08, the area, true to five significant figures, is 0·0050265; but, if d is slightly greater or less than the given amount, the corresponding area is greater or less. Thus, if d is 0·079, the area is 0·0049018; and, if 0·081 is 0·005153, and hence, if there is any uncertainty in the second significant figure, not more than one significant figure can be retained in the answer.

Assuming d to denote a measured length, and therefore probably slightly in error, it will be absurd to use an accurate value of π. This constant has been calculated to over seven hundred significant figures; its value is 3·1416 to five significant figures, and this number is usually sufficiently exact for all practical purposes. A good value to use for nearly all practical calculations, indeed, is the number $\frac{22}{7}=3{\cdot}1428$. The number 3·142 is usually used with four-figure logarithms, and it should be noticed that there are comparatively few calculations outside the range of four-figure logarithms.

Ex. 9. Let x denote the diameter of a circle. A small error in the measured value of x may be denoted by δx. Calculate the proportional error in the area.

For an alteration in the diameter denoted by δx the corresponding change in the area may be denoted by δA.

$$A=\frac{\pi}{4}x^2. \qquad \text{(i)}$$

Also $$A+\delta A=\frac{\pi}{4}(x+\delta x)^2=\frac{\pi}{4}\{x^2+2x\delta x+(\delta x)^2\}. \qquad \text{(ii)}$$

As δx is a small quantity, its square will be too small to affect the result.

Subtracting (i) from (ii) we obtain

$$\delta A=\frac{\pi}{4}(2x\delta x)+\frac{\pi}{4}(\delta x)^2. \qquad \text{(iii)}$$

Dividing (iii) by (i) and omitting the last term as being too small to affect the result.

∴ the proportional error in the calculated result is twice that made in the measurement of x.

Ex. 10. Let x denote the radius of a circle;

$$\text{the area } y = \pi x^2. \quad \text{(i)}$$

Let the radius increase by an amount δx, then the increase in the area is given by

$$y + \delta y = \pi(x + \delta x)^2 = \pi\{x^2 + 2x\delta x + (\delta x)^2\}, \quad \text{(ii)}$$

or $$y + \delta y = \pi x^2 + \{2x\delta x + (\delta x)^2\}\pi.$$

Subtract (i) from (ii),

$$\therefore \ \delta y = \pi\{2x\delta x + (\delta x)^2\};$$

$$\therefore \ \delta y = 2\pi x\delta x + \pi(\delta x)^2.$$

Now if δx is exceedingly small, the increase in the area is simply the circumference of a circle of radius x multiplied by the change of radius.

Ex. 11. Let V denote the volume of a sphere of diameter x.

Then $$V = \frac{\pi}{6}x^3, \quad \text{(i)}$$

also $$V + \delta V = \frac{\pi}{6}(x + \delta x)^3 = \frac{\pi}{6}\{x^3 + 3x^2\delta x + 3x(\delta x)^2 + (\delta x)^3\}.$$

As δx is small, we need only retain the first two terms.

Subtracting (i) from (ii),

$$\delta V = \frac{\pi}{6}(3x^2\delta x). \quad \text{(iii)}$$

Dividing (iii) by (i),

$$\therefore \ \frac{\delta V}{V} = \frac{3\delta x}{x}.$$

Hence, the proportional error in the calculated volume is three times that made in the measurement of the diameter. In each of the preceding cases, certain terms have been rejected when such terms were small in comparison with a larger one It will be found that, if an exact determination of the numerical value of such terms is made, no appreciable effect is produced in the result. It is important that this should be verified by the student. It clearly applies in the preceding cases, and it may be shown to apply always when, as in raising a number to a given power or extracting a root, one or two terms of a series are sufficient.

Ex. 12. Find the first five terms of the square root of $1+x$, and use the result to obtain the square root of 101.

$$\sqrt{1+x}=(1+x)^{\frac{1}{2}}.$$

Therefore, by using the binomial theorem, we obtain

$$(1+x)^{\frac{1}{2}}=1+\tfrac{1}{2}x-\tfrac{1}{8}x^2+\tfrac{1}{16}x^3-\tfrac{5}{128}x^4+\dots;$$

$$\therefore\ \sqrt{101}=\sqrt{(100+1)}=10\sqrt{(1+\tfrac{1}{100})}$$

$$=10(1+\tfrac{1}{200}-\tfrac{1}{80000}+\tfrac{1}{16000000}-\text{ etc.})$$

$$=10(1+0\cdot005-0\cdot0000125+0\cdot0000000625)$$

$$=10\cdot049875.$$

By the approximate rule $(1+x)^n=1+nx$,

we obtain $\qquad 10(1+0\cdot005)=10\cdot05.$

Zero and infinity.—Probably one of the greatest difficulties met with by a beginner is the meaning to be attached to the words zero and infinity. He is probably familiar with two meanings which may be attached to the former. Thus, in reference to numbers we might say $4-4$ is zero, meaning that by the subtraction of four from four we obtain a result which has no magnitude. Another form may be roughly shown by considering $4-3\cdot999\ \dots$, in which the difference between the two magnitudes may be made exceedingly small; or, as it is often expressed, when the magnitude of the number representing the difference is made indefinitely small such a quantity may be called zero. In a similar manner, if x and x' are two points on a curve and close together, the distance apart may be indicated either by $x'-x$ or by δx, where δx denotes a small increment of x, which may be either positive or negative. Again, if one number be multiplied by another, the product becomes less and less as one of the numbers diminishes; hence, $b\times 0=0$, or 0 is the limit of bx when x becomes 0.

It is important, also, to understand clearly what is meant by "infinity." Thus, 1 divided by $\frac{1}{100}$ is 100. Similarly, 1 divided by $\frac{1}{1000000}$ is one million. By diminishing the denominator, the result may be made of any magnitude. Hence, as the divisor approaches 0, the quotient becomes an exceedingly great number, and when the denominator is actually 0, the quotient is said to have an infinitely large value, or to be infinite (written as ∞).

The tangent of an angle is the ratio of the sine to the cosine of the angle, or $\tan\theta = \frac{BC}{AB}$ (p. 15); when the angle approaches 90°, the base AB (Fig. 106) becomes exceedingly small; the height becomes equal to the radius of the circle when the angle is 90° and the base is 0; $\therefore \tan 90° = \infty$. Similarly, $\operatorname{cosec}\theta = \frac{AC}{BC}$; as the angle θ approaches 0°, the side BC becomes indefinitely small, and in the limit, when the angle becomes 0°, the side BC is zero, and $\therefore \operatorname{cosec} 0° = \infty$. Conversely, as the value of a fraction diminishes by increasing the denominator, it follows that when the denominator becomes indefinitely great, the value of the fraction or its limit is 0. Thus, the value of the fraction $\frac{a}{x}$, when x becomes indefinitely great, is zero.

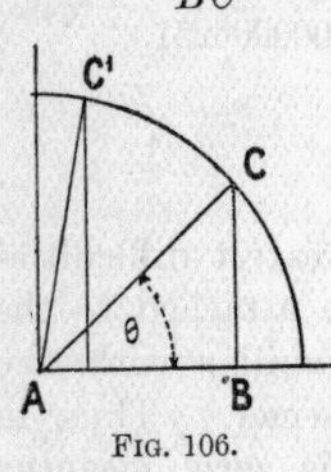

FIG. 106.

Undetermined forms.—When given values are substituted for x in a fraction, the expression sometimes assumes the form $\frac{0}{0}$, known as an **undetermined form.** There are various methods which may be used to ascertain the value of such an expression. One consists in writing the given expression in factors, removing factors common to both numerator and denominator, and in this manner the factor which reduces the numerator and denominator to the undetermined form may be eliminated.

Ex. 13. Find the value when $x=2$ of the fraction

$$\frac{2x^3-7x^2+12}{x^3-7x+6}.$$

Substituting the value $x=2$, the given fraction assumes the form $\frac{0}{0}$. Writing the given expression in the form of factors, we have

$$\frac{2x^3-7x^2+12}{x^3-7x+12}=\frac{(x-2)(2x^2-3x-6)}{(x-2)(x^2+2x-3)}.$$

Cancel the common factor $x-2$, then $\frac{2x^2-3x-6}{x^2+2x-3}$, and this, when $x=2$, becomes $= -\frac{4}{5}$.

Limits.—The undetermined form $\frac{0}{0}$ may be used to illustrate the meaning of a limit. Thus, to find the limit of $\frac{a^2-b^2}{a-b}$, when b approaches to the value of a and ultimately becomes equal to it.

So long as b differs from a, the given expression has a definite value. When b becomes equal to a, the expression assumes the form $\frac{0}{0}$. But as $a^2-b^2=(a+b)(a-b)$, we obtain

$$\frac{a^2-b^2}{a-b}=a+b \text{ by division.}$$

When $b=a$, this becomes $2a$.

It is important to bear in mind that $\frac{0}{0}$ may have any value whatever.

Ex. 14. Let $$y=x^2, \quad \text{.......................(i)}$$
and let x receive a slight increment denoted by δx, then y becomes $y+\delta y$;
$$\therefore\ y+\delta y=(x+\delta x)^2=x^2+2x\delta x+(\delta x)^2 \quad \text{..............(ii)}$$

Subtract (i) from (ii) and divide by δx;

$$\therefore\ \frac{\delta y}{\delta x}=2x+\delta x \quad \text{..........................(iii)}$$

When the numerical values of x and δx are known, the value of $\frac{\delta y}{\delta x}$ can at once be obtained from (iii). As δx is made smaller and smaller, the value approaches $2x$ in the limit. When δx is zero, we obtain $\frac{\delta y}{\delta x}=2x$, from which when x is known the numerical value can be found; also when δx is zero, the preceding is written in the form $\frac{dy}{dx}=2x$.

EXERCISES. XXXIII.

Find the value of

1. $\frac{x^3+x^2-5x+3}{x^4-2x^3-x^2+4x-2}$ when $x=1$.

2. $\frac{(x^2-a^2)^{\frac{3}{2}}+x-a}{(1+x-a)^3-1}$ when $x=a$.

3. $\frac{x^3+2x^2-14x-3}{x^2-x-6}$ when $x=3$.

4. Show that the limit of $\frac{a^3 - b^3}{a - b}$ when $b = a$ is $3a^2$.

5. Write down and simplify the middle term of the expansion of $\left(1 + \frac{8x}{15}\right)^6$.

6. Find the third term, also the two middle terms, of $(a+b)^{11}$.

7. Expand $(x \pm a)^6$. 8. $(5 - 4x)^4$.

9. What is the fifth term of $(x+a)^{16}$?

10. Find by means of a series an approximate value of $\sqrt[3]{7}$.

11. Expand $(\sqrt{a} \pm \sqrt{x})^4$.

Numerical value of e.—The value of $\left(1 + \frac{1}{n}\right)^n$ when n increases without limit is denoted by the letter e, where e is the base of the Naperian logarithms. On p. 280 we have found that when n is a large number, or in other words when $\frac{1}{n}$ is a small number and a is not large compared with n, then $\left(1 + \frac{1}{n}\right)^a = 1 + \frac{a}{n}$ approximately.

Ex. 1. If $n = 1000$ and $a = 5$,

$$\left(1 + \frac{1}{1000}\right)^5 = 1 + \frac{5}{1000} = 1{\cdot}005$$

with an error of 1 in 100,000.

The value of $\left(1 + \frac{1}{1000}\right)^{1000}$ may be obtained by the Binomial Theorem, p. 278, as follows:

$$\left(1 + \frac{1}{1000}\right)^{1000} = 1 + 1000\frac{1}{1000} + 1000\frac{(1000-1)}{2}\left(\frac{1}{1000}\right)^2$$

$$+ \frac{1000(1000-1)(1000-2)}{2 \,.\, 3}\left(\frac{1}{1000}\right)^3$$

$$+ \frac{1000(1000-1)(1000-2)(1000-3)}{2 \,.\, 3 \,.\, 4}\left(\frac{1}{1000}\right)^4$$

$$+ \text{etc.}$$

$$= 1 + 1 + \frac{1}{2}\left(1 - \frac{1}{1000}\right) + \frac{1}{6}\left(1 - \frac{3}{1000}\right) + \frac{1}{24}\left(1 - \frac{6}{1000}\right)$$

$$+ \text{etc.},$$

neglecting such terms as $\frac{2}{6}\left(\frac{1}{1000}\right)^2$, $\frac{11}{24}\left(\frac{1}{1000}\right)^3$, etc.

Hence, $$\left(1+\frac{1}{1000}\right)^{1000}=1+1+\frac{1}{2}+\frac{1}{6}+\frac{1}{24}+\frac{1}{120}+\frac{1}{720},$$

neglecting terms $\frac{1}{2000}$, $\frac{3}{6000}$, $\frac{6}{24000}$, etc.;

$$\therefore \left(1+\frac{1}{1000}\right)^{1000}=2{\cdot}718$$

with an error of about 1 in 2000.

From the preceding it will be seen that, if a approaches equality with n, the equation $\left(1+\frac{1}{n}\right)^a=1+\frac{a}{n}$ is very far from being true.

Now by the binomial theorem, when n is a positive integer,

$$\left(1+\frac{1}{n}\right)^n=1+n\,.\,\frac{1}{n}+\frac{n(n-1)}{1\,.\,2}\,.\,\frac{1}{n^2}+\ldots$$

$$=1+1+\frac{1}{1\,.\,2}\left(1-\frac{1}{n}\right)+\frac{1}{1\,.\,2\,.\,3}\left(1-\frac{1}{n}\right)\left(1-\frac{2}{n}\right).\quad\ldots\ldots\text{(i)}$$

The $(r+1)$th term of the series is

$$\frac{1}{1\,.\,2\,.\,3\ldots r}\left(1-\frac{1}{n}\right)\left(1-\frac{2}{n}\right)\ldots\left(1-\frac{r-1}{n}\right),$$

which is obviously positive and an increasing function of n. The number of terms also increases with n; hence

$$\left(1+\frac{1}{n}\right)^n \text{ increases as } n \text{ increases.}$$

But $$\left(1+\frac{1}{n}\right)^n<1+1+\frac{1}{1\,.\,2}+\frac{1}{1\,.\,2\,.\,3}+\ldots+\frac{1}{1\,.\,2\ldots n},$$

i.e., $$<1+1+\frac{1}{2}+\frac{1}{2^2}+\ldots+\frac{1}{2^{n-1}}.$$

This is a G.P. whose sum is less than 3;

$$\therefore \left(1+\frac{1}{n}\right)^n<3,$$

so that as n tends to infinity, $\left(1+\frac{1}{n}\right)^n$ tends to a finite positive limit which is denoted by the number e.

Hence from (i), as n is indefinitely increased,

$$e=1+1+\frac{1}{2!}+\frac{1}{3!}+\ldots+\frac{1}{r!}+\ldots,$$

where $r!=1.2.3\ldots r$, and is called *factorial* r.

This series will give the numerical value of e to any degree of accuracy required.

Ex. 2. Calculate the numerical value of e to five decimal places.

$$1+1+\frac{1}{2}=2{\cdot}500000,\quad \frac{1}{2.3}=0{\cdot}166666,\quad \frac{1}{2.3.4}=0{\cdot}041666,$$

$$\frac{1}{2.3.4.5}=0{\cdot}008333,\quad \frac{1}{2.3.4.5.6}=0{\cdot}001388,$$

$$\frac{1}{\lfloor 7}=0{\cdot}000198,\quad \frac{1}{\lfloor 8}=0{\cdot}000024,\quad \frac{1}{\lfloor 9}=0{\cdot}000003,$$

by addition the numerical value of e is 2·718282.

Expansion of powers of e.—We may now proceed to obtain a series which will enable the values of any power of e such as e^x to be obtained.

By the Binomial Theorem, if $1/n<1$,

$$\left(1+\frac{1}{n}\right)^{nx}=1+nx\frac{1}{n}+\frac{nx(nx-1)}{\lfloor 2}\frac{1}{n^2}$$
$$+\frac{nx(nx-1)(nx-2)}{\lfloor 3}\frac{1}{n^3}+\ldots$$
$$=1+x+\frac{1}{2!}x\left(x-\frac{1}{n}\right)+\ldots.$$

Putting $x=1$,

$$\left(1+\frac{1}{n}\right)^n=1+1+\frac{1}{2!}\left(1-\frac{1}{n}\right)+\ldots.$$

But $$\left\{\left(1+\frac{1}{n}\right)^n\right\}^x=\left(1+\frac{1}{n}\right)^{nx};$$

$$\therefore\ \left\{1+1+\frac{1}{2!}\left(1-\frac{1}{n}\right)+\ldots\right\}^x$$
$$=1+x+\frac{x}{2!}\left(x-\frac{1}{n}\right)+\ldots.$$

Hence, assuming these series remain equal as n is indefinitely increased; when n tends to infinity,

$$e^x = 1 + x + \frac{x^2}{2!} + \ldots + \frac{x^r}{r!} + \ldots .$$

Hence it follows at once that

$$e^{ax} = 1 + ax + \frac{a^2x^2}{\lfloor 2} + \frac{a^3x^3}{\lfloor 3} + \ldots + \frac{a^rx^r}{\lfloor r} + \ldots, \quad \ldots\ldots\ldots(i)$$

and, putting $a = -1$,

$$e^{-x} = 1 - x + \frac{x^2}{2!} - \frac{x^3}{3!} + \ldots + (-1)^r \frac{x^r}{r!} + \ldots . \quad \ldots\ldots\ldots(ii)$$

Ex. 3. Calculate to four decimal places the value of e^x when $x = 1{\cdot}2$.

From (i) we obtain, where $a = 1$,

$$1 + x = 2{\cdot}20000, \quad \frac{x^2}{2} = 0{\cdot}72000, \quad \frac{x^3}{2 \cdot 3} = 0{\cdot}28800,$$

$$\frac{x^4}{\lfloor 4} = 0{\cdot}08640, \quad \frac{x^5}{\lfloor 5} = 0{\cdot}02064, \quad \frac{x^6}{\lfloor 6} = 0{\cdot}00413,$$

$$\frac{x^7}{\lfloor 7} = 0{\cdot}00071, \quad \frac{x^8}{\lfloor 8} = 0{\cdot}00011, \quad \text{the sum is } 3{\cdot}32000.$$

Other values of x, *e.g.* 0·4, 0·8, 1·6, 2·0, etc., may in like manner be assumed and the corresponding values of e^x obtained.

From the series for e^x it will be obvious that when x is 0, $e^0 = 1$.

When x is indefinitely great, or (as usually expressed) when x is infinite, e^x is infinite;

$$\therefore \; e^\infty = \infty .$$

Also, since $e^{-x} = \frac{1}{e^x} = 0$, when x is infinite, e^x has a range of positive values from zero to ∞, as x changes from $-\infty$ to $+\infty$. That its value cannot be negative if x is real may be seen from the graph on p. 141.

Expansion a^x.—The series for a^x is readily deduced from that of e^x.

Since e^c can have any positive value from zero to infinity, it follows that if a is any real positive quantity whatever, we can always find c, so that $e^c = a$.

Thus if $a=2$, $c=0{\cdot}693147$ to 6 places of decimals, an $e^{0{\cdot}693147}=2$. In fact, we see from the definition of logarithm p. 49, $c=\log_e a$, if $e^c=a$.

But $$a^x=e^{cx}=1+cx+\frac{c^2x^2}{\lfloor 2}+\frac{c^3x^3}{\lfloor 3}+\ldots+\frac{c^rx^r}{\lfloor r}+\ldots;$$

$$\therefore\ a^x=1+x\log_e a+\frac{(x\log_e a)^2}{\lfloor 2}+\ldots+\frac{(x\log_e a)^r}{\lfloor r}+\ldots,$$

and $$a^{bx}=1+bx\log_e a+\frac{(bx\log_e a)^2}{\lfloor 2}+\ldots+\frac{(bx\log_e a)^r}{\lfloor r}+\ldots$$

We collect here for reference the four expansions alread obtained.

$$(a)\qquad \mathbf{e}=\mathbf{1}+\mathbf{1}+\frac{\mathbf{1}}{\lfloor \mathbf{2}}+\frac{\mathbf{1}}{\lfloor \mathbf{3}}+\ldots+\frac{\mathbf{1}}{\lfloor \mathbf{r}}+\ldots;$$

$$(b)\qquad \mathbf{e}^x=\mathbf{1}+\mathbf{x}+\frac{\mathbf{x}^2}{\lfloor \mathbf{2}}+\frac{\mathbf{x}^3}{\lfloor \mathbf{3}}+\ldots+\frac{\mathbf{x}^r}{\lfloor \mathbf{r}}+\ldots;$$

$$(c)\qquad \mathbf{e}^{ax}=\mathbf{1}+\mathbf{ax}+\frac{\mathbf{a}^2\mathbf{x}^2}{\lfloor \mathbf{2}}+\frac{\mathbf{a}^3\mathbf{x}^3}{\lfloor \mathbf{3}}+\ldots+\frac{\mathbf{a}^r\mathbf{x}^r}{\lfloor \mathbf{r}};$$

$$(d)\qquad \mathbf{a}^{bx}=\mathbf{1}+\mathbf{bx}\log_e \mathbf{a}+\frac{(\mathbf{bx}\log_e \mathbf{a})^2}{\lfloor \mathbf{2}}+\frac{(\mathbf{bx}\log_e \mathbf{a})^3}{\lfloor \mathbf{3}}+\ldots.$$

The last is the most general of the preceding series; fron this one the remaining series may be obtained by givin particular values to b and x, and substituting e for a.

Expansion of $\log_e(1+x)$.—Take the series

$$a^z=1+z\log_e a+\frac{z^2(\log_e a)^2}{\lfloor 2}+\frac{z^3(\log_e a)^3}{\lfloor 3}+\ldots,$$

and let $$a=1+x;$$

$$\therefore\ (1+x)^z=1+z\log_e(1+x)+\frac{z^2}{\lfloor 2}\{\log_e(1+x)\}^2+\ldots.$$

But, by the Binomial Theorem, p. 278,

$$(1+x)^z=1+zx+\frac{z(z-1)x^2}{\lfloor 2}+\frac{z(z-1)(z-2)}{\lfloor 3}x^3+\ldots$$
$$+\frac{z(z-1)(z-2)(z-3)\ldots(z-r+1)}{\lfloor r}x^r+\ldots$$
$$=1+z\left\{x-\frac{x^2}{2}+\frac{1.2}{\lfloor 3}x^3+\ldots+(-1)^{r-1}\frac{1.2.3\ldots(r-1)}{\lfloor r}x^r+\ldots\right\}$$
$$+z^2\left(\frac{x^2}{2}+\ldots\right)+\ldots.$$

This is only true when x is less than 1, for the Binomial Theorem is only applicable in such a case. Hence, if x is < 1,

$$1+z\left\{x-\frac{x^2}{2}+\frac{x^3}{3}-\frac{x^4}{4}+\frac{x^5}{5}-\dots\right\}+z^2\left\{\frac{x^2}{2}+\dots\right\}+\dots$$

$$=1+z\log_e(1+x)+\frac{z^2}{\lfloor 2}\{\log_e(1+x)\}^2+\dots$$

for all values of z. Therefore, the coefficient of any power of z on one side of the identity is equal to that of the similar power on the other, provided x is not > 1.

Selecting the coefficients of the first power of z, we obtain the series

$$\log_e(1+x)=x-\frac{x^2}{2}+\frac{x^3}{3}-\frac{x^4}{4}+\frac{x^5}{5}\dots.$$

This holds when x is not greater than unity. But when x is greater than unity it is obviously infinite in value for an infinite number of terms. But $\log_e(1+x)$ is finite, if x is finite; hence the above cannot be true if $x > 1$.

Calculation of logarithms.—From the preceding series it is possible to calculate a table of logarithms to the base e.

Ex. 4. In the preceding series (i) put $x=\frac{1}{2}$, and we obtain

$$\log_e\tfrac{3}{2}=\tfrac{1}{2}-\tfrac{1}{2}(\tfrac{1}{2})^2+\tfrac{1}{3}(\tfrac{1}{2})^3-\tfrac{1}{4}(\tfrac{1}{2})^4+\dots,$$

or $$\log_e 3-\log_e 2=\tfrac{1}{2}-\tfrac{1}{2}(\tfrac{1}{2})^2+\tfrac{1}{3}(\tfrac{1}{2})^3-\tfrac{1}{4}(\tfrac{1}{2})^4+\dots$$

$$=0{\cdot}549305-0{\cdot}143840;$$

$$\therefore \log_e 3-\log_e 2=0{\cdot}405465.$$

In a similar manner, the series may be used to calculate the numerical values of $\log_e 2$, $\log_e 3$, ...

Thus, substituting $x=\frac{1}{3}$ in the series for $\log(1+x)$, we obtain

$$\log_e 4-\log_e 3=0{\cdot}287682,$$

$$\therefore 2\log_e 2-\log_e 3=0{\cdot}287682;$$

also $$\log_e 3-\log_e 2=0{\cdot}405465,$$

$$\therefore \text{ by addition } \log_e 2=0{\cdot}693147,$$

and $$\log_e 3=1{\cdot}098612;\ \text{also}\ \log_e 4=1{\cdot}386294.$$

Other selected values may be calculated in like manner.

The preceding method is much too laborious for general use in calculations. More convenient formulae may be obtained as follows:

Thus, $$\log_e(1+x)=x-\frac{x^2}{2}+\frac{x^3}{3}-\frac{x^4}{4}+\dots;$$

$$\therefore \log_e(1-x)=-x-\frac{x^2}{2}-\frac{x^3}{3}-\frac{x^4}{4}-\dots.$$

The latter is obtained from the former by writing $-x$ for x.

Subtracting,

$$\therefore \log_e(1+x)-\log_e(1-x)=2\left(x+\frac{x^3}{3}+\frac{x^5}{5}+\dots\right),$$

or $$\log_e\frac{1+x}{1-x}=2\left(x+\frac{x^3}{3}+\frac{x^5}{5}+\dots\right). \quad \text{.......(ii)}$$

If x is small it is only necessary to retain and calculate the values of two or three terms in the series (ii).

Ex. 5. Given $\log_e 9=2{\cdot}197224$, find the value of $\log_e 11$.

If $x=\frac{1}{10}$, $$\log_e\frac{1+x}{1-x}=\log_e 11-\log_e 9$$
$$=2\left\{\frac{1}{10}+\frac{1}{3\times 10^3}+\dots\right\}.$$

A series in which it is necessary to retain only a few terms.

It will be obvious that if a series for $\log_e(n+1)-\log_e n$ can be obtained in which the successive terms in the series decrease very rapidly, then it will be possible, when $\log_e n$ is known, to obtain $\log_e(n+1)$, and therefore the logarithms of all numbers consecutively.

Now $$\log_e(n+1)-\log_e n=\log_e\frac{1+n}{n}.$$

Let $$\frac{1+n}{n}=\frac{1+x}{1-x},$$

$$\therefore (1+n)(1-x)=n(1+x); \quad \therefore x=\frac{1}{2n+1}.$$

Now substitute this value of x obtained in the series for $\log_e\frac{1+x}{1-x}$;

$$\log_e\frac{n+1}{n}=2\left\{\frac{1}{2n+1}+\frac{1}{3(2n+1)^3}+\frac{1}{5(2n+1)^5}+\dots\right\}.$$

A series in which the successive terms decrease very rapidly.

Calculation of common logarithms.—To calculate common logarithms or logarithms to base 10, we may, as indicated on p. 54, divide the logarithm of a number to base e by $\log_e 10$.

Thus $\log_e 2 = 0{\cdot}69315$ and $\log_e 10 = 2{\cdot}30258$;

$$\therefore \log_{10} 2 = \frac{0{\cdot}69315}{2{\cdot}30258} = 0{\cdot}30103.$$

Proceeding in this manner it would be possible to change the logarithms of all numbers calculated to base e into common logarithms.

The number $\dfrac{1}{\log_e 10} = 0{\cdot}4342945$ is called the **modulus** of the common system of logarithms, and is often represented by the letter μ.

Thus, the series for $\log_e \dfrac{n+1}{n}$ and the value of μ enables us to calculate common logarithms directly, for

$$\log_{10} \frac{n+1}{n} = \mu \log_e \frac{n+1}{n}.$$

Hence,
$$\log_{10} \frac{n+1}{n} = 2\mu \left\{ \frac{1}{2n+1} + \frac{1}{3(2n+1)^3} + \ldots \right\}.$$

The work is further simplified by the fact that

$$\log_{10} (10^r \times n) = r + \log_{10} n.$$

Thus
$$\log_{10} 1{\cdot}0561 = \log_{10} 10561 - 4,$$

since
$$1{\cdot}0561 = \frac{10561}{10^4}.$$

Ex. 6. Calculate $\log_{10} 10{\cdot}001$ to 7 decimal places.

$$\log_{10} 10{,}001 = \log 10{,}000 + \frac{2 \times 0{\cdot}4342945}{20{,}001}$$
$$= 4 + 0{\cdot}0000434;$$

$$\therefore \log 10{\cdot}001 = 1{\cdot}0000434.$$

Similarly,
$$\log_{10} 10{,}002 = \log 10{,}001 + \frac{2 \times 0{\cdot}4342945}{20{,}003}$$
$$= 4{\cdot}0000868.$$

EXERCISES. XXXIV.

1. The values of $\log_e 2$, $\log_e 3$, are $0{\cdot}69315$, and $1{\cdot}09861$ respectively, calculate and tabulate the logarithms of 5, 6, 7, 8, 9, and 10 to base e in each case to 5 significant figures.

2. Given $\log_e 30 = 3{\cdot}401197$, calculate to 5 significant figures the numerical values of the logarithms of 31, 32, 33, 34, 35, 36, 37, 38, 39, and 40.

3. Find series for the expressions

$$\frac{e^x + e^{-x}}{2}, \quad \frac{e^x - e^{-x}}{2}, \quad \frac{e^{ax} + e^{-ax}}{2}, \quad \frac{e^{ax} - e^{-ax}}{2}.$$

4. Taking $\log_e 1{\cdot}1 = 0{\cdot}09531$, test the identity

$$(1{\cdot}1)^2 = 1 + 2\log_e 1{\cdot}1 + \frac{(2\log_e 1{\cdot}1)^2}{\lfloor 2} + \ldots + \frac{(2\log_e 1{\cdot}1)^x}{\lfloor r}$$

to four decimal places.

5. Given $\log_{10} 4{\cdot}1110 = 0{\cdot}6139475$, calculate the logarithms of numbers of 6 significant figures between 4·1110 and 4·1120.

6. Take $\log_{10} 3420$ from the tables at the end of the book and calculate logs of numbers between 3420 and 3430 to at least 4 decimal places. Compare your answers with the tables.

Hint. Use $n = 3420$, not 34,200 as before;

$$\therefore \log_{10} 3421 = \log 3420 + \frac{2\mu}{2(3420)+1}.$$

Using the formulae $(1 \pm a)^n = 1 \pm na$ etc., p. 282. Verify the following:

7. If there is a possible error of 2 per cent. in the radius of a circle, the possible error in the calculated area will be 4 per cent.

Given $r = 5{\cdot}23$ in., show that the possible error is 3·4 sq. in.

8. The area of a triangle is calculated by the formula $\frac{1}{2}bc \sin A$. If an error of 3 per cent. excess is made in measuring the side b, and 2 per cent. defect in measuring the side c, show that the calculated value of the area will be 1 per cent. excess.

Given $b = 13{\cdot}1$ ft. $c = 7{\cdot}2$ ft., $A = 40°$, show that the error is 0·31 square feet.

9. The torsional rigidity of a length of wire is obtained from the formula $N = 8\pi Il \div t^2 r^4$. If an error of 2 per cent. defect is made in the observed value of l, $1\frac{1}{2}$ per cent. excess in t, and 2 per cent. excess in r, show that the resulting error in the calculated value of N is 13 per cent. Given $I = 34{,}300$, $l = 38{\cdot}2$, $t = 6{\cdot}28$, $r = 0{\cdot}04$, show that the probable error in the value of N is $4{\cdot}58 \times 10^{10}$.

CHAPTER XIV.

RATE OF INCREASE. SIMPLE DIFFERENTIATION.

Rate of increase.—Most students are probably familiar with what is meant by such a statement as the following:—The population of a country in 1901 was 3,000,000 in excess of that in 1891, thus giving an **average rate of increase** of 300,000 per year during the ten years. The calculation involved is simply the increase of population for the 10 years divided by 10, and this gives what is called the average rate of increase per year. This average rate of increase, though useful to the statistician, is not sufficiently definite for mathematical purposes. Such a rate does not, for instance, give the rate of increase for any one year; this might be 200,000 during 1898 and 400,000 during 1899 without altering the average rate during the ten years.

Probably a better illustration is obtained from a table such as the following, in which the relation between y and x is $y=x^2$, and in which for values of x corresponding values of y are given.

From such a table we are able to ascertain the average, and also the actual, rate of increase of a given quantity.

x	4·000	4·0001	4·001	4·01	4·1
y	16·0000	16 00080001	16·008001	16·0801	16·81

The amount by which one value of x has increased, to form a second value x, is called an **increment** of x. Thus, referring to the table and subtracting 4·0 from 4·1 we obtain 0·1; this is the increment of x which is being considered; and

$16{\cdot}81-16{\cdot}0=0{\cdot}81$ is the corresponding increment of y. The average rate of increase of y, as x increases from 4·0 to 4·1, is the increment of y divided by the corresponding increment of x, and is equal to

$$\frac{0{\cdot}81}{0{\cdot}1}=8{\cdot}1.$$

Taking other values from the table, we have, between $x=4{\cdot}0$ and 4·01, the ratio:

$$\frac{\text{increment of } y}{\text{increment of } x}=\frac{0{\cdot}0801}{0{\cdot}01}=8{\cdot}01.$$

Between $x=4{\cdot}0$ and $x=4{\cdot}001$ $=\dfrac{0{\cdot}008001}{0{\cdot}001}=8{\cdot}001.$

Between $x=4{\cdot}0$ and $x=4{\cdot}0001=\dfrac{0{\cdot}00080001}{0{\cdot}0001}=8{\cdot}0001.$

Thus, the average rate of increase of y is a variable quantity which depends on the magnitude of the increment of x. Further, as the increment is diminished, the corresponding increment of y also diminishes, and the average rate approaches a value 8. The approximation becomes closer and closer as the increment of x is diminished, and ultimately, when the increment of x is made indefinitely small, the ratio has the value 8, and this is the actual rate of increase of y when $x=4$.

The value 8 is then said to be the **limit** of the ratio of the increment of y to the corresponding increment of x.

As the expression "increment of y" occurs frequently, the symbol δy is used to denote an increment of y, and the above ratio is written $\dfrac{\delta y}{\delta x}$.

The expression "the limit of $\dfrac{\delta y}{\delta x}$ when δx diminishes without limit" is written in the form

$$\underset{\delta x=0}{\mathrm{Lt}}\ \frac{\delta y}{\delta x}.$$

The final value of δx *will be zero*, and the result obtained is called the **differential coefficient of y.** This is the definition in its algebraic form of a differential coefficient.

Comparing this, step by step, with the example given, we obtain for one particular case

$$\left.\begin{array}{l}\delta y = 0{\cdot}81\\ \delta x = 0{\cdot}1\end{array}\right\},$$

the ratio $\frac{\delta y}{\delta x}$ having a numerical value of 8·1 or $8+\delta x$.

Again, for a second case, $\delta y = 0{\cdot}0801$ and $\delta x = 0{\cdot}01$,

or $$\frac{\delta y}{\delta x} = \frac{0{\cdot}0801}{0{\cdot}01} = 8{\cdot}01, \text{ or } 8+\delta x,$$

and so on as far as possible.

It is obvious, however, that we may proceed to make δx less and less, and shall not come to a stop until it is absolutely zero. When this occurs, $8+\delta x$ becomes $8+0$ or 8—a perfectly definite result, which does not depend on the increment taken. Or, in other words, we have reached a limit to the value of $\frac{\delta y}{\delta x}$, and we call it a differential coefficient, writing it $\frac{dy}{dx}$.

It must be carefully noticed that in $\frac{dy}{dx}$, $\frac{d}{dx}$ is a symbol of an operation just as $\div$ indicates division, or $\times$ indicates multiplication, and therefore it *does not mean* $d\times x$ and $d\times y$; the symbol $\frac{dy}{dx}$ simply indicates a rate of increase.

The relation between two variables x and y from which the preceding numbers may be calculated being given by

$$y = x^2. \qquad \text{(i)}$$

Let $x+\delta x$ denote a slightly larger value of x, and $y+\delta y$ the corresponding value of y. Then we obtain from (i), by substitution,

$$\begin{aligned} y+\delta y &= (x+\delta x)^2 \\ &= x^2 + 2x\delta x + (\delta x)^2. \qquad \text{(ii)} \end{aligned}$$

Subtract (i) from (ii),

$$\delta y = 2x\delta x + (\delta x)^2.$$

Divide both sides by δx;

$$\therefore \frac{\delta y}{\delta x} = 2x + \delta x.$$

Comparison with the preceding tabulated numbers will explain the meaning when $x=4$ of $\frac{\delta y}{\delta x}=8+\delta x$, and for the reasons already given when δx becomes zero we write $\frac{dy}{dx}$ instead of $\frac{\delta y}{\delta x}$, and say that the differential coefficient of y is 8 when x has the value 4.

Ex. 1. From the definition

$$\frac{dy}{dx}=\mathrm{Lt}_{\delta x=0}\frac{\delta y}{\delta x},$$

find $\frac{dy}{dx}$ when

$$y=10+5x+3x^2. \quad \text{(i)}$$

The equation (i) must be true for all values of y and x.

Hence

$$y+\delta y=10+5(x+\delta x)+3(x+\delta x)^2$$
$$=10+5x+5\delta x+3x^2+6x\delta x+3(\delta x)^2. \quad \text{(ii)}$$

Subtracting (i) from (ii),

$$\delta y=5\delta x+6x\delta x+3(\delta x)^2,$$

or

$$\frac{\delta y}{\delta x}=5+6x+3\delta x.$$

Now make $\delta x=0$; this also makes $\frac{\delta y}{\delta x}$ become $\frac{dy}{dx}$, and we obtain

$$\mathrm{Lt}_{\delta x=0}\frac{\delta y}{\delta x}=\left[\frac{dy}{dx}\right]=5+6x. \quad \text{(iii)}$$

Expressing (iii) in words we may say "The limit of the ratio of the increment of y to the increment of x, when the latter is made zero, is called the differential coefficient of y with respect to x, and is equal, in the case considered, to $5+6x$."

Ex. 2. Show that when

$$y=x^3,\ u=x^4,\ v=5x^2,$$

then

$$\frac{dy}{dx}=3x^2,\ \frac{du}{dx}=4x^3,\ \frac{dv}{dx}=10x;$$

also when $y=ax^3$,

$$\frac{dy}{dx}=3ax^2.$$

$\frac{dy}{dx}$ has been defined as $\mathrm{Lt}_{\delta x=0}\frac{\delta y}{\delta x}$,

and in order to find its actual value the relation between x and y must be known. This is expressed by saying that y is some function of x, or

$$y=f(x) \quad \text{(i)}$$

As before $y+\delta y$ and $x+\delta x$ are simultaneous values;

$$\therefore\ y+\delta y=f(x+\delta x). \qquad \text{(ii)}$$

Subtract (i) from (ii);

$$\therefore\ \delta y=f(x+\delta x)-f(x).$$

Substitute this value in the definition above, and

$$\frac{dy}{dx}=\text{Lt}_{\delta x=0}\frac{f(x+\delta x)-f(x)}{\delta x}.$$

This is the usual expression for defining a differential coefficient and is more convenient for use.

Ex. 3. Given that $y=3x^3+9x$, find $\frac{dy}{dx}$.

$$\frac{dy}{dx}=\text{Lt}_{\delta x=0}\frac{\{3(x+\delta x)^3+9(x+\delta x)\}-(3x^3+9x)}{\delta x}$$

$$=\text{Lt}_{\delta x=0}\frac{3\{3x^2\delta x+3x(\delta x)^2+(\delta x)^3\}+9\delta x}{\delta x}$$

$$=\text{Lt}_{\delta x=0}\{9x^2+9x\delta x+3(\delta x)^2+9\}.$$

Apply the limiting condition, *i.e.* put $\delta x=0$, and $\therefore\ \frac{dy}{dx}=9x^2+9$.

The differential coefficients of certain expressions such as $y=x^n$, $y=\sin x$, etc., are of the utmost importance; the results when obtained should be committed to memory.

Differential coefficient x^n.—If $y=x^n$, then, from the definition just given, the average rate of increase of y with respect to x is

$$\frac{dy}{dx}=\text{Lt}_{\delta x=0}\frac{(x+\delta x)^n-x^n}{\delta x}$$

$$=\text{Lt}_{\delta x=0}\frac{x^n\left(1+\frac{\delta x}{x}\right)^n-x^n}{\delta x}$$

$$=\text{Lt}_{\delta x=0}\frac{x^n\left\{\left(1+\frac{\delta x}{x}\right)^n-1\right\}}{\delta x}.$$

Since $\frac{\delta x}{x}$ is <1 we may apply the Binomial Theorem (p. 278) to the expansion of $\left(1+\frac{\delta x}{x}\right)^n$, and therefore

$$\left(1+\frac{\delta x}{x}\right)^n=1+\frac{n\delta x}{x}+\frac{n(n-1)}{\underline{|2}}\left(\frac{\delta x}{x}\right)^2+\frac{n(n-1)(n-2)}{\underline{|3}}\left(\frac{\delta x}{x}\right)^3+\ldots;$$

$$\therefore \quad \left(1+\frac{\delta x}{x}\right)^n - 1 = \frac{n\delta x}{x} + \frac{n(n-1)}{\underline{|2}}\left(\frac{\delta x}{x}\right)^2 + \text{etc.},$$

and

$$\frac{\left(1+\frac{\delta x}{x}\right)^n - 1}{\delta x} = \frac{n}{x} + \frac{n(n-1)}{\underline{|2}}\frac{1}{x^2}(\delta x) + \text{etc.}$$

The remaining terms will contain increasing powers of δx as multipliers, and will therefore disappear in the limit, when δx is made zero.

Hence, the value of $\frac{dy}{dx}$ is $x^n \times \frac{n}{x} = nx^{n-1}$;

$$\therefore \text{ when } y = x^n, \quad \frac{dy}{dx} = nx^{n-1}.$$

Differential coefficient of sin x.—To obtain the differential coefficient when $y = \sin x$, we have, by definition,

$$\frac{dy}{dx} = \mathrm{Lt}_{\delta x=0}\frac{\sin(x+\delta x) - \sin x}{\delta x},$$

and by Trigonometry (p. 28),

$$\sin(x+\delta x) - \sin x = 2\cos\left(x+\frac{\delta x}{2}\right)\sin\frac{\delta x}{2};$$

$$\therefore \quad \frac{dy}{dx} = \mathrm{Lt}_{\delta x=0}\frac{\cos\left(x+\frac{\delta x}{2}\right)\sin\frac{\delta x}{2}}{\frac{\delta x}{2}}. \quad \text{..................(i)}$$

Now the value of $\frac{\sin A}{A}$, when A is very small and measured in radians, is very nearly unity, and when A is zero the ratio is exactly 1;

$$\therefore \quad \frac{\sin\frac{\delta x}{2}}{\frac{\delta x}{2}} = 1, \text{ also } \cos\left(x+\frac{\delta x}{2}\right) = \cos x, \text{ when } \delta x = 0.$$

Hence, $\frac{dy}{dx} = \cos x$ from (i).

Differential coefficient of cos x.—The value of $\frac{dy}{dx}$, when $y = \cos x$, may be obtained in a similar manner to the preceding;

$$\therefore \quad \frac{dy}{dx} = \mathrm{Lt}_{\delta x=0}\frac{\cos(x+\delta x) - \cos x}{\delta x},$$

and by Trigonometry (p. 28), this

$$=\mathrm{Lt}_{\delta x=0}\frac{-\sin\left(x+\frac{\delta x}{2}\right)\sin\frac{\delta x}{2}}{\frac{\delta x}{2}};$$

$$\therefore\ \frac{dy}{dx}=-\sin x,$$

since $$\mathrm{Lt}_{\delta x=0}\frac{\sin\frac{\delta x}{2}}{\frac{\delta x}{2}}=1.$$

Differential coefficient of e^x.—The differential coefficient of $y=e^x$ may be obtained as follows:

By definition $\frac{dy}{dx}$ is the limiting value of

$$\frac{\delta y}{\delta x}=\frac{e^{x+\delta x}-e^x}{\delta x}$$

when δx is made zero,

$$i.e.\ \frac{dy}{dx}=\mathrm{Lt}_{\delta x=0}\frac{e^x e^{\delta x}-e^x}{\delta x}$$

$$=e^x\frac{e^{\delta x}-1}{\delta x}.$$

But, as on p. 292,

$$e^{\delta x}=1+\delta x+\frac{(\delta x)^2}{\lfloor 2}+\ldots,$$

$$\therefore\ \frac{dy}{dx}=\mathrm{Lt}_{\delta x=0}\,e^x\times\frac{\left(1+\delta x+\frac{(\delta x)^2}{\lfloor 2}+\ldots\right)-1}{\delta x}$$

$$=\mathrm{Lt}_{\delta x=0}e^x\left\{1+\frac{\delta x}{\lfloor 2}+\frac{(\delta x)^2}{\lfloor 3}+\ldots\right\}.$$

Now, when δx becomes zero, all terms in the brackets, except the first, disappear;

$$\therefore\ \frac{dy}{dx}=e^x.$$

The last result may be obtained as follows:
Let $y = e^x$.

Now, $$e^x = 1 + x + \frac{x^2}{\lfloor 2} + \frac{x^3}{\lfloor 3} + \dots \text{ (see p. 292)};$$

$$\therefore \frac{dy}{dx} = \frac{d}{dx}(e^x) = \frac{d}{dx}\left(1 + x + \frac{x^2}{\lfloor 2} + \frac{x^3}{\lfloor 3} + \dots\right).$$

Differentiating,

$$\therefore \frac{d}{dx}(e^x) = 0 + 1 + x + \frac{x^2}{\lfloor 2} + \frac{x^3}{\lfloor 3} + \dots.$$

It will be noticed that the series obtained by differentiation is identical with the original series;

$$\therefore \frac{d}{dx}(e^x) = e^x.$$

In other words, **the rate of increase, or differential coefficient, of e^x, is the function itself.** This remarkable result, as indicated on pp 474, 477, 479, 587, is known as the **compound interest law.**

Differentiation of $\log_e x$.—Let $y = \log_e x$;

$$\therefore \frac{dy}{dx} = \text{Lt}_{\delta x = 0} \frac{\log_e(x + \delta x) - \log_e x}{\delta x}.$$

But the difference of two logarithms is the logarithm of their quotient (p. 51);

$$\therefore \frac{dy}{dx} = \text{Lt}_{\delta x = 0} \frac{\log_e \frac{x + \delta x}{x}}{\delta x}$$

$$= \text{Lt}_{\delta x = 0} \frac{\log_e\left(1 + \frac{\delta x}{x}\right)}{\delta x}.$$

Now, using the expansion for $\log_e\left(1 + \frac{\delta x}{x}\right)$ (p. 293), we obtain

$$\frac{dy}{dx} = \text{Lt}_{\delta x = 0}\left\{\frac{\delta x}{x} - \frac{1}{2}\left(\frac{\delta x}{x}\right)^2 + \frac{1}{3}\left(\frac{\delta x}{x}\right)^3 - \dots\right\} \div \delta x$$

$$= \text{Lt}_{\delta x = 0}\left\{\frac{1}{x} - \frac{1}{2}\frac{\delta x}{x^2} + \frac{1}{3}\frac{(\delta x)^2}{x^3} - \text{etc.}\right\}$$

$$= \frac{1}{x}.$$

Hence, the differential coefficient of $\log_e x$ is $\frac{1}{x}$.

Geometrical meaning of $\frac{dy}{dx}$.—In order to make the meaning of $\frac{dy}{dx}$, or of a *rate of increase*, clear, it may be necessary to consider the properties of the tangent line at a given point on a curve, particularly with regard to the angle made by the line with the axis of x, or as it is called the **slope of the line.**

If we take a line PQR (Fig. 107), its inclination to the axis of x, or the slope of the line, may be measured by several different methods.

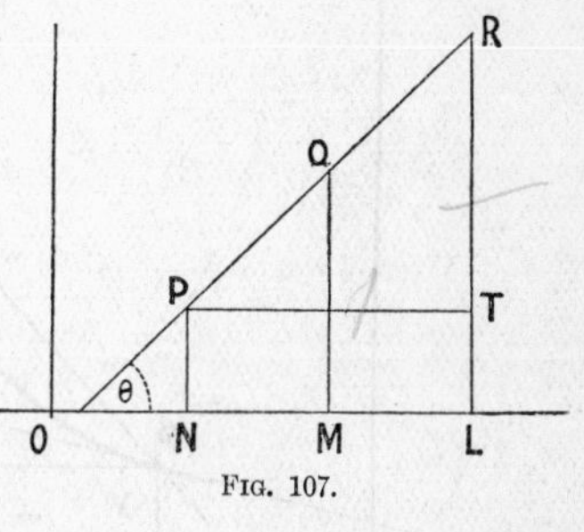

Fig. 107.

A length PR may be measured along the incline and the height of R, RT, above P obtained. Then the ratio $\frac{RT}{PR}$ or $\sin\theta$ is called by surveyors and others, the gradient or the slope of the road. It is usually expressed as a fraction having unity for its numerator, such as $\frac{1}{10}$, $\frac{1}{100}$, etc.

A much more convenient method for mathematical purposes is given by the ratio of RT to PT;

$$\therefore \tan\theta = \frac{RT}{PT}.$$

θ is known as the **slope** and $\tan\theta$ as the **gradient** of the line.

Tangent to a curve.—The tangent to a curve at a given point is defined as the straight line touching the curve at the point. In the case of a curve which passes through a series of plotted points, the line joining two points on the curve close to each other can be determined by diminishing the distance between them. In this manner the approximation to the tangent at a point may be made to any degree of accuracy and the tangent is the limit; *i.e.* when the points forming two consecutive points coincide on the curve.

Gradient of a curve.—The gradient of a curve at a given point may be defined as the tangent of the angle (made by the tangent to the curve at that point) with the axis of x.

Meaning of differential coefficient at a point on a curve.—Suppose PSQ to be a portion of a curve found by plotting $y=f(x)$. Taking the algebraic form of expression for $\frac{dy}{dx}$ and applying it to the geometrical case illustrated in Fig. 108.

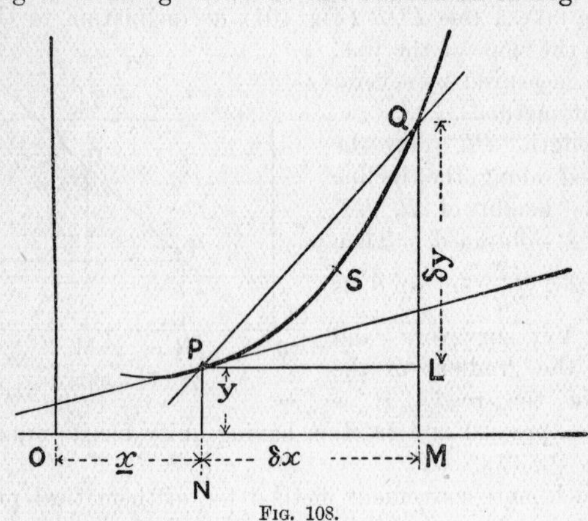

FIG. 108.

If $y=f(x)$,

then $$\frac{dy}{dx}=\text{Lt}_{\delta x=0}\frac{f(x+\delta x)-f(x)}{\delta x},$$

and since $f(x)=y$ and $f(x+\delta x)=y+\delta y$ it may be written

$$\frac{dy}{dx}=\text{Lt}_{\delta x=0}\frac{(y+\delta y)-y}{\delta x}.$$

Let y denote PN and $QM=y+\delta y$, then NM will be denoted by δx. $$\frac{dy}{dx}=\text{Lt}_{\delta x=0}\frac{QM-PN}{NM}.$$

But $QM-PN$ is equal to QL and $NM=PL$, whilst

$$\frac{QL}{PL}=\tan\phi.$$

But $\tan\phi$ has been defined as the gradient of the line PQ;

$\therefore$ replacing $\frac{QM-PN}{NM}$ by the words "the gradient of the line PQ," we obtain

$$\frac{dy}{dx}=\text{Lt}_{\delta x=0}, \text{ "the gradient of the line } PQ.\text{"}$$

Now, as δx decreases, *i.e.* as Q approaches nearer and nearer to P, PQ also approximates closer and closer to the tangent PT, and will become the tangent at P when $\delta x=0$, *i.e.*

"$\text{Lt}_{\delta x=0}$, the slope of the line PQ." now becomes the slope of the tangent at P.

Also, as $y=PN$, it follows that the differential coefficient of PN, with respect to x, is equal to the slope of the tangent at P.

Ex. 4. $y=\frac{1}{2}x^2$.

By the algebraic method,

$$\frac{dy}{dx}=\text{Lt}_{\delta x=0}\frac{\frac{1}{2}(x+\delta x)^2-\frac{1}{2}x^2}{\delta x}$$

$$=x.$$

Now plot the curve from $y=0$ to $y=1$.

This is shown by the curve in Fig. 109, p. 308.

Put the set square in the position indicated in Fig. 109, and draw the tangent at the point P as carefully as possible, P being the point for which $x=1$.

Measure the angle θ, and obtain its tangent from Table VI., or measure $\tan\theta$ directly from the figure by making NT equal to unity, and measuring on the vertical scale the length of MT, this is seen to be unity;

$$\therefore \tan\theta=\frac{MT}{NT}=\frac{1}{1}=1.$$

We have already found that $\frac{dy}{dx}=x$, and therefore for the point P, where $x=1$, $\frac{dy}{dx}=1$.

In a similar manner, other points on the curve may be selected, and the numerical values of $\frac{dy}{dx}$ can be calculated by

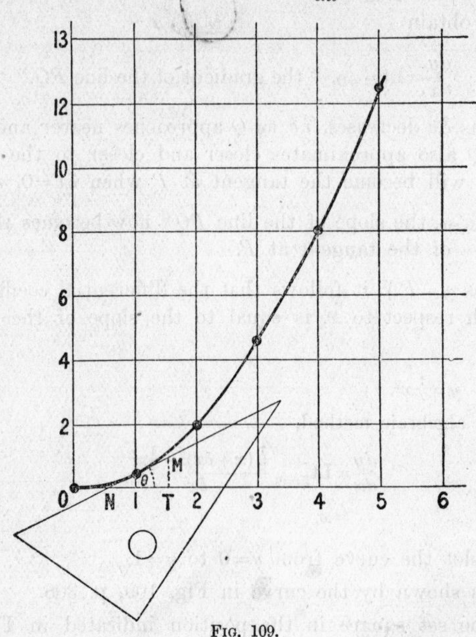

Fig. 109.

measuring the tangent of the angle made between the tangent to the curve and the axis of x.

EXERCISES. XXXV.

In each of the following, from the given value of y, find the value of $\frac{dy}{dx}$.

1. $y = x^4 + 3x^3 - x^2 + 5$.
2. $y = Ax^n$.
3. $y = \sin ax$.
4. $y = A \sin ax$.
5. $y = A \cos ax$.
6. $y = \sqrt{x^3}$.
7. Find $\frac{ds}{dt}$ from $s = v_0 t + \frac{1}{2}at^2$.

8. Illustrate that if $y=\sin x$, then $\frac{dy}{dx}=\cos x$ by working out the following table:

Angle in degrees.	Angle in radians.	y or $\sin x$.	δx	δy	$\frac{\delta y}{\delta x}$	Average value of $\frac{\delta y}{\delta x}$
40°	0·698131	0·642788				
40°·1	0·699877	0·644124				
40°·2	0·701622	0·645458				

9. If $u=\sin x$, and $v=\cos x$, determine by first principles the values of $\frac{du}{dx}$ and $\frac{dv}{dx}$.

Hence, or otherwise, find the value of $\frac{dy}{dx}$ where $y=\tan x$.

10. Determine the values of

$$\frac{d(a\sin bx)}{dx}, \quad \frac{d(a\cos bx)}{dx}, \quad \frac{d(ax^n)}{dx}.$$

11. $u=a\cos(bx+c)$, $v=\log(a+bx)$. Determine the values of

$$\frac{du}{dx}, \frac{dv}{dx}.$$

Find the differential coefficient in each of the following cases:

12. $y=\sqrt{a^2-x^2}$.

13. $y=\cot x$.

14. $y=\log ax$.

15. $y=a^x$.

16. $y=\sin ax^n$.

17. $v=\frac{a-t}{t}$.

18. $v=\sqrt{a^2-t^2}$.

19. $y=\log x^2$.

20. $y=4x^2+13x+4$.

21. $y=5x^2-9x+2$.

22. $y=x^5+4x^3$.

23. $y=2x^{-\frac{3}{2}}$.

24. $pv^{1·408}=c$, find $\frac{dp}{dv}$.

25. $s=\frac{1}{2}ft^2$, find $\frac{ds}{dt}$.

26. $v=ft$, find $\frac{dv}{dt}$.

CHAPTER XV.

DIFFERENTIATION.

THE definitions and principles of the preceding chapter are probably sufficient to enable the student to find the rate of increase, or the differential coefficient, of any function with respect to its variable, provided there is sufficient data given with regard to the function.

The labour thus involved may be reduced by the use of certain rules.

[Such rules have an undoubted advantage from a labour-saving point of view; but, as they may in some cases hide the steps in the work, and as it is so easy a matter for a student to use such rules without understanding them, it may be desirable to explain somewhat fully how some of these rules may be obtained.]

Differential coefficient of a constant.—As a constant is, from definition, an invariable quantity, and admits of no variation, it follows that if $y=c$, then δy, which denotes an increase in the value of y, is zero; and, therefore, all values of $\frac{\delta y}{\delta x}$ are zero, and consequently the limit $\frac{dy}{dx}=0$. Now, it will be obvious that $y=c$ denotes a line parallel to the axis of x and at a distance c from it. Hence, the tangent of the inclination, *i.e.* $\frac{dy}{dx}$ is zero.

Differentiation of a sum of functions.—This problem has been illustrated in a former chapter, but the general proof may with advantage be given here.

Let $$y=u+v+w,$$
where u, v, and w are each functions of x; and let $u+\delta u$, $v+\delta v$,

and $w+\delta w$ be the values of these functions when x has become $x+\delta x$.

Then, by definition,

$$\frac{dy}{dx}=\text{Lt}_{\delta x=0}\left\{\frac{(u+\delta u+v+\delta v+w+\delta w)-(u+v+w)}{\delta x}\right\}$$

$$=\text{Lt}_{\delta x=0}\left\{\frac{\delta u}{\delta x}+\frac{\delta v}{\delta x}+\frac{\delta w}{\delta x}\right\}.$$

But, making δx zero, which is an independent operation for each fraction, we obtain

$$\frac{dy}{dx}=\text{Lt}_{\delta x=0}\frac{\delta u}{\delta x}+\text{Lt}_{\delta x=0}\frac{\delta v}{\delta x}+\text{Lt}_{\delta x=0}\frac{\delta w}{\delta x}.$$

But $\text{Lt}_{\delta x=0}\frac{\delta u}{dx}=\frac{du}{dx}$, and so on for the others;

$$\therefore\ \frac{dy}{dx}=\frac{du}{dx}+\frac{dv}{dx}+\frac{dw}{dx}.$$

This form is most convenient for use, but it is often necessary to use more cumbrous expressions than u, v, and w for functions of the independent variable; and for this reason, the same operations are repeated exactly as follows:

Let $$y=F(x)+f(x)+\phi(x),$$

where $F(x)$, $f(x)$, and $\phi(x)$ denote functions of the variable x and do not contain the variable y; when x becomes $x+\delta x$, then y becomes

$$y+\delta y=F(x+\delta x)+f(x+\delta x)+\phi(x+\delta x);$$

$$\therefore\ \frac{dy}{dx}=\text{Lt}_{\delta x=0}\left\{\frac{F(x+\delta x)-F(x)+f(x+\delta x)-f(x)+\phi(x+\delta x)-\phi(x)}{\delta x}\right\}$$

$$=\text{Lt}_{\delta x=0}\left\{\frac{F(x+\delta x)-F(x)}{\delta x}+\frac{f(x+\delta x)-f(x)}{\delta x}+\frac{\phi(x+\delta x)-\phi(x)}{\delta x}\right\}.$$

Now $\text{Lt}_{\delta x=0}\left\{\frac{F(x+\delta x)-F(x)}{\delta x}+\frac{f(x+\delta x)-f(x)}{\delta x}+\dots\right\}$

is equal to

$$\text{Lt}_{\delta x=0}\frac{F(x+\delta x)-F(x)}{\delta x}+\text{Lt}_{\delta x=0}\frac{f(x+\delta x)-f(x)}{\delta x}+\dots,$$

because it is obvious that each term is independent of the others, since δx is put zero in each.

Also $\text{Lt}_{\delta x=0}\dfrac{F(x+\delta x)-F(x)}{\delta x}=\dfrac{dF(x)}{dx}$,

or the differential coefficient of $F(x)$.

Hence, $$\frac{dy}{dx}=\frac{dF(x)}{dx}+\frac{df(x)}{dx}+\frac{d\phi(x)}{dx}.$$

We may express the result in words as follows: **The differential coefficient of the sum of a series of functions is the sum of the differential coefficients of each of the respective functions.**

$dF(x)$ is often written $F'(x)$, and similarly for the others.

Ex. 1. $y=x^3+x^2$;

$$\frac{dy}{dx}=3x^2+2x.$$

Ex. 2. $y=a+x+x^2+x^3+x^4$;

$$\frac{dy}{dx}=0+1+2x+3x^2+4x^3.$$

Differentiation of a function of a function.—The meaning of the term function of a function of x will be clear from the following examples:

Ex. 3. Let $y=\sqrt{(1+x^2)}$. ....(1)

This is a function of a function of x.

If we substitute a letter such as z for the quantity in the bracket, we obtain from (1)

$$y=\sqrt{z};$$

where $z=1+x^2$,

z is a function of x, and y is a function of z.

Hence y, a function of z,—which is itself a function of x,—is said to be a function of a function of x.

Ex. 4. Similarly, if $y=\cos(x^2)$,

let $x^2=z$;

$$\therefore\ y=\cos z.$$

$\therefore$ y is the cosine of a function of z, and is a function of a function of x.

We can obtain in each case, with some labour, the differential coefficient of a complex function from first principles. Referring to Ex. 3, let

$$y=\sqrt{(1+x^2)};$$

$$\therefore \frac{dy}{dx}=\text{Lt}_{\delta x=0}\frac{\sqrt{1+x^2+2x\delta x+(\delta x)^2}-\sqrt{(1+x^2)}}{\delta x}$$

$$=\text{Lt}_{\delta x=0}\frac{(1+x^2)^{\frac{1}{2}}}{\delta x}\left[\left\{1+\frac{\delta x(2x+\delta x)}{1+x^2}\right\}^{\frac{1}{2}}-1\right].$$

By the binomial theorem,

$$\left\{1+\frac{\delta x(2x+\delta x)}{1+x^2}\right\}^{\frac{1}{2}}=1+\frac{1}{2}\frac{\delta x(2x+\delta x)}{1+x^2}-\frac{1}{8}\frac{(2x+\delta x)^2}{(1+x^2)^2}\delta x^2+\text{etc.}$$

$$\therefore \frac{dy}{dx}=\text{Lt}_{\delta x=0}\frac{(1+x^2)^{\frac{1}{2}}}{\delta x}$$

$$\times\left\{1+\frac{1}{2}\frac{\delta x(2x+\delta x)}{1+x^2}-\frac{1}{8}\left(\frac{2x+\delta x}{1+x^2}\right)^2\delta x^2+\text{etc.}-1\right\}$$

$$=\text{Lt}_{\delta x=0}(1+x^2)^{\frac{1}{2}}\left\{\frac{1}{2}\frac{2x+\delta x}{1+x^2}-\frac{1}{8}\left(\frac{2x+\delta x}{1+x^2}\right)^2\delta x+\dots\right\}$$

$$=\text{Lt}_{\delta x=0}(1+x^2)^{\frac{1}{2}}\left[\frac{x}{1+x^2}-\left\{\frac{1}{8}\left(\frac{2x+\delta x}{1+x^2}\right)^2-\frac{1}{2(1+x^2)}\right\}\delta x\right],$$

and hence,
$$\frac{dy}{dx}=(1+x^2)^{\frac{1}{2}}\frac{x}{1+x^2}=\frac{x}{(1+x^2)^{\frac{1}{2}}}.$$

This may be written in the form

$$\frac{dy}{dx}=\frac{1}{2}(1+x^2)^{-\frac{1}{2}}\times 2x.$$

Again referring to (3), if

$$z=1+x^2,\ \text{then}\ y=z^{\frac{1}{2}},$$

and
$$\frac{dy}{dz}=\frac{1}{2}z^{-\frac{1}{2}}=\frac{1}{2}(1+x^2)^{-\frac{1}{2}};$$

$$\frac{dz}{dx}=\frac{d}{dx}(1+x^2)=2x;$$

$$\therefore \frac{dy}{dx}=\frac{dy}{dz}\frac{dz}{dx}.$$

Let $y=f(z)$ where $z=F(x)$, then $y=f\{F(x)\}$.

If x increases to $x+\delta x$, z will increase to $z+\delta z$ where

$$z+\delta z=F(x+\delta x)$$

and
$$\delta z=F(x+\delta x)-F(x).$$

Using $z+\delta z$, we can calculate $y+\delta y$ from $y=f(z)$.

This result will be the same as if $x+\delta x$ had been substituted directly in $y=f\{F(x)\}$.

Under these conditions we can say that

$$\frac{\delta y}{\delta x}=\frac{\delta y}{\delta z}\times\frac{\delta z}{\delta x},$$

because δz is the same in the ratio $\frac{\delta z}{\delta x}$ as in $\frac{\delta y}{\delta z}$. Also δy is the same in the ratio $\frac{\delta y}{\delta z}$ as in $\frac{\delta y}{\delta x}$. This will be true no matter how small δx is.

If we now assume δx to be made smaller and smaller without limit. Then

$$\frac{dy}{dx}=\frac{dy}{dz}\cdot\frac{dz}{dx}.$$

Thus, to calculate $\frac{dy}{dx}$ where $y=f(z)=f\{F(x)\}$, we may first find $\frac{dy}{dz}$ from $y=f(z)$, then $\frac{dz}{dx}$ from $z=F(x)$, and the product of the results is $\frac{dy}{dx}$.

Geometrical illustration.—The preceding considerations may be illustrated graphically as follows:

In Fig. 110, (i) represents $z=F(x)$, $z=x^{\frac{1}{2}}$;

(ii) „ $y=f(z)$, $y=\cos z$;

(iii) „ $y=f\{F(x)\}$, $y=\cos x^{\frac{1}{2}}$.

Take $x=Op$ and $x+\delta x=Oq$. Draw the corresponding ordinates of (i). Measure in (ii) $Ot=Pp$, $Os=Qq$,

i.e. $Ot=z$ and $Os=z+\delta z$.

Since from (i) $Pp=z$ and $Qq=z+\delta z$,

in (iii), $Or=Op=x$,

$Ov=Oq=x+\delta x$.

Then $Rr=Tt=y$,

$Vv=Ss=y+\delta y$;

$\therefore\ Vl=Sm$ and $Rl=pq$.

It follows, therefore, that

$$\frac{Sm}{Tm}\times\frac{Qn}{Pn}=\frac{Sm}{Pn}=\frac{Vl}{Rl}.$$

Now, if pq be made smaller and smaller without limit till it becomes zero,

$\frac{Sm}{Tm}$ becomes $\frac{dy}{dz}$, *i.e.* slope of (ii) at T,

$\frac{Qn}{Pn}$ becomes $\frac{dz}{dx}$, *i.e.* slope of (i) at P,

and $\frac{Vl}{Rl}$ becomes $\frac{dy}{dx}$, *i.e.* slope of (iii) at R.

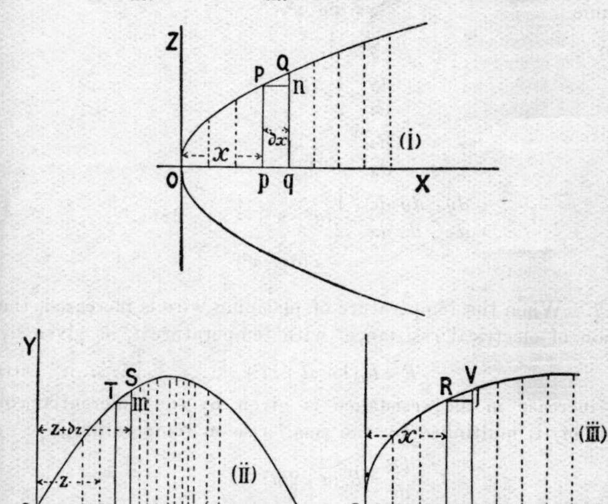

FIG. 110.—To show that $\frac{dy}{dx}=\frac{dy}{dz}\cdot\frac{dz}{dx}$.

P, T and R being three corresponding points as described.

$$\therefore\ \frac{dy}{dz}\frac{dz}{dx}=\frac{dy}{dx}.$$

The relation $\frac{dy}{dx}=\frac{dy}{dz}\frac{dz}{dx}$ is of great use in complicated expressions.

Ex. 5. Thus, if $y=(x+x^2)^2$. ....(i)

Let $z=x+x^2$, then (i) becomes $y=z^2$.

Then $$\frac{dz}{dx}=1+2x;$$

also $$\frac{dy}{dz}=2z,$$

$$\frac{dy}{dx}=\frac{dy}{dz}\cdot\frac{dz}{dx}=2z(1+2x)$$
$$=2(x+x^2)(1+2x).$$

Ex. 6. Let $y=\sqrt{(a^2-x^2)}$.

Assume $z=a^2-x^2$.

Then $$y=z^{\frac{1}{2}},$$
$$\frac{dy}{dz}=\frac{1}{2}z^{-\frac{1}{2}};$$

also, $$\frac{dz}{dx}=-2x;$$

$$\therefore\ \frac{dy}{dx}=\frac{dy}{dz}\frac{dz}{dx}=\frac{1}{2}(a^2-x^2)^{-\frac{1}{2}}\times(-2x)$$
$$=-x(a^2-x^2)^{-\frac{1}{2}}.$$

Ex. 7. When the temperature of platinum wire is increased, the variation of electrical resistance, with temperature t, is given by

$$R=R_0(1+\alpha t+\beta t^2). \qquad \text{(i)}$$

The increase in the resistance is given by the differential coefficient of (i) multiplied by the small rise in temperature;

$$\frac{dR}{dt}=R_0(\alpha+2\beta t).$$

Ex. 8. Find $\frac{dy}{dx}$ when $y=\sin x^2$.

Put $$z=x^2;\ \therefore\ \frac{dz}{dx}=2x.$$

$$y=\sin z;\ \therefore\ \frac{dy}{dz}=\cos z.$$

$$\therefore\ \frac{dy}{dx}=\frac{dy}{dz}\frac{dz}{dx}=\cos z\times 2x$$
$$=2x\cos x^2.$$

Ex. 9. Find $\frac{dy}{dx}$ when $y=(x^2+4)^4$.

Put $$z=x^2+4\ ;\ \therefore\ \frac{dz}{dx}=2x.$$

$$y=z^4\ ;\ \therefore\ \frac{dy}{dz}=4z^3.$$

Hence, $$\frac{dy}{dx}=\frac{dy}{dz}\cdot\frac{dz}{dx}=4z^3\times 2x$$
$$=8x(x^2+4)^3.$$

Ex. 10. Find $\frac{dy}{dx}$ when $y=\frac{1}{x^2+x+c}$.

Let $$z=x^2+x+c,\ \therefore\ \frac{dz}{dx}=2x+1,$$

and $$y=\frac{1}{z};\ \therefore\ \frac{dy}{dz}=-z^{-2}.$$

$$\therefore\ \frac{dy}{dx}=-\frac{2x+1}{(x^2+x+c)^2}.$$

Ex. 11. If x increases uniformly at the rate of 0·001 ft. per sec., at what rate is the expression $(1+x)^3$ increasing per second, when x becomes 9?

Let $z=1+x$, then $y=z^3$,

$$\frac{dz}{dx}=1 \text{ and } \frac{dy}{dz}=3z^2.$$

Substituting, $$\frac{dy}{dx}=\frac{dy}{dz}\frac{dz}{dx}=3(1+x)^2.$$

When x becomes 9 this gives 300, or y increases 300 times as quickly as x.

But x increases 0·001 ft. per sec.;

$\therefore$ y increases at $300\times 0{\cdot}001=0{\cdot}3$ ft. per sec.

Differential coefficient of the product of two functions.

Ex. 1. Let $$y=x^2\cos x.$$

This is a typical representative of a large family of functions. Its differential coefficient may be found by either of the following methods:

$$\frac{dy}{dx} = \text{Lt}_{\delta x=0}\left[\frac{(x+\delta x)^2\cos(x+\delta x) - x^2\cos x}{\delta x}\right]$$

$$= \text{Lt}_{\delta x=0}\left[\frac{x^2\{\cos(x+\delta x) - \cos x\} + 2x\delta x\cos(x+\delta x) + (\delta x)^2\cos(x+\delta x)}{\delta x}\right]$$

$$= \text{Lt}_{\delta x=0}\left[\frac{x^2\{\cos(x+\delta x) - \cos x\}}{\delta x} + 2x\cos(x+\delta x) + \delta x\cos(x+\delta x)\right]$$

$$= \text{Lt}_{\delta x=0}\left[\frac{x^2\times 2\sin\left(x+\frac{\delta x}{2}\right)\times\left(-\sin\frac{\delta x}{2}\right)}{\delta x} + 2x\cos(x+\delta x) + \delta x\cos(x+\delta x)\right];$$

$$\therefore \frac{dy}{dx} = -x^2\sin x + 2x\cos x.$$

Instead of the preceding method of solution, the result could be obtained as follows:

$$\frac{dy}{dx} = \text{Lt}_{\delta x=0}\left[\frac{(x+\delta x)^2\cos(x+\delta x) - x^2\cos x}{\delta x}\right]$$

$$= \text{Lt}_{\delta x=0}\left[\frac{(x+\delta x)^2\cos(x+\delta x) - (x+\delta x)^2\cos x + (x+\delta x)^2\cos x - x^2\cos x}{\delta x}\right].$$

$(x+\delta x)^2\cos x$ has been added and subtracted in the numerator, then, by rearrangement of the terms, we obtain

$$\frac{dy}{dx} = \text{Lt}_{\delta x=0}\left\{\frac{(x+\delta x)^2\{\cos(x+\delta x) - \cos x\}}{\delta x} + \frac{(x+\delta x)^2 - x^2}{\delta x}\cos x\right\}.$$

But we have already found that

$$\text{Lt}_{\delta x=0}\left\{\frac{\cos(x+\delta x) - \cos x}{\delta x}\right\}$$

is the differential coefficient of $\cos x$, or $\frac{d}{dx}(\cos x)$.

Similarly, $$\text{Lt}_{\delta x=0}\left\{\frac{(x+\delta x)^2 - x^2}{\delta x}\right\}$$

is the differential coefficient of x^2, or $\frac{d}{dx}(x^2)$.

Now, in the limit, $(x+\delta x)^2$ is x^2;

$$\therefore \frac{dy}{dx} = x^2\frac{d}{dx}(\cos x) + \cos x\frac{d}{dx}(x^2)$$

$$= -x^2\sin x + 2x\cos x.$$

These operations apply to any case, and the following proof is only a repetition, using symbols instead of the preceding concrete case. Comparison should be made step by step.

Thus, instead of x^2 and $\cos x$, write $f(x)$ and $F(x)$, respectively.

Then, $$y=f(x)\times F(x).$$

Hence, $$y+\delta y=f(x+\delta x)\times F(x+\delta x),$$

$$\therefore \frac{dy}{dx}=\text{Lt}_{\delta x=0}\left[\frac{f(x+\delta x)\times F(x+\delta x)-f(x)\times F(x)}{\delta x}\right].$$

This may be written in the form

$$\frac{dy}{dx}=\text{Lt}_{\delta x=0}\left[\frac{f(x+\delta x)\times F(x+\delta x)-f(x+\delta x)\times F(x)+f(x+\delta x)\times F(x)-f(x)\times F(x)}{\delta x}\right]$$

$$=\text{Lt}_{\delta x=0}\left[f(x+\delta x)\frac{F(x+\delta x)-F(x)}{\delta x}+\frac{f(x+\delta x)-f(x)}{\delta x}F(x)\right].$$

But $$\text{Lt}_{\delta x=0}\left\{\frac{F(x+\delta x)-F(x)}{\delta x}\right\} \text{ is } \frac{d}{dx}F(x),$$

i.e. the differential coefficient of $F(x)$ with respect to x.

Also $$\text{Lt}_{\delta x=0}\left\{\frac{f(x+\delta x)-f(x)}{\delta x}\right\} \text{ is } \frac{d}{dx}f(x).$$

Similarly, $f(x+\delta x)$ becomes $f(x)$.

Hence $$\frac{dy}{dx}=f(x)\frac{d}{dx}F(x)+F(x)\frac{d}{dx}f(x).$$

The following demonstration is very general, and perhaps better for comparison with the example.

Let $y=u\times v$, where u and v are functions of x.

When x increases to $x+\delta x$, y becomes $y+\delta y$, u becomes $u+\delta u$, and v becomes $v+\delta v$;

$$\therefore\ y+\delta y=(u+\delta u)(v+\delta v),$$

and $$\frac{\delta y}{\delta x}=\frac{(u+\delta u)(v+\delta v)-uv}{\delta x}$$

$$=u\frac{\delta v}{\delta x}+\left(v\frac{\delta u}{\delta x}\right)+\frac{\delta u\delta v}{\delta x}.$$

Now, as δx becomes smaller and smaller,
$\frac{\delta v}{\delta x}$ approaches nearer and nearer to $\frac{dv}{dx}$, $\frac{\delta u}{\delta x}$ to $\frac{du}{dx}$, $\frac{\delta y}{\delta x}$ to $\frac{dy}{dx}$, and $\frac{\delta u \cdot \delta v}{\delta x}$ becomes 0.

Hence, in the limit,

$$\frac{dy}{dx}=u\frac{dv}{dx}+v\frac{du}{dx}. \quad \text{.........................(i)}$$

The preceding important result may be stated in words as follows :—**The differential coefficient of the product of two functions is the sum of the products of each function by the differential coefficient of the other.**

As a first use of this theorem consider

$$y=\text{const.}\times f(x).$$

Then $$\frac{dy}{dx}=\text{const.}\times\frac{df(x)}{dx}+f(x)\frac{d(\text{const.})}{dx}.$$

But the differential coefficient of a constant is zero ;

$$\therefore \frac{dy}{dx}=\text{const.}\times\frac{df(x)}{dx},$$

or is simply the product of the same constant and the differential coefficient of the function. Simple examples which may easily be verified may be manufactured as follows :

Ex. 2. Let $$y=20x^6,$$

$$\frac{dy}{dx}=120x^5.$$

As $20x^6=4x^4\times 5x^2$, we can also obtain the result from (i) as follows :

$$\frac{dy}{dx}=4x^4\times 10x+5x^2\times 16x^3=120x^5.$$

In a similar manner, when $y=uvw$,

$$\frac{dy}{dx}=uv\frac{dw}{dx}+vw\frac{du}{dx}+uw\frac{dv}{dx}.$$

To obtain familiarity with the method it may be advisable, as in the preceding case, to select some fairly easy example and proceed to apply the rule to it.

Ex. 3. Let $$y=24x^9=2x^2\times 3x^3\times 4x^4,$$

$$\frac{dy}{dx}=2x^2\times 3x^3\times\frac{d(4x^4)}{dx}+2x^2\times 4x^4\times\frac{d(3x^3)}{dx}+3x^3\times 4x^4\times\frac{d(2x^2)}{dx}$$

$$=96x^8+72x^8+48x^8=216x^8,$$

and this can be verified readily, because if $y=24x^9$,

$$\frac{dy}{dx}=9\times 24x^8=216x^8.$$

Ex. 4. A rectangular slab of wrought iron is heated and its linear dimensions increase at the rate 0·01 inch per sec. Find the rate at which its volume is increasing at the instant when the dimensions are 4, 3, and 12 inches respectively.

If $y=uvw$, where u, v, and w are functions of t, the time denoting three edges of the solid mutually at right angles, then

$$\frac{dy}{dt}=vw\frac{du}{dt}+uw\frac{dv}{dt}+uv\frac{dw}{dt}. \qquad\text{(ii)}$$

But y denotes the volume of the solid, and $\therefore\ \frac{dy}{dt}$ denotes the rate of increase of volume due to change of temperature.

Hence, at the instant when the three dimensions are 4, 3, and 12, the rate of increase of the volume is obtained from (ii) by substituting the given values, and is

$$(36\times 0{\cdot}01)+(48\times 0{\cdot}01)+(12\times 0{\cdot}01)=96\times 0{\cdot}01;$$

$$\therefore\ \frac{dV}{dt}=0{\cdot}96 \text{ cub. in. per sec.}$$

Ex. 5. Find $\frac{dy}{dx}$ when $y=(x^3+a)(3x^2+b)$.

$$\frac{dy}{dx}=(x^3+a)\frac{d(3x^2+b)}{dx}+(3x^2+b)\frac{d(x^3+a)}{dx}$$

$$=(x^3+a)6x+(3x^2+b)3x^2$$

$$=15x^4+3bx^2+6ax.$$

Ex. 6. Find $\frac{dy}{dx}$ when $y=(a+x)(b+x)(c+x)$.

$$\frac{dy}{dx}=(b+x)(c+x)\frac{d(a+x)}{dx}+\dots$$

$$=3x^2+2(a+b+c)x+ab+ac+bc$$

Ex. 7. Find $\frac{dy}{dx}$ when $y=a(bx^2)^4$.

Let $z=bx^2$.

Then $y=az^4$,

$$\frac{dy}{dz}=4az^3 \text{ and } \frac{dz}{dx}=2bx;$$

$$\therefore \frac{dy}{dx}=4az^3\times 2bx=4a(bx^2)^3\times 2bx$$

$$=8abx(bx^2)^3=8ab^4x^7.$$

EXERCISES. XXXVI.

Find in each of the following cases the value of $\frac{dy}{dx}$; verify the result obtained by calculation from first principles.

1. $y=7x^2$.
2. $y=3\sin x$.
3. $y=\cos 3x$.
4. $y=5\cos(2x+3)$.
5. $y=\log 6x$.
6. $y=A\log x^3$.
7. $y=3e^{2x}$.
8. $y=Ae^{-kx}$.

Find the values of $\frac{ds}{dt}$ in the following examples:

9. $s=3t^2-4t+7$.
10. $s=At^2+Bt+c$.
11. $s=3\sin(4t+9)$.
12. $s=7\cos^2(6t^3+9t+5)$.
13. $s=14e^{\frac{t}{8}}+9\sin 8t$.
14. $s=11e^t\sin(6t+7)$.
15. $s=Ae^{bt}\sin(ct+f)$.

Quotient of two functions.—To obtain a general expression for the differentiation of the quotient of two functions we may proceed as follows:

Let $y=\frac{f(x)}{F(x)}$,

$$\frac{dy}{dx}=\text{Lt}_{\delta x=0}\left[\frac{\frac{f(x+\delta x)}{F(x+\delta x)}-\frac{f(x)}{F(x)}}{\delta x}\right]$$

$$=\text{Lt}_{\delta x=0}\left[\frac{F(x)f(x+\delta x)-f(x)F(x+\delta x)}{F(x)F(x+\delta x)\delta x}\right];$$

therefore,

$$\frac{dy}{dx}=\text{Lt}_{\delta x=0}\left[\frac{F(x)f(x+\delta x)-F(x)f(x)+F(x)f(x)-f(x)F(x+\delta x)}{F(x)F(x+\delta x)\delta x}\right].$$

In the numerator $f(x)F(x)$ has been added and subtracted; this allows $\frac{dy}{dx}$ to be put into the following form:

$$\frac{dy}{dx}=\text{Lt}_{\delta x=0}\left[\frac{F(x)\frac{f(x+\delta x)-f(x)}{\delta x}-f(x)\frac{F(x+\delta x)-F(x)}{\delta x}}{F(x)F(x+\delta x)}\right],$$

and finally, taking the limiting values of the functions in the numerator and denominator,

$$\frac{dy}{dx}=\frac{F(x)\frac{d}{dx}f(x)-f(x)\frac{d}{dx}F(x)}{\{F(x)\}^2}$$

Alternative proof.—An alternate form of proof of the preceding result may be obtained.

Thus, let $y=\frac{u}{v}$,

$$\frac{dy}{dx}=\text{Lt}_{\delta x=0}\left[\frac{\frac{u+\delta u}{v+\delta v}-\frac{u}{v}}{\delta x}\right]$$

$$=\text{Lt}_{\delta x=0}\left[\frac{v\frac{\delta u}{\delta x}-u\frac{\delta v}{\delta x}}{v(v+\delta v)}\right].$$

Hence,
$$\frac{dy}{dx}=\frac{v\frac{du}{dx}-u\frac{dv}{dx}}{v^2}.$$

Or, **the differential coefficient of a quotient of two functions is the product of the denominator and the differential coefficient of the numerator, minus the product of the numerator and the differential coefficient of the denominator, divided by the denominator squared** This important rule may be tested as follows:

Ex. 1. $y=\frac{10x^6}{2x^2}$, y is really $5x^4$, but consider it as a quotient.

Then
$$\frac{dy}{dx}=\frac{2x^2\frac{d}{dx}(10x^6)-10x^6\frac{d}{dx}(2x^2)}{(2x^2)^2},$$

$$=\frac{2x^2\times 60x^5-40x^7}{4x^4}=20x^3.$$

As $y=5x^4$, we see that $\frac{dy}{dx}=20x^3$.

Ex. 2. $y=\tan x$, find $\frac{dy}{dx}$.

By our rule, since $y=\frac{\sin x}{\cos x}$,

$$\frac{dy}{dx}=\frac{\cos x\frac{d}{dx}(\sin x)-\sin x\frac{d}{dx}(\cos x)}{\cos^2 x}$$

$$=\frac{\cos^2 x+\sin^2 x}{\cos^2 x}=\frac{1}{\cos^2 x}=\sec^2 x.$$

From first principles,

$$\frac{dy}{dx}=\mathrm{Lt}_{\delta x=0}\left[\frac{\tan(x+\delta x)-\tan x}{\delta x}\right]$$

$$=\mathrm{Lt}_{\delta x=0}\left[\frac{\sin(x+\delta x)\cos x-\sin x\cos(x+\delta x)}{\delta x\,.\,\cos x\cos(x+\delta x)}\right]$$

$$=\mathrm{Lt}_{\delta x=0}\left[\frac{\sin\{(x+\delta x)-x\}}{\delta x\cos x\cos(x+\delta x)}\right]$$

$$=\mathrm{Lt}_{\delta x=0}\left[\frac{\sin\delta x}{\delta x}\cdot\frac{1}{\cos x\cos(x+\delta x)}\right].$$

In the limit, when $\delta x=0$, $\left[\frac{\sin\delta x}{\delta x}\right]=1$ (p. 383),

$$\frac{dy}{dx}=\frac{1}{\cos^2 x}=\sec^2 x.$$

Differentiation of inverse functions.—We proceed to prove that

$$\frac{dy}{dx}\times\frac{dx}{dy}=1.$$

By definition $\frac{dy}{dx}=\mathrm{Lt}_{\delta x=0}\frac{\delta y}{\delta x}$,

and $\frac{dx}{dy}=\mathrm{Lt}_{\delta y=0}\frac{\delta x}{\delta y}$,

therefore, $\frac{dy}{dx}\cdot\frac{dx}{dy}=\mathrm{Lt}_{\delta x=0}\frac{\delta y}{\delta x}\times\mathrm{Lt}_{\Delta y=0}\frac{\Delta x}{\Delta y}$.

Now the product of the limiting values of two or more functions is equal to the limit of the products, and therefore

$$\frac{dy}{dx}\cdot\frac{dx}{dy}=\mathrm{Lt}_{\substack{\delta x=0\\ \Delta y=0}}\left[\frac{\delta y}{\delta x}\times\frac{\Delta x}{\Delta y}\right].$$

Before the limit is taken, δy and δx are of any value corresponding to each other, as are also Δx and Δy, and, as we have seen previously, the limit is independent of such quantities. Since this is the case, make $\Delta y = \delta y$, and then Δx will $= \delta x$, and we have

$$\frac{dy}{dx} \cdot \frac{dx}{dy} = \text{Lt}_{\substack{\delta x=0 \\ \delta y=0}} \left[\frac{\delta y}{\delta x} \times \frac{\delta x}{\delta y} \right] = 1.$$

Ex. 1.
$$y = x^3, \quad \text{then } x = y^{\frac{1}{3}};$$

$$\therefore \frac{dy}{dx} = 3x^2, \quad \text{and} \quad \frac{dx}{dy} = \frac{1}{3} y^{-\frac{2}{3}} = \frac{1}{3} \frac{1}{x^2};$$

$$\therefore \frac{dy}{dx} \times \frac{dx}{dy} = 3x^2 \times \frac{1}{3x^2} = 1.$$

Ex. 2.
$$y = x^2; \quad \therefore x = \pm y^{\frac{1}{2}},$$

$$\frac{dy}{dx} = 2x \quad \text{and} \quad \frac{dx}{dy} = \pm \frac{1}{2} y^{-\frac{1}{2}} = \frac{1}{2x},$$

where the $\pm$ signs agree with those before;

$$\therefore \frac{dy}{dx} \times \frac{dx}{dy} = 2x \times \frac{1}{2x} = 1.$$

Ex. 2*a*. If $y = \log_e x$, $\quad \therefore x = e^y$.

$$\frac{dx}{dy} = e^y; \quad \therefore \frac{dy}{dx} = \frac{1}{x}.$$

Geometrical proof.—A geometrical proof that $\frac{dy}{dx} \cdot \frac{dx}{dy} = 1$ may be obtained as follows:

Let $Q'PQ$ (Fig. 111) be a portion of a curve representing

$$y = f(x).$$

Then, as on p. 305,

$$\frac{dy}{dx} = \text{Lt}_{\delta x=0} \frac{QM}{PM} \quad \text{(Fig. 111)}$$

$$= \tan \theta.$$

Again,
$$\frac{dx}{dy} = \text{Lt}_{\Delta y=0} \frac{\Delta x}{\Delta y}.$$

Now, as Δy gets less and less, Q' must get nearer to point P, and eventually PQ' will coincide with the tangent at P; and the angle ϕ will become equal to θ.

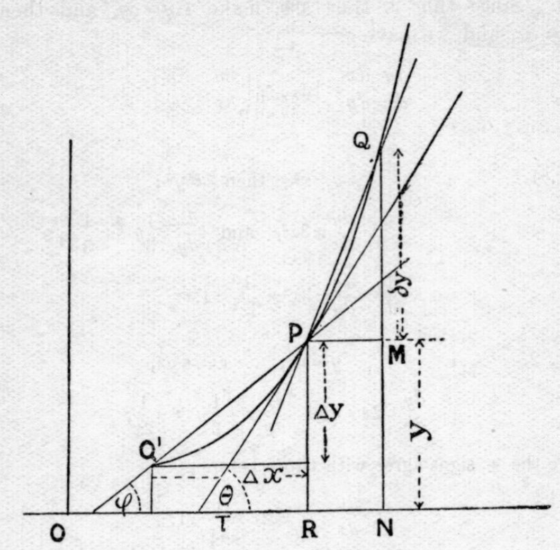

FIG. 111.—To show that $\frac{dy}{dx} \cdot \frac{dx}{dy} = 1$.

But $\frac{\Delta x}{\Delta y} = \cot \phi$, and, therefore, in the limit, when ϕ becomes θ,

$$\text{Lt}_{\Delta y=0}\left[\frac{\Delta x}{\Delta y}\right] \text{ becomes } \cot \theta ;$$

$$\therefore \frac{dy}{dx} \cdot \frac{dx}{dy} = \text{Lt}_{\delta x=0}\left[\frac{QM}{PM}\right] \times \text{Lt}_{\delta y=0}\left[\frac{-\Delta x}{-\Delta y}\right]$$

$$= \tan \theta \times \cot \theta = 1.$$

The theorem that $\frac{dy}{dx} \cdot \frac{dx}{dy} = 1$ or $\frac{dy}{dx} = \frac{1}{\frac{dx}{dy}}$ is very useful in finding the rates of increase, or differential coefficients, of certain functions as follows:

Ex. 3. Let $$y=\sin^{-1}\frac{x}{a}.$$

Since $$y=\sin^{-1}\frac{x}{a},\ \frac{x}{a}=\sin y,$$

$$\frac{dx}{dy}=a\cos y=a\sqrt{1-\sin^2 y};$$

$$\therefore\ \frac{dy}{dx}=\frac{1}{\sqrt{a^2-x^2}}.$$

Ex. 4. Let $y=\sin^{-1}x$, a particular case of the preceding example,

then $$\frac{dy}{dx}=\frac{1}{\sqrt{1-x^2}}.$$

Similarly, if $$y=\cos^{-1}\frac{x}{a},$$

$$\frac{dy}{dx}=-\frac{1}{\sqrt{a^2-x^2}}.$$

Thus if $y_1=\sin^{-1}x$ and $y_2=\cos^{-1}x$; y_1+y_2 has for its least value $\frac{1}{2}\pi\left(\text{but in any case is constant}=\frac{4n+1}{2}\pi\right)$;

$$\therefore\ \frac{dy_1}{dx}+\frac{dy_2}{dx}=\frac{d(\frac{1}{2}\pi)}{dx}=0.$$

Hence $$\frac{dy_1}{dx}=-\frac{dy_2}{dx};\ \therefore\ \frac{d(\sin^{-1}x)}{dx}=-\frac{d(\cos^{-1}x)}{dx},$$

so $$\frac{d(\tan^{-1}x)}{dx}=-\frac{d(\cot^{-1}x)}{dx}.$$

Ex. 5. Let $$y=\cos^{-1}\frac{x}{a};$$

$$\therefore\ a\cos y=x$$

$$-a\sin y\frac{dy}{dx}=1;$$

$$\therefore\ \frac{dy}{dx}=-\frac{1}{a\sqrt{1-\cos^2 y}}=-\frac{1}{a\sqrt{1-\frac{x^2}{a^2}}}$$

$$=-\frac{1}{\sqrt{a^2-x^2}}.$$

Ex. 6. Let $$y=\tan^{-1}\frac{x}{a}.$$

Here
$$x=a\tan y;$$
$$\therefore\ \frac{dx}{dy}=a\sec^2 y=a(1+\tan^2 y)$$
$$=a\left\{1+\left(\frac{x}{a}\right)^2\right\};$$
$$\therefore\ \frac{dy}{dx}=\frac{1}{a\left(1+\frac{x^2}{a^2}\right)}=\frac{a}{a^2+x^2}.$$

Ex. 7. Similarly, if $$y=\cot^{-1}\frac{x}{a},$$

then
$$\frac{dy}{dx}=-\frac{a}{x^2+a^2}.$$

These cases of inverse functions, viz.
$$\sin^{-1}\frac{x}{a},\ \cos^{-1}\frac{x}{a},\ \tan^{-1}\frac{x}{a},\ \cot^{-1}\frac{x}{a},$$
are of great importance in the application of mathematics to physical and mechanical sciences.

Ex. 8. Let $$y=x^{\frac{1}{m}};$$
$$\therefore\ x=y^m,$$
$$\frac{dx}{dy}=my^{m-1};$$
$$\therefore\ \frac{dy}{dx}=\frac{1}{my^{m-1}}.$$

Substitute in (ii) the value of y from (i);
$$\therefore\ \frac{dy}{dx}=\frac{1}{m\left(x^{\frac{1}{m}}\right)^{m-1}}=\frac{1}{m}x^{\left(\frac{1}{m}-1\right)}.$$

Ex. 9. If the diameter of a circle increases at the rate of 0·01 inch per second, at what rate is the area increasing when the initial diameter is 10 inches?

Here, if x denote the diameter, and δx the increase in length;

then
$$\text{area}=y=\frac{\pi}{4}x^2, \quad\text{......(i)}$$

and
$$y+\delta y=\frac{\pi}{4}(x+\delta x)^2=\frac{\pi}{4}\{x^2+2x\delta x+(\delta x)^2\}. \quad\text{......(ii)}$$

Subtracting (i) from (ii) and dividing by δx,

$$\frac{\delta y}{\delta x}=\frac{\pi}{4}\times 2x+\frac{\pi}{4}\delta x.$$

Hence, average rate of increase when $x=10$ is given by

$$\frac{\delta y}{\delta x}=0{\cdot}7854\times 20+0{\cdot}7854\times \delta x.$$

It will be seen that the second term on the right hand side becomes smaller and smaller as δx is diminished. Finally, when δx is indefinitely small, the actual rate of increase,

or $$\frac{dy}{dx}=15{\cdot}708.$$

That is, the area changes 15·708 times as quickly as the diameter at this point, or is increasing $15{\cdot}708\times 0{\cdot}01$ sq. in. per sec. $=0{\cdot}15708$ sq. in. per sec.

Ex. 10. If the diameter of a spherical soap-bubble increases uniformly at the rate of 0·1 inch per second, at what rate is the volume increasing when the diameter is 3 inches?

Let V denote the volume and x the diameter.

Then $$V=\frac{\pi}{6}x^3, \quad\text{(i)}$$

also $$V+\delta V=\frac{\pi}{6}(x+\delta x)^3=\frac{\pi}{6}\{x^3+3x^2\delta x+3x(\delta x)^2+(\delta x)^3\}. \quad\text{(ii)}$$

Subtracting (i) from (ii) and dividing by δx,

$$\frac{\delta V}{\delta x}=\frac{\pi}{6}\{3x^2+3x\delta x+(\delta x)^2\}.$$

When x is 3, we obtain for average rate of increase

$$\frac{\delta V}{\delta x}=0{\cdot}5236\{27+9\times \delta x+(\delta x^2)\}.$$

When δx is indefinitely small,

$$\frac{dV}{dx}=0{\cdot}5236\times 27=14{\cdot}137\,;$$

$\therefore$ rate of increase of volume is $14{\cdot}137\times 0{\cdot}1=1{\cdot}4137$ cubic inches per second.

Ex. 11. If the radius of a soap-bubble is increasing at the rate of 0·05 inch per second, at what rate is the capacity increasing when the radius becomes one inch?

V = volume of a sphere $=\frac{4}{3}\pi r^3$, where r denotes the radius of the sphere;

$$\therefore \frac{dV}{dr}=4\pi r^2;$$

$$\therefore \delta V=4\pi r^2\delta r, \text{ when } \delta r \text{ is small}, =4\pi\times 1^2\times 0{\cdot}05$$

$$=0{\cdot}2\pi \text{ cub. in. per sec.} \quad =0{\cdot}6283 \text{ cub. in. per sec.}$$

Tangent, subtangent, and subnormal.—Let P (Fig. 112) be a point on the curve $y=f(x)$, the coordinates of the point P being $OM=x$ and $MP=y$.

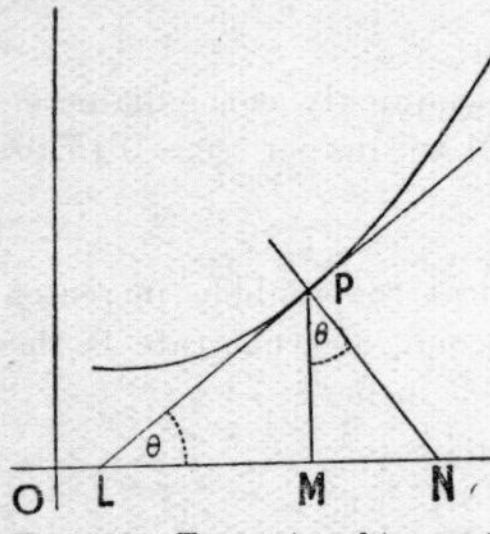

FIG. 112.—Tangent, subtangent, and subnormal to a curve.

If L be the point where the tangent at P cuts the axis of x, and if PN is a line perpendicular to PL and meeting the axis of x at N, then LP is the **tangent**, PN is the **normal**, LM is the **subtangent**, and MN the **subnormal** to the curve at P.

If θ denotes the angle which the tangent makes with the axis of x, then the angle $PNM=\frac{\pi}{2}-\theta$.

$$\frac{PM}{LM}=\tan\theta=\frac{dy}{dx}.$$

$$\therefore \textbf{Subtangent}=LM=y\div\frac{dy}{dx}=\mathbf{y\frac{dx}{dy}}. \quad \text{(i)}$$

Also
$$\frac{MN}{PM}=\tan\theta=\frac{dy}{dx};$$

$$\therefore \textbf{subnormal}=MN=\mathbf{y\frac{dy}{dx}}. \quad \text{(ii)}$$

The lengths of the normal PN and tangent PL are easily obtained.

Thus,
$$PN=\sqrt{PM^2+MN^2}=\sqrt{y^2+y^2\left(\frac{dy}{dx}\right)^2};$$

$$\therefore \textbf{normal}=PN=\mathbf{y\sqrt{1+\left(\frac{dy}{dx}\right)^2}}.$$

Similarly, **tangent** $=PL=\sqrt{PM^2+ML^2}=\dfrac{y\sqrt{1+\left(\frac{dy}{dx}\right)^2}}{\frac{dy}{dx}}$.

Ex. **1.** Draw a tangent and normal at a given point P on the curve $y^2=4ax$. Plotting on squared paper, a curve called a parabola is obtained as in Fig. 113.

Differentiating, we obtain

$$2y\frac{dy}{dx}=4a;$$

$$\therefore \frac{dy}{dx}=\frac{4a}{2y}=\frac{2a}{y}.$$

From (ii),

$$\text{subnormal}=y\frac{dy}{dx}=2a.$$

From (i),

$$\text{subtangent}=y\frac{dx}{dy}=\frac{y^2}{2a}=2x.$$

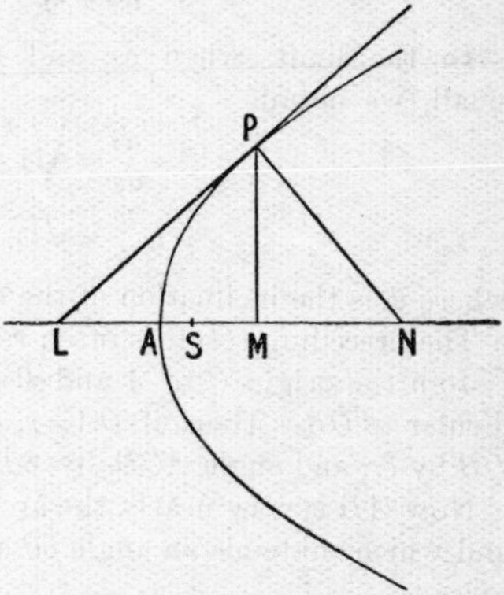

To draw the tangent at P, make $ML=2AM$ (Fig. 113) and join P to L, then PL is the tangent at P.

FIG. 113.—Tangent and normal to a parabola.

To draw the normal, make $MN=2AS$ and join NP, then PN is the normal required.

Length of curve.—Let A and B be two points near together on the curve NAM (Fig. 114).

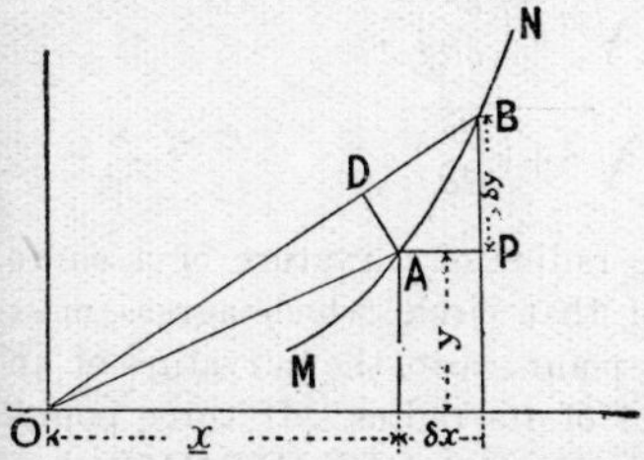

FIG. 114.—Length of a curve.

Let the coordinates of point A be denoted by (x, y); and of B by $(x+\delta x, y+\delta y)$.

If s denote length of curve, then AB will be represented by δs.

As AB is a very small length of curve, we may assume it to form the hypotenuse of a right-angled triangle, of which PA and PB are the two perpendicular sides.

Since $AP=\delta x$ and PB is δy,

$$(\delta s)^2=(\delta x)^2+(\delta y)^2;$$

dividing by $(\delta x)^2$,

$$\left(\frac{\delta s}{\delta x}\right)^2=1+\left(\frac{\delta y}{\delta x}\right)^2;$$

$$\therefore\ \frac{\delta s}{\delta x}=\sqrt{1+\left(\frac{\delta y}{\delta x}\right)^2}.$$

In the limit, when δx and therefore δy are indefinitely small, we obtain

$$\frac{ds}{dx}=\sqrt{1+\left(\frac{dy}{dx}\right)^2} \quad \text{..........................(i)}$$

$$=\sqrt{1+\tan^2\phi}=\sec\phi,$$

where ϕ is the inclination of the tangent to the axis of x.

The preceding result is often required in polar coordinates.

Join the origin O to A and B (Fig. 114). Draw AD perpendicular to OB. Then, if $OA=r$, $OB=OD+DB$, we may denote DB by δr, and angle AOD by $\delta\theta$.

Now AD is very nearly the arc of a circle, whose radius is r, and which subtends an angle $\delta\theta$ at the centre of the circle this gives.

$AD=r\delta\theta$, whence we obtain from the right-angled triangle ADB,

$$(\delta s)^2=(r\delta\theta)^2+(\delta r)^2;$$

or taking the square root and dividing by $\delta\theta$,

$$\frac{\delta s}{\delta\theta}=\sqrt{r^2+\left(\frac{\delta r}{\delta\theta}\right)^2};$$

$$\therefore \text{ in the limit } \frac{ds}{d\theta}=\sqrt{r^2+\left(\frac{dr}{d\theta}\right)^2}.$$

Radius of curvature.—The radius of curvature of a curve at any point is the radius of that circle which agrees most nearly with the curve at that point; also, the curvature of an arc of a circle is the reciprocal of its radius. If three points ABC be taken near together on a curve DE (Fig. 115), then a circle can be drawn through the three points, as the distance between the points is diminished, the circle will more and more nearly coincide with the curve; or, the circle drawn through three points, indefinitely near each other, gives the radius and centre of the circle of curvature at the point.

The slope of the line passing through the two points A and B is written $\frac{\delta y}{\delta x}$; the change in $\frac{\delta y}{\delta x}$, in passing from B to C, is the change in the angle itself multiplied by $\sec^2\phi$. This increase in $\frac{\delta y}{\delta x}$ divided by the length of arc BC is therefore the average curvature from B to C, *i.e.* $\frac{d\phi}{ds}=\frac{1}{\rho}$.

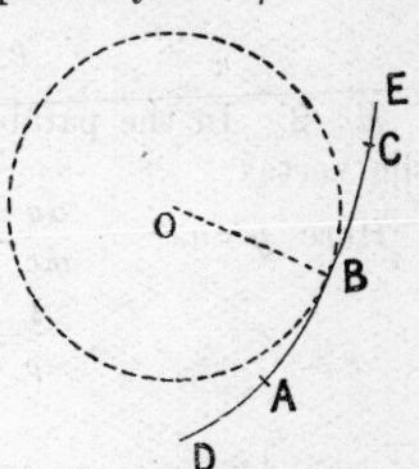

FIG. 115.—Radius of curvature.

Let ρ denote radius of curvature at B.

Now write $\quad u=\tan\phi=\frac{dy}{dx}$;

and consider u, ϕ, $\frac{du}{dx}$ to be functions of x. Take the differential coefficient of this equation;

$$\therefore \frac{du}{dx}=\sec^2\phi\frac{d\phi}{dx}=\frac{d\left(\frac{dy}{dx}\right)}{dx}, \quad \text{(i)}$$

the latter is abbreviated into $\frac{d^2y}{dx^2}$.

To obtain $\frac{d\phi}{dx}$ we use the relation

$$\frac{d\phi}{dx}=\frac{d\phi}{ds}\cdot\frac{ds}{dx}=\frac{1}{\rho}\frac{1}{\cos\phi}.$$

Substituting this value in (i), we obtain

$$\frac{1}{\rho}\sec^3\phi=\frac{d^2y}{dx^2},$$

also $$\sec^2\phi=1+\tan^2\phi=1+\left(\frac{dy}{dx}\right)^2;$$

$$\therefore \rho=\frac{\left\{1+\left(\frac{dy}{dx}\right)^2\right\}^{\frac{3}{2}}}{\frac{d^2y}{dx^2}}. \quad \text{(ii)}$$

Ex. 1. Find the radius of curvature at the point $x=0{\cdot}6$ on the curve $y=2x^3$.

As $y=2x^3$, $\frac{dy}{dx}=6x^2=2{\cdot}16$ when $x=0{\cdot}6$.

$$\frac{d^2y}{dx^2}=12x=12\times 0{\cdot}6=7{\cdot}2;$$

$$\therefore\ \rho=\frac{\{1+(2{\cdot}16)^2\}^{\frac{3}{2}}}{7{\cdot}2}=1{\cdot}874.$$

Ex. 2. In the parabola $y=ax^2$, find the radius of curvature at the vertex.

Here $y=ax^2$ $\therefore$ $\frac{dy}{dx}=2ax$ and $\frac{d^2y}{dx^2}=2a$;

$$\therefore\ \frac{1}{\rho}=\frac{2a}{(1+4a^2x^2)^{\frac{3}{2}}};$$

$$\therefore\ \rho=\frac{1}{2a}\ \text{when}\ x=0.$$

When, as often occurs in engineering problems, the curve is a very flat one and nearly parallel to the axis of x, then the length δs may be taken to be simply the change in x. The approximation being closer as the curve is flatter; when δs becomes indefinitely small we may denote the curvature by the change in

$$\frac{dy}{dx},\ \text{i.e.}\ \frac{d}{dx}\left(\frac{dy}{dx}\right)=\frac{d^2y}{dx^2}.$$

Hence, instead of the more accurate expression given by Eq. (ii) we can use—especially in problems dealing with beams—the approximate expression $\frac{1}{\rho}=\frac{d^2y}{dx^2}$. A result which could be obtained by putting $\frac{dy}{dx}=0$ in (ii).

EXERCISES. XXXVII.

Differentiate the following with regard to x:

1. If $y=\frac{20x^6}{2x^2}$.

2. $y=\frac{2x^4}{a^2-x^2}$.

3. $\frac{x^2}{(a+x^3)^2}$.

4. $\tan x$.

5. $\frac{1-x}{\sqrt{1+x^2}}$.

6. (i) $\frac{mx+n}{px+q}$, (ii) $\frac{1}{x^n}$.

7. (i) $y=\frac{1+x}{\sqrt{1+x^2}}$, (ii) $y=x^a \log x$.

8. $y=\frac{(x+1)^2}{x^2+1}$.

9. $y=e^{\sin x}$.

10. $y=\log_a \sin^{-1}x$.

11. $\cos\sqrt{x^2+a^2}$.

12. $\sin\sqrt{x^2+a^2}$.

13. $\log\sqrt{x^2+a^2}$.

14. $y=\sin^{-1}x^2$.

15. If $u=(x+1)(x^2+1)$, find $\frac{du}{dx}$.

16. $\tan^{-1}\frac{2x}{1-x^2}$

17. $\log\sqrt[4]{\frac{1+x}{1-x}}+\frac{1}{2}\tan^{-1}x$.

18. $\log\frac{x-a}{x+a}$.

19. $\frac{\cos 3x+\cos x}{\sin 3x-\sin x}$.

Find $\frac{du}{dx}$:

20. $u=\log_e(x+\sqrt{a^2+x^2})$.

21. $u=\tan^{-1}\frac{2x}{1-x^2}$.

22. $u=(a^2-x^2)^{\frac{3}{2}}$.

23. $u=\log_e\frac{x^2+\sqrt{x^2-1}}{x^2-\sqrt{x^2-1}}$.

24. $u=\frac{\sin mx}{(\cos x)^m}$.

25. $u=\sin^{-1}\frac{x}{\sqrt{1+x^2}}$.

26. $(a+bx)x^3$.

27. $\sqrt{x^2+a^2}$.

28. $\sin^2 x$.

29. $\sin^3 x\cos x$.

30. $(ax+x^2)^2$.

31. $e^x\cos x$.

32. $x^c\log_a x$.

33. $x\sqrt{(a^2-x^2)}$.

34. $\tan^{-1}\frac{1}{\sqrt{x^2-1}}$.

35. $\frac{\sin^{-1}x}{\sqrt{1-x^2}}$.

36. If y is the area of a circle of radius x, show that

$$\frac{dy}{dx}=2\pi x.$$

37. If y denotes the surface of a sphere of radius x,

$$\frac{dy}{dx}=8\pi x.$$

Show also that $\frac{dy}{dx}=4\pi x^2$, where y denotes the volume.

38. The volume of a spherical balloon is increasing at the rate of c cubic feet per second when the diameter is x feet. What is the rate of increase of the superficial area of the balloon at that instant?

CHAPTER XVI.

RATES OF INCREASE. VELOCITY. ACCELERATION AND FORCE.

Rates of increase.—Probably everyone is more or less familiar with the statement that the average speed, or velocity, of a train is 50 miles per hour. Thus, suppose a train takes 8 hours for a journey of 400 miles, then to obtain the average speed, the number denoting the distance is divided by the number denoting the time. Or, more shortly, the distance divided by the time gives an average speed of 50 miles per hour. But, during the 8 hours the train has many times reduced its speed, stopped altogether, and increased its speed again, so that the average rate of 50 miles an hour gives no measure of its speed at any given instant, such as when passing a station on the line of route. How can we proceed to measure the speed of the train when passing such a place? We might perhaps set out a distance of 176 yards, close to the station, and measure as accurately as possible the time, say 6 seconds or $\frac{1}{600}$ hour, which a given point in the train takes to pass over the distance: then, the distance divided by the time $\frac{1}{10} \div \frac{1}{600} = 60$ miles per hour, gives us the average speed or velocity of the train during 6 seconds while passing over 176 yards.

If instead of 176 yards we use the symbol δs, and instead of 6 seconds the symbol δt, then we have the average speed for this interval of time expressed by $\frac{\delta s}{\delta t}$. Now, as δt, and therefore δs, get smaller and smaller, this result gets more and more nearly equal to the actual velocity of the train at the station. But the distance and time may be made so small that we have no means of measuring them. It would therefore be impossible to find exactly the limit of this expression when $\delta t=0$. If we could get the limit $\left(\text{which is expressed by } \frac{ds}{dt}\right)$, we should find the actual velocity when the train passes a given point at the station. Thus, if s represents the space moved over by a body, and t the time measured from some convenient instant, then the actual velocity, or the rate of increase of space with time, is denoted by $\frac{ds}{dt}$.

In many cases it is possible to express the relation between s and t by means of a formula, and hence to find the value of $\frac{ds}{dt}$ from the known motion of the body. For example, in the case of a falling body starting from rest at a time when $t=0$, we have

$$s=\tfrac{1}{2}gt^2,$$

where $g=32{\cdot}2$ feet per second per second;

$$\therefore \frac{ds}{dt}=\text{Lt}_{\delta t=0}\frac{\frac{1}{2}g(t+\delta t)^2-\frac{1}{2}gt^2}{\delta t}$$

$$=gt.$$

As $\frac{ds}{dt}$ simply denotes velocity, we may replace it by v and thus obtain the well-known law,

$$v=gt. \qquad \text{(i)}$$

In the preceding consideration, v indicated the rate of change of space with time; so, in the same manner, the acceleration of a moving body, which may be denoted by a, is the rate of change of velocity with the time;

$$\therefore a=\frac{dv}{dt}.$$

From (i),
$$\frac{dv}{dt}=\text{Lt}_{\delta t=0}\frac{g(t+\delta t)-gt}{\delta t}$$

$$=g.$$

Thus, we arrive at a result already well known, that the acceleration of a falling body is g, a constant.

Ex. 1. A body falls from rest according to the law $s=16{\cdot}1t^2$, where s is the space passed over in t seconds. Find the actual velocity of the body when t is 1 second.

We may, from the given equation, find the space passed over in a fractional part of a second, and, by dividing the space by the time, obtain the average velocity.

Thus, we may take such values of t as 1 and 1·1, 1 and 1·01, and 1 and 1·001, the approximation being closer and closer to the actual value as the interval is diminished. From time 1 to time 1·1 seconds, the space passed over is, from the given equation,

$$16{\cdot}1\{(1{\cdot}1)^2-1^2\}=3{\cdot}381 \text{ feet,}$$

described in 0·1 second;

$\therefore$ average velocity during 0·1 second $=\dfrac{3{\cdot}381}{0{\cdot}1}=33{\cdot}81$ feet per second.

The average velocity during the 0·01 second from $t=1$ to $t=1{\cdot}01$ is

$$16{\cdot}1\{(1{\cdot}01)^2-1^2\}\div 0{\cdot}01=32{\cdot}361 \text{ feet per second.}$$

From $t=1$ to $t=1{\cdot}001$, it is

$$16{\cdot}1\{(1{\cdot}001)^2-1^2\}\div 0{\cdot}001=32{\cdot}2161 \text{ ft. per sec.}$$

Taking smaller and smaller intervals of time, we find that the average velocity approaches nearer and nearer to the value 32·2, and ultimately we obtain, when t is one second, the actual velocity as 32·2 feet per second.

It should be noticed that if t be taken as 0·99 and 1·01, two values separated by an interval of 1 second, then

$$\text{average velocity}=16{\cdot}1\{1{\cdot}01)^2-(0{\cdot}99)^2\}\div{\cdot}02$$
$$=32{\cdot}2 \text{ ft. per sec.,}$$

and this result follows no matter how much the two intervals may differ from one second, provided their mean is one second.

This will readily be understood when we remember that for such a law of motion the velocity is proportional to the time.

The preceding results are readily obtained by means of Algebra. The coordinates of any point on the curve

$$s=16{\cdot}1t^2 \qquad \text{(i)}$$

may be denoted by (s, t), and those of a point near it by $s+\delta s$ and $t+\delta t$.

Substituting these values in (i),

$$s+\delta s=16{\cdot}1(t+\delta t)^2=16{\cdot}1\{t^2+2t\delta t+(\delta t)^2\}. \qquad \text{(ii)}$$

Subtracting (i) from (ii),

$$\delta s = 32{\cdot}2t\delta t + 16{\cdot}1(\delta t)^2.$$

Dividing by δt, $\dfrac{\delta s}{\delta t} = 32{\cdot}2t + 16{\cdot}1\delta t.$ ....(iii)

When δt is made zero, then the last term $16{\cdot}1\delta t$ is zero, and (iii) becomes

$$\frac{ds}{dt} = 32{\cdot}2t.$$

Hence, the actual value, when t is 1, is 32·2.

Ex. 2. At the end of a time t seconds it is observed that a body has passed over a distance s feet, reckoned from some starting point. If it is known that

$$s = 5t + 0{\cdot}5t^2, \quad \text{.................................(i)}$$

what is the velocity at the time t? Plot the curve.

Find the average velocity at a time $t=4{\cdot}1$, $4{\cdot}01$, $4{\cdot}001$. Hence, find the actual velocity at a time $t=4$.

Assuming values 0, 1, 2, ... for t, values of s can be found. Thus, when t is 2, $\quad s = 5 \times 2 + 0{\cdot}5 \times 4 = 12.$

Other values of s are tabulated:

t	0	1	2	3	4	5	6	7
s	0	5·5	12	19·5	28	37·5	48	59·5

When t is 4·1, $\quad s = (5 \times 4{\cdot}1) + \{0{\cdot}5 \times (4{\cdot}1)^2\}$

$$= 28{\cdot}905;$$

$$\therefore \delta t \text{ is } 4{\cdot}1 - 4 = 0{\cdot}1 \text{ and } \delta s = 28{\cdot}905 - 28 = 0{\cdot}905.$$

Hence, $\quad \dfrac{\delta s}{\delta t} = \dfrac{0{\cdot}905}{0{\cdot}1} = 9{\cdot}05.$

Similarly, when t is 4·01, $\delta s = 0{\cdot}09005$;

$$\therefore \frac{\delta s}{\delta t} = 9{\cdot}005.$$

When t is 4·001, then

$$s = (5 \times 4{\cdot}001) + \{0{\cdot}5 \times (4{\cdot}001)^2\} = 28{\cdot}0090005;$$

$$\therefore \delta s = 0{\cdot}0090005 \text{ and } \delta t = 0{\cdot}001;$$

$$\therefore \frac{\delta s}{\delta t} = \frac{0{\cdot}0090005}{0{\cdot}001} = 9{\cdot}0005.$$

It is obvious that, as δt is made less and less, the values of $\frac{\delta s}{\delta t}$ are approaching 9; this is confirmed by simple differentiation.

Thus, if $$s = 5t + 0{\cdot}5t^2,$$

then $$\frac{ds}{dt} = 5 + t = 9, \text{ when } t \text{ is } 4.$$

Hence, the actual velocity, when t is 4, is 9 ft. per sec.

The following construction is an easy verification. The value just obtained for v denotes the tangent of the angle made with the axis of x by the line touching the curve at the point P; using the edge of a set-square and a hard, sharp pencil, such a line as in Fig. 116 may be drawn with some approach to accuracy.

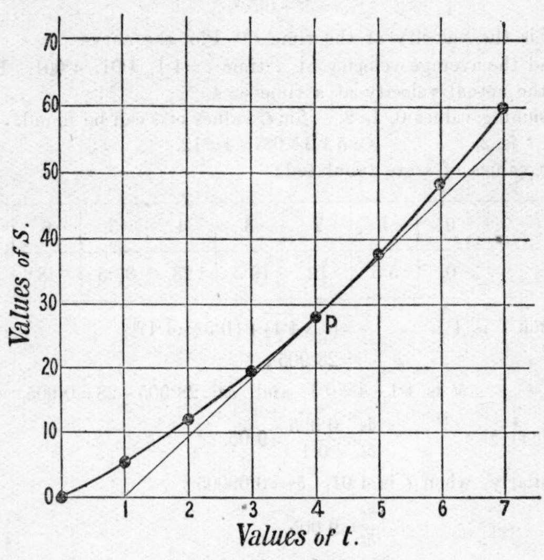

FIG. 116.—Slope of a curve.

Ex. 3. If $$y = 2{\cdot}4 - 1{\cdot}2x + 0{\cdot}2x^2, \qquad \text{(i}$$

find $\frac{dy}{dx}$, and plot two curves from $x=0$ to $x=4$, showing how y and $\frac{dy}{dx}$ depend upon x.

From (i), $\frac{dy}{dx} = -1{\cdot}2 + 0{\cdot}4x$. ....(ii)

To plot the two curves given by (i) and (ii), we may, in the usual manner, assume values of x, and calculate values of y.

Thus, from (i), when $x=2$,

$$y = 2{\cdot}4 - 2{\cdot}4 + 4 \times 0{\cdot}2 = 0{\cdot}8.$$

Similarly, when $x=2$, from (ii),

$$\frac{dy}{dx} = -1{\cdot}2 + 2 \times 0{\cdot}4 = -0{\cdot}4.$$

Values of x and y and $\frac{dy}{dx}$ may be tabulated as follows

x	0	1	2	3	4
y	2·4	1·4	0·8	0·6	0·8
$\frac{dy}{dx}$	−1·2	−0·8	−0·4	0·0	0·4

By plotting values of x and y, the curve ab in Fig. 117 is obtained.

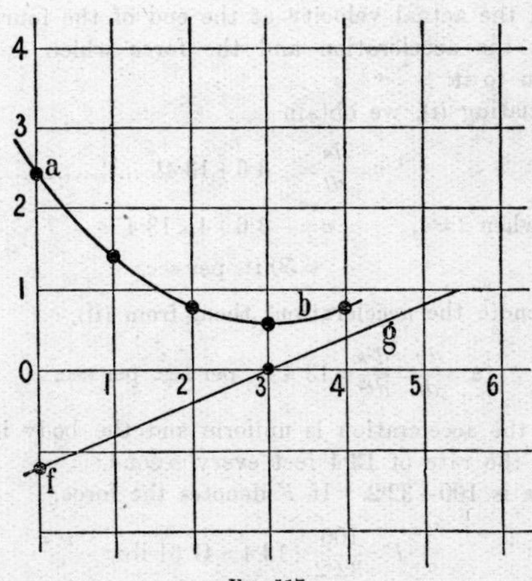

Fig. 117.

By plotting the values x and $\frac{dy}{dx}$, the straight line fg (Fig. 117) passes through the plotted points.

Force.—In books on Mechanics it is shown that the force F, necessary to give an acceleration a to a body of mass M, is represented by the product of the mass and the acceleration.

$$F = Ma.$$

The mass of a body in gravitation units is its weight divided by g, the acceleration of a body falling freely under the action of gravity, where $g = 32{\cdot}2$ ft. per sec. per sec.

Ex. 4. Find the force required to give a body weighing 100 lbs. an acceleration of 20 ft. per sec. per sec.

$$F = \frac{100}{g} \times 20 = 62{\cdot}1 \text{ lbs.}$$

[The unit of force is the weight of 1 lb.]

Ex. 5. A body weighing 100 lbs. passes through the space s feet measured from some zero point in its path at the time t seconds, measured from some zero of time; the law of motion is

$$s = 12{\cdot}2 - 3{\cdot}6t + 6{\cdot}7t^2. \quad \text{.......................(i)}$$

(i) Find the actual velocity at the end of the fourth second.

(ii) Find the acceleration and the force which is giving this acceleration to it.

Differentiating (i), we obtain

$$v = \frac{ds}{dt} = -3{\cdot}6 + 13{\cdot}4t. \quad \text{.......................(ii)}$$

Hence, when $t = 4$, $\quad v = -3{\cdot}6 + 4 \times 13{\cdot}4$

$$= 50 \text{ ft. per sec.}$$

Let a denote the acceleration, then, from (ii),

$$a = \frac{dv}{dt} = \frac{d^2s}{dt^2} = 13{\cdot}4 \text{ ft. per sec. per sec.}$$

That is, the acceleration is uniform and the body increases its velocity at the rate of 13·4 feet every second.

The mass is $100 \div 32{\cdot}2$. If F denotes the force,

then $$F = \frac{100}{32{\cdot}2} \times 13{\cdot}4 = 41{\cdot}61 \text{ lbs.}$$

A velocity of 50 ft. per sec. is conveniently denoted by 50 *f.s.* Similarly, an acceleration of 13·4 ft. per sec. per sec. would be written 13·4 *f.s.s.*

In many practical cases the relation between space and time and velocity and time is not known, and an approximate value of $\frac{ds}{dt}$ or $\frac{d^2s}{dt^2}$ is all that can be found. The following example indicates some methods which may be used to find such an approximate value.

Ex. 6. There is a piece of mechanism whose weight is 200 lbs. The following values of s in feet show the distance of its centre of gravity (as measured on a skeleton drawing) from some point in its straight path at the time t seconds from some era of reckoning. Find its velocity at the time 2·01, its acceleration at the time $t=2·05$ and the force in pounds which is giving this acceleration to it.

s	0·3090	0·4931	0·6799	0·8701	1·0643	1·2631
t	2	2·02	2·04	2·06	2·08	2·10

As the values of t differ by 0·02 sec., we may take $\delta t=0·02$, and δs will be obtained by subtracting consecutive values of s. This procedure enables values of δs to be tabulated. Thus

$$0·4931-0·3090=0·1841;$$

other values similarly obtained are given in the following table.

$$\text{Velocity at time } 2·01 \text{ is } 0·1841 \div 0·02.$$

In a similar manner, by subtracting consecutive values of δs, we may obtain the numerical values of $\delta^2 s$. These may be tabulated as follows:

s	0·3090, 0·4931, 0·6799, 0·8701, 1·0643, 1·2631.
δs	0·1841, 0·1868, 0·1902, 0·1942, 0·1988.
$\delta^2 s$	0·0027, 0·0034, 0·0040, 0·0046.

$$\text{The mean value of } \delta^2 s=\tfrac{1}{4}(0·0027+0·0034+0·0040+0·0046)$$
$$=0·0037.$$

$$\text{Acceleration}=\frac{\delta^2 s}{\delta t^2}=\frac{0·0037}{(0·02)^2}=\frac{0·0037}{0·0004}$$
$$=9·25 \text{ ft. per sec. per sec.}$$

As mass is $\frac{200}{32·2}$, $\therefore$ force $=\frac{200}{32·2}\times 9·25=57·5$ lbs.

Circular motion.—When a particle of mass m is moving in a circular path of radius r with velocity v, or with an angular velocity ω, in passing from a position P to P_1, although the magnitude of the velocity is unaltered, the direction is changed from that of the tangent at P (Fig. 118) to that of the tangent at P_1. The change in the direction of the vector V may be set out, as in Fig. 118, by making Oa and Ob each equal in magnitude to v, the former parallel to the tangent at P, the latter to the tangent at P_1; the total vector change is represented by the line ab. But it is obvious that ab is made up of a series of vectors obtained by taking points P_2 and P_3, etc., between P and P_1. The result becomes nearer and nearer to the actual value as the points P_2, P_3, etc., approach each other. Finally, when P_2, P_3, etc., are consecutive points on the circle, then the vector change at any instant is an indefinitely small arc of a circle of radius v. Thus, the vector change, or acceleration, is in the direction of the tangent at a, and is therefore along the radius PC.

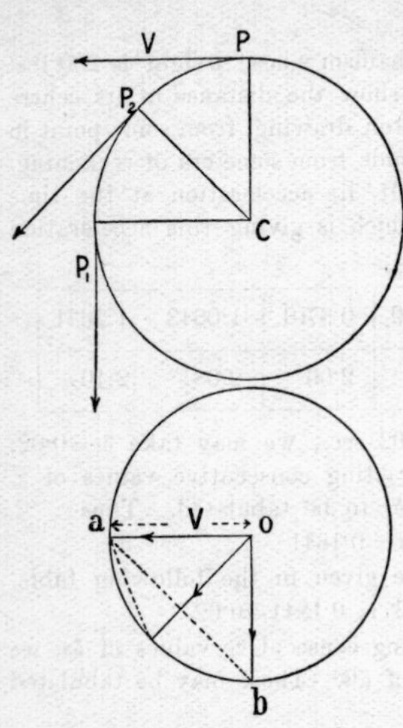

FIG. 118.—Motion in a circle.

To find the magnitude, let t be the time, in seconds, of one revolution of P. Then, from the relation $s=vt$, we obtain

$$2\pi r=vt; \quad \therefore \ t=\frac{2\pi r}{v}. \qquad \text{(i)}$$

Also ...... (vector change per unit time) $\times t=2\pi v$,

or $$\text{acceleration}=a=\frac{2\pi v}{t}.$$

Substitute the value of t from (i);

$$\therefore \ a=\frac{v^2}{r}.$$

Harmonic motion.—If a point P (Fig. 119) is moving in a circular path of radius r with uniform speed v ft. per sec., then the acceleration of P at any instant is directed towards C, and its magnitude is given by $\frac{v^2}{r}$.

The point M (Fig. 119), the projection of P on a diameter AA', moves with **simple harmonic motion,** usually denoted by the letters S.H.M.

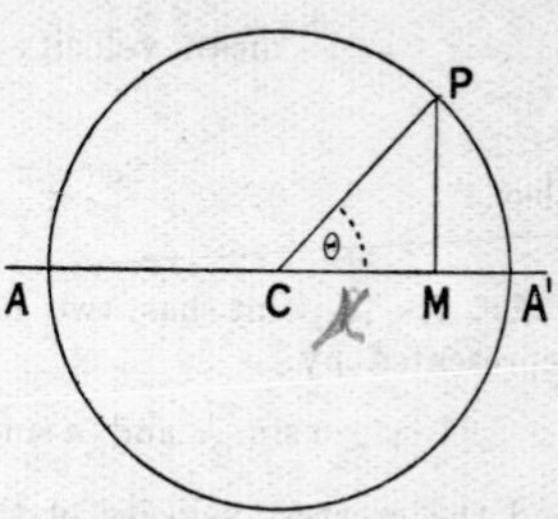

Fig. 119.—Harmonic motion.

The acceleration of M is the resolved part of the acceleration of P, and is therefore

$$\frac{v^2}{r}\cos\theta = \omega^2 r\cos\theta,$$

where ω denotes the constant angular velocity of P, and θ is the angle PCM.

Let x denote the distance CM, *i.e.* the distance of M from its mean position.

Then, the acceleration of

$$M = \omega^2 r \times \frac{x}{r} = \omega^2 x. \quad \text{(i)}$$

If the direction C to A' in the usual manner be taken to be positive, then (i) becomes $-\omega^2 x$, indicating that the direction of the acceleration is from A' to C.

The maximum value of x occurs when P is at A or A', where $x=r$. Hence, maximum acceleration of M is $\omega^2 r$.

Since Force = Mass × Acceleration, it follows from (i) that the force F, acting on a body of mass m moving with S.H.M. is given by $F = m\omega^2 x$.

The maximum value of the velocity occurs when M passes through C.

When a point is moving with S.H.M. the maximum velocity may be obtained by multiplying its mean velocity by $\frac{\pi}{2}$.

If v is the velocity of the point P in the auxiliary circle, the maximum velocity of M occurs when M is at the middle of its path, and is then v or ωr.

If T is the periodic time of a vibration, then

$$\omega=\frac{2\pi}{T},$$

$$\text{mean velocity}=\frac{\text{distance}}{\text{time}}=\frac{4r}{\frac{2\pi}{\omega}}=\frac{2\omega r}{\pi},$$

also
$$\frac{2\omega r}{\pi}\times\frac{\pi}{2}=\omega r=\text{max. vel.}$$

Ex. 7. A point has two harmonic motions, in the same line, represented by

$$a\sin\frac{\pi t}{2} \text{ and } a\sin\left(\frac{\pi t}{2}+\frac{\pi}{2}\right) \text{ respectively;}$$

find the greatest velocity of the resultant motion.

Let R denote the resultant velocity;

$$\therefore\ R=a\sin\frac{\pi t}{2}+a\sin\left(\frac{\pi t}{2}+\frac{\pi}{2}\right),$$

or, if
$$\phi=\frac{\pi t}{2},$$

then
$$R=a\sin\phi+a\sin\left(\phi+\frac{\pi}{2}\right).$$

To find the maximum value differentiate and equate to zero in the usual manner (see p. 356);

$$\therefore\ \frac{dR}{d\phi}=a\cos\phi+a\cos\left(\phi+\frac{\pi}{2}\right);$$

$$\therefore\ a\cos\phi+a\cos\left(\phi+\frac{\pi}{2}\right)=0,$$

or
$$\cos\phi=-\cos\left(\phi+\frac{\pi}{2}\right)=\sin\phi;$$

$$\therefore\ \tan\phi=1, \text{ giving } \phi=45°.$$

Hence,
$$R=\frac{a}{\sqrt{2}}+\frac{a}{\sqrt{2}}=a\sqrt{2}.$$

We may obtain the same result as follows:

$$a\sin\phi+a\sin\left(\phi+\frac{\pi}{2}\right)=a\sqrt{2}\sin\left(\phi+\frac{\pi}{4}\right);$$

$$\therefore\ \text{maximum value is } a\sqrt{2}.$$

The direction of motion of P is usually taken to be in the opposite direction to the hands of a clock, or anticlockwise;

but in dealing with (say) the mechanism of a direct-acting engine, no such restriction is necessary; the motion may and often does occur in a clockwise direction.

If, as in Fig. 120, a rod PQ be attached to P, the direction of motion of Q being always in the line QC, then the motion of Q, for uniform motion of P is not S.H.M. but approaches more to it the longer the link PQ becomes. The maximum values of the acceleration of Q occur when P is at A or A', and are given in magnitude by the formula $\omega^2 r\left(1 \pm \frac{r}{l}\right)$.

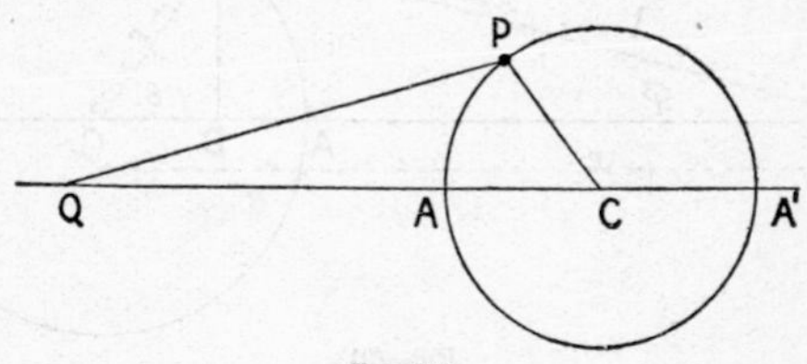

FIG. 120.

The maximum forces acting on Q therefore occur when P is at A or A', and are, in each case, the product of the mass of the reciprocating parts and the acceleration.

It will be noticed that when l is great compared with r, the term $\frac{r}{l}$ becomes very small and may be neglected; the acceleration may be taken to be simply $\omega^2 r$. Such a case occurs in an eccentric and valve rod in which the motion of the valve is often assumed to be S.H.M.

The case when the motion of Q is assumed to be S.H.M. is usually referred to as a rod of infinite length, or more shortly as an infinite rod. When the rod is comparatively short, say 2, 3, 4, etc., times the length of the crank, then the preceding equation may be used to find the magnitude of the maximum acceleration of Q, and hence of the maximum force at Q.

In the formula $m\omega^2 r\left(1 \pm \frac{r}{l}\right)$, where m is the mass of the reciprocating parts, ω the angular velocity of the crank assumed to be constant, l the length of the rod PQ (Fig. 121), and r the length of the crank CP.

Let the crank PC make an angle θ with QC, and let ϕ denote the angle PQC. From P, draw PD perpendicular to QC, and let $PD=y$.

If x denote the distance QC, then

$$x=QD+DC=l\cos\phi+r\cos\theta,$$

$$\frac{dx}{dt}=-l\frac{d\phi}{dt}\sin\phi-r\frac{d\theta}{dt}\sin\theta.\quad\text{(i)}$$

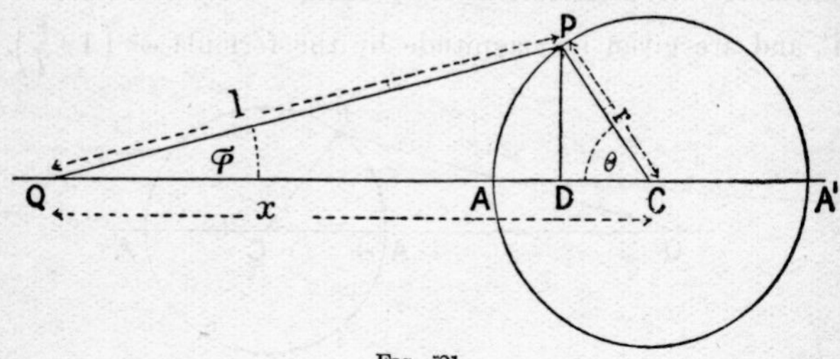

FIG. 121.

If ω' denote the angular velocity of QP,

then $$\frac{d\phi}{dt}=\omega' \text{ and } \frac{d\theta}{dt}=\omega;$$

by differentiating (i) with regard to t,

$$\frac{d^2x}{dt^2}=-l\frac{d^2\phi}{dt^2}\sin\phi-l\left(\frac{d\phi}{dt}\right)^2\cos\phi-r\frac{d^2\theta}{dt^2}\sin\theta-r\left(\frac{d\theta}{dt}\right)^2\cos\theta.\quad\text{(ii)}$$

P is a point on the rod PQ and also on the crank CP. Therefore, $l\sin\phi=r\sin\theta$.

Differentiating this gives $\omega' l\cos\phi=\omega r\cos\theta$,

$$\text{or } \omega'=\frac{\omega r}{l}\times\frac{\cos\theta}{\cos\phi}.$$

When P is at A, $\phi=0$ and $\theta=0$, substitute in (ii);

$$\therefore\ \frac{d^2x}{dt^2}=-\frac{l\omega^2r^2}{l^2}-\omega^2r=-\omega^2r\left(1+\frac{r}{l}\right),$$

and when P is at A', $\phi=0$ and $\theta=\pi$;

$$\therefore\ \frac{d^2x}{dt^2}=+\omega^2r\left(1-\frac{r}{l}\right).$$

In each of these expressions the negative sign indicates that the direction of the acceleration is negative, *i.e.* tending to decrease x.

Ex. 8. In a direct-acting engine (Fig. 120) the crank CP is 0·5 feet long and makes 125 revolutions per minute. The mass of the reciprocating parts is m. Find the forces acting at Q when the point P is at a dead-point, A or A',

(*a*) when the connecting rod is infinite,

(*b*) when the length of the connecting rod is three times the crank.

(*a*) Here $\omega = \frac{2\pi \times 125}{60} = \frac{125\pi}{30}$ radians per sec.,

$$F = \frac{m \times (125\pi)^2}{30^2} \times 0{\cdot}5$$
$$= m \times 85{\cdot}7;$$

(*b*)
$$F = m\omega^2 r\left(1 \pm \frac{r}{l}\right)$$
$$= m \times 85{\cdot}7(1 + \tfrac{1}{3}), \text{ or } m \times 85{\cdot}7(1 - \tfrac{1}{3})$$
$$= m \times 85{\cdot}7 \times \tfrac{4}{3}, \text{ or } m \times 85{\cdot}7 \times \tfrac{2}{3}$$
$$= 114{\cdot}2m, \text{ or } 57{\cdot}1m.$$

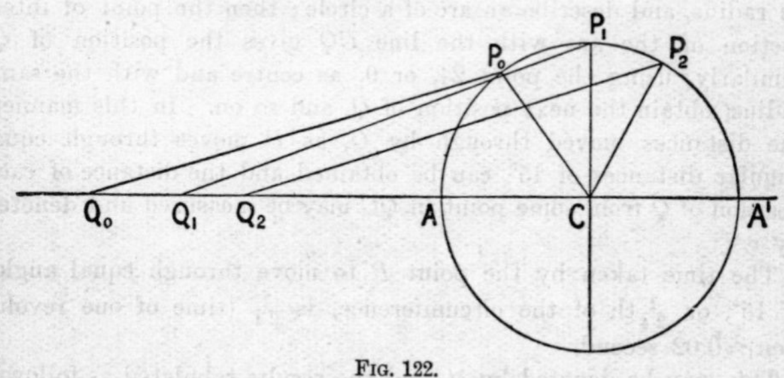

Fig. 122.

Graphical methods.—The velocity and acceleration of Q may be obtained by assuming P to move through small distances P_0P_1, P_1P_2, during small intervals of time δt, and then measuring the distances Q_0Q_1, Q_1Q_2, moved through by Q (Fig. 121). The distances moved through by Q may be denoted by x; then, subtracting consecutive values, we obtain values of δx. Proceeding in this manner, a series of such distances moved through by Q may be obtained and tabulated. From such a table, values of $\frac{\delta x}{\delta t}$ can be calculated. Similarly, values of $\frac{\delta v}{\delta t}$ or $\frac{\delta^2 x}{\delta t^2}$ can be found; from the latter results an approximate value of the force acting on Q at any given instant—and producing the acceleration of Q—can be obtained.

The method adopted may be seen from the following example :

Ex. 9. In a direct-acting engine mechanism (Fig. 120), $CP=6$ in. $(=0·5$ ft.), and $PQ=1·5$ ft., the crank CP makes 125 revolutions per min. in a clockwise direction. The weight of the reciprocating parts at Q is 100 lbs. Find the magnitude of the force at Q for a given position of P.

To obtain the distances moved through by Q draw a diagram (Fig. 122) to a scale (say) of 0·1 in. $=1$ ft. The circle denoting the path of the crank pin P may be divided into 24 equal parts, corresponding to equal angular intervals at 15°.

To determine the position of Q when P is at point (23) on the circle, use the point as centre and the length of the rod $=1·5$ ft. as radius, and describe an arc of a circle ; then the point of intersection of the arc with the line CQ gives the position of Q. Similarly, using the point 24, or 0, as centre and with the same radius, obtain the next position of Q, and so on. In this manner, the distances moved through by Q, as P moves through equal angular distances of 15°, can be obtained and the distance of each position of Q from some point in QC may be measured and denoted by x.

The time taken by the point P to move through equal angles of 15°, or $\frac{1}{24}$th of the circumference, is $\frac{1}{24}$ (time of one revolution) $=0·02$ second.

This may be denoted by δt, and the results tabulated as follows:

Position of P. No.	Displacement of Q $=x$ feet.	δx.	δt.	Velocity $\frac{\delta x}{\delta t}$.	δv.	Acceleration $a=\frac{\delta v}{\delta t}$.
23	0·022					
		−0·022	0·02	−1·10		
					2·20	110
0	0·000					
		0·022	0·02	1·10		
					2·10	105
1	0·022					
		0·064	0·02	3·20		
					1·75	87·5
2	0·086					
		0·099	0 02	4·95		
					1·20	60·0
3	0·185					
		0·123	0·02	6·15		
4	0·308					

By taking the differences of the various tabulated values of x in column 2, a series of values δx, as in column 3, are obtained. The ratio $\frac{\delta x}{\delta t}$ gives approximately the velocity of Q at each given instant.

In like manner, by taking the differences of consecutive values of v, column 6, giving numerical values of δv, can be obtained. Finally, the acceleration at each position is approximately given by $\frac{\delta v}{\delta t}$.

If W denotes the weight of the reciprocating parts, then $W \div g$ is the mass, and when W is known, the force acting at any point of the stroke can be ascertained.

EXERCISES. XXXVIII.

1. A body is observed at the instant when it is passing a point P. From subsequent observations it is found that in any time t seconds, measured from this instant, the body has described s feet (measured from P) where s and t are connected by the equation $s=2t+4t^2$. Find the average speed of the body between the interval $t=1$ and $t=1{\cdot}1$ between $t=1$ and $t=1{\cdot}001$ and between $t=1$ and $t=1{\cdot}0001$ and deduce the actual speed when t is exactly 1.

2. Suppose that a curve has been plotted such that the ordinates and abscissae represent distance and time respectively, what will be represented by the slope of the curve at any point on it? Obtain an expression for the slope if the distance s and time t are connected by the equation

$$s=5t+2{\cdot}1t^2.$$

Give the numerical value at the instant when $t=5$.

3. At the end of a time t seconds it is observed that a body has passed over a distance s feet reckoned from some starting point. If $s=25+150t-5t^2$, find the velocity at a time t and give the value when $t=7$. Find also the acceleration and the force causing this acceleration if the weight of the body is 100 lbs.

4. A train starts from rest and its speeds at the ends of the first, second, third, fourth, fifth and sixth minutes are 9·8, 13·75, 16·95, 19·6, 21·9 and 24 miles per hour respectively. Plot a curve showing the relation between speed and time, and between acceleration and time, deduce approximately the velocity and acceleration at the end of the sixth minute.

5. A body has passed through the space s feet measured from some zero point in its path at the time t seconds measured from some zero of time; the law of motion is

$$s=12{\cdot}2-3{\cdot}6t+6{\cdot}7t^2.$$

Calculate the average velocity of the body

(i) for the next tenth of a second following the completion of the fourth second.

(ii) for the next $\frac{1}{100}$th of a second following the completion of the fourth second.

(iii) for the next $\frac{1}{1000}$th of a second following the completion of the fourth second.

Hence deduce the actual velocity at the end of the fourth second.

6. A piston makes n revolutions per second and drives a crank of length r through a connecting rod of length l. Show that the acceleration at the ends of the strokes are

$$4\pi^2n^2r\left(1+\frac{r}{l}\right) \text{ and } 4\pi^2n^2r\left(1-\frac{r}{l}\right).$$

7. A body weighing 50 lbs. has passed through the space s feet measured from some zero point in its path at the time t seconds measured from some zero of time; the law of motion is

$$s=1{\cdot}2-0{\cdot}6t+1{\cdot}7t^2.$$

Find the acceleration when t is 7 and the force giving this acceleration to it.

8. The following values of s, in feet, show the distance of the centre of gravity of a piece of mechanism weighing 100 lbs. from some point in its straight path at the time t seconds. Find the velocity and the acceleration at the time $t=0{\cdot}085$; find also the force which is giving this acceleration to it.

s	0·088	0·2226	0·3612	0·5038	0·6505	0·8011
t	0·06	0·07	0·08	0·09	0·10	0·11

9. In the mechanism shown (Fig. 123) C and D are fixed centres of motion, the linear scale of the figure being $\frac{1}{8}$ full size, CB is a crank (6″ long) rotating in a clockwise direction at a speed of 8 radians per sec. DA is an oscillating lever and AB a connecting link. Draw a diagram which shall give the acceleration of any point in the link BA, and state the magnitude and direction of the acceleration of the point E.

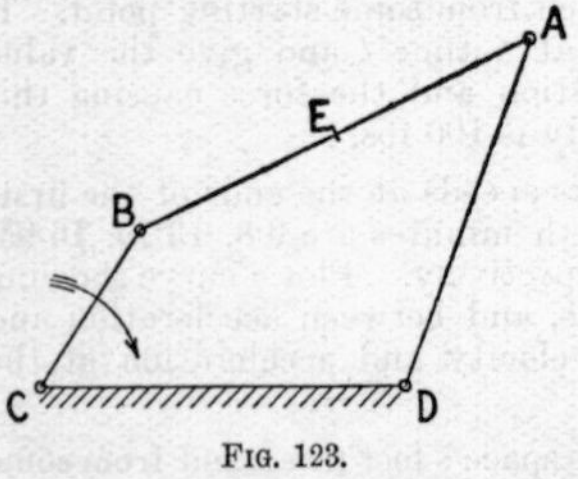

FIG. 123.

10. In a direct-acting engine mechanism (Fig. 120) a crank CP rotates about a fixed centre C, and the end of the connecting rod PQ moves in the line QC.

Given $CP=5$ in., $PQ=16$ in.; speed 120 revolutions per min.

Find by means of careful graphical construction, measurement, tabulation, and calculation, the displacement, velocity and acceleration of Q as P moves through equal distances of $\frac{1}{24}$th the circumference.

Complete the following table:

Position of P.	Displacement of $Q=x$ feet.	δx.	δt.	Velocity $v=\delta x \div \delta t$.	δv.	Acceleration $a=\delta v \div \delta t$.
0	0					
			0·0208	0·87		
1	0·0183				1·67	80·3
		0·0183				
2	0·0725		0·0208	2·54		
		0·0542				
3	0·1542					
4						

11. The sketch (Fig. 124) shows a mechanism called a "quick return motion," where CP is a crank rotating with constant speed, the end of the rod PQ moving in the straight line QM.

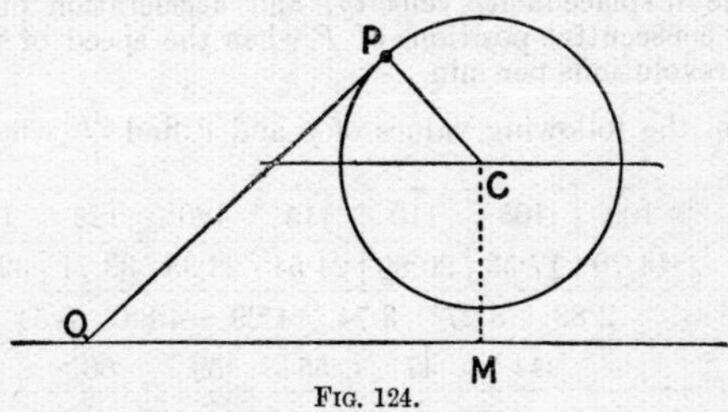

Fig. 124.

Given $CP=5$ in., $PQ=16$ in., and $CM=7$ in.; speed 120 revolutions per min.; determine as in the preceding exercise the displacement, velocity, and acceleration of the point Q.

Set out curves representing these quantities (a) on a time base, (b) on a displacement base.

12. CP (Fig. 121) is a crank which rotates clockwise about C at a uniform speed of 1·5 radians per second. PD is a perpendicular on a fixed horizontal line. The position shown is that for which the time $t=0$; the figure is $\frac{1}{4}$ full size.

If y is the distance of D from C at any time t (positive when to the right of C) and is given by $y=a \sin(qt+e)$, find the numerical values of a, q and e in this case. Also draw the position of the crank and of D when $t=3$, and measure the value of y.

13. In Fig. 125, a diagram of a radial valve gear is given, the point Q moving in the straight line XQ.

Given $CP=5''$, $PR=QM=12''$, $RQ=14''$, $RS=4''$, angle $PSL=30°$.

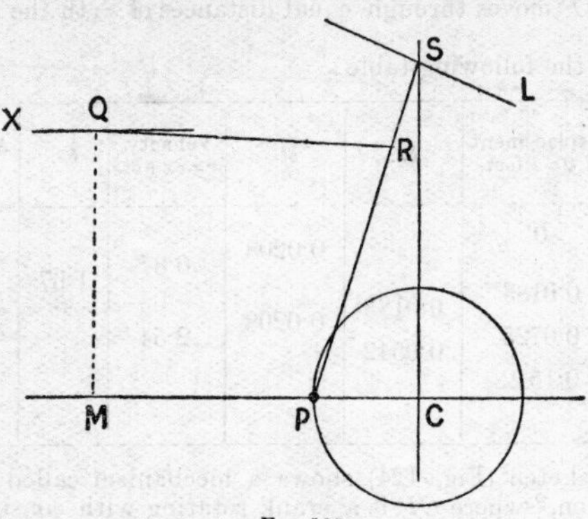

FIG. 125.

Find the displacement, velocity, and acceleration of Q for a number of consecutive positions of P when the speed of the crank CP is 120 revolutions per min.

14. From the following values of p and θ find $\frac{dp}{d\theta}$ when $\theta=115$.

θ	100		105		110		115		120		125		130
p	14·70		17·53		20·80		24·54		28·83		33·71		39·25
Δ_1		2·83		3·27		3·74		4·29		4·88		5·54	
Δ_2			·44		·47		·55		·59		·66		
Δ_3				·03		·08		·04		·07			

Subtracting consecutive values of p we obtain Δ_1 thus

$$17·53-14·7=2·83, \text{ etc.}$$

Similarly Δ_2 is obtained by subtraction, *i.e.* $3·27-2·83=·44$ etc.

A sloping line through 24·54 will pass through 3·74, ·47, ·03 or 4·29, ·59, ·07. As the difference in θ is 5;

$$\therefore \frac{dp}{d\theta}=\tfrac{1}{5}(\Delta_1+\tfrac{1}{2}\Delta_2+\tfrac{1}{3}\Delta_3+\tfrac{1}{4}\Delta_4+\dots)=\tfrac{1}{5}(3·74+\tfrac{1}{2}\times ·47+\tfrac{1}{3}\times ·03+\dots)=0·79$$

$$\text{or } \frac{dp}{d\theta}=\tfrac{1}{5}(\Delta_1-\tfrac{1}{2}\Delta_2+\tfrac{1}{3}\Delta_3)=\tfrac{1}{5}(4·29-\tfrac{1}{2}\times ·59+\tfrac{1}{3}\times ·07)=·803,$$

CHAPTER XVII.

MAXIMA AND MINIMA.

Maxima and minima.—It has already been shown (p. 306) that the slope of the curve representing $y=f(x)$ is equal to $\frac{dy}{dx}$. In Fig. 126 the graph of a function $y=f(x)$ is shown, and the changes in the slope of this curve may be seen from the varying inclinations of the lines touching the curve at various points.

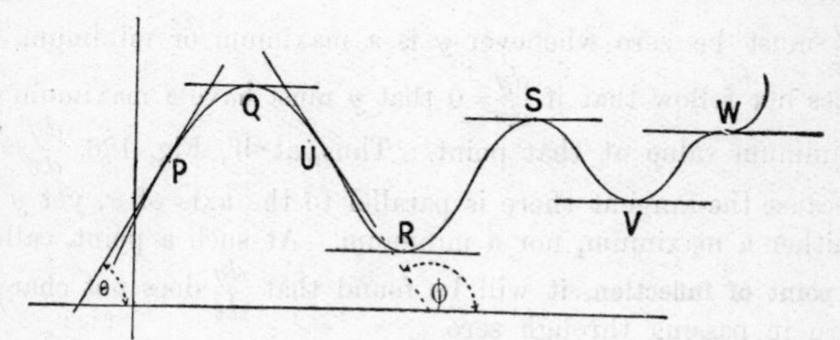

Fig. 126.—Maxima and minima.

Thus, at a point P, $\frac{dy}{dx}=\tan\theta$, and as θ is less than 90° the slope of the curve at P is positive, *i.e.* $\frac{dy}{dx}$ is positive. At U, $\frac{dy}{dx}=\tan\phi$ and is negative. If the curve has been continuous between P and U, then $\frac{dy}{dx}$ must have had a zero value at some intermediate point, or in other words, the tangent to the curve must have been parallel to the axis of x. Such a point is shown at Q. At each of the points R, S, V, and W, $\frac{dy}{dx}$ must also be zero. It will be seen that the ordinate at Q is a little greater than any ordinate near to it on either side; it is said to be a *maximum* ordinate, or a maximum value of y.

The ordinate at V is less than any adjacent to it on either side, and is called a *minimum* ordinate.

DEF. When y increases with increase of x to a certain value and then diminishes, it is said to have a **maximum** value where the change occurs; and when y diminishes to a certain value and then increases, a **minimum** value is obtained. In either case $\frac{dy}{dx}=0$. So the maximum value of a function may be defined as a value greater than either the one just before it or just after it. Or, in other words, $\frac{dy}{dx}$ changes from $+$ to $-$ as the curve passes through a maximum point. Similarly, if $\frac{dy}{dx}$ changes from $-$ to $+$ in passing through zero, the point where $\frac{dy}{dx}$ is zero is a *minimum* point.

Points of inflection.—It should be noted that although $\frac{dy}{dx}$ must be zero whenever y is a maximum or minimum, it does not follow that if $\frac{dy}{dx}=0$ that y must have a maximum or minimum value at that point. Thus, at W, Fig. 126, $\frac{dy}{dx}=0$, because the tangent there is parallel to the axis of x, yet y is neither a maximum, nor a minimum. At such a point, called **a point of inflection**, it will be found that $\frac{dy}{dx}$ does not change sign in passing through zero.

It will be seen from Fig. 126 that the terms maximum and minimum are relative, and that we can have one maximum value, as at Q, greater than another maximum, as at S.

The method of procedure in finding maximum or minimum values of a function y will be seen in the following example:

Ex. 1. Find for what values of x the function

$$y=x^3-6x^2+9x-12,$$

is a maximum or a minimum. Give the maximum and minimum values of y.

Since $$y=x^3-6x^2+9x-12; \quad \text{.........................(i)}$$

$$\therefore \frac{dy}{dx} = 3x^2 - 12x + 9.$$

But when y is a maximum or minimum, $\frac{dy}{dx} = 0$.

To find what values of x make $\frac{dy}{dx}$ zero, we solve the equation

$$3x^2 - 12x + 9 = 0,$$

and obtain $\qquad x = 1$ and $x = 3$.

It remains to determine which of these values makes y a maximum and which makes it a minimum.

In Eq. (i), substitute $\qquad x = 1$;

$$\therefore y = 1 - 6 + 9 - 12 = -8; \quad \therefore y = -8.$$

Now, when $x = 0{\cdot}999$, a value slightly less than 1, find the value of y;

$$\therefore y = -8{\cdot}000003.$$

Also, when

$$x = 1{\cdot}001,$$
$$y = -8{\cdot}000003.$$

Hence y increases, algebraically, as x increases from $0{\cdot}999$ to $x = 1$, and diminishes as x increases from 1 to $1{\cdot}001$ (since $-8{\cdot}000003$ is < -8).

Hence, at $x = 1$, y has the maximum value -8.

Another method of testing will be applied at $x = 3$. *

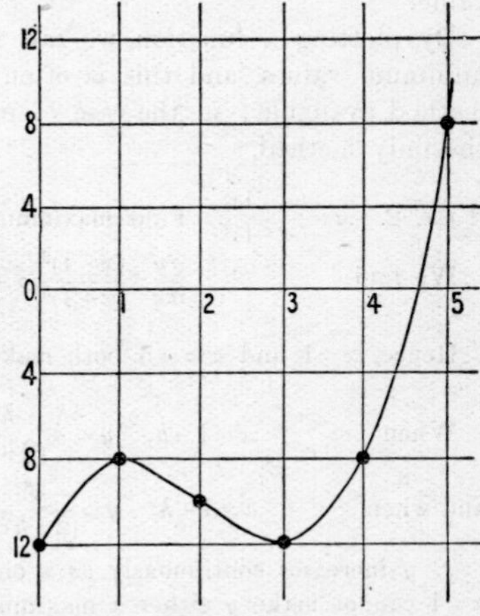

FIG. 127.—Graph of $y = x^3 - 6x^2 + 9x - 12$.

In Fig. 127 it is evident that $\frac{dy}{dx}$ is positive for a value of x slightly less than that giving y a maximum, and negative for a value of x a little greater than this; also $\frac{dy}{dx}$ is negative for x less than, and positive for x greater than, that making y a minimum.

$$\text{Now,} \quad \frac{dy}{dx} = 3(x^2 - 4x + 3); \text{ when } x = 2{\cdot}99, \frac{dy}{dx} = -0{\cdot}0603;$$

* See p. 385.

when $$x=3{\cdot}01, \frac{dy}{dx}=+0{\cdot}0603,$$
or $\frac{dy}{dx}$ changes from $-^{ve}$ to $+^{ve}$ as x increases from 2·99 to 3·01.

Hence $x=3$ gives a minimum value of $y=-12$. Fig. 127 shows the graph of $y=x^3-6x^2+9x-12$.

It will be noticed in Fig. 126 that maximum and minimum values of y occur alternately. This is always so; between two consecutive maximum values of y there must be one, and only one minimum value, and between consecutive minimum values, one maximum. For after y is a maximum it decreases and must, before it can increase again to reach another maximum, have stopped decreasing, and so have had a minimum value.

By plotting a function we can always find maximum and minimum values, and this is often the readiest and simplest method available; in the case of experimental numbers it is the only method.

Ex. 2. $y=\frac{(x-1)^3}{(x+1)^2}$. Find maximum and minimum values of y.

We find $$\frac{dy}{dx}=\frac{(x-1)^2}{(x+1)^3}(x+5).$$

Hence, $x=1$ and $x=-5$ both make $\frac{dy}{dx}$ zero.

When $$x=1-h, \quad y=-\frac{h^3}{(2-h)^2},$$
and when $$x=1+h, \quad y=\frac{h^3}{(2+h)^2};$$

$\therefore$ y increases continuously as x changes from $1-h$ to $1+h$, so $x=1$ cannot make y either a maximum or minimum. Apply the same test at $x=-5$, we find that y is a maximum there.

Ex. 3. If $$y=\sin^3\theta\cos\theta, \quad \text{.............................(i)}$$
show that y is a maximum when $\theta=60°$.

Substituting various values, 10°, 20°, etc., for θ, the corresponding values of y can be calculated from (i).

Thus, when $\theta=40°$,
$$\sin 40°=0{\cdot}6428, \quad \cos 40°=0{\cdot}7660;$$
$$\therefore\ y=(0{\cdot}6428)^3\times 0{\cdot}7660=0{\cdot}2033.$$

Other values of y may be obtained in like manner and tabulated as follows:

θ	20°	40°	60°	80°	90°
y	0·0376	0·203	0·325	0·166	0

Plotting these values as in Fig. 128, the maximum value of y occurs at m when $\theta=60°$.

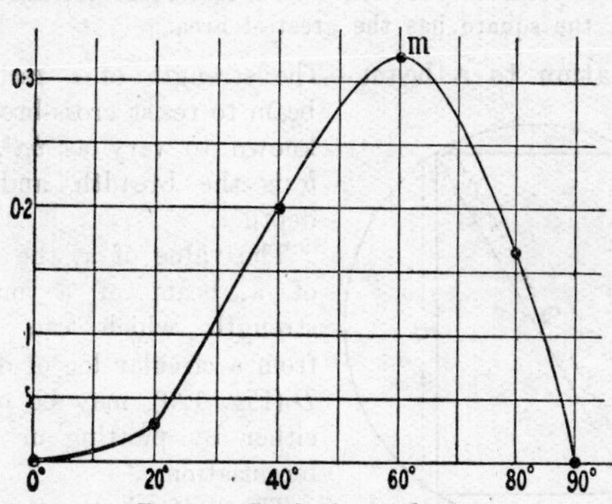

FIG. 128.—Graph of $y=\sin^3\theta\cos\theta$.

We have $$y=\sin^3\theta\cos\theta;$$

$$\therefore\ \frac{dy}{d\theta}=-\sin^3\theta\sin\theta+3\cos\theta\sin^2\theta\cos\theta=-\sin^4\theta+3\sin^2\theta\cos^2\theta,$$

or a maximum value this must vanish;

$$\therefore\ 3\sin^2\theta\cos^2\theta-\sin^4\theta=0.$$

The solutions of this equation are $\theta=n\pi$ or $n\pi+(-1)^{n-1}\frac{\pi}{3}$. This gives $\theta=60°$.

Ex. 4. To divide a given number into two parts so that their product is a maximum.

Let a be the given number, and x one of the parts, then the remaining part is $a-x$. The product is $x(a-x)$.

If $$y=x(a-x)=ax-x^2,$$

or a maximum.

By differentiation, $\frac{dy}{dx}=a-2x=0$ for a maximum;

$$\therefore\ x=\frac{a}{2}.$$

A result which gives a maximum value of y, as may easily be proved.

Hence, the two parts must be equal.

It will be noticed that this is the same problem as to divide a line into two parts such that the rectangle on the two parts as sides is a maximum. Hence, of all rectangles having a given perimeter, the square has the greatest area.

Application to a beam.—The strength of a rectangular beam to resist cross-breaking is known to vary as bd^2, where b is the breadth, and d the depth.

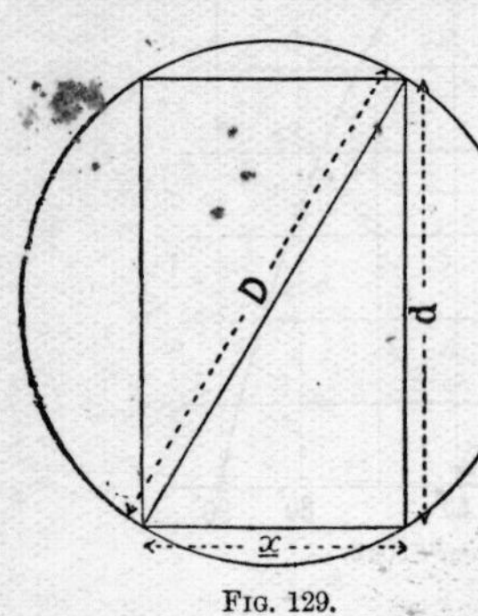

Fig. 129.

The value of x, the breadth of a beam of a maximum strength which can be cut from a circular log of diameter D (Fig. 129), may be obtained either by plotting or by differentiation.

Thus, if d be the depth then $d=\sqrt{D^2-x^2}$, and putting

$$y=bd^2=x(D^2-x^2), \quad \text{.........................(i)}$$

we obtain $$\frac{dy}{dx}=D^2-3x^2,$$

and therefore for a maximum $\left(\text{i.e. } \frac{dy}{dx}=0\right)$,

$$x=\frac{D}{\sqrt{3}}. \quad \text{...(ii)}$$

Ex. 5. Let the diameter D be 9 in. Then, giving a series of values to x, values of y can be calculated and tabulated as follows:

x	0	1	2	3	4	5	6	7	8	9
y	0	80	154	216	260	280	270	224	136	0

By plotting the values of x and y a curve may be drawn through the plotted points as in Fig. 130. The maximum value, *i.e.* the point on the curve at which the tangent is horizontal, is seen to be between $x=5$ and $x=6$, viz. at a. Also, from such a curve, we can find within what limits the breadth may vary so as not to weaken the beam more than a certain percentage, say 10 or 15 per cent.

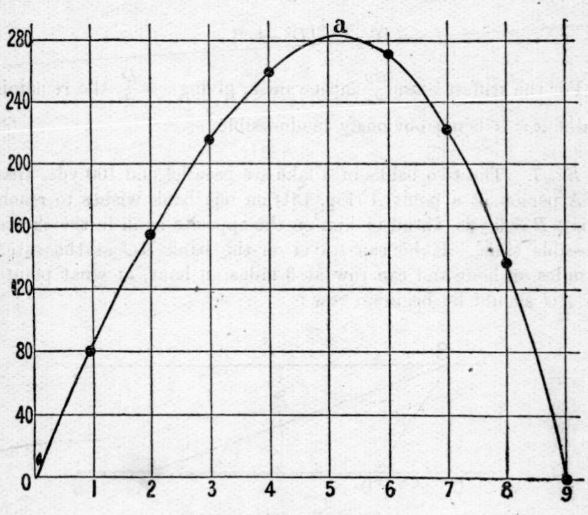

Fig. 130.—Graph of $y=x(81-x^2)$.

Now, making $D=9$ in (ii), we have

$$x=\frac{9}{\sqrt{3}}=3\sqrt{3}=5{\cdot}196 \text{ in.}$$

The maximum value of y can readily be obtained either from the curve or by substituting the value of x in (i).

Thus, $$y=3\sqrt{3}(81-27)=162\sqrt{3}=280{\cdot}58.$$

Stiffest beam.—The deflection of a beam due to a given load is inversely proportional to the breadth and the cube of the depth of the beam.

Ex. 6. If D is the diameter of a cylindrical log of timber, and if x denote the breadth, then the depth d is $\sqrt{D^2-x^2}$.

Hence, putting $y=xd^3$;

$$y=x(D^2-x^2)^{\frac{3}{2}},$$

$$\frac{dy}{dx}=(D^2-x^2)^{\frac{3}{2}}+\frac{3}{2}x(D^2-x^2)^{\frac{1}{2}}\times(-2x)$$

$$=(D^2-x^2)^{\frac{1}{2}}\{D^2-4x^2\}.$$

For the stiffest beam $\frac{dy}{dx}$ must vanish, giving $x=\frac{D}{2}$, the remaining value $x=D$ being obviously inadmissible.

Ex. 7. The two banks of a lake are parallel and 100 yds. apart. A person at a point A (Fig. 131) on one bank wishes to reach a point B 300 yds. ahead of him on the opposite bank in the shortest possible time. If he can travel on the bank AC at the rate of 5 miles an hour and can row at 3 miles an hour, at what point D in AC should he begin to row?

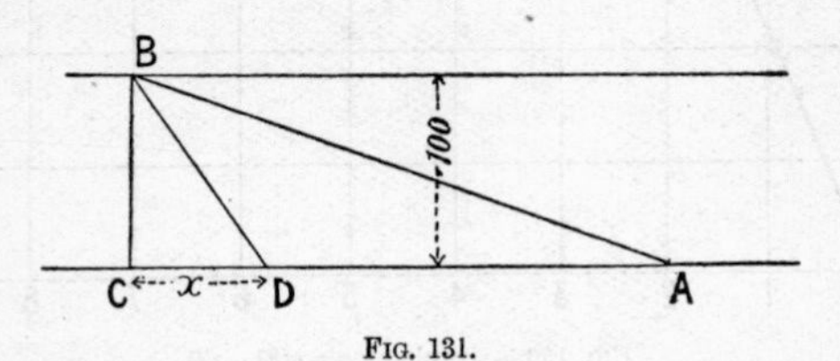

FIG. 131.

Draw CB perpendicular to AC and let the distance CD be denoted by x yards. Then, $AD=(300-x)$ yd.

The distance $DB=\sqrt{100^2+x^2}$ yd.,

and time taken from D to B is

$$\frac{\sqrt{100^2+x^2}}{3\times1760}\text{ hours.}$$

Along the bank the distance $AD=(300-x)$ yd. and time taken from A to D

$$=\frac{300-x}{5\times1760}\text{ hours.}$$

The total time $t=\frac{\sqrt{100^2+x^2}}{3\times 1760}+\frac{300-x}{5\times 1760}$ hours

$$=\frac{5\sqrt{100^2+x^2}+900-3x}{15\times 1760}$$

s to be a minimum;

$$\therefore \frac{dt}{dx}=\frac{5\times\frac{1}{2}(100^2+x^2)^{-\frac{1}{2}}\times 2x-3}{15\times 1760}=0$$

for a maximum or minimum,

whence $$\frac{5x}{\sqrt{100^2+x^2}}-3=0.$$

Hence, $16x^2=9\times 100^2$, $\therefore\ x=\pm 75$ yds.

It is obvious that the negative value is not applicable, hence $x=75$ yds.

Ex. 8. **Height of rectangle of maximum area inscribed in a given triangle.**

Let ABC (Fig. 132) be the given triangle, the base AB equal to a, and the altitude h.

Let GD, one of the sides of the rectangle, be denoted by x, and the base, FG, by y.

Height of triangle $DEC=h-x$,

and $h:(h-x)=AB:DE$ (similar $\triangle$s),

or $h:h-x=a:y$;

$$\therefore\ y=\frac{a(h-x)}{h}.$$

Area of rectangle

$$=x\times y=\frac{a}{h}(h-x)x;$$

$$\therefore\ A=ax-\frac{ax^2}{h},$$

$$\frac{dA}{dx}=a-\frac{2ax}{h}=0$$

for a maximum or minimum,

giving $2x=h$; $\therefore\ x=\frac{h}{2}$,

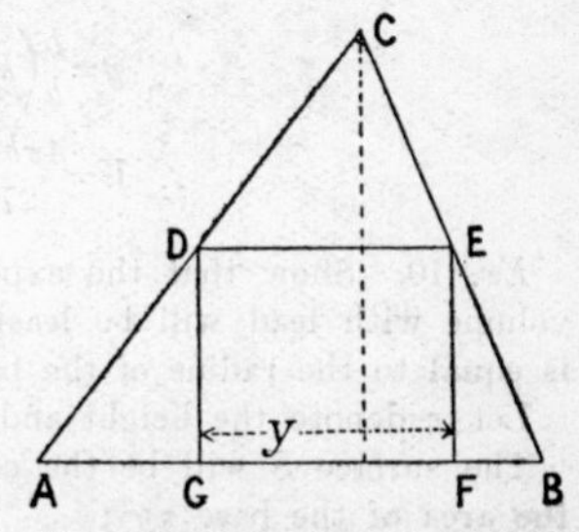

FIG. 132.—Rectangle of maximum area inscribed in a triangle.

which makes A a maximum; therefore altitude of rectangle must be one-half of the altitude of the triangle.

Ex. 9. **To find the dimensions of the cylinder of greatest volume which can be obtained from a given right cone.**

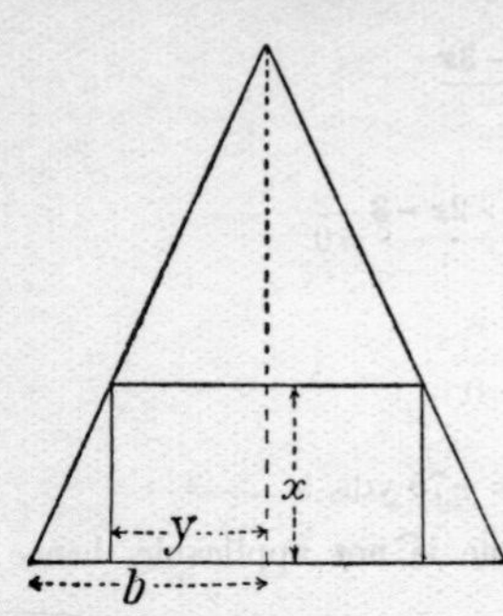

FIG. 133.—Cylinder of greatest volume in a cone.

Let h denote the height of the cone, and b the radius of the base (Fig. 133). Also let x and y denote the corresponding dimensions for the cylinder.

Then $V=\pi y^2\times x,$ ....(i)

also $h:(h-x)=b:y;$

$$\therefore\ y=\frac{b(h-x)}{h}, \text{ ....(ii)}$$

and $$V=\frac{\pi b^2}{h^2}(h-x)^2x, \text{ .....(iii)}$$

as b and h are both constant, to obtain the maximum value of (iii) it is only necessary when differentiating to consider the terms $(h-x)^2x$.

Let $$V'=(h-x)^2x=h^2x-2hx^2+x^3.$$

Then $$\frac{dV'}{dx}=h^2-4hx+3x^2;$$

$$\therefore\ 3x^2-4hx=-h^2.$$

Solving this, we find $x=h$ or $\frac{h}{3}$. The former is inadmissible.

Hence, substituting the value $x=\frac{h}{3}$ in (ii),

$$y=\frac{b}{h}\left(h-\frac{h}{3}\right)=\frac{2}{3}b;$$

$$\therefore\ V=\frac{4\pi hb^2}{27}.$$

Ex. 10. Show that the expense of lining a cylinder of given volume with lead will be least when the depth of the cylinder is equal to the radius of the base.

Let x denote the height and y the radius of the base.

The surface S will be the convex surface $2\pi xy$ together with the area of the base πy^2;

$$\therefore\ S=2\pi xy+\pi y^2, \text{ ....(i)}$$

$$V=\text{volume}=\pi y^2x;$$

$$\therefore\ x=\frac{V}{\pi y^2}. \text{ ....(ii)}$$

Substitute in (i); $\therefore\ S=\dfrac{2\pi V}{\pi y^2}y+\pi y^2=\dfrac{2V}{y}+\pi y^2,$

$$\frac{dS}{dy}=-\frac{2V}{y^2}+2\pi y;$$

$$\therefore\ y^3=\frac{V}{\pi}\ \text{for a minimum.}$$

From (ii), $$x^3=\frac{V^3}{\pi^3 y^6}=\frac{V^3}{\pi^3\times\dfrac{V^2}{\pi^2}}=\frac{V}{\pi}=xy^2\ \text{from (ii).}$$

Hence $x=y$, or the height of the cylinder is equal to the radius of the base.

We may consider the preceding problem as an example of a more general method. Thus, taking the equations for the surface and volume respectively of a cylinder,

$$S=\pi y(2x+y),$$

where x denotes the height of the cylinder and y the radius of its base,

$$V=\pi y^2 x.$$

Two conditions are to be satisfied. $\dfrac{dS}{dx}$ must be zero for a minimum. (Either x or y might have been chosen as the independent variable.)

Also V is to be constant, or $\dfrac{dV}{dx}$ must be zero.

$$\frac{dS}{dx}=0\ \text{gives}\ y\left(2+\frac{dy}{dx}\right)+(2x+y)\frac{dy}{dx}=0, \quad\text{(i)}$$

and $$\frac{dV}{dx}=0\ \text{gives}\ y^2+2xy\frac{dy}{dx}=0. \quad\text{(ii)}$$

To find the relation between x and y eliminate $\dfrac{dy}{dx}$;

$$\therefore\ \text{from (ii)},\ \frac{dy}{dx}=-\frac{y}{2x}.$$

Substitute this value in (i);

$$\therefore\ y\left(2-\frac{y}{2x}\right)-(2x+y)\frac{y}{2x}=0,$$

or $$2-\frac{y}{2x}=1+\frac{y}{2x},$$

or $$\frac{y}{x}=1,$$

i.e. $$y=x.$$

Ex. 11. From a circular disc of thin sheet copper a piece in the shape of a sector is cut out in such a way that the remainder can be bent into the form of a right circular conical funnel. What is the least possible diameter for the disc if the capacity of the funnel is to be one pint? [1 pint=34·66 cub. in.]

Let r denote the length of a slant side of cone, and x the radius of the base of the cone.

$$V = \text{volume of cone} = \frac{\pi}{3}x^2\sqrt{r^2-x^2}, \qquad \text{(i)}$$

and the volume has to be constant, viz. 1 pint; $\therefore \dfrac{dV}{dx}=0.$

But the minimum value of the diameter, or the radius, being required,

$$\therefore \frac{dr}{dx}=0. \qquad \text{(ii)}$$

From $\dfrac{dV}{dx}=0$

we obtain
$$2x\sqrt{r^2-x^2}+\frac{1}{2}\frac{2r\dfrac{dr}{dx}-2x}{\sqrt{r^2-x^2}}\times x^2=0. \qquad \text{(iii)}$$

Substituting from (ii),

$$\therefore \ 2(r^2-x^2)-x^2=0,$$

or
$$r=\sqrt{\frac{3}{2}}x. \qquad \text{(iv)}$$

From (i) and (iv), since 1 pint=34·66 cub. in.,

$$34{\cdot}66=\frac{\pi}{3}\times\frac{2}{3}r^3\left(1-\frac{2}{3}\right)^{\frac{1}{2}},$$

or
$$r^3=\frac{9\sqrt{3}\times 34{\cdot}66}{2\pi};$$

$$\therefore \ r=4{\cdot}413 \text{ in.},$$

or the least diameter is 8·826 inches.

Ex. 12. It is known that the weight of coal in tons consumed per hour in a certain vessel is $0{\cdot}3+0{\cdot}001v^3$, where v is the speed in knots (or nautical miles per hour). For a voyage of 1,000 nautical miles, tabulate the time in hours, and the total coal consumption for various values of v. If the wages, interest on cost of vessel, etc., are represented by the value of 1 ton of coal per hour, tabulate for each value of v the total cost, stating it in the alue of tons of coal, and plot on squared paper. About what alue of v gives the greatest economy?

Let t denote the time (in hours), and s the distance described, hen

$$s=vt. \quad \text{(i)}$$

Total cost in tons of coal consumption

$$=C=t+(0{\cdot}3+0{\cdot}001v^3)t. \quad \text{(ii)}$$

Also t may be expressed in terms of v from (i);

$$\therefore \; t=sv^{-1}=1000v^{-1}.$$

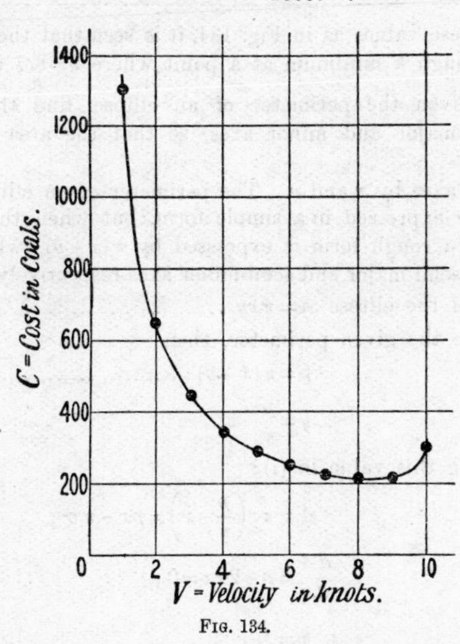

FIG. 134.

Substituting in (ii),

$$C=1000v^{-1}+(0{\cdot}3+0{\cdot}001v^3)\,1000v^{-1}$$
$$=1300v^{-1}+v^2,$$

$$\frac{dC}{dv}=-1300v^{-2}+2v=0 \text{ for a minimum};$$

$$\therefore \; v^3=650 \text{ gives a minimum},$$

ence $\quad v=8{\cdot}66$ knots,

r, the minimum value for v may be obtained by plotting on quared paper.

Tabulating each value of v, we obtain the following table:

v	1	2	3	4	5	6	7	8	9	10
t	1000	500	333	250	200	167	143	125	111	100
Tons of coal consumed	301	154	109	91	85	86	92	101·5	114	130
Total cost -	1301	654	442	341	285	253	235	226·5	225	230

Plotting these values as in Fig. 134, it is seen that the total cost C passes through a minimum at a point where $v = 8{\cdot}7$ (roughly).

Ex. 13. Given the perimeter of an ellipse, find the relation between the major and minor axes, so that the area may be a maximum.

Denote the axes by x and y. The perimeter of an ellipse cannot be accurately expressed in a simple form, but when the axes are nearly equal a rough form is expressed by $\pi(x+y)$, when x and y denote the semi-major and semi-minor axes respectively.

The area of the ellipse $A = \pi xy$. ....(i)

If p denote the given perimeter, then

$$p = \pi(x+y); \qquad \text{(ii)}$$

$$\therefore\ y = \frac{p}{\pi} - x.$$

Substituting this value in (i);

$$\therefore\ A = \pi x\left(\frac{p}{\pi} - x\right) = px - \pi x^2;$$

$$\therefore\ \frac{dA}{dx} = p - 2\pi x = 0;$$

$$\therefore\ x = \frac{p}{2\pi},$$

or, the given ellipse must have its semi-axes equal, and that form is a circle.

Prof. Boys, F.R.S., has suggested the use of elliptical water pipes to prevent the pipes bursting during frosty weather. The expansion of the water due to freezing tends to make the internal cross-section become more circular, that is, to increase its area; and the internal volume of the pipe would be correspondingly enlarged.

Ex. 14. When is $x^{\frac{2}{\gamma}} - x^{1+\frac{1}{\gamma}}$ a maximum, γ being 1·4? Also show, by two or three values near the maximum, and on either side, that the value obtained is a maximum.

Let $y = x^{\frac{2}{\gamma}} - x^{1+\frac{1}{\gamma}}$.

Substituting the given value for γ,

$$y = x^{\frac{2}{1\cdot4}} - x^{\frac{1+1\cdot4}{1\cdot4}};$$

$$\therefore\ y = x^{\frac{10}{7}} - x^{\frac{12}{7}}, \qquad \text{(i)}$$

$$\frac{dy}{dx} = \frac{10}{7}x^{\frac{3}{7}} - \frac{12}{7}x^{\frac{5}{7}}.$$

For a maximum value $\frac{dy}{dx} = 0$;

$$\therefore\ \frac{10}{7}x^{\frac{3}{7}} - \frac{12}{7}x^{\frac{5}{7}} = 0,$$

or

$$5x^{\frac{3}{7}} = 6x^{\frac{5}{7}};\quad \therefore\ x^3 = (1\cdot2)^7 x^5;$$

$$\therefore\ x^2 = \frac{1}{(1\cdot2)^7} = \left(\frac{10}{12}\right)^7,$$

$$2\log x = 7(\log 10 - \log 12);$$

$$\therefore\ x = 0\cdot5282.$$

Insert this value in (i) and calculate the corresponding value of y. Thus, when $x = 0\cdot5282$, from (i),

$$y = 0\cdot5282^{\frac{10}{7}} - 0\cdot5282^{\frac{12}{7}} = 0\cdot0669.$$

Calculate values of y on each side of the maximum, and tabulate as follows:

Values of x	0·4	0·52	0·5282	0·53	0·6
y	0·0627	0·0668	0·0669	0·0668	0·0652

Ex. 15. Determine the speed most economical in fuel when steaming *against* a tide, supposing the resistance to the ship to vary as the square of the velocity, and that the fuel burnt per hour is proportional to the product of resistance and speed.

Let v miles per hour be the constant velocity of the tide, and V miles per hour the velocity of the ship. Then, the velocity of the ship relative to the bank is $V - v$ miles per hour;

$\therefore$ time required to steam a distance of m miles is $\frac{m}{V-v}$ hours.

But the resistance to motion is proportional to V^2, and the fuel burnt per hour to $V \times V^2 = V^3$;

$\therefore$ fuel burnt per hour $= KV^3$, where K is some constant;

$\therefore$ to steam m miles requires $F = \frac{m}{V-v} \times KV^3$ lbs. of fuel.

We have to find what value of V makes F a minimum.

$$\frac{dF}{dV} = mK \times \frac{3V^2(V-v) - V^3}{(V-v)^2}$$

$$= mK \times \frac{2V^3 - 3V^2 v}{(V-v)^2}.$$

This is zero when $V=0$ or $V = \frac{3v}{2}$.

$V=0$ is inadmissible. Hence, $V = \frac{3}{2}v$ gives the speed at which the minimum quantity is burnt.

Taking $v=5$ miles per hour, and that $K=0{\cdot}0016$, plot the curve connecting fuel per mile per hour in tons, if $K=0{\cdot}0016$, and V varies from $V=5\frac{1}{2}$ to $V=10$. Show that we can depart considerably from $V=7\frac{1}{2}$, the most economical speed without altering F very much.

[This is shown by the graph of F and V being flat in the neighbourhood of $V=7\frac{1}{2}$.]

EXERCISES. XXXIX.

1. The sum of two numbers is 33; find the numbers when the sum of their squares is a minimum.

2. For what value of x is $3x - 4x^3$ a minimum? Is there a maximum?

3. Find the turning values of $x + \frac{1}{x}$.

4. Find the area of the greatest rectangle whose perimeter is 10 feet.

5. Divide a line into two parts so that the sum of the squares on the two parts shall be a minimum.

Find the maximum and minimum values of the following:

6. $3x^4 + 8x^3 - 24x^2 - 96x + 112$.

7. $2x^3 - 17x^2 + 44x - 30$.

8. $\frac{x^3}{3x^2 - a^2}$.

9. Prove that the greatest value of

$$\frac{2x\sqrt{9+3x^2}}{9+7x^2} \text{ is } \tfrac{1}{2}.$$

10. Divide 12 into two parts, (i) so that the least multiplied by the square of the greatest shall be a maximum; (ii) so that the least multiplied by the cube of the greatest shall be a maximum.

11. Find maximum and minimum values of $y=\cos(ax+b)$.

12. Find the value of x for which $y=\dfrac{a}{x}+bx$ is a minimum; find the numerical value when $a=8$, $b=2$.

13. Find the maximum and minimum values of

(i) $y=(x-3)^3(x^2-3x-3)$, (ii) $y=x^3(x-4)$, (iii) $y=x^{2n+1}(x-2n)$.

14. Find maximum and minimum values of $\sqrt{a+x}+\sqrt{a-x}$.

15. Find the least area of sheet metal that can be used to make a cylindrical gasometer, whose volume is 10 million cub. ft., the one closed end being flat. Give the dimensions of the gasometer.

16. Find the volume of the greatest cylindrical parcel which may be sent by parcel post. Given that the combined length and girth must not be greater than 6 feet.

17. Find the values of x which will make $\sin(x-a)\cos x$ a maximum or minimum.

18. Determine the maximum and minimum values of $f(x)$ when

$$f(x)=(x-2)^4(x-4)^2.$$

19. Find the values of x which make $x(a-x)^2(2a-x)^3$ a maximum or minimum.

20. Find the least area of canvas that can be used to construct a conical tent whose cubical capacity is 800 cub. feet.

21. Show that the maximum and minimum values of $y=\dfrac{x^2}{1+x^2}$ are $\frac{1}{2}$ and $-\frac{1}{2}$ respectively.

22. The hypotenuse of a right-angled triangle is given; find the lengths of the other sides when the area is a maximum.

23. Find the maximum and minimum values of

(i) $x^3-6x^2+9x+10$, (ii) $\sqrt{4a^2x^3-2ax^3}$.

24. A cylindrical cistern made of sheet metal is required to hold 00 gallons of water. Find the dimensions when the cost of the material is a minimum. (*a*) No cover, (*b*) closed top and bottom.

CHAPTER XVIII.

SUCCESSIVE DIFFERENTIATION. TAYLOR'S AND MACLAURIN'S THEOREMS.

Successive differentiation.—In the process of differentiatior we have already found that when an expression contains x tc any power, its differential contains x to a power lower by unity; we may consider such a differential of a function as a new function, and proceed to determine its differential.

Ex. 1. Let $y=f(x)$, where $f(x)=3x^4$, $\frac{dy}{dx}=12x^3$.

As the differential contains x^3 we may proceed to differ entiate it as a new function. The differential of $12x^3$ is $36x^2$ and is called the second differential of $f(x)$, and may be denoted by

$$\frac{d\left(\frac{dy}{dx}\right)}{dx}.$$

This expression is more conveniently written in the usua form $\frac{d^2y}{dx^2}$.

Repeating the process, the third differential $\frac{d^3y}{dx^3}=72x$ i obtained; and similarly, $\frac{d^4y}{dx^4}=72$. As this, the fourth, differ ential does not contain x, all succeeding differential coefficient will be zero.

Care must be taken not to confuse $\frac{d^2y}{dx^2}$ with $\left(\frac{dy}{dx}\right)^2$. Th former denotes the differential of the differential of y witl respect to x, the latter is the square of the differential of y

If u and v are functions of x, it can easily be shown that

$$\frac{d^n(uv)}{dx^n}=u\frac{d^nv}{dx^n}+n\frac{du}{dx}\frac{d^{n-1}v}{dx^{n-1}}+\frac{n(n-1)}{1.2}\frac{d^2u}{dx^2}\frac{d^{n-2}v}{dx^{n-2}}+\text{etc.}+\frac{d^nu}{dx^n}v.$$

This is called the **Theorem of Leibnitz.**

If we differentiate $y=uv$, we find, as on p. 320,

$$\frac{dy}{dx}=u\frac{dv}{dx}+v\frac{du}{dx}.$$

Differentiating again, this becomes

$$\frac{d^2y}{dx^2}=u\frac{d^2v}{dx^2}+\frac{du}{dx}\frac{dv}{dx}+\frac{dv}{dx}\frac{du}{dx}+v\frac{d^2u}{dx^2}$$

$$=u\frac{d^2v}{dx^2}+2\frac{du}{dx}\frac{dv}{dx}+v\frac{d^2u}{dx^2}.$$

In a similar manner, from the third differentiation,

$$\frac{d^3y}{dx^3}=u\frac{d^3v}{dx^3}+3\frac{du}{dx}\frac{d^2v}{dx^2}+3\frac{d^2u}{dx^2}\frac{dv}{dx}+v\frac{d^3u}{dx^3},$$

and, generally,

$$\frac{d^ny}{dx^n}=u\frac{d^nv}{dx^n}+n\frac{du}{dx}\frac{d^{n-1}v}{dx^{n-1}}+\frac{n(n-1)}{1.2}\frac{d^2u}{dx^2}\frac{d^{n-2}v}{dx^{n-2}}+\ldots+\frac{d^nu}{dx^n}v,$$

in which the coefficients follow the law of the Binomial Theorem. Hence the result follows.

The simplest case of successive differentiation occurs with the function $y=e^x$, in which all the differential coefficients are equal to the original functions.

Ex. 2. Let $y=ax^4$.

Then $$\frac{dy}{dx}=4ax^3,\ \frac{d^2y}{dx^2}=12ax^2,\ \frac{d^3y}{dx^3}=24ax.$$

A convenient notation is to write

$$y=f(x),$$

then $$\frac{dy}{dx}=f'(x),\ \frac{d^2y}{dx^2}=f''(x),\ \text{etc.}$$

Thus, if $$f(x)=ax^4,\ \text{then}\ f'(x)=4ax^3,$$

$$f''(x)=12ax^2,\ f'''(x)=24ax.$$

Ex. 3. Let $y=a\sin x$.

Then $$\frac{dy}{dx}=a\cos x=a\sin\left(x+\frac{\pi}{2}\right),$$

$$\frac{d^2y}{dx^2}=\frac{d(a\cos x)}{dx}=-a\sin x=a\sin\left(x+2\cdot\frac{\pi}{2}\right).$$

Similarly, $$\frac{d^3y}{dx^3}=-a\cos x=a\sin\left(x+3\cdot\frac{\pi}{2}\right).$$

Ex. 4. Let $y=a\sin bx$.

$$\frac{dy}{dx}=ab\cos bx=ab\sin\left(bx+\frac{\pi}{2}\right),$$

$$\frac{d^2y}{dx^2}=-ab^2\sin bx=ab^2\sin\left(bx+2\frac{\pi}{2}\right),$$

$$\frac{d^3y}{dx^3}=-ab^3\cos bx=ab^3\sin\left(bx+3\frac{\pi}{2}\right),$$

and $$\frac{d^ny}{dx^n}=ab^n\sin\left(bx+n\frac{\pi}{2}\right).$$

Implicit functions.—So far we have confined our attention to functions in which y occurs alone on the left hand side of the equation. Such are called **explicit functions**; in contradistinction an **implicit function** is one in which the variable y is not expressed directly as a function of x. We proceed to show how to find the differential coefficient of such an expression. The method adopted may be seen from the following examples:

Ex. 5. $$2yx+ay^2=bx^2. \quad\text{(i)}$$

Differentiating according to x, we obtain

$$2y+2x\frac{dy}{dx}+2ay\frac{dy}{dx}=2bx,$$

dividing by 2 and rearranging,

$$(ay+x)\frac{dy}{dx}=bx-y;$$

$$\therefore\ \frac{dy}{dx}=\frac{bx-y}{ay+x}. \quad\text{(ii)}$$

This equation admits of being reduced to a simpler form by using Eq. (i).

Thus, from (i), $$bx^2-yx=ay^2+yx,$$

or $$x(bx-y)=y(ay+x);$$

$$\therefore \frac{y}{x} = \frac{bx - y}{ay + x}.$$

Substitute this value in (ii), and we obtain

$$\frac{dy}{dx} = \frac{y}{x}.$$

For verification (i) may be treated as a quadratic for y;

$$\therefore y = \frac{-x \pm \sqrt{x^2 + abx^2}}{a}$$

$$= \frac{x}{a}(-1 \pm \sqrt{1 + ab});$$

$$\therefore \frac{dy}{dx} = \frac{1}{a}(-1 \pm \sqrt{1 + ab}) = \frac{y}{x}.$$

Ex. 6. The equation

$$xy = c^2 \text{ or } y = \frac{c^2}{x} \text{ ....(i)}$$

is known as the rectangular hyperbola;

$$\therefore \frac{dy}{dx} = -\frac{c^2}{x^2}.$$

Now, consider it as an implicit function, in which case we have, by differentiating both sides (xy being the product of two functions of x),

$$x\frac{dy}{dx} + y = 0;$$

$$\therefore \frac{dy}{dx} = -\frac{y}{x}.$$

Substitute the value of y from (i), and we find as before that

$$\frac{dy}{dx} = -\frac{c^2}{x^2}.$$

Partial differentiation.—In the preceding example, in which the relation betweeen x and y may be denoted by $f(xy) = 0$, the result obtained by differentiation is precisely the same as would be obtained by differentiating the given expression, firstly with regard to x assuming y to be constant, and secondly with regard to y assuming x to remain constant, and finally taking the quotient with the opposite sign.

The process of differentiating with respect to one only of two or more variables is known as **partial differentiation.** It is usually denoted by such symbols as $\frac{\partial f}{\partial x}$ and $\frac{\partial f}{\partial y}$, which read as the partial differential coefficient of $f(x, y)$ with respect to x, and a corresponding expression for y, or shortly, "the partial with respect to x," "the partial with respect to y."

Ex. 7. Let $f(x, y)=2yx+ay^2-bx^2=0.$

Differentiating first with respect to x, keeping y constant, we find

$$\frac{\partial f}{\partial x}=2y-2bx.$$

Next differentiating with regard to y, keeping x constant,

$$\frac{\partial f}{\partial y}=2x+2ay.$$

In order to convert $\frac{\partial f}{\partial y}$, which is a differentiation with respect to y, into one with respect to x, we must multiply by $\frac{dy}{dx}$, or the differential coefficient of y with respect to x.

Then,
$$\frac{\partial f}{\partial x}+\frac{\partial f}{\partial y}\frac{dy}{dx}=2y-2bx+2(x+ay)\frac{dy}{dx}=0,$$

or
$$y-bx+(x+ay)\frac{dy}{dx}=0;$$

$$\therefore \frac{dy}{dx}=-\frac{y-bx}{x+ay}=\frac{bx-y}{ay+x}=\frac{y}{x},$$

or for all implicit relations between two variables such as x and y, we have

$$\frac{\partial f}{\partial x}+\frac{\partial f}{\partial y}\frac{dy}{dx}=0;$$

$$\therefore \frac{dy}{dx}=-\frac{\frac{\partial f}{\partial x}}{\frac{\partial f}{\partial y}}.$$

EXERCISES. XL.

1. If $y=x^4+3x^3-x^2+5$, find $\frac{d^2y}{dx^2}$ and $\frac{d^3y}{dx^3}$.

2. $y=\sin ax$, find $\frac{dy}{dx}$ and $\frac{d^2y}{dx^2}$.

3. $y = A \sin ax$, find $\dfrac{dy}{dx}$ and $\dfrac{d^2y}{dx^2}$.

4. $y = A \cos ax$, find $\dfrac{dy}{dx}$ and $\dfrac{d^2y}{dx^2}$.

5. $y = \sqrt{x^3}$, find $\dfrac{d^2y}{dx^2}$.

6. $s = v_0 t + \frac{1}{2}at^2$, find $\dfrac{d^2s}{dt^2}$.

7. $x = A \sin nt + B \cos nt$, prove that $\dfrac{d^2x}{dt^2} + n^2x = 0$.

8. $y = e^{-x} \cos x$, prove that $\dfrac{d^4y}{dx^4} + 4y = 0$.

9. $x = \theta^2 \log \theta$, prove that $\dfrac{d^3x}{d\theta^3} = \dfrac{2}{\theta}$.

10. $x = \tan \theta + \sec \theta$, prove that $\dfrac{d^2x}{d\theta^2} = \dfrac{\cos \theta}{(1 - \sin \theta)^2}$.

11. Show by means of the following examples that

$$\frac{\partial^2 u}{\partial y \partial x} = \frac{\partial^2 u}{\partial x \partial y}:$$

$$\text{(i)}\ u = \frac{x^2 y}{a^2 - y^2};\quad \text{(ii)}\ u = x \sin y + y \sin x.$$

12. If $u = (x^2 + y^2 + z^2)^{-\frac{1}{2}}$, prove that $\dfrac{\partial^2 u}{\partial x^2} + \dfrac{\partial^2 u}{\partial y^2} + \dfrac{\partial^2 u}{\partial z^2} = 0$.

13. If $y = \dfrac{\cos(2 \tan^{-1} x)}{1 + x^2}$, show that

$$(1 + x^2)\frac{d^2y}{dx^2} + 6x\frac{dy}{dx} + 6y = 0.$$

Maclaurin's Theorem.—It is frequently necessary to expand an algebraical or trigonometrical function into an infinite series. Examples are furnished in the expansion of a series by the Binomial Theorem, and various methods have already been given for the expansion of such expressions as $(a + x)^x$, e^x, a^x, $\log_e(1 + x)$, etc., in a series of ascending powers of x. We may now find a general theorem by means of which all the preceding, as well as others, may be expanded

Let y denote some function of x, or $y = f(x)$. Assuming that this function, when expanded, can be represented by a series of ascending powers of x, whose coefficients A, B, C, ... do not contain x, we may write

$$y = f(x) = A + Bx + Cx^2 + Dx^3 + Ex^4 + \dots\dots\dots\dots \text{(i)}$$

Differentiating,

$$\frac{dy}{dx}=B+2Cx+3Dx^2+4Ex^3+\ldots.$$

Differentiating again,

$$\frac{d^2y}{dx^2}=2C+3.2Dx+4.3Ex^2+\ldots,$$

and $$\frac{d^3y}{dx^3}=2.3D+4.3.2Ex+\ldots.$$

Now, as the series must be true for all values of x, it must be true for the value $x=0$; and, therefore, if the expressions (y), $\left(\frac{dy}{dx}\right)$, $\left(\frac{d^2y}{dx^2}\right)$, etc., denote the values of y, $\frac{dy}{dx}$, $\frac{d^2y}{dx^2}$, etc., for the particular case when $x=0$, we obtain

$$(y)=A, \quad \left(\frac{dy}{dx}\right)=B,$$

$$\left(\frac{d^2y}{dx^2}\right)=2C, \quad \left(\frac{d^3y}{dx^3}\right)=2.3D, \text{ etc.};$$

or $$A=(y), \quad B=\left(\frac{dy}{dx}\right), \quad C=\frac{1}{1.2}\left(\frac{d^2y}{dx^2}\right),$$

$$D=\frac{1}{1.2.3}\left(\frac{d^3y}{dx^3}\right), \qquad E=\frac{1}{1.2.3.4}\left(\frac{d^4y}{dx^4}\right), \text{ etc.}$$

Substituting these values in Eq. (i),

$$y=(y)+\left(\frac{dy}{dx}\right)x+\frac{1}{1.2}\left(\frac{d^2y}{dx^2}\right)x^2+\frac{1}{1.2.3}\left(\frac{d^3y}{dx^3}\right)x^3+,\ldots \text{(ii)}$$

or $$y=f(x)_0+xf'(x)_0+\frac{x^2}{1.2}f''(x)_0+\frac{x^3}{1.2.3}f'''(x)_0+,\ldots\ldots \text{(iii)}$$

in which the given function $y=f(x)$ is represented in a series of ascending powers of x with constant coefficients.

The result given by (ii) or (iii) is known as **Maclaurin's Theorem.**

If any function x be changed into $x+h$, then the differential coefficient will be the same whether we suppose x to vary uniformly and h to remain constant, or h to vary and x to remain constant.

It is an easy matter to see that this is so from a simple example as follows:

Let
$$y=x^3.$$
Then, when x becomes $x+h$, we may write
$$y'=(x+h)^3.$$
On the supposition that x varies and h remains constant, we obtain
$$\frac{\partial y'}{\partial x}=3(x+h)^2.$$
Also if h varies and x is constant,
$$\frac{\partial y'}{\partial h}=3(x+h)^2\,;$$
$$\therefore\ \frac{\partial y'}{\partial x}=\frac{\partial y'}{\partial h}.$$

Taylor's Theorem.—A theorem of great importance, known as Taylor's Theorem, may now be stated.

Let
$$y=f(x),$$
and let y' denote the new function when x becomes $x+h$;
$$\therefore\ y'=y+Ah+Bh^2+Ch^3+\dots \quad \text{(i)}$$
whose coefficients A, B, C, etc., contain x but not h.

Differentiate on the supposition that x is constant and h varies;
$$\therefore\ \frac{\partial y'}{\partial h}=A+2Bh+3Ch^2+\dots \quad \text{(ii)}$$
Next let x vary and h remain constant, then
$$\frac{\partial y'}{\partial x}=\frac{\partial y}{\partial x}+\frac{\partial A}{\partial x}h+\frac{\partial B}{\partial x}h^2+\text{etc.} \quad \text{(iii)}$$
As the left-hand sides of Equations (ii) and (iii) are equal, the two series are identical, and therefore the coefficients of the same powers of h are equal;
$$\therefore\ A=\frac{\partial y}{\partial x},\quad B=\frac{1}{2}\frac{\partial A}{\partial x},\quad C=\frac{1}{3}\frac{\partial B}{\partial x},\quad D=\frac{1}{4}\frac{\partial C}{\partial x},\ \text{etc.}, \dots$$
Substituting in B the value of A;
$$\therefore\ B=\frac{1}{2}\frac{\partial A}{\partial x}=\frac{1}{1\,.\,2}\frac{\partial^2 y}{\partial x^2}.$$

Similarly, $$C=\frac{1}{1.2.3}\frac{\partial^3 y}{\partial x^3}, \text{ etc.}$$

Now, substituting these values in (i),

$$y'=y+h\frac{\partial y}{\partial x}+\frac{h^2}{1.2}\frac{\partial^2 y}{\partial x^2}+\frac{h^3}{1.2.3}\frac{\partial^3 y}{\partial x^3}+\dots,$$

or, $$f(x+h)=f(x)+hf'(x)+\frac{h^2f''(x)}{1.2}+\frac{h^3f'''(x)}{1.2.3}+\dots, \quad \dots\dots\text{(iv)}$$

where $f'(x)$, $f''(x)$, etc., refer to differentiation with respect to x only. This is **Taylor's Theorem.**

Ex. 1. Let $$f(x)=x^n,\ f(x+h)=(x+h)^n,$$

$$f'(x)=nx^{n-1},\ f''(x)=n(n-1)x^{n-2}, \text{ etc.};$$

$$\therefore\ (x+h)^n=x^n+nhx^{n-1}+\frac{n(n-1)h^2x^{n-2}}{1.2}+\dots,$$

the well-known binomial expansion.

Examples of the use of Taylor's Theorem.—A few examples of the use of Taylor's Theorem are given; others of a similar kind may easily be obtained if necessary.

Ex. 2. Given $\sin 30°=0·5$, find the value of $\sin 30° 30'$.

In this case h is the radian measure of $30'$;

$$\therefore\ 30'=\frac{3·14159\times 30}{60\times 180}=0·0087.$$

From Equation (iv), we find

$$f(x)=\sin 30°=0·5,\ f'(x)=\cos 30°=0·866,$$

$$f''(x)=-\sin 30°=-0·5,\ f'''(x)=-\cos 30°=-0·866.$$

Substituting these values in Eq. (iv), we find

$$\sin 30° 30'=\sin 30°+0·0087\times\cos 30°+\frac{(0·0087)^2(-\sin 30°)}{1.2}+\text{etc.}$$

$$=0·5+0·0087\times 0·866-\frac{(0·0087)^2}{1.2}\times 0·5\ \dots+\text{etc.}$$

$$=0·5+0·0075342-0·000018922=0·5075.$$

Development of $\log_e(1+x)$.—The development of this series has already been found (p. 293); it may also be obtained by Taylor's Theorem.

Ex. 3. Let $y=\log_e x,\ y'=\log_e(x+h)$,

$$\frac{dy}{dx}=\frac{1}{x},\ \frac{d^2y}{dx^2}=-\frac{1}{x^2},\ \frac{d^3y}{dx^3}=\frac{2}{x^3},\ \frac{d^4y}{dx^4}=-\frac{2.3}{x^4}+\text{etc.}$$

Substituting these values in Taylor's Theorem, we obtain

$$\log_e(x+h)=\log_e x+\frac{h}{x}-\frac{h^2}{2x^2}+\frac{h^3}{3x^3}-\frac{h^4}{4x^4}+\dots.$$

Substituting unity for x, and x for h, then, since

$$\log_e 1=0,$$

$$\log_e(1+x)=\frac{x}{1}-\frac{x^2}{2}+\frac{x^3}{3}-\frac{x^4}{4}+\dots,$$

the same result as that already found on p. 293.

Maclaurin's Theorem can easily be obtained from Taylor's Theorem, thus:

$$f(x+h)=f(x)+\frac{h}{1}f'(x)+\frac{h^2}{1.2}f''(x)+\dots.$$

Now put $x=0$, and for h write x, and we find

$$f(x)=f(x)_0+xf'(x)_0+\frac{x^2}{1.2}f''(x)_0+\dots.$$

The meaning attached to the symbols may be shown by $f''(x)_0$, which indicates that $f(x)$ is to be differentiated twice with respect to x, and finally put $x=0$ in the result.

Ex. 4. Expand the function $y=\sin x$ in a series of ascending powers of x.

$y=\sin x$; $\therefore$ when $x=0$, $(y)=0$, or $f(x)=0$.

$\frac{dy}{dx}=\cos x$; $\therefore$ when $x=0$, $f'(x)=\cos 0=1$.

Also $f''(x)=-\sin x$, when $x=0$; $\therefore f''(x)=0$.

$f'''(x)=-\cos x$, when $x=0$; $\therefore f'''(x)=-1$.

Substituting these values in (iii) of Maclaurin's Theorem,

$$\therefore\ y=\sin x=x-\frac{x^3}{3!}+\frac{x^5}{5!}-\frac{x^7}{7!}+\dots.$$

Similarly, if $y=\cos x$, we obtain

$$\cos x=1-\frac{x^2}{2!}+\frac{x^4}{4!}-\frac{x^6}{6!}+\dots.$$ (See p. 512.)

It should be remembered that in each of these series, x is in *radians* and not degrees.

Exponential Values of sin x and cos x.—From the series obtained in Ex. 4 (p. 381), $\sin x$ and $\cos x$ may be expressed in terms of the exponential function by the use of $\sqrt{-1}$ or i. Thus $\cos x + i \sin x$

$$=\left(1-\frac{x^2}{2!}+\frac{x^4}{4!}-\ldots\right)+i\left(x-\frac{x^3}{3!}+\frac{x^5}{5!}-\ldots\right)$$

$$=1+ix-\frac{x^2}{2!}-\frac{ix^3}{3!}+\frac{x^4}{4!}+\ldots.$$

Now $i^{2r}=-1$ or $+1$ and $i^{2r+1}=-i$ or $+i$ according as r is odd or even (see pp. 112-3); hence the above series may be written

$$1+ix+\frac{i^2x^2}{2\,!}+\frac{i^3x^3}{3\,!}+\frac{i^4x^4}{4\,!}+\ldots$$

$$=e^{ix};$$

$$\therefore\ \cos x+i\sin x=e^{ix}. \quad \ldots\ldots\ldots\ldots\ldots\ldots\ldots\ldots\ldots\ldots\text{(i)}$$

And $(\cos x+i\sin x)(\cos x-i\sin x)=\cos^2x-i^2\sin^2x$

$$=\cos^2x+\sin^2x=1;$$

$$\therefore\ e^{ix}(\cos x-i\sin x)=1,$$

or $$\cos x-i\sin x=1/e^{ix}=e^{-ix}. \quad \ldots\ldots\ldots\ldots\ldots\ldots\text{(ii)}$$

Solving (i) and (ii) for $\cos x$ and $\sin x$,

$$2\cos x=e^{ix}+e^{-ix} \quad \text{and} \quad 2i\sin x=e^{ix}-e^{-ix}.$$

Value of sin x.—The value of $\sin x$ can be obtained to any requisite degree of accuracy by using a few terms of the series (p. 381), viz.:

$$\sin x=x-\frac{x^3}{3!}+\frac{x^5}{5!}-\ldots.$$

Thus, for an angle of 30°, as sin 30° = 0·5236 radians, we obtain by substitution

$$\sin 30^\circ=0{\cdot}5236-\frac{(0{\cdot}5236)^3}{6}+\frac{(0{\cdot}5236)^5}{120}$$

$$=0{\cdot}5236-0{\cdot}0239+0{\cdot}0003=0{\cdot}5000.$$

Thus, $\sin 30^\circ=0{\cdot}5$.

Similarly, $$\sin 60^\circ=1{\cdot}0472-\frac{(1{\cdot}0472)^3}{6}+\frac{(1{\cdot}0472)^5}{120}-\frac{(1{\cdot}0472)^7}{5040}$$

$$=1{\cdot}0472-0{\cdot}1914+0{\cdot}0105-0{\cdot}0003=0{\cdot}8660.$$

Calculation of the value of cos x.—The numerical value of the cosine of a given angle may also be determined by means of the appropriate series.

Ex. 5. Calculate the numerical value of cos 30°.

We have $$\cos x = 1 - \frac{x^2}{2!} + \frac{x^4}{4!} - \dots,$$

and as $30° = 0·5236$ radians, we obtain, by substitution,

$$\cos 30° = 1 - \frac{(0·5236)^2}{2} + \frac{(0·5236)^4}{24}$$
$$= 1 - 0·1371 + 0·0031 = 0·8660.$$

In a similar manner other values may be calculated and the results compared with those in Table V.

Since $$\sin x = x - \frac{x^3}{3!} + \frac{x^5}{5!} - \text{etc.},$$

we have, dividing by x,

$$\frac{\sin x}{x} = 1 - \frac{x^2}{3!} + \frac{x^4}{5!} - \text{etc.};$$

$$\therefore \ \mathrm{Lt}_{x=0}\left[\frac{\sin x}{x}\right] = \mathrm{Lt}_{x=0}\left[1 - \frac{x^2}{3!} + \text{etc.}\right] = 1.$$

Small angles.—If the angle x be so small that x^2 and all succeeding terms can be omitted, then from the preceding series $\sin x = x$, or **when an angle is small, its sine is approximately equal to the circular measure of the angle and its cosine is approximately equal to unity.**

Series for tan x.—The series for $\tan x$ may be obtained from Maclaurin's Theorem.

$$f(x) = f(0) + \frac{x}{1}f'(0) + \frac{x^2}{2!}f''(0) + \dots.$$

Here $f(x) = \tan x$; $\quad \therefore f(0) = 0.$

$f'(x) = 1 + \tan^2 x = 1 + [f(x)]^2$; $\quad \therefore f'(0) = 1.$

$f''(x) = 2f(x)f'(x)$; $\quad \therefore f''(0) = 0.$

$f'''(x) = 2f''(x)f(x) + 2[f'(x)]^2$; $\quad \therefore f'''(0) = 2$, etc.

$f^{iv}(0) = 0,$ $\quad f^{v}(0) = 16.$

Hence, by substitution,

$$\tan x = x + \frac{x^3}{3} + \frac{2x^5}{15} + \dots.$$

Maxima and minima.—We have already found (p. 356) that if, at a point denoting a maximum value on a curve, the abscissa x receives a small increment, the corresponding value of y is less than its preceding value. Or, the slope of the curve becomes negative. In other words, the tangent to a curve making a positive angle with the axis of x varies until at a point indicating a maximum value it becomes horizontal. When x is increased past this point, the inclination of the tangent is in a negative direction. For a minimum value the inclination of the tangent varies from negative through zero to positive.

Thus, if $y=f(x)$, and $f(a)$ is a maximum or minimum value. Then $f(a)$ will be a maximum value of $f(x)$ if $f'(x)$ changes from a positive to a negative value as x passes through a; and $f(a)$ will be a minimum value if $f'(x)$ changes from a negative to a positive value as x passes through a.

Analytically, by **Taylor's Theorem**, let $y=f(x)$, and let x become $x+\delta x$, then, since $f'(x)=0$, we have

$$f(x+\delta x)=f(x)+\frac{f''(x)}{1 \, . \, 2}(\delta x)^2+\dots \dots\dots\dots\dots \text{(i)}$$

Also, if x becomes $x-\delta x$, we get

$$f(x-\delta x)=f(x)+\frac{f''(x)}{1 \, . \, 2}(-\delta x)^2+\dots$$

$$=f(x)+\frac{f''(x)}{1 \, . \, 2}(\delta x)^2+\dots \dots\dots\dots\dots \text{(ii)}$$

From (i) and (ii), we see that if the second term $f''(x)$ be positive, then in both expressions the values of the right-hand side of the expression is greater than $f(x)$. Therefore the value of the ordinate y diminishes in passing from the point $x-\delta x$ to the point x, and y is said to have a minimum value. Similarly, if $\frac{d^2y}{dx^2}$ or $f''(x)$ is negative, the value of y is a maximum. In this way obtain a rule which may be thus stated:

If $y=f(x)$, the value or values which denote a maximum or minimum are obtained by determining the value or values which make $f'(x)=0$. To ascertain whether the values obtained denote a maximum or a minimum, find the value of $\frac{d^2y}{dx^2}$ or

$f''(x)$ and substitute for x. If the resulting value is negative, it corresponds to a maximum, and to a minimum if the value is positive.

Ex. 1. Determine the values of x which make $x^3-6x^2+9x-12$ a maximum or a minimum.

Let
$$y=x^3-6x^2+9x-12,$$
$$\frac{dy}{dx}=3x^2-12x+9.$$

When y is a maximum or minimum,
$$\frac{dy}{dx}=0\,;$$
$$\therefore\ 3x^2-12x+9=0, \qquad \text{(i)}$$
or
$$x^2-4x+3=0 \text{ or } (x-1)(x-3)=0\,;$$
$$\therefore\ x=1 \text{ or } 3.$$

Differentiating (i), we obtain
$$\frac{d^2y}{dx^2}=6x-12\,;$$

$\therefore$ when $x=1$, $\frac{d^2y}{dx^2}=-6$, a negative quantity, and therefore corresponds to a maximum.

Similarly, when $x=3$, $\frac{d^2y}{dx^2}=6$, a positive quantity.

Hence, $x=1$ corresponds to a maximum value.
and $x=3$ " " minimum "

The rule may be stated thus:—**An expression will be a maximum when the value of x, which makes $\frac{dy}{dx}$ zero, gives $\frac{d^2y}{dx^2}$ a negative sign, and a minimum when the value of x gives $\frac{d^2y}{dx^2}$ a positive sign.**

It will be noticed that this expresses only in a different form the rule already used in determining maxima and minima by plotting.

Points of inflexion.—It may happen that both $\frac{dy}{dx}$ and $\frac{d^2y}{dx^2}$ vanish for the same value of x. In that case, we do not necessarily have a maximum or a minimum. Reference to Fig. 126 will show a point, W, where this is so.

If this happens $\frac{d^2y}{dx^2}$ should be differentiated again and the values that made $\frac{d^2y}{dx^2}$ vanish, as well as $\frac{dy}{dx}$ zero, should be substituted in $\frac{d^3y}{dx^3}$.

If after substitution the result is not zero, then the point considered is a point of inflexion; but if it is zero, then the differentiation must again be tried to find whether the new differential vanishes. The process must be repeated until we obtain a differential which does not vanish. If the first non-vanishing coefficient is of **odd** order it is a **point of inflection**; if of **even** order it is a **turning point**, *i.e.* one that is either a maximum or a minimum.

Ex. 2. Let

$$y = x^3 - 3x^2 + 3x - 13,$$

$$\frac{dy}{dx} = 3x^2 - 6x + 3 = 3(x-1)^2,$$

which vanishes when $x = 1$.

Differentiating again;

$$\therefore \frac{d^2y}{dx^2} = 6(x-1),$$

and this is also zero when $x=1$;

$\therefore$ differentiate again, and obtain

$$\frac{d^3y}{dx^3} = 6.$$

But this result does not contain x, and is not zero when $x=1$, and therefore the point $x=1$ is neither a maximum nor a minimum, but a point of inflexion; that is to say, the tangents to the curve on either side of the point are inclined in the same (positive or negative) direction to the tangent at the point itself.

Ex. 3. Find the maximum and minimum values (if any) of y when

$$y = x^4 - 8x^3 + 24x^2 - 32x,$$

$$\frac{dy}{dx} = 4(x^3 - 6x^2 + 12x - 8) = 4(x-2)^3,$$

and this is zero when $x=2$.

Hence, differentiating again,

$$\frac{d^2y}{dx^2} = 12(x-2)^2, \text{ and this is zero when } x=2.$$

Again, $\frac{d^3y}{dx^3}=24(x-2)$, and this is zero when $x=2$.

$$\frac{d^4y}{dx^4}=24.$$

In this case the first differential which does not vanish is of even order.

Thus $x=2$ gives a minimum value of y.

Each of these cases, Exs. 2 and 3, can be simplified; the first, by the substitution of z for $x-1$, becomes $y=z^3-12$.

The second, by putting $x-2=v$, becomes $y=v^4+16$.

In each case the resulting expression may be treated in the usual manner.

EXERCISES. XLI.

1. Expand $\log_e(1+x)$.

2. Expand as far as x^4:

(i) $\log(x+\sqrt{x^2+a^2})$; (ii) $(e^x+e^{-x})^n$.

3. Expand, by Maclaurin's Theorem, $\tan^4 x$ in terms of x to three terms.

Find the first and second differential coefficients of the following:

4. x^x. **5.** $xe^{\tan x}$. **6.** $\tan^{-1}x$.

Find the nth differential coefficients of:

7. $x^2\log x$. **8.** x^3e^x.

9. Expand $\tan^{-1}x$ in a series of ascending powers of x by Maclaurin's Theorem.

10. Expand $\sin^{-1}(x+h)$ to three terms by Taylor's Theorem.

11. Expand $e^x\log_e(1+x)$ by Maclaurin's Theorem.

12. Expand $\sin x$ in terms of x by Maclaurin's Theorem to three terms.

13. Show that the series for $\cos x$ may be obtained by differentiating the series for $\sin x$.

14.
$$\cos x+i\sin x=e^{ix},$$
$$\cos x-i\sin x=e^{-ix} \quad \text{(pp. 512, 584).}$$

Hence,
$$\cos^2 x+\sin^2 x=1,$$
$$\sin 2x=2\sin x\cos x,$$
and
$$(\cos x+i\sin x)^n=e^{nix}=\cos nx+i\sin nx.$$

If c is the chord of an arc of a circle, a the chord of half the arc, and l its length; prove that $l=\frac{1}{3}(8a-c)$. (p. 192.)

CHAPTER XIX.

INTEGRATION.

Integration.—We may consider integration as the inverse process of differentiation. Thus, for example, from a relation connecting x and y, the process by which $\frac{dy}{dx}$ is obtained is called **differentiation.** Conversely, given a differential expression, the previous process may sometimes be reversed and the **integral** obtained, the object being to determine the expression, or function, from which the given differential expression has been obtained. We are able in this way, to write down, in many cases, the original expression by mere inspection. Or, we may make use of a rule which is readily seen from the corresponding rule in differentiation.

Ex. 1. Thus, if $y=x^3$,

$$\frac{dy}{dx}=3x^2.$$

This may be written in the form

$$dy=3x^2dx.$$

Integrating,
$$\int dy=\int 3x^2dx,$$

or
$$y=x^3.$$

These, and similar expressions, may be obtained by using the following rule:

To find the integral of a power of x, add unity to the index and divide by the index thus increased.

[As any constant quantity connected with a function by a positive, or negative, sign (indicating addition or subtraction) disappears during differentiation; therefore, a constant, which may conveniently be denoted by C, must be added after integration; its value is determined from the conditions of the given problem.]

An important exception to this rule is furnished when $n=-1$, or the quantity to be integrated is $\frac{1}{x}$. This will, however, be recognized to be the inverse of the differentiation of $\log x$.

Thus, if $\quad y=\log_e x, \quad \frac{dy}{dx}=\frac{1}{x};$

and if $\quad y_1=\frac{1}{x}, \quad \int y_1 dx=\log_e x,$

The symbol $\int y_1 dx$ is read as "**the integral of y_1 with respect to x.**"

As illustrations of the meaning of integration consider the two progressions, arithmetical and geometrical.

The integral as the sum of a series in arithmetical progression.—In the series

$$a^2+2a^2+3a^2+\ldots+na^2, \quad \ldots\ldots\ldots\ldots\ldots\ldots\text{(i)}$$

the sum of n terms is $\frac{a^2\times n(n+1)}{2}$ (p. 269).

Now, as the number of terms may be of any magnitude, it is possible, if a is altered inversely as n, to make na always the same, say equal to x.

Thus, the sum becomes $\frac{x(x+a)}{2}$. ……………………………(ii)

Now, as na is to remain constant, it follows that as n becomes greater and greater, a becomes less and less, and eventually, when a becomes zero, the sum of the series from (ii) is $\frac{x^2}{2}$.

We may with advantage rewrite the original series and put δx instead of a.

$$(\delta x)^2+2(\delta x)^2+\ldots+n(\delta x)^2.$$

But, as before, $n\delta x=x$. Thus, we find

$$(\delta x)^2+\ldots+x\,\delta x.$$

This is obviously an ordinary arithmetical progression, and the sum of the series, which may be denoted by Σ, gives

$$\Sigma\{n(\delta x)^2\}=\Sigma\{x\,\delta x\}=\frac{(\delta x)^2 n(n+1)}{2}=\frac{x(x+\delta x)}{2}$$

by the usual formula.

So long as δx is assumed to be of any magnitude, the sum may be found by the preceding expression. If, now, we assume δx to be zero, we may write the integration sign $\int$ instead of the summation sign Σ, and also dx instead of δx, and we obtain

$$\int x\,dx=\frac{x^2}{2}.$$

It may perhaps be easier to follow this proof if the various steps are interpreted graphically. For this purpose, take in the usual manner, two perpendicular axes, mark off horizontally distances equal to a, and vertically distances b, $2b$, $3b$, ... nb, as in Fig. 135.

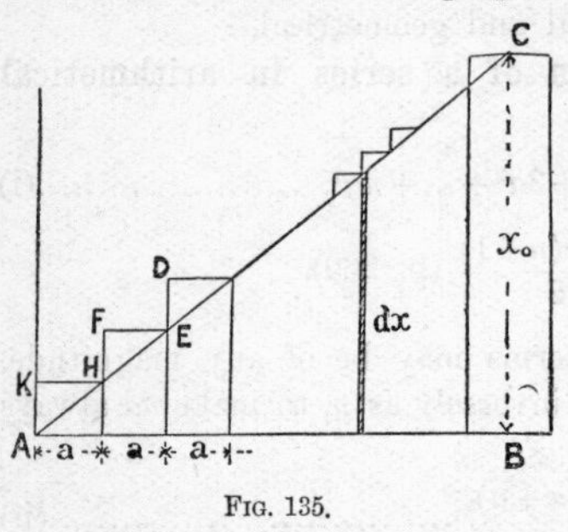

FIG. 135.

The area of the first rectangle, its two sides AK and KH, is ab, or the first term of the given series. Similarly, the area of the second rectangle represents the second term, and so on, the last term being nab. AB is equal to na, and the assumption that na is constant implies that AB and BC are to be constant lengths; the sum of the series is the sum of all the rectangles into which the figure may be assumed to be divided, and is equal to the area of the triangle ABC together with the area of n half squares.

$$\therefore \text{ sum of series}=\frac{AB\times BC}{2}+\frac{nab}{2}$$

$$=\frac{n^2ab+nab}{2}=\frac{n(n+1)ab}{2},$$

i.e. the ordinary summation formula.

Now assume n to become very great. Then, since AB is to remain the same, the length a must be very small, and the size of the half squares will become very small.

Finally, when a is made indefinitely small, the corners of the squares will all lie on the line AC, and the sum of the series will be the area of $ABC=\frac{n^2ab}{2}$.

But, in the preceding case, na was denoted by x_0 and also $=b$;

$$\therefore \quad \frac{n^2a^2}{2}=\frac{x_0^{\,2}}{2}=\int x\,dx,$$

where x is 0 for the first term and x_0 for the last.

Geometrical progression.—Consider the geometrical series

$$a+ar^a+ar^{2a}+ar^{3a}+\ldots+ar^{ma-1}.$$

The sum $=\frac{a(r^{ma}-1)}{r^a-1}$.

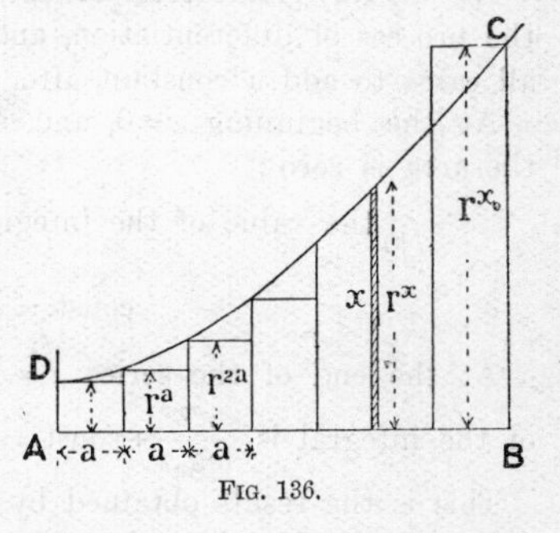

FIG. 136.

As in the previous solution, we may represent the sum graphically.

The area of the stepped figure (Fig. 136) gives the sum of the series. Now, make $r^{ma}=\text{const.}=r^{x_0}$;

$\therefore \; ma=\text{const.}=x_0$.

Next assume m to become indefinitely large, and a very small. The steps in the curve (Fig. 136) will disappear and a continuous curve will be obtained. Also r^{ma-1} will be very nearly equal to the next ordinate to it, or, in other words,

$$r^{ma-1}=r^{x_0};$$

$$\therefore \text{ sum of series}=\frac{a(r^{x_0}-1)}{r^a-1}.$$

Expand r^a by the exponential theorem (p. 292)

$$r^a=1+a\log_e r+\frac{a^2\log_e{}^2 r}{2\,!}+\text{etc.};$$

$$\therefore \text{ sum of series}=\frac{r^{x_0}-1}{\log_e r+\frac{a\log_e{}^2 r}{2\,!}+\text{etc.}}$$

Now make a zero; that is, make the curve continuous, and the sum of the series becomes

$$\frac{r^{x_0}-1}{\log_e r}.$$

If for a we substitute dx, the series will be written

$$dx + r^{dx}dx + r^{2dx}dx + \ldots + r^{mdx}dx,$$

or $\int r^x dx$, where the value of x is 0 at the beginning, and x_0 at the end of the series.

The differential coefficient of $\frac{r^x}{\log_e r}$ is equal to $r^x dx$;

$$\therefore \int r^x dx = \frac{r^x}{\log_e r} + C.$$

As already indicated, added constants disappear during the process of differentiation, and therefore it is necessary in all cases to add a constant after integration.

At the beginning $x=0$, and, since no terms are included the area is zero;

$$\therefore \text{ the value of the integral is } \frac{1}{\log_e r} + \text{const.} = 0;$$

$$\therefore \text{ const.} = -\frac{1}{\log_e r}.$$

At the end of the series $x = x_0$ and $r^x = r^{x_0}$, and the value of the integral is $\frac{r^{x_0}}{\log_e r} + \text{const.} = \frac{r^{x_0}}{\log_e r} - \frac{1}{\log_e r} = \frac{r^{x_0}-1}{\log_e r}$.

This is the result obtained by the preceding method.

The reason for the subtraction appears from the fact that only a small portion of the curve is used in order to obtain the resultant area, but by containing the geometrical series backwards, as $\ldots + ar^{-2a} + ar^{-a} + a + ar^a + ar^{2a} + \ldots$, the curve would gradually reach the axis of x. The unknown constant is the area between this produced part of the curve and the axes of x and y.

The operation just performed is called **integration between limits**, and when the area $ABCD$ is required, it is necessary to obtain **the integral of** $r^x dx$ **between the limits** $x=0$ **and** $x=x_0$.

This is written as $\int_0^{x_0} r^x dx.$

The rule for such an integration is: **first find the general integral,** *i.e.* in this case $\frac{r^x}{\log_e r}$; **then subtract the result of substituting the lower limit in the integral from the result of substituting the upper limit.** In this case 0 and x_0 respectively;

$$\therefore \int_0^{x_0} r^x dx = \left[\frac{r^x}{\log_e r}\right]_0^{x_0} = \frac{r^{x_0}}{\log_e r} - \frac{1}{\log_e r}$$

$$= \frac{r^{x_0} - 1}{\log_e r}.$$

These examples show three distinct methods which may be used to find the integral of a given function.

(*a*) **By the summation of a series in which the terms alter gradually.**

(*b*) **By the process of finding an area.**

(*c*) **By inverting the process of differentiation.**

Obviously the result of integrating a given function by each of the methods should be identical, but it should be noticed that the first method is frequently impossible, the last two (*b*) and (*c*) are those in general use.

It will be noticed that the first two methods are identical, the character of (*a*) is algebraical, that of (*b*) is graphical. But as there are many series the algebraical terms of whose sum is unknown, or, useless from this point of view, we are practically restricted to (*b*) and (*c*).

To obtain the general connection between integration, regarded as the inverse process of differentiation and obtaining an area, we may proceed as follows:

If $y=f(x)$, then when the form of the function is known, the process of differentiation can be carried out by the methods already described, and we obtain $\frac{dy}{dx}=f'(x)$, which is, in general, some other function of x.

Now, plot $y=f(x)$ and x, and make x and y zero together; also plot $\frac{dy}{dx}=f'(x)$ and x.

If $\frac{\delta y}{\delta x}$ is plotted instead of $\frac{dy}{dx}$, we should obtain a steppe curve, as indicated by the dotted lines (Fig. 137). The are of the rectangle M_1N_1RQ is $\frac{\delta y}{\delta x} \times \delta x$.

Now, y is the sum of all the small increments, from th place where $x=0$ to the place where $x=ON_1$,

i.e. $$\sum_{x=0}^{x=ON_1} \delta y = \sum_{x=0}^{x=ON_1} \frac{\delta y}{\delta x}\delta x, \quad \ldots\ldots\ldots\ldots\ldots\ldots(\text{i}$$

and this is obviously equal to the

area of the stepped figure OCP_1N_1. ....(i

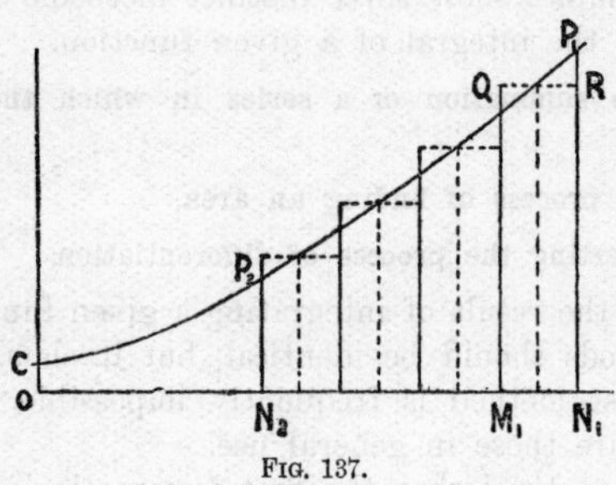

FIG. 137.

Hence, make δx indefinitely small, and $\frac{\delta y}{\delta x}$ becomes $\frac{dy}{dx}$ and we write dx instead of δx, and $\int_0^{ON_1} \frac{dy}{dx}dx$ instead of (i)

Or, write $f'(x)$ for $\frac{dy}{dx}$, and the preceding becomes

$$\therefore\ y = \int_0^{ON_1} f'(x)dx = \text{area of figure } OCP_1N_1,$$

the steps having disappeared.

Similarly, the area OCP_2N_2 is $\int_0^{ON_2} f'(x)\,dx = y_1.$

Hence, $y - y_1 =$ area OCP_1N_1 minus area OCP_2N_2, or the are $P_1N_1N_2P_2 = y - y_1 = \int_0^{ON_1} f'(x)dx - \int_0^{ON_2} f'(x)dx.$

This may be written :—**The increase in the value of the integral, as x increases from the value ON_2 to the value ON_1, is equal to the area between the curve $f'(x)$, the ordinates at N_2 and N_1, and the axis of x, and is equal to the value obtained by the inverse process of differentiation, finally substituting in the result the extreme values of x, and subtracting.**

For convenience, $\int^{ON_1} f'(x)dx - \int^{ON_2} f'(x)dx$ is written in the form $\int_{ON_2}^{ON_1} f'(x)dx$.

Ex. 2. Let $f'(x) = \frac{x}{2}$.

As on p. 390, $f(x) = \int f'(x)dx = \frac{x^2}{4} + \text{const.}$

Plot $f^1(x)$. This is a straight line passing through the origin (Fig. 138). The area enclosed by the line, an ordinate at any point, and the axis of x can be obtained. Thus the area enclosed up to point P is $50 \times 25 \div 2 = 625$. Draw a straight line $A_1B_1C_1$ parallel to the axis of x and at any convenient distance from it. Make $A_1P_1 = 625$ (altering the vertical scale for the purpose). Again at a point on the curve where $x = 150$, $y = 75$; area enclosed $= 150 \times 75 \div 2 = 5625$. Proceeding in this manner, any number of points on a curve may be obtained, the ordinates of the curve denoting the area enclosed by the line up to the ordinate passing through the point.

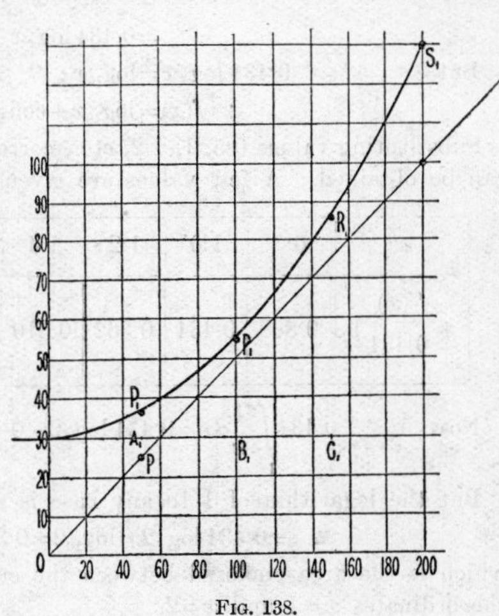

Fig. 138.

Drawing the curve through the points P_1, R_1, S_1, we obtain the parabola $\frac{x^2}{4} + \text{const.}$

It will be seen that the value of the constant is unknown, because by moving the curve $O_1P_1Q_1R_1S_1$ parallel to the axis of y we do not alter the slope at the points, and therefore the shape of the curve remains the same. The constant must therefore be determined otherwise.

If, however, the difference in height between P_1 and R_1 is required, then $R_1C_1 - P_1A_1$ is the value required; and the result is obviously independent of the constant.

As in preceding case the value is

$$\int_{50}^{150} \frac{x}{2}\,dx = \left[\frac{x^2}{4}\right]_{50}^{150} = \frac{150^2}{4} - \frac{50^2}{4} = 5000.$$

From the diagram this is seen to be the area of $APRC$.

Ex. 3. Let $f'(x) = \frac{1}{x} \times 0{\cdot}434$.

Then, as on p. 389, $$f(x) = 0{\cdot}434\int\frac{dx}{x}$$

$$= 0{\cdot}434 \log_e x + \text{const.}$$

But $$0{\cdot}434 \log_e x = \log_{10} x\,;$$

$$\therefore\ f(x) = \log_{10} x + \text{const.}$$

Substituting values 0·5, 1, 1·2, etc., corresponding values of $f'(x)$ can be obtained. A few values are given in the following table:

x	0·5	1·0	1·2	1·4	1·6	1·8	2·0
$f'(x) = 0{\cdot}434\frac{1}{x}$	0·868	0·434	0·362	0·310	0·271	0·241	0·217

Now $$0{\cdot}434\int_1^2 \frac{1}{x}\,dx = 0{\cdot}434 \log_e 2 - 0{\cdot}434 \log_e 1.$$

But the logarithm of 1 to any base is zero, and

$$0{\cdot}434 \log_e 2 = \log_{10} 2 = 0{\cdot}301\,;$$

which is the area enclosed between the curve, the axis of x, and the ordinates $x=1$ and $x=2$.

This result may be readily verified by drawing the curve on squared paper to a fairly large scale, and adding up the whole squares and partial squares enclosed by the curve.

Similarly, the logarithm of 2·5 is the area enclosed by the curve from $x=1$ to $x=2{\cdot}5$, and so on for the logarithm of any number.

Ex. 4. Integrate $\int \frac{dx}{x}$.

The indefinite integral is $\log_e x + C$.
Hence, if the limits are a and b,

$$\int_a^b \frac{dx}{x} = \log_e b - \log_e a.$$

Ex. 5. Find the value of $\int_{\frac{1}{3}}^{1} \frac{dx}{x}$.

$$\int_{\frac{1}{3}}^{1} \frac{dx}{x} = [\log x]_{\frac{1}{3}}^{1} = \log_e 3 = 0{\cdot}4771 \times 2{\cdot}3026 = 1{\cdot}0986.$$

Ex. 6. Find the value of $\int_1^4 x^2 dx$.

$$\int_1^4 x^2 dx = \tfrac{1}{3}[x^3]_1^4 = \tfrac{1}{3}(4^3 - 1^3) = 21.$$

Ex. 7. Show that

$$c\int_a^b x^n dx = \frac{c}{n+1}(b^{n+1} - a^{n+1}).$$

Area of segment of a parabola.—In the curve

$$y = ax^2, \qquad \text{(iii)}$$

$$A = \int ax^2 dx = \frac{a}{3}x^3 + C. \qquad \text{(iv)}$$

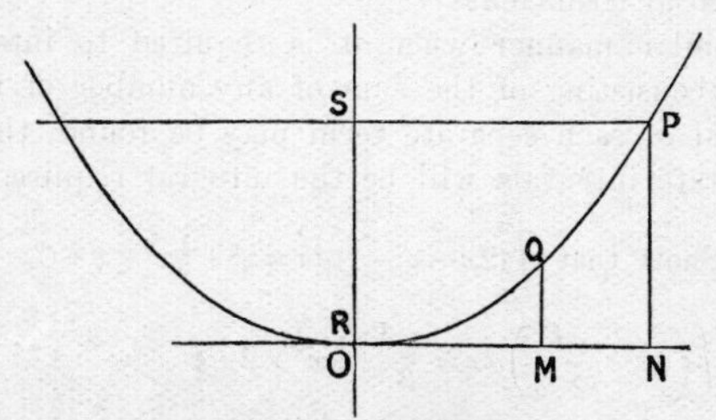

FIG. 139.—Area of a parabola.

The area $ONPR$ (Fig. 139) from $x = 0$ to $x = ON$ (Fig. 139) is given by

$$A = \frac{a}{3} \times ON^3. \qquad \text{(v)}$$

We may eliminate the constant a by substituting in (iii) the values of x and y for any point, such as P.

Thus, $$PN = a \times ON^2;$$

$$\therefore\ a = \frac{PN}{ON^2}.$$

Substituting in (v), we obtain

$$A = \frac{PN}{3 \times ON^2} \times ON^3 = \tfrac{1}{3} . PN \times ON.$$

Hence, **the area of ONPR is one-third the area of the rectangle ONPS.** As there are, for each value of y, two values of x, it follows that the area of the segment of the parabola PSO is $\frac{2}{3}$ that of the rectangle $SONP$, an important result.

Denoting OM by x_2, and ON by x_1, then the area of $MNPQ$ is given by

$$A = \int_{x_2}^{x_1} ax^2 dx = \frac{a}{3}\left(x_1{}^3 - x_2{}^3\right). \quad\text{..................(vi)}$$

A result from which, when the numerical values of a, x_1 and x_2 are known, the value of A can be obtained.

Integration of sum of functions.—When differentiating an expression containing a number of distinct functions connected by the signs plus or minus, it was only necessary to differentiate each singly and obtain the algebraical sum of the differential coefficients.

In a similar manner when it is required to integrate an expression consisting of the sum of any number of functions the integral of each separate term may be found, the sum of these separate integrals will be the integral required.

Ex. 8. Show that $\int (2x + x^2 - 1)\, dx = x^2 + \frac{1}{3}x^3 - x + C.$

Ex. 9. $$\int \left(ax^2 + \frac{1}{2\sqrt{x}}\right) dx = \frac{ax^3}{3} + \tfrac{1}{2}x^{\frac{1}{2}} \times 2 + C$$

$$= \frac{ax^3}{3} + \sqrt{x} + C.$$

We have already found that any constant which is a multiplier or divisor of a given function is a multiplier or divisor of the differential, hence a constant multiplier or divisor following the integration sign may be removed and placed in front of the sign of integration.

The following list of some of the simpler functions and their differential coefficients will be found very useful, the list may easily be extended if necessary; it will be obvious that from such a list the integral of any function agreeing with any of the tabulated or known differential coefficients can be at once written down.

In all the following cases the constant of integration should be added.

If $y=x^n$, $\frac{dy}{dx}=nx^{n-1}$; $\therefore \int nx^{n-1}\,dx$ is x^n.

Hence, from the preceding,

$$\int x^n dx=\frac{x^{n+1}}{n+1},$$

$$y=\log x, \quad \frac{dy}{dx}=\frac{1}{x}; \quad \therefore \int \frac{1}{x}dx=\log x,$$

$$y=e^x, \quad \frac{dy}{dx}=e^x, \quad \int e^x dx=e^x,$$

$$y=\sin x, \quad \frac{dy}{dx}=\cos x, \quad \int \cos x dx=\sin x,$$

$$y=-\cos x, \quad \frac{dy}{dx}=\sin x, \quad \int \sin x dx=-\cos x,$$

$$y=\tan x, \quad \frac{dy}{dx}=\sec^2 x, \quad \int \sec^2 x dx=\tan x,$$

$$y=\sin^{-1} x, \quad \frac{dy}{dx}=\frac{1}{\sqrt{1-x^2}}, \quad \int \frac{1}{\sqrt{1-x^2}}dx=\sin^{-1} x,$$

when $x<1$;

$$y=\tan^{-1} x, \quad \frac{dy}{dx}=\frac{1}{1+x^2}, \quad \int \frac{1}{1+x^2}dx=\tan^{-1} x,$$

$$y=\sec^{-1} x, \quad \frac{dy}{dx}=\frac{1}{x\sqrt{x^2-1}}, \quad \int \frac{1}{x\sqrt{x^2-1}}dx=\sec^{-1} x$$

Thus, if $y=bx^n+C$,

the differential coefficient is

$$\frac{dy}{dx}=nbx^{n-1}. \text{ or } dy=nbx^{n-1}dx.$$

Hence, reversing the process, we see that the integral of $nbx^{n-1}dx$, written $nb\int x^{n-1}dx$,

$$=bx^n+C. \qquad \text{(i)}$$

Ex. 10. $$\tfrac{1}{2}\int x^{-\frac{1}{2}}dx=\frac{\frac{1}{2}x^{-\frac{1}{2}+1}}{\frac{1}{2}}=x^{\frac{1}{2}}+C....$$

Indefinite integral.—The expression (i) is called an **indefinite integral** of the function nbx^{n-1}, the value of the constant C being unknown. In practical applications the value of the constant and the integral can usually be determined from the conditions of the problem.

The preceding integrals are important and should be committed to memory. The following may be reduced to the preceding forms by one or more simple substitutions and rearrangements.

If $$y=-\frac{1}{a}\cos ax, \quad \frac{dy}{dx}=\sin ax;$$

$$\therefore \int \sin ax\, dx=-\frac{1}{a}\cos ax.$$

The result may also be obtained as follows:

Ex. 11. Integrate $\sin ax dx$.

Let $ax=z$, then $\frac{dz}{dx}=a$, or $dx=\frac{dz}{a}$;

$$\therefore \int \sin ax\, dx=\frac{1}{a}\int \sin z\, dz.$$

But, from the preceding table,

$$\int \sin z\, dz=-\cos z;$$

$$\therefore \frac{1}{a}\int \sin z\, dz=-\frac{1}{a}\cos z=-\frac{1}{a}\cos ax.$$

In many cases an integration may be readily effected by means of a suitable simple substitution.

Ex. 12. Find the value of

$$\int \frac{1}{(a+bx)^n}\, dx.$$

Put $a+bx=z$; then $dx=\frac{1}{b}dz$;

$$\therefore \int \frac{1}{(a+bx)^n}\, dx = \frac{1}{b}\int \frac{dz}{z^n}$$

$$= \frac{1}{b}\,\frac{z^{1-n}}{1-n};$$

replace z by $a+bx$;

$$\therefore \int \frac{1}{(a+bx)^n}\, dx = \frac{1}{b(1-n)}\,\frac{1}{(a+bx)^{n-1}}.$$

Ex. 13. Integrate $\int e^{ax}dx.$

Let $ax=z$, then $dx=\frac{dz}{a}$,

and $\int e^{ax}dx = \frac{1}{a}\int e^z dz$

$$= \frac{1}{a}e^z = \frac{1}{a}e^{ax}.$$

In some cases an integration may be effected by more than one method; the results obtained, although perhaps differing in appearance, may by suitable simplification be reduced to the same form. Two such methods are used in the following examples:

Ex. 14. Find the integral of

$$\frac{x^3dx}{x^2-3x+2}.$$

It will be noticed that the numerator contains x to a higher power than the denominator. In such a case it is necessary to divide the numerator by the denominator until the numerator contains x to a lower power than the denominator.

Thus $\frac{x^3}{x^2-3x+2} = x+3+\frac{7x-6}{x^2-3x+2}$;

$$\therefore \int \frac{x^3}{x^2-3x+2}\, dx = \int \left\{x+3+\frac{7x-6}{x^2-3x+2}\right\} dx$$

$$= \frac{x^2}{2}+3x+\int \frac{7x-6}{x^2-3x+2}\, dx.$$

Resolving $\frac{7x-6}{x^2-3x+2}$ into its partial fractions, p. 6, we obtain

$$\frac{7x-6}{x^2-3x+2}=\frac{8}{x-2}-\frac{1}{x-1};$$

$$\therefore \int\frac{7x-6}{x^2-3x+2}dx=8\log(x-2)-\log(x-1).$$

Hence $$\int\frac{x^3}{x^2-3x+2}dx=\frac{x^2}{2}+3x+8\log(x-2)-\log(x-1).$$

Instead of the preceding solution we could write the given integral as follows:

$$\int\frac{x^3}{x^2-3x+2}dx=\frac{x^2}{2}+3x+\int\left\{\frac{7}{2}\left(\frac{2x-3}{x^2-3x+2}\right)+\frac{9}{2}\left(\frac{1}{x^2-3x+2}\right)\right\}dx$$

$$=\frac{x^2}{2}+3x+\frac{7}{2}\int\frac{2x-3}{x^2-3x+2}dx+\frac{9}{2}\int\frac{1}{x^2-3x+2}dx,$$

put $x^2-3x+2=z$;

$$\therefore \frac{dz}{dx}=2x-3,$$

also $\frac{7}{2}\int\frac{2x-3}{x^2-3x+2}dx$ becomes $\frac{7}{2}\int\frac{1}{z}dz=\frac{7}{2}\log z.$

Similarly $$\frac{9}{2}\int\frac{1}{(x-2)(x-1)}dx=\frac{9}{2}\int\left\{\frac{1}{x-2}-\frac{1}{x-1}\right\}dx$$

$$=\frac{9}{2}\log(x-2)-\frac{9}{2}\log(x-1).$$

Collecting the terms we find

$$\int\frac{x^3}{x^2-3x+2}dx=\frac{x^2}{2}+3x+\frac{7}{2}\log(x^2-3x+2)+\frac{9}{2}\log(x-2)-\frac{9}{2}\log(x-1)$$

This result appears to differ from the previous one, but

$\frac{7}{2}\log(x^2-3x+2)$ may be written $\frac{7}{2}\log(x-2)+\frac{7}{2}\log(x-1)$;

$$\therefore \int\frac{x^3}{x^2-3x+2}dx=\frac{x^2}{2}+3x+\frac{7}{2}\log(x-2)+\frac{7}{2}\log(x-1)+\frac{9}{2}\log(x-2)$$

$$-\frac{9}{2}\log(x-1)$$

$$=\frac{x^2}{2}+3x+8\log(x-2)-\log(x-1).$$

Ex. 15. If $pv^s = c$ where c is a constant, find

$$\int p\,dv.$$

Here it is necessary to express p in terms of v.

Thus, since $$pv^s = c,$$
then $$p = cv^{-s};$$
substitute for p; $$\therefore \int p\,dv = c\int v^{-s}\,dv$$
$$= c\frac{v^{-s+1}}{-s+1}.$$

Thus, let $s = 0{\cdot}8$; then, $p = cv^{-0{\cdot}8}$;

$$\therefore c\int v^{-0{\cdot}8}\,dv = \frac{cv^{0{\cdot}2}}{0{\cdot}2} = 5cv^{0{\cdot}2}.$$

Let $s = 1$; then $$c\int v^{-1}\,dv = c\int \frac{1}{v}\,dv$$
$$= c\log_e v.$$

Ex. 16. The rate (per unit increase of volume) of the reception of heat by a gas is h, p is its pressure, and v its volume, and c is a known constant.

If $$pv^s = c, \quad \text{(i)}$$
and c being constant, find h where

$$h = \frac{1}{\gamma - 1}\left\{v\frac{dp}{dv} + \gamma p\right\}. \quad \text{(ii)}$$

If h is always 0, find what s must be.

From (i) $$p = cv^{-s}; \quad \text{(iii)}$$
$$\therefore \frac{dp}{dv} = -scv^{-s-1}.$$

Substituting this value in (ii),

$$h = \frac{1}{\gamma - 1}\{v(-scv^{-s-1}) + \gamma p\};$$

$$\therefore h = \frac{1}{\gamma - 1}\{-scv^{-s} + \gamma p\}. \quad \text{(iv)}$$

Substituting from (iii) in (iv), we obtain

$$h = \frac{1}{\gamma - 1}(-sp + \gamma p),$$

when $h = 0$ we have $$\frac{p(\gamma - s)}{\gamma - 1} = 0;$$
giving $$s = \gamma.$$

Automatic integration.—Many instruments are in use by which integration is performed automatically. Familiar examples are furnished by meters of various kinds, such as gas and water meters. Thus, assume an orifice, or tap, in connection with a water meter; then, if v denotes the velocity of the issuing water, the quantity which flows in a time t may be denoted by Q, where $Q=\int_0^t vdt$. This quantity is duly registered on the dial in front of the meter. In a similar manner, the dials of a gas meter record the number of cubic feet of gas which passes through the meter.

It must not be inferred that it is possible to integrate any given algebraic expression for some, as $\int\frac{dx}{\sqrt{(1+x^5)}}$, $\int\frac{dx}{\sqrt{(x^7+3)}}$ and others, have only been obtained by approximate methods. Thus, the form of the differential cannot always be derived from an algebraical expression. In such a case the method adopted is to obtain an approximate value by the aid of series, etc.

Approximate methods.—In practical cases, such as finding the area or volume of an irregular figure, it frequently happens that the value of a definite integral cannot be obtained, and some approximate method must replace a more accurate integration. Hence, it becomes necessary to ascertain what formulae may be used for the purpose.

There are several methods by which, when numerical values of x and y are known, an approximate value of $\int_a^b ydx$ can be found. Of these the following are important:

Simpson's Parabolic Rules, viz., the *one-third* and the *three-eighths* rules.

Weddle's rule, the **trapezoidal** and the **mid-ordinate** rules.

Simpson's First Rule.—This important rule, also called Simpson's *one-third* rule, may be used when values of the ordinates of a given area, or volume, at equal distances are known, and when there is an *odd* number of such ordinates. It may be written in the form:

$$\Sigma=\frac{s}{3}(A+4B+2C);$$

where Σ denotes the area when the ordinates are linear, and volume when the ordinates denote areas; s is the common distance between the ordinates, A the sum of the end ordinates, B the sum of the even ordinates, and C the sum of the odd

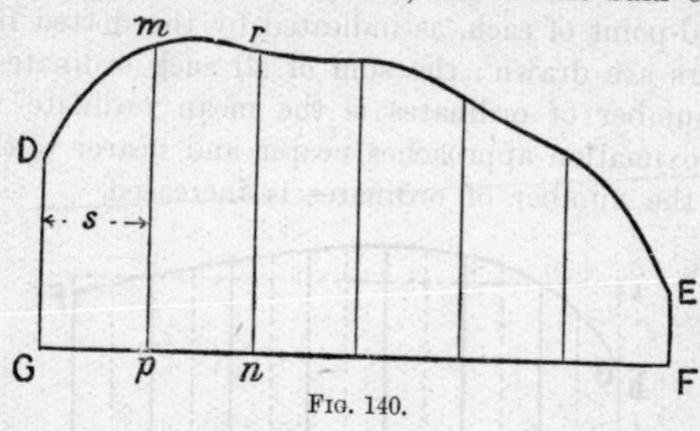

FIG. 140.

ordinates. If, as in Fig. 140, there are seven ordinates, then the rule may be written

$$\text{Area } DGFE=\int_0^6 f(x)dx=\frac{s}{3}\{y_0+y_6+4(y_1+y_3+y_5)+2(y_2+y_4)\}.$$

Simpson's Second Rule.—Simpson's second or *three-eighths rule*, may be used when there is an *even* number of ordinates.

$$\therefore\ A=\int_0^6 f(x)dx=\frac{3s}{8}\{y_0+y_6+2y_3+3(y_1+y_2+y_4+y_5)\}.\ *$$

Weddle's Rule.—This rule is applicable when there are 7 equidistant ordinates, and on the assumption that the boundary is a continuous curve the results are probably more accurate than those obtained by Simpson's Rules. The rule may be stated as follows:

$$A=\frac{3s}{10}\{y_0+y_2+y_3+y_4+y_6+5(y_1+y_3+y_5)\}.$$

Trapezoidal Rule.—The so-called trapezoidal rule is usually more easily manipulated than the preceding formulae, but the results are not so accurate as those obtained by Simpson's and Weddle's rules. The rule for 7 ordinates may be stated as follows:

$$A=s\{\tfrac{1}{2}(y_0+y_6)+y_1+y_2+y_3+y_4+y_5\}.$$

* For eight or more *even* ordinates, apply the second rule to the first four and first rule to the remainder.

Mid-ordinate Rule.—If h is the mean ordinate of an irregular figure $DEFG$ (Fig. 141), then the product of h and the length DE is the area of the figure.

The base DE is divided into a number of equal parts, and at the mid-point of each, as indicated by the dotted lines, perpendiculars are drawn; the sum of all such ordinates divided by the number of ordinates is the mean ordinate required. The approximation approaches nearer and nearer to the actual value as the number of ordinates is increased.

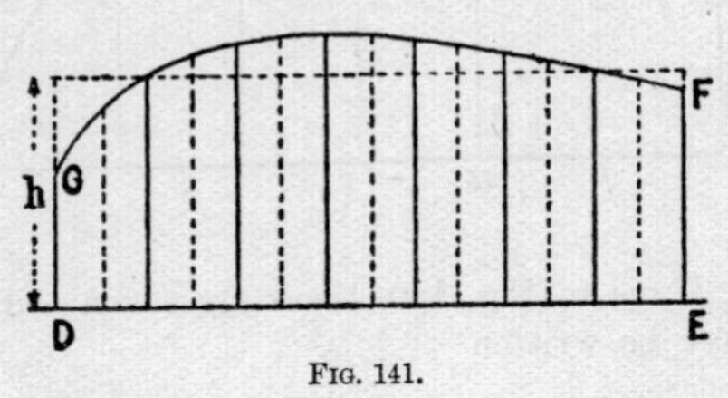

FIG. 141.

The sum of the ordinates is readily obtained by using a strip of paper and marking off a length equal to the first, and at the end of the first a length equal to the second, etc.

Ex. 17. Find the area of the curve $y=x^2$, between the values $x=1$ and $x=7$.

Let A denote the area

$$\therefore \ A=\int_1^7 x^2 dx=\left[\frac{x^3}{3}\right]_1^7.$$

Substituting the given limits, we find

$$A=\frac{1}{3}(7^3-1^3)=\frac{342}{3}=114.$$

To avoid mistakes it is advisable to write the indefinite integral in square brackets as shown, and afterwards to substitute and simplify.

It is instructive to compare the accurate result obtained by integration with the value found by using Simpson's Rule.

Ex. 18. To find the area of the curve $y=x^2$, between the values $x=1$ and $x=7$.

For values of $x=1$, 2, etc., calculate and tabulate values of y as follows:

x	1	2	3	4	5	6	7
y	1	4	9	16	25	36	49

By Simpson's Rule the area of the curve from 1 to 7, is

$$\frac{1}{3}\{1+49+4(4+16+36)+2(9+25)\}=\frac{342}{3}=114.$$

The area obtained is that of a parabola and therefore the result agrees with that obtained by integration. Simpson's parabolic rules give accurate results in such cases, even if only three equidistant ordinates are given. Thus, in the preceding example, using the three ordinates 1, 16 and 49. Then, as the common distance is 3,

$$\text{area}=\frac{3(1+49+4\times 16)}{3}=\frac{342}{3}=114.$$

In fact Simpson's Rule proceeds on the assumption that the curve is a parabola, and consequently the nearer any given case approaches to this form, the greater the accuracy obtained by the rule.

Ex. 19. Find the volume of a log of timber 36 feet long, the areas of cross-sections at equal intervals of 6 feet being as follows: 8·20, 5·68, 4·04, 2·92, 2·16, 1·54, 1·02, sq. ft. respectively.

I. **Simpson's First Rule.**

Sum of end ordinates $=8{\cdot}20+1{\cdot}02=9{\cdot}22$.

,, ,, even ,, $=5{\cdot}68+2{\cdot}92+1{\cdot}54=10{\cdot}14$.

,, ,, odd ,, $=4{\cdot}04+2{\cdot}16=6{\cdot}20$.

$$\text{Volume}=\tfrac{6}{3}(9{\cdot}22+4\times 10{\cdot}14+2\times 6{\cdot}20)$$
$$=2\times 62{\cdot}18=124{\cdot}36 \text{ cub. ft.}$$

II. **Simpson's Second Rule.**

$$V=\frac{3\times 6}{8}\{8{\cdot}20+1{\cdot}02+2\times 2{\cdot}92+3(5{\cdot}68+4{\cdot}04+2{\cdot}16+1{\cdot}54)\}$$
$$=\tfrac{9}{4}(9{\cdot}22+5{\cdot}84+3\times 13{\cdot}42)$$
$$=124{\cdot}47 \text{ cub. ft.}$$

III. **Weddle's Rule.**

$$V=\frac{3\times 6}{10}\{8{\cdot}20+4{\cdot}04+2{\cdot}92+2{\cdot}16+1{\cdot}02+5(5{\cdot}68+2{\cdot}92+1{\cdot}54)\}$$
$$=\tfrac{18}{10}(18{\cdot}34+50{\cdot}70)$$
$$=\frac{9\times 69{\cdot}04}{5}=124{\cdot}272 \text{ cub. ft.}$$

IV. **Trapezoidal Rule.**

$$V=6\{\tfrac{1}{2}(8{\cdot}20+1{\cdot}02)+5{\cdot}68+4{\cdot}04+2{\cdot}92+2{\cdot}16+1{\cdot}54\}$$
$$=6\times 20{\cdot}95=125{\cdot}7 \text{ cub. ft.}$$

V. **Mid-ordinate Rule.** Drawing the mid-ordinates the sum is 20·56;

$$\therefore \text{ Volume}=\frac{20{\cdot}56}{6}\times 36=123{\cdot}4 \text{ cub. ft.}$$

It is important to be able to use more than one method in calculating the area or volume of a given irregular figure, the results obtained by one method may be used as a check on the other.

Ex. 20. Plot the curve $y=2{\cdot}45e^{0{\cdot}4x}$ (i) where $e=2{\cdot}718$. Find the average value of y from $x=0$ to $x=8$.

When values 0, 1, 2, 3 ... are assumed for x corresponding values of y can be calculated. Thus, when $x=0$, from (i)

$$y=2{\cdot}45e^0=2{\cdot}45.$$

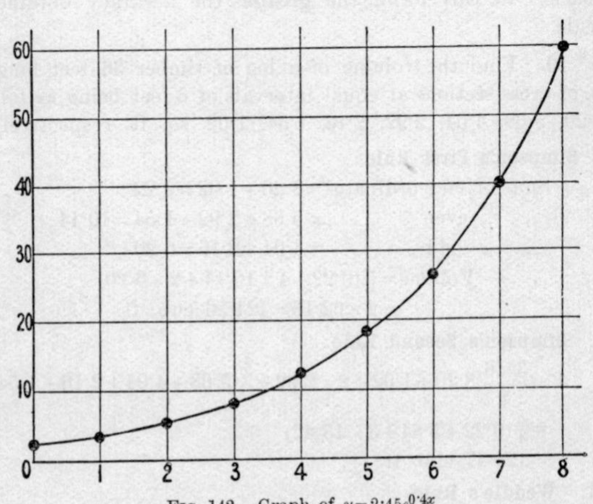

FIG. 142.—Graph of $y=2{\cdot}45e^{0{\cdot}4x}$.

When $x=3,\ y=2{\cdot}45e^{3\times 0{\cdot}4}=2{\cdot}45e^{1{\cdot}2}$,

$$\log y=\log 2{\cdot}45+1{\cdot}2\log 2{\cdot}718=0{\cdot}91036;$$

$$\therefore\ y=8{\cdot}136.$$

Values of x and corresponding values of y are given in the following table:

x	0	1	2	3	4	5	6	7	8
y	2·45	3·656	5·453	8·136	12·13	18·10	27·01	40·29	60·12

The curve is shown in Fig. 142.

The area OAB may be obtained by Simpson's Rule as follows:

Sum of end ordinates $=2·45+60·12=62·57$,

Sum of even ordinates $=3·656+8·136+18·10+40·29=70·182$,

Sum of odd ordinates $=5·453+12·13+27·01=44·593$.

$$A=\tfrac{1}{3}(62·57+4\times 70·182+2\times 44·593)=\frac{432·478}{3}=144·16.$$

Also area $=$ (average ordinate) $\times$ (length of base);

$$\therefore \text{ average value}=\frac{144·16}{8}=18·02.$$

The preceding result may be obtained more accurately by integration. Thus, if $y=Ae^{ax}$, $\dfrac{dy}{dx}=aAe^{ax}$.

Hence
$$\int Ae^{ax}dx=\frac{1}{a}Ae^{ax}+C.$$

Ex. 21. If $y=2·45e^{0·4x}$, find the average value of y from $x=0$ to $x=8$.

$$\therefore \text{ (average value)}\times 8=\int_0^8 2·45e^{0·4x}=\frac{2·45}{0·4}\Big[e^{0·4x}\Big]_0^8$$
$$=6·125\,(e^{3·2}-1)$$
$$=6·125\times 23·54=144·18;$$
$$\therefore \text{ average value}=\frac{144·18}{8}=18·02.$$

Some applications of integration.—Many of the rules and formulae used in mensuration are extremely difficult or impossible to obtain by elementary algebraical methods. There are very few, however, which do not yield to an elementary application of the calculus. The proofs of some of those which are of constant occurrence in practical work are given in the following pages, others may, if necessary, be obtained by similar methods.

Area of a circle.—Let θ denote the angle BCD (Fig. 143), then DCE, a small increase in the angle, will be denoted by $\delta\theta$, and the arc $DE = r\delta\theta$. Draw the chord DE. The area of the triangle $DCE = \frac{1}{2}DE \times CF$ where CF is drawn perpendicular to DE.

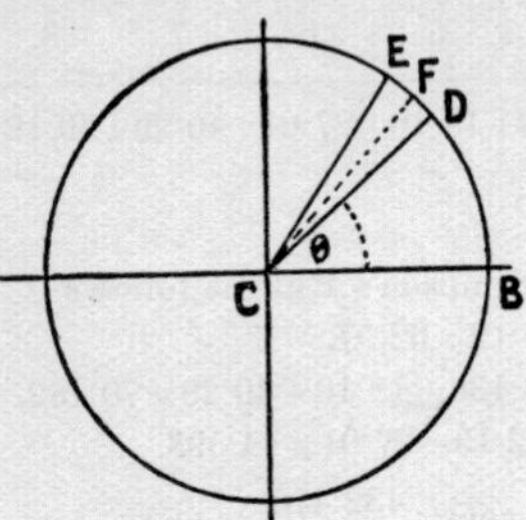

FIG. 143.—Area of a circle.

When the angle becomes indefinitely small, the arc DE becomes equal to the chord DE, and CF becomes r.

$$\therefore \text{ area of triangle} = \tfrac{1}{2}rd\theta \times r$$
$$= \tfrac{1}{2}r^2 d\theta.$$

The sum of all such triangles, θ varying from 0 to 2π, will give the area of the circle.

$$\therefore \text{ area} = \int_0^{2\pi} \frac{1}{2} r^2 d\theta = \frac{r^2}{2}\int_0^{2\pi} d\theta;$$

$$\therefore \text{ area} = \frac{r^2}{2}\left[\theta\right]_0^{2\pi} = \pi r^2. \text{ *}$$

Surface of a cone.—Let r denote the radius of the base, l the length of the slant side ON (Fig. 144), then if AD, BC denote two plane sections perpendicular to the axis of the

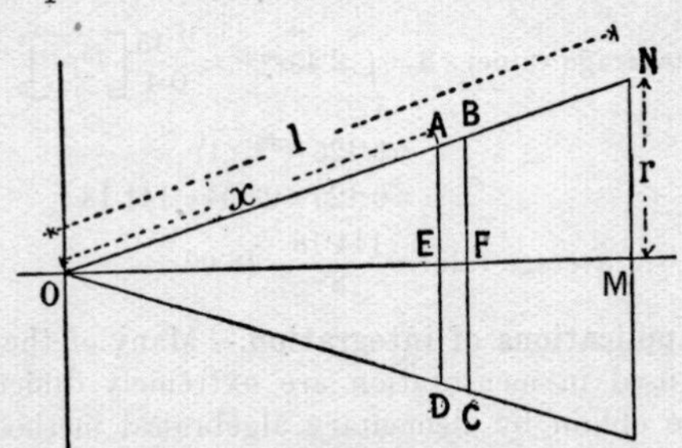

FIG. 144.—Surface of a cone.

cone which cut the cone in two circles shown by the lines AED, BFC respectively, when these planes lie close together, if y denotes the radius AE, the surface

* See footnote, p. 434.

of the slice $ABCD$ is $2\pi y \times EF$ approximately, and this approaches closer and closer to the actual value as the distance EF is made smaller. When the two points E and F are indefinitely near to each other, the points A and B form two consecutive points on the surface, and the expression for the area becomes $2\pi y dx$..................................(i)

It is now necessary to express y in terms of x. Let $OA = x$, then, from the similar triangles OEA and OMN,

$$x : y = l : r;$$

$$\therefore\ y = \frac{xr}{l}.$$

Substitute in (i);

$$\therefore\ \text{area of slice} = \frac{2\pi r x}{l} dx.$$

The total surface from $x = 0$ to $x = l$ may be denoted by S.

$$\therefore\ S = \int_0^l \frac{2\pi r}{l} x dx = \frac{2\pi r}{l} \int_0^l x dx$$

$$= \frac{2\pi r}{l} \left[\frac{x^2}{2}\right]_0^l = \frac{2\pi r l^2}{2l}$$

$$= \pi r l.$$

Hence, we obtain the rule :—**The curved surface of a cone is one-half the perimeter of the base multiplied by the slant height.**

When the total surface is required it is necessary to add the area of the base to this;

$$\therefore\ \text{total surface} = \pi r l + \pi r^2$$

$$= \pi r (l + r).$$

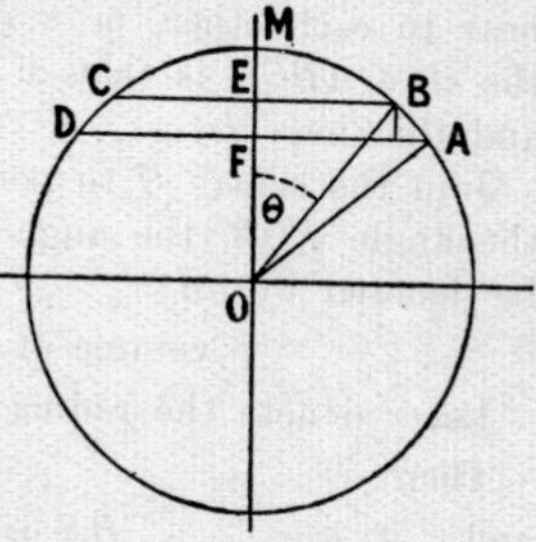

FIG. 145.—Surface and volume of a sphere.

Surface of a sphere.—Any plane section, such as BC, cuts the sphere in a circle; let AD be any other section drawn parallel, and indefinitely near to BC and on the side of BC nearest to the centre of the sphere, then the radius of the circle is slightly larger than that of plane BC.

Let x denote the distance ME, then, when the two sections are indefinitely near to each other, the distance FE will be denoted by dx.

The portion $ABCD$ is a flat circular plate of radius BE and thickness dx.

Join the points B and A to the centre O, then if the angle EOB be denoted by θ, the angle BOA will be represented by $d\theta$.

$$\text{Area of slice } ABCD = 2\pi \times BE \times AB. \quad \ldots\ldots\ldots\ldots\text{(i)}$$

Now $\qquad BE = r\sin\theta$ and $AB = r\,d\theta$.

Substituting in (i),

$$\text{Area of } ABCD = 2\pi r \sin\theta \times r d\theta.$$

The sum of all such slices from $\theta=0$ to $\theta=\frac{\pi}{2}$ will give the surface of the hemisphere and twice this sum will be the surface of the sphere;

$$\therefore \text{ surface of sphere} = 2\int_0^{\frac{\pi}{2}} 2\pi r^2 \sin\theta d\theta$$

$$= 4\pi r^2 \int_0^{\frac{\pi}{2}} \sin\theta d\theta = 4\pi r^2 \Big[-\cos\theta\Big]_0^{\frac{\pi}{2}}$$

$$= 4\pi r^2.$$

Volume of a sphere.—Let AD and BC be two plane sections of the sphere when the two planes are indefinitely near to each other, or a distance dx apart. The volume of the slice $ABCD$ is that of a flat circular plate of radius BE, and thickness dx.

Join the centre O to points B and A. Then, if θ denotes the angle EOB, the angle BOA, a slight increase to θ, will be denoted by $d\theta$;

$$\therefore \text{ volume of } ABCD = \pi \times BE^2 \times dx.$$

Let r denote the radius of the sphere.

Then $\qquad BE = r\sin\theta,$

and $\qquad BN \text{ or } dx = AB\sin BAN$

$$= rd\theta \sin\theta;$$

$$\therefore \text{ volume of } ABCD = \pi r^2 \sin^2\theta \times r\sin\theta d\theta$$

$$= \pi r^3 \sin^3\theta d\theta.$$

The sum of all such slices from 0 to $\frac{\pi}{2}$ will give the volume of the hemisphere, and twice this sum is the volume of the sphere.

$$\therefore \text{ volume of sphere} = 2\int_0^{\frac{\pi}{2}} \pi r^3 \sin^3\theta d\theta = 2\pi r^3 \int_0^{\frac{\pi}{2}} \sin^3\theta d\theta$$

$$= 2\pi r^3 \int_0^{\frac{\pi}{2}} \sin\theta(1-\cos^2\theta)d\theta = 2\pi r^3\left[\int_0^{\frac{\pi}{2}} \sin\theta d\theta - \int_0^{\frac{\pi}{2}} \cos^2\theta \sin\theta d\theta\right]$$

$$= 2\pi r^3\left[-\cos\theta - \left(-\frac{\cos^3\theta}{3}\right)\right]_0^{\frac{\pi}{2}}$$

$$= 2\pi r^3\left[\frac{\cos^3\theta}{3} - \cos\theta\right]_0^{\frac{\pi}{2}} = 2\pi r^3 \times \frac{2}{3} = \frac{4}{3}\pi r^3;$$

or, let MO be taken to be the axis of x, and let x, y denote the co-ordinates of B. Then

$$\text{volume of strip} = \pi y^2 dx;$$

if r denote the radius and V the volume of the sphere,

$$\frac{V}{2} = \pi\int_0^r y^2 dx = \pi\int_0^r (r^2 - x^2)dx = \pi\left[r^2x - \frac{x^3}{3}\right]_0^r = \frac{2}{3}\pi r^3;$$

$$\therefore V = \frac{4}{3}\pi r^3. \text{*}$$

Volume of a cone.—Let r denote the radius of the base, and h the length of the axis of the cone. Any plane section parallel to the base will be a circle.

Let AD and BC (Fig. 146) be two such sections; then when the distance between the sections is indefinitely small, or dx, the area of AD is nearly equal to that of BC.

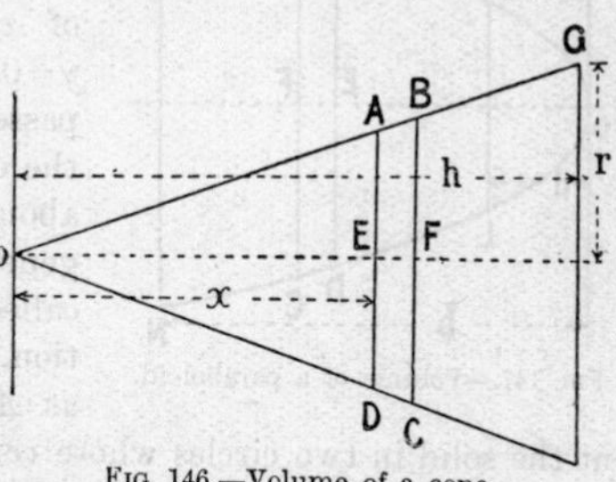

Fig. 146.—Volume of a cone.

Let $OE = x$ and radius $EA = y$.

Volume of $ABCD = \pi y^2 dx$. ....(i)

* or, $V + \delta V = \frac{4}{3}\pi(r+\delta r)^3$; $\therefore \frac{dV}{dr} = 4\pi r^2$.

The cone may be supposed to be divided into a large number of such small sections and the sum of all such will be the volume of the solid.

In Eq. (i) it is necessary to express y in terms of x.

Thus, from the similar triangles OHG and OEA, we find

$$x:y=h:r; \quad \therefore \ y=\frac{rx}{h}.$$

Substitute this value in (i);

$$\therefore \text{ volume of } ABCD=\frac{\pi r^2x^2}{h^2}dx.$$

If V denote the volume of the cone,

$$V=\int_0^h \frac{\pi r^2x^2}{h^2}dx=\frac{\pi r^2}{h^2}\int_0^h x^2dx=\frac{\pi r^2}{h^2}\left[\frac{x^3}{3}\right]_0^h;$$

$$\therefore \ V=\frac{\pi r^2h}{3};$$

$\therefore$ **volume of cone is one-third the product of area of base and height**, or one-third the volume of a cylinder on the same base and the same height.

Volume of a paraboloid.—It follows from the equation of a parabola $y^2=4ax$, that for each value of x, two values of y, equal in magnitude but opposite in sign, may be obtained. Hence, the curve when plotted is symmetrical about the axis of x. Further, as $x=0$ gives $y=0$, the vertex of the curve passes through the origin. If the curve be assumed to rotate about the axis of x, it will generate a solid of revolution called a paraboloid of revolution. Two plane sections, such as AD and BC (Fig. 147) will cut the solid in two circles whose centres are E, F respectively. The volume of the portion $ABCD$ may be taken to be

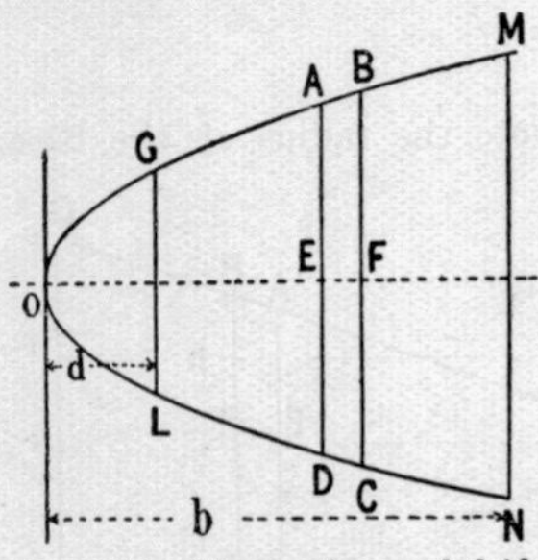

Fig. 147.—Volume of a paraboloid.

$$\pi \times AE^2 \times EF=\pi y^2\delta x,$$

the approximation becoming closer and closer to the actual value as the distance δx is diminished.

When δx is indefinitely small the volume of the slice $ABCD = \pi y^2 dx = 4\pi a x dx$, and the volume of the solid between the planes GL and MN at distances b and d from the origin respectively, is given by

$$V = \pi \int_d^b y^2 dx = 4\pi a \int_d^b x dx$$

$$= 4\pi a \left[\frac{x^2}{2}\right]_d^b = 4\pi a \left(\frac{b^2 - d^2}{2}\right).$$

If the volume be estimated from the origin, then $d=0$.

$$\therefore \ V = \frac{4\pi a b^2}{2} = 2\pi a b^2$$

$$= \tfrac{1}{2}\pi c^2 b \text{ if } c^2 = 4ab$$

(c being the value of y when $x=b$). Therefore volume of segment of paraboloid of revolution is equal to one-half volume of cylinder on same base and same height.

Ex. 22. In the curve

$$y = cx^{\frac{1}{2}}, \qquad \text{(i)}$$

find c if $y=m$ when $x=b$. Let this curve rotate about the axis of x; find the volume V enclosed by the surface of revolution between the two section-planes at $x=a$, and $x=b$.

Also find the numerical value of V when $m=6$, $b=4$, $a=2$, and $c=3$.

Substituting the given values of y and x in (i);

$$\therefore \ m = cb^{\frac{1}{2}};$$

$$\therefore \ c = mb^{-\frac{1}{2}}. \qquad \text{(ii)}$$

It will be seen that as Eq. (i) can be written in the form $y^2 = c^2 x$, it follows that the curve is one-half of a parabola, and therefore by revolution it will generate a paraboloid of revolution.

As in Fig. 147, the volume of a portion $ABCD$ is $\pi y^2 dx$;

$$\therefore \ V = \pi \int_a^b y^2 dx.$$

Now express y in terms of x and the two constants of m and b, substitute the value of c from (ii) in (i), and we obtain

$$y^2 = \frac{m^2}{b} x;$$

$$\therefore \quad V=\frac{m^2\pi}{b}\int_a^b x\,dx=\frac{\pi m^2}{b}\left[\frac{x^2}{2}\right]_a^b$$

$$=\frac{\pi m^2(b^2-a^2)}{2b}.$$

Substitute the given values of a, b, and m;

$$\therefore \quad V=\frac{\pi\times 36(16-4)}{8}=54\pi.$$

Prolate spheroid.—If an ellipse rotates about an axis passing through its major axis, it generates a solid of revolution called a prolate spheroid. If the semi-axes of the ellipse MO and NO (Fig. 148), are a and b respectively, the equation to the ellipse may be written in the form

$$\frac{x^2}{a^2}+\frac{y^2}{b^2}=1 \quad \text{..........(i)}$$

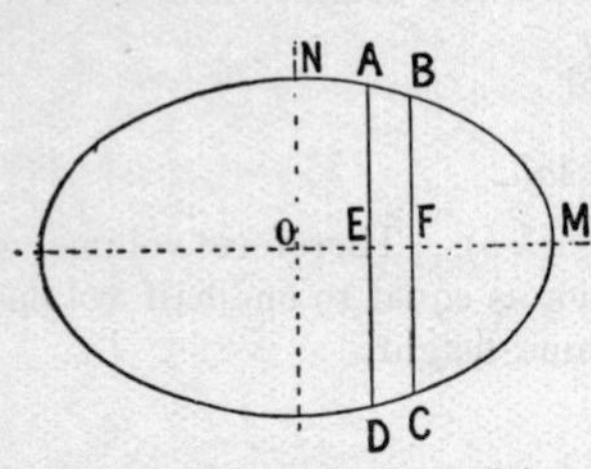

FIG. 148.—Volume of a prolate spheroid.

It will be noticed that when in Eq. (i) $x=0$, $y=\pm b$; and $y=0$, $x=\pm a$. Hence, the centre of the ellipse is at the origin.

Two plane sections AD and BC will cut the spheroid in two circles of radii AE and BF respectively. Let $AE=y$; then, if the distance EF be assumed to be indefinitely small, and denoted by dx,

$$\text{Volume of slice } ABCD=\pi y^2 dx.$$

If V denote the volume;

then
$$V=2\pi\int_0^a y^2 dx.$$

From (i)
$$y^2=\frac{b^2}{a^2}(a^2-x^2);$$

$$\therefore \quad V=\frac{2\pi b^2}{a^2}\int_0^a (a^2-x^2)\,dx=\frac{2\pi b^2}{a^2}\left[a^2x-\frac{x^3}{3}\right]_0^a=\frac{4}{3}\pi ab^2.$$

It will be noticed that when $b=a$, the volume is that of a sphere of radius a.

Oblate spheroid.—The volume generated by an ellipse rotating about its minor axis is called an *oblate spheroid*, and the volume may be obtained as in the preceding case.

Ex. 23. A curve whose equation is $4y^2=x^3$ is supposed to turn about the axis of x and trace out a surface of revolution. Find the volume of the solid enclosed by the surface of revolution and the two circles traced out by the ordinates at $x=1$ and $x=4$ respectively.

Denoting the volume enclosed by the surface of revolution, and the two circles traced out by the ordinates at $x=1$ and $x=4$ by V,

$$V=\pi\int_1^4 y^2dx=\frac{\pi}{4}\int_1^4 x^3dx;$$

$$\therefore\ V=\frac{\pi}{16}(256-1)=\frac{255\pi}{16}=50 \text{ cub. ft. approx.}$$

Simpson's Rule. Let p be the origin and pm the axis of y (Fig. 140). If s denotes the distance pn, then pG will be $-s$. If the portion of the given curve included between the ordinates y_0 and y_2 can be replaced by a curve of the form $y=a+bx+cx^2$, then it is necessary to determine the three constants a, b, c, so that the curve passes through the three points D, m, r.

Thus, at the point D, $x=-s$, $y=y_0$.

Substituting, $\therefore\ y_0=a-sb+cs^2$ ....(1)

at m, $x=0,\ y=y_1,\ \therefore\ y_1=a$ ....(2)

at r, $x=s,\ y=y_2,\ \therefore\ y_2=a+sb+cs^2.$ ....(3)

From (1) and (3) $\dfrac{y_0+y_2}{2}=a+cs^2=y_1+cs^2;$

$$\therefore\ cs^2=\frac{y_0+y_2}{2}-y_1. \quad\text{......(4)}$$

The area enclosed by the two ordinates y_0 and y_2, and the axis of x and the curve is given by

$$\int_{-s}^{s} y\,dx=\int_{-s}^{s}(a+bx+cx^2)\,dx=2as+\tfrac{2}{3}cs^3.$$

Substituting from (4) and (2)

$$2sy_1+\frac{2}{3}\left(\frac{y_0+y_2}{2}-y_1\right)s=\frac{s}{3}(y_0+y_2+4y_1).$$

This is Simpson's Rule for 3 ordinates, for 7 ordinates, as in Fig. 140, this becomes

$$\frac{s}{3}\{y_0+y_2+4y_1+y_2+y_4+4y_3+y_4+y_6+4y_5\}$$

$$=\frac{s}{3}\{y_0+y_6+4(y_1+y_3+y_5)+2(y_2+y_4)\}.$$

EXERCISES. XLII.

Write down the values of

1. $\int_1^4 x^2 dx, \quad \int_{\frac{1}{3}}^1 \frac{dx}{x}.$

2. $\int x^2 dx, \quad \int (\cos bx)\, dx, \quad \int_{\frac{1}{3}}^1 \frac{dv}{v},$ and $\int_9^{12} x^2 dx,$

where a and b are constants.

3. Find $\int_a^b 2(c+x)\,dx$, when $a=10$, $b=20$, $c=4$.

Give the values of

4. $\int_a^b 3(c+nx^2)^2 2nx\,dx$, when $a=4$, $b=6$, $c=4$, and $n=2$.

(Hint, put $c+nx^2=z$, then $2nx\,dx=dz$.)

Integrate the following:

5. $\int \cos ax\,dx.$

6. $\int \sec^2 ax\,dx.$

7. $\int \frac{1}{1+a^2x^2} dx.$

8. $\int l^{ax}\,dx.$

9. $\int A\cos(a+bx)\,dx.$

10. $\int \frac{1}{1+(a+bx)^2} dx.$

11. $\int (p+qx)^2 dx.$

12. $\int \frac{dx}{\sqrt{1-(a+bx)^2}}$, where $a+bx<1$.

Integrate with respect to x the following functions:

13. $ax^m\,dx,\ (a+bx^n)dx,\ \cos(a+bx)\,dx,\ \frac{dx}{x},\ \frac{dx}{a+bx}.$

14. $\frac{dx}{a^2+x^2}.$

15. $\frac{x\,dx}{a^2-x^2}.$

16. $\frac{dx}{x\sqrt{x^2-a^2}}.$

17. $x^{\frac{p}{q}}dx.$

18. $\frac{x\,dx}{\sqrt{a^4-x^4}}.$

19. $\frac{x\,dx}{(x+1)(x+3)}.$

20. $\frac{d\theta}{\cos^2\theta-\sin^2\theta}.$

21. $\frac{1+\cos\theta\,d\theta}{\theta+\sin\theta}.$

22. $\frac{x\,dx}{(a^2-x^2)^{\frac{7}{2}}}.$

23. $\frac{\tan^2 x\,dx}{4+\tan^2 x}.$

Integrate the following:

24. $x^5\,dx$, $x^{\frac{1}{2}}dx$, $2x^{\frac{1}{2}}dx$, $\sqrt[3]{x^2\,dx}$.

25. $(2x^2+3x+5)\,dx$.

26. $(\sin x+\cos x)\,dx$.

27. $(2\sin 4x\cos 2x)\,dx$.

28. $(\sin 2x\cos 4x)\,dx$.

29. $(2\sin 4x\sin 2x)\,dx$.

30. $(2\cos 4x\cos 2x)\,dx$.

31. $e^{av}\,dv$.

32. $av^{-1\cdot 37}\,dv$.

33. $(at^2+bt+c)\,dt$.

34. $\dfrac{dx}{\sqrt{x^2+a^2}}$.

35. $a^{m+x}\,dx$.

36. $\dfrac{dx}{x\sqrt{a^2+x^2}}$.

37. $x^3(1+x^2)^{-\frac{1}{2}}dx$.

38. $\dfrac{x\,dx}{x^4+a^4}$.

39. $\dfrac{dx}{x^3(a+bx)}$.

40. $\dfrac{x^3\,dx}{\sqrt{1-x^2}}$.

41. $(\sin x)^2\,dx$.

42. $\dfrac{x^2-1}{x^2-4}\,dx$.

43. $2\cdot 4^{2x}\,dx$.

44. $\dfrac{dx}{\cos x}$.

45. $\dfrac{dx}{\sin x}$.

46. There is a curve whose shape may be drawn from the following values of x and y.

x	0	1	2	3	4	5	6	7	8
y	0	1·25	5	11·25	20	31·25	45	61·25	80

Find the relation connecting x and y.

Assuming this curve to rotate about the axis of x; find the volume enclosed by the surface so traced and the end sections where $x=0$ and $x=8$.

47. The shape of a curve may be obtained from the following values of x and y.

Assuming this curve to rotate about the axis of x, find the volume of the solid between the values $x=0$ and $x=32$.

x	0	3	5	7	9	12	16	19	21	23	26	30	32
y	15	12·9	12·35	12·36	12·6	13·6	15·55	16·34	16·6	15·6	13·18	8·7	5·7

CHAPTER XX.

CENTRE OF GRAVITY. MOMENT OF INERTIA.

Moment of a force.—The **moment** of a force, about a given point, is the product of the force and the perpendicular let fall from the given point on the line representing the direction of the force.

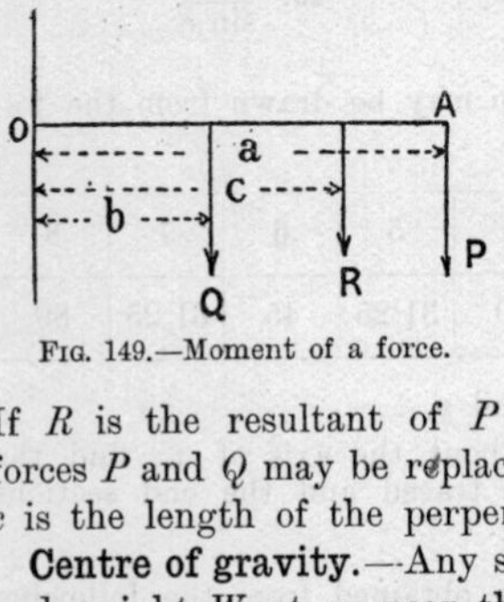

FIG. 149.—Moment of a force.

Thus, let P be a force (Fig. 149) acting at A, and O the given point. From O, draw OA perpendicular to the direction of P. If a denotes the length of this perpendicular, then the moment of P is Pa. Similarly, the moment of Q about O is Qb. If R is the resultant of P and Q, *i.e.* $R=P+Q$, then the forces P and Q may be replaced by R, if $R\times c=Pa+Qb$, where c is the length of the perpendicular from O on R.

Centre of gravity.—Any small portion of matter, of mass M and weight W, at or near the Earth's surface, is acted on by a force $W=Mg$ (where g is the acceleration due to gravity). As a body may be assumed to be an aggregate of small parts, and the forces due to these constitute a large number of parallel forces, the single force (or resultant) equal to their sum is called the **weight of the body.** The point in a body at which this single force may be assumed to act, whatever be the position of the body, is called the **centre of gravity** of the body. The term is, for convenience, used to denote a centre of an area, a centre of figure, or even a linear centre. Such a point is in many cases easily obtained. Thus, it would be the centre of a circle, the point of intersection of the diagonals of a rectangle, etc.

The centre of gravity of an irregular figure, especially when of comparatively small size, may be obtained by experimental methods. Thus, with a template, the exact shape of the figure may be cut out of a sheet of tin, cardboard, zinc, etc., and when such a template is freely suspended, the centre of gravity is in the vertical line passing through the point of support. In this manner two vertical lines can be drawn, and the point of their intersection is the centre of gravity of the figure. Another convenient method is to balance the figure on a knife edge and mark the line on it along which the figure balances; two such lines determine, as before, the position of the centre of gravity.

There are comparatively few bodies which have a centre of gravity, what is usually meant is the **centre of mass, or centre of area.**

Ex. 1. Find the centre of gravity of four bodies, weights 4, 2, 3, and 1 respectively, and arranged as in Fig. 150, their distances from a point O being 2, 7, 11, and 13 units of length respectively.

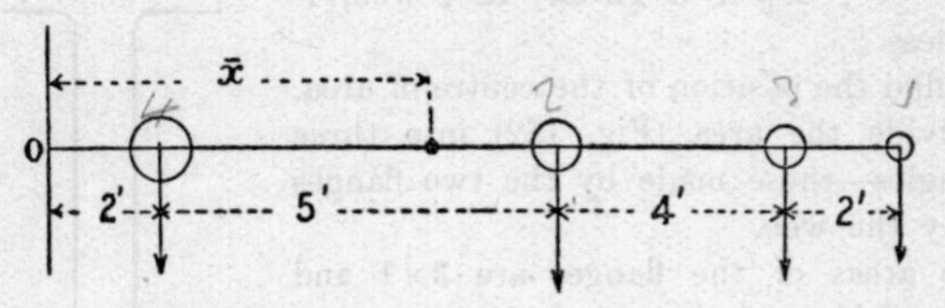

FIG. 150.—Centre of gravity.

Let the four weights in Fig. 150 be assumed to be rigidly connected together by a weightless rod or wire. To find the centre of gravity, or the point where a single force can be applied so that they remain in equilibrium, we may proceed as follows:

The four bodies shown give rise to four parallel forces, the sum of the moments of these four forces about any line, such as oy, must be equal to the moment of the resultant about the same line. Let $\bar{x}$ denote the distance of the resultant from oy.

Then, the sum of the moments will be

$$(4 \times 2)+(2 \times 7)+(3 \times 11)+(1 \times 13)=68.$$

The moment of the resultant is

$$(4+2+3+1)\bar{x};$$

$$\therefore\ 10\bar{x}=68,$$

or

$$\bar{x}=6\cdot 8.$$

Hence, the resultant acts at a point 6·8 from *oy*. If a single upward force equal to 10 were applied at this point, the system would remain in equilibrium.

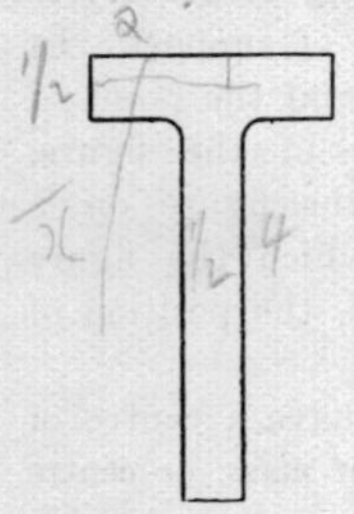

Fig. 151.—Centre of area of a T-section.

Ex. 2. Find the centre of area of the T-section (Fig. 151), flange $2'' \times \frac{1}{2}''$, web $4'' \times \frac{1}{2}''$.

The position of the centre of area may be obtained by taking moments about the upper edge. Let $\bar{x}$ denote the distance of the centre of area from the upper edge.

The areas of the two rectangles are $2'' \times \frac{1}{2}''$, and $4'' \times \frac{1}{2}''$, or 1 and 2 sq. in. respectively.

Hence, $$\bar{x} \times 3 = 1 \times \tfrac{1}{4} + 2 \times 2\cdot 5;$$

$$\therefore\ x = \frac{5\cdot 25}{3} = 1\cdot 75.$$

Ex. 3. Find the centre of area of a section of a cast iron girder of the following dimensions: flanges, $3'' \times 1''$ and $9'' \times 1''$; depth of girder, $12''$; web, $1''$ thickness.

To find the position of the centre of area, we divide the area (Fig. 152) into three rectangles—those made by the two flanges and by the web.

The areas of the flanges are 3×1 and 9×1, and that of the web is 10×1 sq. in.

Hence, if $\bar{x}$ denotes the distance of the centre of area from the base AB,

Then

$$\bar{x}(3+9+10)=9\times 0\cdot 5+10\times 6+3\times 11\cdot 5;$$

$$\therefore\ 22\bar{x}=99,\ \text{ or }\ \bar{x}=4\cdot 5.$$

Fig. 152.—Section of girder.

Hence, the centre of area of the given figure, is at a distance $4\frac{1}{2}$ inches from the base AB.

If $ABCD$ (Fig. 153) represents an irregular figure of uniform thickness, then the weights of the small strips into which the body may be assumed to be divided may be denoted by w_1,

$_2$, w_3 ... and the distances of their centres from E by x_1, $_2$, x_3 .... Then, if $\bar{x}$ is the distance of the centre of gravity rom E, and W the total weight,

$$\bar{x}=\frac{w_1x_1+w_2x_2+w_3x_3+\dots}{w_1+w_2+w_3+\dots}=\frac{\Sigma(wx)}{\Sigma w}$$

$$=\frac{\Sigma(wx)}{W}.\qquad\text{(i)}$$

The preceding equation will determine the position of the entre when the given body is symmetrical about a line such s EF. When this is not the case, two calculations which re expressed by $\bar{x}=\frac{\Sigma wx}{W}$, $\bar{y}=\frac{\Sigma wy}{W}$ must be made.

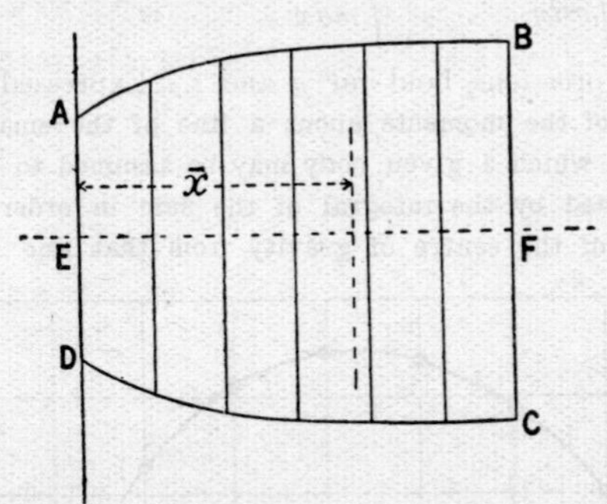

FIG. 153.—Centre of area of an irregular figure.

In the general case, the co-ordinates of the centre of gravity are obtained from

$$\bar{x}=\frac{\Sigma(wx)}{\Sigma w},\ \bar{y}=\frac{\Sigma(wy)}{\Sigma w},\ \bar{z}=\frac{\Sigma(wz)}{\Sigma w}\qquad\text{(ii)}$$

It is frequently convenient to apply the term centre of gravity to bodies which have no weight, such as geometrical figures, lines and planes. In such cases we mean the point which would be the centre of gravity if the body was of uniform density, or its weight was proportional to its length, area or volume. To obtain the weight of a body from its area of cross-section and length, it would be necessary to introduce common factors in Eq. (ii); these could then be cancelled, leaving simply volumes, areas, or lengths instead of weights.

Application of Integration.—The centre of gravity of a surface in which the boundary consists of a curved line may be obtained approximately by Eq. (ii). Strictly, however, the sub-divisions should be made indefinitely small, and the problem is therefore one requiring the integral calculus. When the process of integration can be applied, it affords the most rapid and also the most accurate method of obtaining the centre of gravity. Thus, if $\bar{x}$, $\bar{y}$, $\bar{z}$ have the same meanings as before,

then $\bar{x}=\dfrac{\int wxdx}{\int wdx}$, or $\bar{x}=\dfrac{\int mxdx}{\int mdx}$, where m denotes unit mass.

Similar expressions hold for y and z. Expressed in words, **the integral of the moments about a line of the small portions of mass into which a given body may be assumed to be divided, must be divided by the integral of the sum in order to obtain the distance of the centre of gravity from that line.**

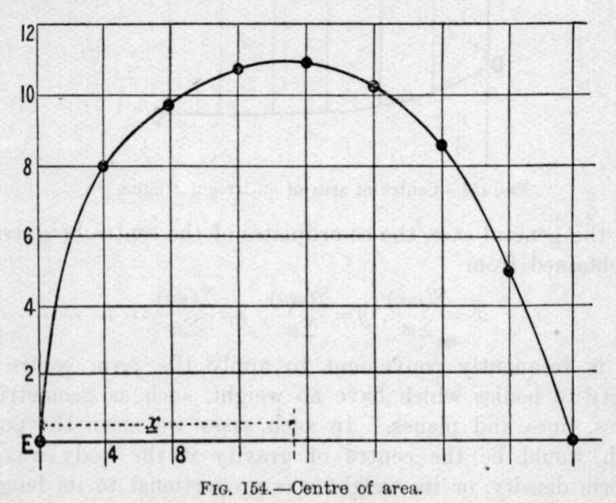

FIG. 154.—Centre of area.

Ex. 4. The half ordinates in feet of a symmetrical area (Fig. 154) are 0, 8·0, 9·6, 10·8, 11·0, 10·2, 8·6, 5·0, 0 ; find the area and the position of the centre of gravity, the common interval being 4 ft.

The area of a strip of the curve of width dx and height y is $y\,dx$, its moment about a line perpendicular to the axis of x and passing through E is $xy\,dx$. The sum of all such terms is expressed by $\int xy\,dx$. Similarly, the area enclosed by the curve is $\int y\,dx$. The integral in each case being taken between suitable limits.

$$\bar{x} = \int xy\,dx \div \int y\,dx.$$

Tabulating the given values, we obtain

(i) x	0	4	8	12	16	20	24	28	32
(ii) y	0	8·0	9·6	10·8	11·0	10·2	8·6	5·0	0
(iii) xy	0	32·0	76·8	129·6	176·0	204·0	206·4	140·0	0
(iv) y^2	0	64	92·16	116·6	121	104	73·96	25	0

The values in (iii) are obtained by multiplying the numbers in (i) and (ii). The sum of the numbers in (iii) can be found by Simpson's rule.

Thus, $\int xy\,dx = \frac{2940{\cdot}8 \times 4}{3}$ approx. Similarly, from

(ii) $\int y\,dx = \frac{194{\cdot}4 \times 4}{3}$; $\quad \therefore\ \bar{x} = \frac{2940{\cdot}8}{194{\cdot}4} = 15{\cdot}13$

where $\bar{x}$ denotes the distance from E of a line parallel to the axis of y and passing through the centre of gravity.

The volume of the solid generated by the rotation of the curve about the axis of x is $\pi\int y^2\,dx$. The sum of the values of y^2 in (iv) is found by Simpson's rule to be $604{\cdot}22 \times 4$;

$$\therefore \text{ volume of solid} = 4\pi \times 604{\cdot}22 = 7593{\cdot}8.$$

Guldinus's Theorem.—Suppose an area BG (Fig. 155) is connected by means of a thin bar GD to an axis OO in the plane of the area.

If the area be made to revolve about the axis, it will generate a ring, the cross-section of which will be the area BG. Let A denote the area of BG, and V denote the volume of the ring. If a denotes an exceedingly small area at a distance,

y, from the axis, then in one revolution the volume generated is $2\pi ay$;

$$\therefore \quad V = \Sigma(2\pi ay) = 2\pi\Sigma(ay).$$

If $\bar{r}$ denote the distance of the centre of area from the axis, then

$$\Sigma(ay) = \bar{r}A, \text{ also } \Sigma a = A;$$

$$\therefore \quad V = 2\pi\bar{r}A. \quad \text{(i)}$$

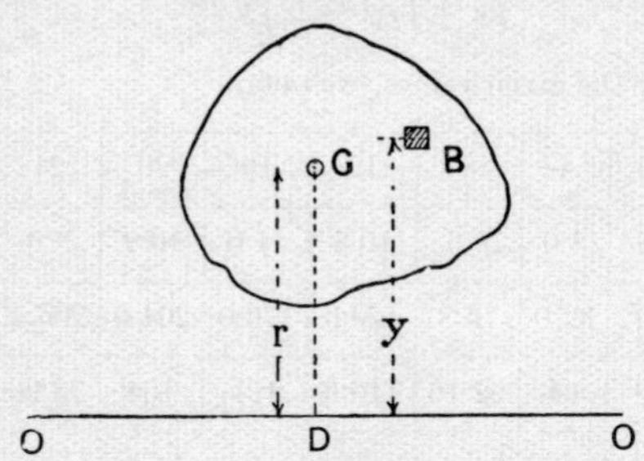

FIG. 155.—To illustrate Guldinus's Theorem.

This result may be expressed in words as follows:

The volume generated by the revolution of a plane figure about any external axis in its plane is equal to the product of the area and the distance moved through by the centre of gravity of the area.

Thus, the volume traced out by an irregular figure can be obtained when the area and the position of the centre of area are known.

Surface.—Let BG (Fig. 155) denote a closed curve, then the revolution of the curve about the axis OO will generate a surface. A very short length of the curve, which may be denoted by δs, at a distance x from the axis, will generate a strip of area $2\pi x\delta s$, and if S denotes the whole surface generated, then

$$S = 2\pi\Sigma(x\delta s).$$

If $\bar{r}$ denotes the distance of the centre of gravity and s the total length of the curve, then $\Sigma(x\delta s) = \bar{r}\Sigma\delta s = \bar{r}s$.

$\therefore$ surface generated $= 2\pi\bar{r}s$, or in words, **the surface traced out by the revolution of a curve about an axis in its own plane is equal to the product of the perimeter of the curve into the distance moved through by the centre of gravity of the curve.**

Conversely, when the length of a curve and the surface generated by the curve are known, the position of the centre of area or centre of gravity can be obtained (see p. 221).

If a rectangle $ABCD$ (Fig. 156) revolves about one of its sides, as AB, it will trace out a cylinder, radius AD, and length AB. When one side, as CE, is a curved line, the volume traced out by the figure may be obtained to any required degree of accuracy by using any of the approximate rules, Simpson's Mid-ordinate, etc.

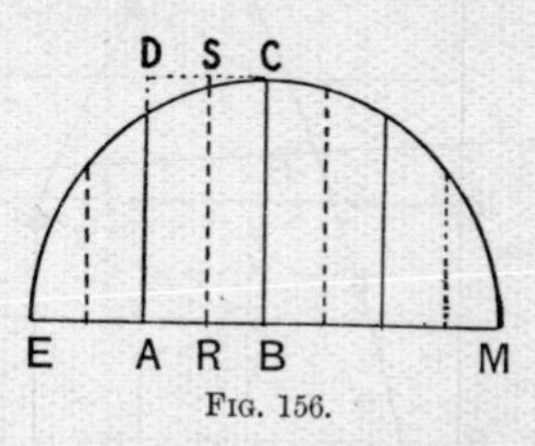

FIG. 156.

The volume, traced out by the figure ECM (Fig. 156), may be found by dividing the figure into a number of parts, then, denoting the common distance AB by δx and the successive radii by y_1, y_2, etc., the volume traced out

$$=\delta x\{\pi y_1^2+\pi y_2^2+\ldots\}.$$

Ex. 5. Find the volume traced out by the semicircle in Fig. 156.

As shown in Fig. 156, the given figure is divided into four equal parts, the mid-ordinates being 1·3, 1·9, 1·9 and 1·3, the common distance 1;

$$\therefore \text{ volume}=\pi\times 2(1{\cdot}3^2+1{\cdot}9^2)=10{\cdot}6\pi$$
$$=33{\cdot}31.$$

Ex. 6. A circle $1\frac{3}{4}$ inches radius rotates about an axis 7 inches from the centre of the circle. Find the surface and volume generated.

$$\text{Length of curve}=2\pi\times 1\tfrac{3}{4}, \text{ also } \bar{x}=7;$$
$$\therefore \text{ surface generated}=2\pi\times 1\tfrac{3}{4}\times 2\pi\times 7=49\pi^2$$
$$=484 \text{ sq. in.}$$
$$A=\pi\times(1\tfrac{3}{4})^2 \text{ sq. in.};$$
$$\therefore \text{ volume}=2\pi\bar{x}A=2\pi\times 7\times\pi\times(1\tfrac{3}{4})^2$$
$$=14\pi^2(1{\cdot}75)^2=423{\cdot}5 \text{ cub. in.}$$

Ex. 7. There is a curve whose shape may be drawn from the following values of x and y:

x in feet,	3	3·5	4·2	4·8
y in inches,	10·1	12·2	13·1	11·9

Imagine this curve to rotate about the axis of x, describing a surface of revolution.

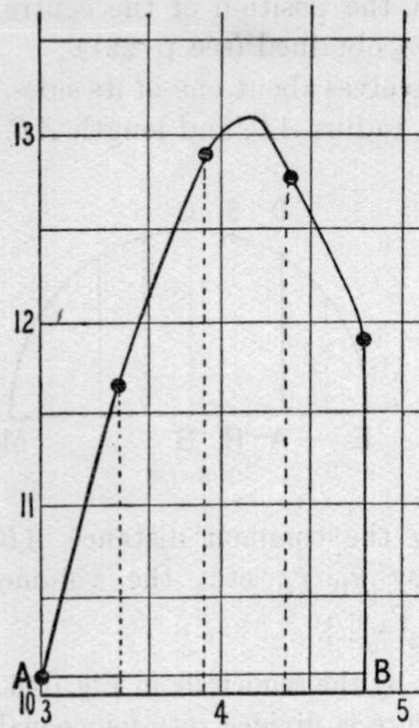

FIG. 157.—Volume of an irregular figure.

What is the volume enclosed by this surface and the two end sections where $x=3$ and $x=4{\cdot}8$?

Plotting the given values of x and y, a curve, as in Fig. 157, may be obtained.

The base AB is $4{\cdot}8-3{\cdot}0=1{\cdot}8$. Dividing this distance into 3 equal parts, the common distance is 0·6 ft., the mid-ordinates are 11·6, 12·9, and 12·7;

$$\therefore \text{ vol.} = 0{\cdot}6 \times 12 \times \pi(11{\cdot}6^2+12{\cdot}9^2+12{\cdot}7^2)$$
$$=3328{\cdot}27\pi \text{ cub. in.}$$
$$=10456 \text{ cub. in.}$$
$$=6{\cdot}05 \text{ cub. ft.}$$

Semicircle.—Let $EBDF$ (Fig. 158) be a semicircle of radius r, and B and A two points on the circumference. Through A and B draw two planes AD and BC parallel to the base EF, and at a distance apart represented by AN. When the points A and B are indefinitely near to each other, the distance between the planes may be denoted by dx. Join B to O. Then, if θ denotes the angle BOE, the small increase to the angle BOE, shown by the small angle AOB, will be represented by $d\theta$. The area of the slice $ABCD = BCdx$, but

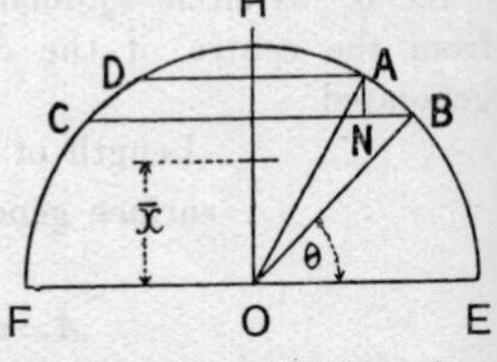

FIG. 158—Centre of area of a semicircle.

$$BC = 2r\cos BOE = 2r\cos\theta,$$

and
$$dx = AB\cos\theta = r\cos\theta d\theta;$$

$$\therefore \text{ area of slice } ABCD = 2r^2\cos^2\theta d\theta,$$
$$\text{moment about } FE = 2r^2\cos^2\theta d\theta \times x,$$

and
$$x = r\cos BOH = r\sin\theta;$$

$$\therefore \text{ moment} = 2r^3\cos^2\theta\sin\theta d\theta.$$

$$\text{Area of semicircle} = \frac{\pi r^2}{2};$$

$$\therefore \bar{x} \times \frac{\pi r^2}{2} = \int_0^{\frac{\pi}{2}} 2r^3 \cos^2\theta \sin\theta d\theta;$$

$$\therefore \bar{x} \times \frac{\pi r^2}{2} = 2r^3 \int_0^{\frac{\pi}{2}} \cos^2\theta \sin\theta d\theta$$

$$= 2r^3 \left[-\frac{\cos^3\theta}{3} \right]_0^{\frac{\pi}{2}} = \frac{2r^3}{3};$$

$$\therefore \bar{x} = \frac{2r^3 \times 2}{3 \times r^2 \times \pi} = \frac{4r}{3\pi} = 0{\cdot}4244r \text{ approx. } \ldots\ldots\ldots\text{(i)}$$

Hemisphere.—Using the notation and diagram of the preceding case, the sections made by the two planes *AD* and *BC* will be circles of diameters *AD* and *BC* respectively. The areas of the two circles may be taken to be the same when the distance between the planes is indefinitely small. The volume of the portion *ABCD* will be that of a flat circular disc of radius $\frac{BC}{2} = r_1$ and thickness dx.

$$\therefore \text{volume of } ABCD = \pi r_1^2 \times dx,$$

$$r_1 = r\cos\theta \text{ and } dx = AB\cos\theta = r\cos\theta d\theta;$$

$$\therefore \text{mass of } ABCD = m\pi r^3 \cos^3\theta d\theta,$$

$$\text{moment of mass about base} = m\pi r^3 \cos^3\theta d\theta \times p,$$

and

$$p = r\sin\theta;$$

$$\therefore \text{moment} = m\pi r^4 \cos^3\theta \sin\theta d\theta.$$

Also,

$$\text{mass of hemisphere} = \tfrac{2}{3} m\pi r^3;$$

$$\therefore \bar{x} \times \tfrac{2}{3} m\pi r^3 = \int_0^{\frac{\pi}{2}} m\pi r^4 \cos^3\theta \sin\theta d\theta,$$

or

$$\bar{x} \times \tfrac{2}{3} m\pi r^3 = m\pi r^4 \int_0^{\frac{\pi}{2}} \cos^3\theta \sin\theta d\theta$$

$$= m\pi r^4 \left[-\frac{\cos^4\theta}{4} \right]_0^{\frac{\pi}{2}}$$

$$= \frac{m\pi r^4}{4};$$

$$\therefore \bar{x} = \frac{m\pi r^4 \times 3}{m \times 4 \times 2\pi r^3} = \tfrac{3}{8} r;$$

or, the centre of gravity is $\frac{3}{8}$ths of the radius, measured from the base of the hemisphere.

Centre of gravity of a right cone.—Let the axis of the cone be horizontal and coincide with the axis of x as in Fig. 159. Let $\bar{x}$ denote the distance of the centre of gravity from an axis passing through the vertex O and parallel to the base.

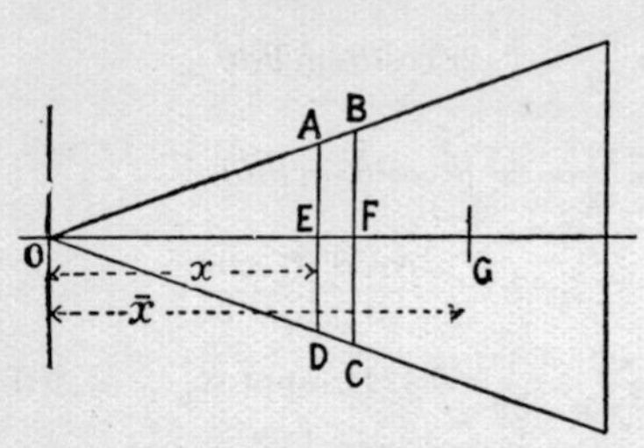

FIG. 159.—Centre of gravity of a right cone.

The sections made by two planes AD and BC, parallel to the base of the cone, will be two circles having slightly different radii. The radius AE, when the distance between the planes is indefinitely small, may be taken to be the same as BF.

Thus, $$\text{volume } ABCD = \frac{\pi r^2 x^2}{h^2} dx,$$

where r denotes the radius of the base and h the length of the axis at the cone.

If m is the mass of unit volume, then moment about O is

$$\frac{m\pi r^2 x^2}{h^2} x dx = \frac{m\pi r^2 x^3}{h^2} dx.$$

If $\bar{x}$ is the distance of the centre of gravity, then the total mass of the cone multiplied by $\bar{x}$ is equal to the sum of the moments of all the indefinitely thin slices into which the body is assumed to be divided.

$$\therefore \quad \frac{m\pi r^2 h}{3} \times \bar{x} = \frac{m\pi r^2}{h^2} \int_0^h x^3 dx$$

$$= \frac{m\pi r^2}{h^2} \left[\frac{x^4}{4}\right]_0^h = \frac{m\pi h^2 r^2}{4};$$

$$\therefore \quad \bar{x} = \tfrac{3}{4} h;$$

or, the centre of gravity is at a point $\frac{3}{4}$ the length of the axis measured from O.

Moment of inertia.—**When the mass of every element of a body is multiplied by the square of its distance from a given axis, the product is called the moment of inertia about that axis.**

Moment of inertia of a thin rod.—The moment of inertia of a thin rod AB (Fig. 160), of length l, about an axis passing through one end and perpendicular to its length, is obtained as follows:

The moment of inertia of a small element dx at a distance x from the axis is mx^2dx, where m denotes the mass of unit length. Hence, the moment of inertia of the rod will be

$$\int_0^l mx^2dx.$$

Denoting this expression by I, we have

$$I=\left[\frac{mx^3}{3}\right]_0^l=\frac{ml^3}{3}.$$

If M denotes the total mass of the rod, then, since

$$M=ml,$$

$$I=\frac{Ml^2}{3} \text{............(i)}$$

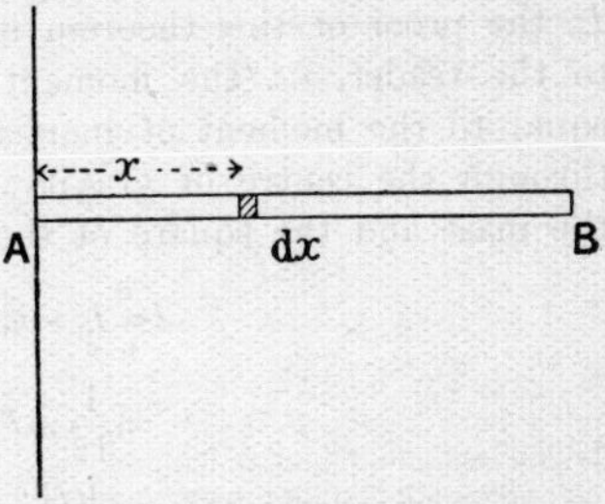

FIG. 160.—Moment of inertia of a rod.

The value of I for an axis passing through the middle point of the rod, or through its centre of gravity, would be obtained in like manner, the limits of the integral being $\frac{l}{2}$ and $-\frac{l}{2}$,

or
$$I=\left[\frac{mx^3}{3}\right]_{-\frac{l}{2}}^{\frac{l}{2}}=\frac{ml^3}{24}+\frac{ml^3}{24}=\tfrac{1}{12}ml^3$$

$$=\frac{Ml^2}{12} \text{..................................(ii)}$$

Ex. 1. Find the moment of inertia of a thin rod weighing 8 lbs. and 6 ft. long.

(a) About an axis passing through one end and perpendicular to its length.

(b) About an axis passing through its middle point and parallel to the preceding axis ($g=32$).

Here $M=\frac{8}{32}$.

(a) Substitute in (i), $\therefore\ I=\frac{8\times 6^2}{32\times 3}=3.$

(b) $I=\frac{8}{32}\times\frac{36}{12}=\frac{3}{4}.$

A convenient notation is to denote the moment of inertia of a given figure about an axis passing through the centre of area, or centre of gravity, by the symbol I_0, and about any parallel axis by the symbol I.

Thus, the preceding result would be written as $I_0 = \frac{Ml^2}{12}$.

The moment of inertia of the rod about a parallel axis passing through one end may be deduced from the value of I_0, the proof of this theorem is very simple and may be left to the reader, *i.e.* the moment of inertia about any axis is equal to the moment of inertia about a parallel axis passing through the centre of gravity, together with the product of the mass and the square of the distance between the axes.

$$\therefore\ I = I_0 + ml \times \left(\frac{l}{2}\right)^2$$

$$= \frac{1}{12} ml^3 + \frac{ml^3}{4} = \frac{ml^3}{3}$$

$$= \frac{Ml^2}{3}.$$

Moment of inertia of a rectangle.—Let b denote the breadth, or width, of the rectangle and d its depth (Fig. 161). The moment of inertia about a horizontal axis G lying in the plane of the rectangle, passing through the centre of area, may be obtained by assuming the figure to consist of an indefinite number of thin slices each of the thickness dx. The moment of inertia of such a slice at a distance x from the axis (Fig. 161) is $bdx \times x^2$, and the moment of inertia of the rectangle is the sum of the moments of inertia of all such slices;

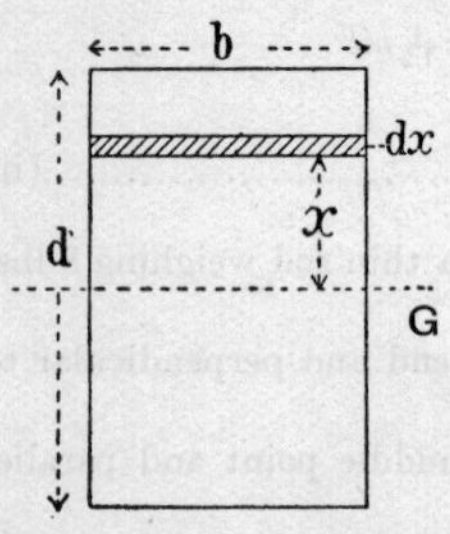

FIG. 161.—Moment of inertia of a rectangle.

$$\therefore\ I_0 = \int_{-\frac{d}{2}}^{\frac{d}{2}} bdx \times x^2 = b\int_{-\frac{d}{2}}^{\frac{d}{2}} x^2 dx$$

$$= \left[\frac{bx^3}{3}\right]_{-\frac{d}{2}}^{\frac{d}{2}} = \frac{bd^3}{12}.$$

Moment of inertia of a T-section.—The section, as in Fig. 151, consists of two rectangles. The moment of inertia of each rectangle about an axis passing through its centre of area can be obtained by substitution in the formula $I=\frac{1}{12}bd^3$.

Ex. 2. Find the moment of inertia of the T-section (Fig. 151) about an axis in the plane of the figure, and passing through the centre of area.

The value of I for the upper rectangle is $\frac{1}{12}\times 2\times(\frac{1}{2})^3=\frac{1}{48}$, and for the lower rectangle $\frac{1}{12}\times\frac{1}{2}\times 4^3=\frac{8}{3}$.

The moment of inertia of the whole section can now be obtained about any axes parallel to the preceding axes; one of the most useful axes is the line passing through the centre of area of the figure. Let I_0 denote the moment of inertia of the figure about the centre of area. The distance between the axis of the upper rectangle and the line through the centre of area of the whole figure is $1\frac{1}{2}''=\frac{3}{2}''$. The corresponding distance for the lower flange is $\frac{3}{4}''$, also area of upper rectangle is $2''\times\frac{1}{2}''=1$ sq. in., and the lower is $4\times\frac{1}{2}=2$ sq. in.

$$\therefore\ I_0=\frac{1}{48}+1\times\left(\frac{3}{2}\right)^2+\frac{8}{3}+2\times\left(\frac{3}{4}\right)^2$$
$$=\frac{291}{48}\text{ inch units.}$$

In a similar manner the value of I for an axis passing through (say) the outer edge of the upper rectangle may be obtained.

Ex. 3. Find the moment of inertia of the given cross-section (Fig. 152) about an axis in the plane of the figure, and passing through G, the centre of area.

The position of G has already been found to be at a distance of $4\frac{1}{2}$ inches from AB.

The given section may be assumed to be divided into three rectangles, the value of I can be obtained and finally I_0.

For lower rectangle, $I=\dfrac{9\times 1^3}{12}$;

$$\therefore\ I_0=\frac{9\times 1^3}{12}+9\times 1\times 4^2=144{\cdot}75\text{ inch units.}$$

For upper rectangle, $I=\dfrac{3\times 1^3}{12}$;

$$\therefore\ I_0=\frac{1}{4}+3\times 1\times 7^2=147{\cdot}25.$$

For web, $I=\dfrac{1\times 10^3}{12}$;

$$\therefore\ I_0=\frac{1000}{12}+10\times 1\times(1{\cdot}5)^2=83{\cdot}33+22{\cdot}5=105{\cdot}83;$$

$$\therefore\ I_0=144{\cdot}75+147{\cdot}25+105{\cdot}83=397{\cdot}83\text{ inch units.}$$

Moment of inertia of a thin disc.—The moment of inertia of a thin disc, of radius r, about an axis passing through the centre of the disc and perpendicular to its plane is obtained as follows:

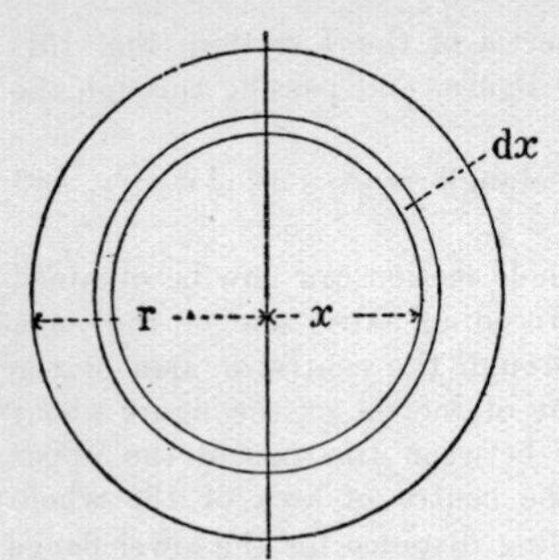

FIG. 162.—Moment of inertia in a circle.

The moment of inertia of an indefinitely thin annulus of thickness dx, and at a distance x from the axis (Fig. 162), would be its area $2\pi x\,dx$* multiplied by the square of its distance from the given axis, or

$$2\pi x dx \times x^2 = 2\pi x^3 dx. \quad \ldots\ldots\text{(i)}$$

The value of I_0 will be the sum of an indefinite number of such annuli, or the sum of all such expressions as (i) from $x=0$ to $x=r$.

$$\therefore \; I_0 = \int_0^r 2\pi x^3 dx = 2\pi \left[\frac{x^4}{4}\right]_0^r$$

$$= \frac{\pi r^4}{2}. \quad \ldots\ldots\ldots\ldots\ldots\ldots\ldots\ldots\text{(ii)}$$

The moment of inertia of the area of a circle about any diameter is half the preceding result, or $\frac{\pi r^4}{4}$. This value is required when dealing with the bending of a beam of circular section, and may be readily obtained by taking, instead of annuli, strips or slices parallel to the diameter.

Moment of inertia of a cylinder about its axis.—If r denotes the radius and l the length of the cylinder, m the mass of unit volume, then, as in the preceding case, the moment of inertia of an annulus of thickness dx, at a distance x from the axis, is the mass, $2\pi x dx l \times m$, multiplied by x^2 and $= 2\pi m l x^3 dx$;

$$\therefore \; I_0 = \int_0^r 2\pi m l x^3 dx = 2\pi m l \left[\frac{x^4}{4}\right]_0^r = \frac{\pi m l r^4}{2}. \quad \ldots\ldots\ldots\ldots\text{(ii)}$$

* Hence the area of a circle is the integral of $2\pi x\,dx$ between the limits, $x=0$, $x=r$.

If M denotes the total mass of the cylinder, then

$$M = m\pi r^2 l;$$

$$\therefore \text{ from (ii) } I_0 = \frac{Mr^2}{2}.$$

Moment of inertia of a hollow cylinder.—The moment of inertia of a hollow cylinder, external and internal radii R and r respectively, may be obtained by the preceding method, or inferred from (ii).

$$\therefore \ I_0 = \frac{\pi ml}{2}(R^4 - r^4),$$

but

$$M = \pi ml(R^2 - r^2);$$

$$\therefore \ I_0 = \frac{M(R^2 + r^2)}{2}.$$

It will be noticed that this result reduces to the preceding when $r = 0$.

Radius of gyration.—It is often convenient to consider the total mass of a body as though it were concentrated at a point in a body. The distance of this point from the axis is called the **radius of gyration.**

Thus, the moment of inertia of a rod about one end is $\frac{1}{3}Ml^2$.

Let k denote the distance from the axis of a point such that the whole mass of the rod may be assumed to be collected, or to act, at the point; then,

$$I = \tfrac{1}{3}Ml^2 = Mk^2; \quad \therefore \ k = \frac{l}{\sqrt{3}}.$$

Similarly, as the **polar moment of inertia** of a circle of radius R is $\frac{MR^2}{2}$, the radius of gyration is given by

$$Mk^2 = \frac{MR^2}{2}; \quad \therefore \ k = \frac{R}{\sqrt{2}}.$$

In the case of a hollow circle or cylinder radii R and r respectively,

$$Mk^2 = \frac{M}{2}(R^2 + r^2); \quad \therefore \ k = \frac{1}{\sqrt{2}}\sqrt{R^2 + r^2}.$$

Moment of inertia of a fly-wheel.—Usually a fly-wheel consists of a heavy rim connected by arms to its centre. In calculating the moment of inertia of such a wheel, only that of the rim is taken into account. If necessary, a small percentage of this may be added to the mass of the rim to allow for the arms and boss of the wheel. If R and r respectively denote the external and internal radii of the rim of the wheel, then the mean radius, or $\frac{1}{2}(R+r)$, is often taken as the radius of gyration.

It is easy to ascertain what amount of error is involved in this assumption when the magnitudes of R and r are given.

Ex. 4. For such a fly-wheel let $R=4$ and $r=3$.

Then $$\tfrac{1}{2}(R+r)=\tfrac{1}{2}(4+3)=3{\cdot}5\,;$$

giving $$I_0=\frac{M(3{\cdot}5)^2}{2}.$$

But $$k=\frac{1}{\sqrt{2}}\sqrt{4^2+3^2}=\frac{5\sqrt{2}}{2}=\frac{7{\cdot}07}{2}\,;$$

$$\therefore\ k=3{\cdot}538\,;$$

$$\therefore\ I_0=\frac{M(3{\cdot}538)^2}{2},$$

or an error of 2 per cent.

Ex. 5. Find the moment of inertia of a pulley, the cross-section being of the form shown in Fig. 163.

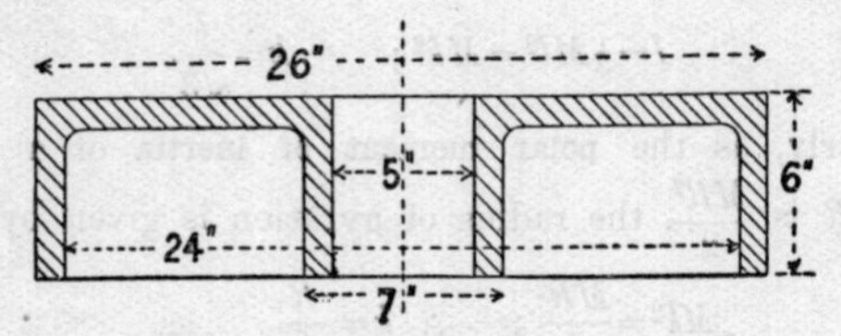

Fig. 163.—Moment of inertia of a pulley.

The moment of inertia of a disc or hollow cylinder can be obtained from tables, but a tabulated value cannot be obtained for the section of a wheel or pulley such as in Fig. 163, and the value of the moment of inertia must be obtained by calculation.

In such a case, we may assume the given section to be made up of three cylinders, the diameters of the outer one being 26 inches and 24 inches respectively and the length 6 inches. The next is a cylinder of length or thickness 1 inch, and of 24 inches external and 7 inches internal diameter; and the dimensions of the inner are 7 inches and 5 inches diameter respectively, and 6 inches long. The moment of inertia of the system is the sum of the moments of its separate parts.

The value of I for a hollow cylinder about its geometrical axis is given by $\frac{M(R^2+r^2)}{2}$, where M denotes the mass, R and r the external and internal radii respectively.

The mass of a hollow cylinder is $\pi m(R^2-r^2)l$, where l denotes the length of the cylinder, and m the mass of unit volume of the material.

$$\text{Mass of outer ring } A=\pi m\left\{\left(\frac{26}{2}\right)^2-\left(\frac{24}{2}\right)^2\right\}6=150\pi m.$$

Similarly, the mass of the ring B is given by

$$\pi m\left\{12^2-\left(\frac{7}{2}\right)^2\right\}=131{\cdot}75\pi m,$$

and mass of ring C is

$$\frac{\pi m}{4}(7^2-5^2)6=36\pi m.$$

The moment of inertia of the whole will simply be the sum of the various rings into which the figure has been assumed to be divided.

$$\therefore\ I=\pi m\left\{\left(150\times\frac{13^2+12^2}{2}\right)+\left(131{\cdot}75\times\frac{12^2+\left(\frac{7}{2}\right)^2}{2}\right)\right.$$
$$\left.+\left(36\times\frac{\left(\frac{7}{2}\right)^2+\left(\frac{5}{2}\right)^2}{2}\right)\right\}$$
$$=\pi m(23475+10293+333)$$
$$=\pi m\times 34101.$$

As the weight of 1 cub. in. of cast iron is 0·26 lb.;

$$\therefore\ \text{mass of 1 cub. in.}=\frac{0{\cdot}26}{32{\cdot}2}.$$

Hence $I=\frac{\pi \times 0{\cdot}26 \times 34101}{32{\cdot}2}=865{\cdot}2$ lb. inch units.

Usually the result is required in pound feet units, hence the preceding result must be divided by 12^2 or 144, giving $I=6{\cdot}008$ lb. ft. units.

Moment of inertia of a cylinder.—The moment of inertia of a cylinder, about an axis passing through its centre of gravity and perpendicular to its length, may be thus determined. Let r denote the radius and l the length of the cylinder. We may assume the cylinder to be composed of an indefinite number of thin discs each of thickness dx.

The moment of inertia of such a disc at a distance x from the axis (Fig. 164) is $\pi r^2 m \times x^2 dx$, where m denotes the mass of unit volume.

Mass of disc is $m \times$ volume $= m\pi r^2 dx$.

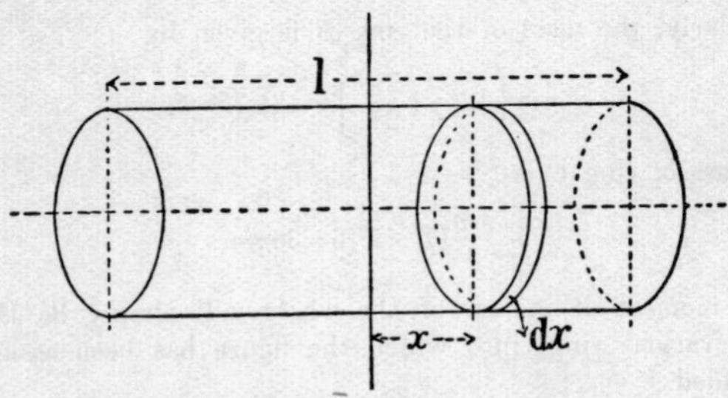

FIG. 164.—Moment of inertia of a cylinder.

Also the moment of inertia of the disc about its own diameter is $\frac{m\pi r^4}{4}dx$.

Hence,
$$I_0=\pi m r^2\int_{-\frac{l}{2}}^{\frac{l}{2}} x^2 dx+\int_{-\frac{l}{2}}^{\frac{l}{2}}\frac{\pi r^4}{4} m\, dx$$

$$=\pi m r^2\left[\frac{x^3}{3}\right]_{-\frac{l}{2}}^{\frac{l}{2}}+\frac{1}{4}\pi m r^4 l$$

$$=\frac{2\pi m r^2 l^3}{24}+\frac{1}{4}\pi m r^4 l. \quad \text{.............................(1)}$$

Also, if M denotes the mass of the cylinder, then

$$M=\pi m r^2 l.$$

Substitute in (i), and obtain

$$I_0=M\left(\frac{r^2}{4}+\frac{l^2}{12}\right). \quad \text{..............................(ii)}$$

It follows at once from (ii) that if the radius of the cylinder is very small compared with its length, then the first term in (ii) may be neglected and the value of I_0 becomes $\frac{Ml^2}{12}$, as on p. 431, for a thin rod.

Similarly, if l is very small compared with r, we obtain $I=\frac{Mr^2}{4}$, the value of I for a thin disc.

EXERCISES XLIII.

In the following exercises the letters C.G. denote centre of gravity or centre of area, and the letter I_0 denotes the moment of inertia about an axis passing through the centre of gravity and in the plane of the figure.

1. The dimensions of a T-section, as in Fig. 151, are as follows: the upper flange is $2'' \times \frac{1}{2}''$ and the web $3'' \times \frac{1}{2}''$; find the distance of the C.G. from the extreme edge of the upper flange and the value of I_0 about an axis passing through the C.G. in the plane of the figure.

2. The dimensions of a rectangular strip of steel are: width $0{\cdot}7''$, depth $0{\cdot}1''$. If $E=3{\cdot}6\times 10^7$ and $M=100$, find the value of r from the formula $r=\frac{EI_0}{M}$.

3. The breadth or width of a rectangular beam is $2''$, its depth $3''$; find the value of f from the formula $M=\frac{f}{y}I_0$, given $M=8000$ and $y=1$.

4. The flanges of a girder of the form shown in Fig. 152 are $4''\times 1''$ and $6''\times 1''$, and the web $1''$; the depth of the girder is $10''$. Find the distance of the C.G. from the outer edge of the larger flange and the value of I_0.

5. A form of rail section is given in Fig. 165. Find the area of the cross-section, the position of its C.G., the value of I_0, and the radius of gyration k. Width of bottom $=6\frac{1}{2}''$.

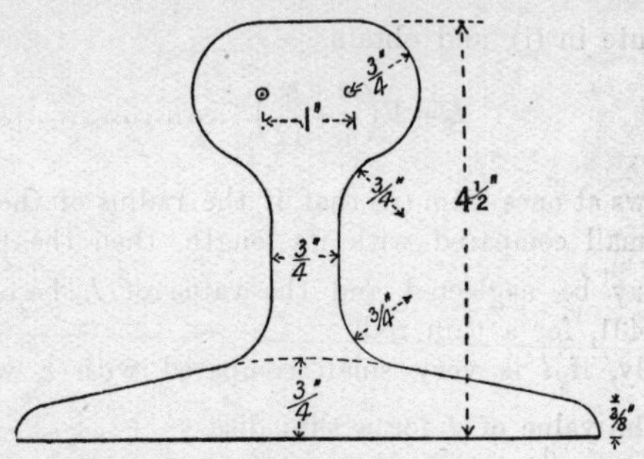

FIG. 165.—Rail section.

6. ABC (Fig. 166) is a segment of a parabola cut off by a chord AC normal to the axis; if b is the length of the chord and h its distance from the vertex B, show that its area is $\frac{2}{3}hb$ and its centre of gravity is $\frac{3}{5}h$ from B.

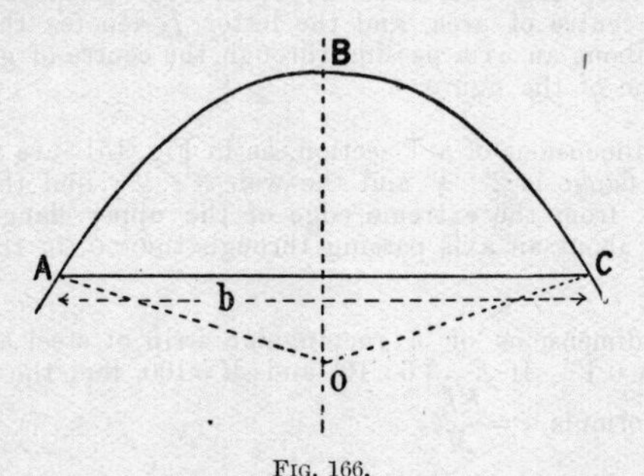

FIG. 166.

7. If ABC (Fig. 166) be assumed to be a circular sector centre O, radius r, and angle $AOB=\theta$, show that the distance of the centre of gravity from O is $\frac{2}{3}r\frac{\sin\theta}{\theta}$.

8. If the cylinder (Fig. 164) be replaced by a rectangular prism (flat bar) of length l, width b and depth d. Show that

$$I_0=M\left(\frac{l^2}{12}+\frac{b^2}{12}\right).$$

CHAPTER XXI.

INTEGRATION BY PARTIAL FRACTIONS. INTEGRATION BY PARTS. FOURIER'S SERIES. FOURIER'S THEOREM.

Integration by partial fractions.—When it is required to integrate an expression of the form $\frac{7x-1}{1-5x+6x^2}$, in which the denominator can be resolved into the product of a series of linear or quadratic factors, as, in this case, $(1-3x)(1-2x)$, it is often the best way to break the fraction up into a series of partial fractions, p. 6.

Thus $\frac{7x-1}{(1-3x)(1-2x)}=\frac{4}{1-3x}-\frac{5}{1-2x}$;

$$\therefore \int\frac{(7x-1)\,dx}{1-5x+6x^2}=4\int\frac{dx}{1-3x}-5\int\frac{dx}{1-2x}$$

$$=-\frac{4}{3}\int\frac{d(3x)}{3x-1}+\frac{5}{2}\int\frac{d(2x)}{2x-1}$$

$$=-\frac{4}{3}\log(3x-1)+\frac{5}{2}\log(2x-1)$$

$$=\log\frac{(2x-1)^{\frac{5}{2}}}{(3x-1)^{\frac{4}{3}}}.$$

Ex. 1. Integrate $\frac{x^2-7x+1}{x^3-6x^2+11x-6}$.

Here the denominator is $(x-1)(x-2)(x-3)$.

$$\therefore \int\frac{(x^2-7x+1)\,dx}{x^3-6x^2+11x-6}=\int\left\{-\frac{5}{2}\cdot\frac{1}{x-1}+\frac{9}{x-2}-\frac{11}{2}\cdot\frac{1}{x-3}\right\}dx$$

$$=-\frac{5}{2}\int\frac{dx}{x-1}+9\int\frac{dx}{x-2}-\frac{11}{2}\int\frac{dx}{x-3}$$

$$=-\frac{5}{2}\log(x-1)+9\log(x-2)-\frac{11}{2}\log(x-3).$$

When the denominator contains repeated factors, one or more of the constants may be determined, as in the preceding example, the remaining constants being obtained by differentiation. The method will be understood from the following example :

Ex. 2. Integrate $\dfrac{dx}{x^3 - x^2 - x + 1}$.

The factors of $x^3 - x^2 - x + 1$ are $(x-1)^2(x+1)$.

Let
$$\frac{1}{x^3 - x^2 - x + 1} = \frac{A}{x-1} + \frac{B}{(x-1)^2} + \frac{C}{x+1}. \quad \text{..................(i)}$$

Notice that the two terms $\dfrac{A}{x-1}$ and $\dfrac{B}{(x-1)^2}$ occur for twice repeated roots. Similarly, three terms would be used for three times repeated roots, etc.

From (1)
$$1 = A(x-1)(x+1) + B(x+1) + C(x-1)^2$$
$$= A(x^2-1) + B(x+1) + C(x-1)^2. \quad \text{.......................(ii)}$$

Let $x=1$; $\quad \therefore \ 1 = 2B$, or $B = \frac{1}{2}$.

To determine the numerical values of A and C we may differentiate each side of equation (ii): for that equation obviously holds true for all values of x, and hence the differential coefficients of the two sides of the equation are equal.

Differentiating (ii),
$$0 = 2Ax + B + 2Cx - 2C \quad \text{.........................(iii)}$$
$$= 2Ax + \tfrac{1}{2} + 2C(x-1).$$

Put $x=1$; $\quad \therefore \ 2A = -\frac{1}{2}$; $\quad \therefore \ A = -\frac{1}{4}$.

Differentiating (iii),
$$2A + 2C = 0, \text{ or } 2C = \tfrac{1}{2};$$
$$\therefore \ C = \tfrac{1}{4}.$$

Hence, substituting these values,
$$\frac{1}{x^3 - x^2 - x + 1} = -\frac{1}{4(x-1)} + \frac{1}{2(x-1)^2} + \frac{1}{4(x+1)};$$
$$\therefore \int \frac{dx}{x^3 - x^2 - x + 1} = -\frac{1}{4}\int \frac{dx}{(x-1)} + \frac{1}{2}\int \frac{dx}{(x-1)^2} + \frac{1}{4}\int \frac{dx}{(x+1)}$$
$$= -\frac{1}{4}\log(x-1) - \frac{1}{2}\,\frac{1}{(x-1)} + \frac{1}{4}\log(x+1).$$

Integration by parts.—The differential of the product of u and v, where u and v are functions of x, has been obtained on p. 320;

$$\therefore \frac{d}{dx}(uv)=u\frac{dv}{dx}+v\frac{du}{dx}.$$

Hence, integrating,

$$uv=\int u\frac{dv}{dx}\,dx+\int v\frac{du}{dx}\,dx,\ldots\ldots\ldots\ldots\text{(iv)}$$

or

$$\int u\frac{dv}{dx}dx=uv-\int v\frac{du}{dx}dx.$$

Thus, in the case of the product of two functions, in which the integral is not easily obtainable, it is possible by using Eq. (iv) to express the integral in a form more easily dealt with than was the original expression, and thus, by successive steps, to reduce the unknown integrals to known forms.

It is very important that the rule and its various applications should be clearly made out, and it is therefore advisable to commence with a few simple expressions which may easily be verified.

Ex. 3. Let $u=3x^2$ and $v=4x^3$.

Also $\frac{du}{dx}=6x$ and $\frac{dv}{dx}=12x^2$;

$$\therefore \int 3x^2\times 12x^2dx=3x^2\times 4x^3-\int 4x^3\times 6xdx;$$

or

$$\int 36x^4dx=12x^5-\int 24x^4dx;$$

$$\therefore \frac{36x^5}{5}=12x^5-\frac{24x^5}{5}=\frac{36x^5}{5}.$$

Ex. 4. Integrate $x^n\log x dx$.

Let $u=\log x$ and $dv=x^n dx$;

$$\therefore \frac{du}{dx}=\frac{1}{x} \text{ and } v=\frac{x^{n+1}}{n+1};$$

$$\therefore \int x^n\log x dx=\log x\frac{x^{n+1}}{n+1}-\int\frac{x^n}{n+1}dx$$

$$=\frac{x^{n+1}}{n+1}\left(\log x-\frac{1}{n+1}\right).$$

Ex. 5. Integrate $e^x \sin x dx$.

Let $$u = \sin x \text{ and } dv = e^x dx,$$

$$\frac{du}{dx} = \cos x, \qquad v = e^x.$$

$$\int e^x \sin x dx = e^x \sin x - \int e^x \cos x dx. \quad \ldots\ldots\ldots\ldots\text{(i)}$$

Again $$\int e^x \cos x dx = e^x \cos x + \int e^x \sin x dx, \quad \ldots\ldots\ldots\ldots\text{(ii)}$$

by repeating the operation;

$$\therefore \int e^x \sin x dx = \frac{e^x(\sin x - \cos x)}{2},$$

by subtracting Eq. (ii) from Eq. (i) and rearranging the terms.

It will be noticed that it is often possible to obtain a solution by repeated integration by parts. Especially is this the case when one of the factors is of the form x^n, in which case the application is made in such a way as to reduce the index each time; or, in other words, is denoted by u in the formula. The method indicated will now be applied to obtain what are known as **reduction formulae.**

One of the most important formulae of reduction is that of $\sin^m\theta \cos^n\theta d\theta$, the integral being made to depend on another, in which the indices are reduced by two, and thus, by successive applications, the complete integral is obtained.

Since $$\int \sin^m\theta \cos^n\theta d\theta = \int \cos^{n-1}\theta \sin^m\theta d(\sin\theta), \quad \ldots\ldots\ldots\text{(i)}$$

we may, in the formula for integration by parts, assume

$$u = \cos^{n-1}\theta, \qquad v = \frac{\sin^{m+1}\theta}{m+1};$$

$$\therefore \int \sin^m\theta \cos^n\theta d\theta = \frac{\cos^{n-1}\theta \sin^{m+1}\theta}{m+1} + \frac{n-1}{m+1}\int \sin^{m+2}\theta \cos^{n-2}\theta d\theta.$$

Also $$\sin^{m+2}\theta = \sin^m\theta \times \sin^2\theta = \sin^m\theta(1 - \cos^2\theta).$$

Substituting, we have

$$\int \sin^m\theta \cos^n\theta d\theta = \frac{\cos^{n-1}\theta \sin^{m+1}\theta}{m+1} + \frac{n-1}{m+1}\int \sin^m\theta(\cos^{n-2}\theta - \cos^n\theta) d\theta$$

$$= \frac{\cos^{n-1}\theta \sin^{m+1}\theta}{m+1} + \frac{n-1}{m+1}\int \sin^m\theta \cos^{n-2} d\theta - \frac{n-1}{m+1}\int \sin^m\theta \cos^n\theta d\theta;$$

transposing the last term and multiplying both sides by $\frac{m+1}{m+n}$, we obtain

$$\int \sin^m\theta \cos^n\theta d\theta = \frac{\cos^{n-1}\theta \sin^{m+1}\theta}{m+n} + \frac{n-1}{m+n}\int \sin^m\theta \cos^{n-2}\theta d\theta \ldots\text{(ii)}$$

It will be seen from (ii) that after integration by parts the integral is made to depend on another, in which the index of $\cos\theta$ is reduced by two. In a similar manner, the integral (i) could be made to depend on another in which the index of $\sin\theta$ would be reduced by two. Hence, by successive applications, the integral of $\int \sin^m\theta \cos^n\theta d\theta$ can always be reduced to that of $\int \sin\theta d\theta$, $\int \sin\theta \cos\theta d\theta$ or $\int \cos\theta d\theta$ when the indices are integers.

A very important case occurs when a definite integral, the limits being 0 and $\frac{\pi}{2}$, is required (m and n being integers).

Then $$\int_0^{\frac{\pi}{2}} \sin^m\theta \cos^n\theta d\theta = \frac{(m-1)(m-3)\ldots(n-1)(n-3)}{(m+n)(m+n-2)\ldots 4 . 2} \times \phi;$$

the quantity ϕ is unity, except when m and n are both even integers, in which case its value is $\frac{\pi}{2}$.

Ex. 6. Let $m=6$ and $n=4$. Here m and n are both even;

$$\therefore \int_0^{\frac{\pi}{2}} \sin^6\theta \cos^4\theta\, d\theta = \frac{5 . 3 . 1 \times 3 . 1}{10 . 8 . 6 . 4 . 2} \times \frac{\pi}{2} = \frac{3\pi}{512}.$$

Ex. 7. Let $m=6$ and $n=5$;

$$\therefore \int_0^{\frac{\pi}{2}} \sin^6\theta \cos^5\theta\, d\theta = \frac{5 . 3 . 1 \times 4 . 2 . 1}{11 . 9 . 7 . 5 . 3 . 1} = \frac{8}{693}.$$

Ex. 8. $$\int_0^{\frac{\pi}{2}} \sin^2\theta \cos^4\theta\, d\theta = \frac{1 \times 3 \times 1}{6 \times 4 \times 2} \times \frac{\pi}{2} = \frac{\pi}{32}.$$

Ex. 9.

$$\int_0^{\frac{\pi}{2}} \sin^5\theta \cos^3\theta\, d\theta = \frac{4 . 2 . 2}{8 . 6 . 4}\int_0^{\frac{\pi}{2}} \sin\theta \cos\theta\, d\theta = \frac{4 . 2 . 2}{8 . 6 . 4 . 2}\Big[\sin^2\theta\Big]_0^{\frac{\pi}{2}} = \frac{1}{24}.$$

$\sin^n\theta d\theta$ and $\cos^n\theta d\theta$.—These examples may be taken to be special cases of the general formulae; but they are very important, especially in the case of definite integrals, and may be obtained independently as follows:

Integrating by parts, we can connect

$$\int \sin^n\theta d\theta \text{ with } \int \sin^{n-2}\theta d\theta;$$

$$\therefore \int \sin^n\theta d\theta = -\frac{\cos\theta\sin^{n-1}\theta}{n} + \frac{n-1}{n}\int \sin^{n-2}\theta d\theta, \quad \text{......(i)}$$

and

$$\int \cos^n\theta d\theta = \frac{\sin\theta\cos^{n-1}\theta}{n} + \frac{n-1}{n}\int \cos^{n-2}\theta d\theta. \quad \text{.........(ii)}$$

From (i) we obtain, by successive applications,

$$\int \sin^n\theta d\theta$$

$$= -\frac{\cos\theta}{n}\left(\sin^{n-1}\theta + \frac{n-1}{n-2}\sin^{n-3}\theta + \frac{(n-1)(n-3)}{(n-2)(n-4)}\sin^{n-5}\theta + \text{etc.}\right) + A;$$

when n is even, the last term in the bracket is

$$+\frac{(n-1)(n-3)\ldots 3}{(n-2)(n-4)\ldots 2}\sin\theta, \text{ and } A = \frac{(n-1)(n-3)\ldots 3.1}{n(n-2)\ldots 4.2}\theta.$$

When n is odd, the last term in the bracket is

$$+\frac{(n-1)(n-3)\ldots 2}{(n-2)(n-4)\ldots 1}, \text{ and } A=0.$$

From (ii) we obtain, by successive applications,

$$\int \cos^n\theta d\theta$$

$$= \frac{\sin\theta}{n}\left(\cos^{n-1}\theta + \frac{n-1}{n-2}\cos^{n-3}\theta + \frac{(n-1)(n-3)}{(n-2)(n-4)}\cos^{n-5}\theta + \text{etc.}\right) + A;$$

when n is even, the last term in the bracket is

$$+\frac{(n-1)(n-3)\ldots 3}{(n-2)(n-4)\ldots 2}\cos\theta, \text{ and } A = \frac{(n-1)(n-3)\ldots 3.1}{n(n-2)\ldots 4.2}\theta.$$

When n is odd, the last term in the bracket is

$$+\frac{(n-1)(n-3)\ldots 2}{(n-2)(n-4)\ldots 1}, \text{ and } A=0.$$

One of the most important applications of the integration of $\sin^n\theta d\theta$ is the definite integral between the limits 0 and $\frac{\pi}{2}$; $\therefore$ from (1),

$$\int_0^{\frac{\pi}{2}} \sin^n\theta d\theta = -\frac{\cos\theta \sin^{n-1}\theta}{n} + \frac{n-1}{n}\int \sin^{n-2}\theta d\theta.$$

When n is an integer, not less than 2, the first term becomes zero for both the limits $\theta=0$, $\theta=\frac{\pi}{2}$;

$$\therefore \int_0^{\frac{\pi}{2}} \sin^n\theta d\theta = \frac{n-1}{n}\int_0^{\frac{\pi}{2}} \sin^{n-2}\theta d\theta$$

$$= \frac{(n-1)(n-3)}{n(n-2)}\int_0^{\frac{\pi}{2}} \sin^{n-4}\theta d\theta, \text{ etc.}$$

This becomes, when n is even,

$$\int_0^{\frac{\pi}{2}} \sin^n\theta d\theta = \left(\frac{n-1}{n}\right)\left(\frac{n-3}{n-2}\right)\cdots\frac{5}{6}\cdot\frac{3}{4}\cdot\frac{1}{2}\int_0^{\frac{\pi}{2}} 1\, d\theta;$$

$$\therefore \int_0^{\frac{\pi}{2}} \sin^n\theta d\theta = \frac{(n-1)(n-3)\ldots 3.1}{n(n-2)\ldots 4.2}\times\frac{\pi}{2} \quad (n \text{ an even integer}),$$

and $$\int_0^{\frac{\pi}{2}} \sin^n\theta d\theta = \frac{(n-1)(n-3)\ldots 4.2}{n(n-2)\ldots 5.3}\times 1 \quad (n \text{ an odd integer}).$$

Ex. 10. Let $n=4$;

$$\therefore \int_0^{\frac{\pi}{2}} \sin^4\theta\, d\theta = \frac{3.1}{4.2}\times\frac{\pi}{2} = \frac{3\pi}{16}.$$

Ex. 11. $$\int_0^{\frac{\pi}{2}} \sin^8\theta\, d\theta = \frac{7.5.3}{8.6.4.2}\times\frac{\pi}{2} = \frac{35\pi}{256}.$$

Ex. 12. $$\int_0^{\frac{\pi}{2}} \sin^9\theta\, d\theta = \frac{8.6.4.2}{9.7.5.3} = \frac{128}{315}.$$

It is easily seen from the foregoing that

$$\int_0^{\frac{\pi}{2}} \cos^n x\, dx = \int_0^{\frac{\pi}{2}} \sin^n x\, dx.$$

Definite integrals.—The following definite integrals are important in later work, particularly in dealing with vibrations and periodic movements.

$$\int_{-\pi}^{\pi} a_0 \cos nx\, dx = a_0 \left[\frac{\sin nx}{n}\right]_{-\pi}^{\pi} = 0.$$

$$\int_{\pi}^{\pi} \cos mx \cos nx\, dx = \tfrac{1}{2}\int_{-\pi}^{\pi} \{\cos(m+n)x + \cos(m-n)x\}\, dx$$

$$= \tfrac{1}{2}\left[\frac{\sin(m+n)x}{m+n} + \frac{\sin(m-n)x}{m-n}\right]_{-\pi}^{\pi};$$

$\therefore$ when m and n are unequal, $\int_{-\pi}^{\pi} \cos nx \cos mx\, dx = 0$;

when $m = n$,

$$\int_{-\pi}^{\pi} \cos^2 nx\, dx = \tfrac{1}{2}\int_{-\pi}^{\pi} (\cos 2nx + 1)\, dx = \tfrac{1}{2}\left[\frac{\sin 2nx}{2n} + x\right]_{-\pi}^{\pi}$$

$$= \tfrac{1}{2}\{0 + \pi - (-\pi)\} = \pi.$$

Similarly, $$\int_{-\pi}^{\pi} \sin mx \cos nx\, dx = 0,$$

and $$\int_{-\pi}^{\pi} \sin^2 nx\, dx = \pi.$$

$$\int_{-\pi}^{\pi} \sin nx \cos nx\, dx$$

$$= \tfrac{1}{2}\int_{-\pi}^{\pi} \sin 2nx\, dx = \frac{1}{4n}\left[-\cos 2nx\right]_{-\pi}^{\pi} = 0.$$

Fourier's series.—Assuming that between the limits π and $-\pi$,

$$f(x) = a_0 + a_1 \cos x + a_2 \cos 2x + \ldots + a_n \cos nx + \ldots$$
$$+ b_1 \sin x + b_2 \sin 2x + \ldots + b_n \sin nx + \ldots,$$

multiply through by $\cos nx$ and integrate. Then,

$$\int_{-\pi}^{\pi} f(x) \cos nx\, dx = \int_{-\pi}^{\pi} a_0 \cos nx\, dx + \int_{-\pi}^{\pi} a_1 \cos x \cos nx\, dx + \ldots$$

$$+\int_{-\pi}^{\pi} a_n\cos^2 nx\,dx + \ldots \int_{-\pi}^{\pi} b_1 \sin x \cos nx\,dx$$

$$+\int_{-\pi}^{\pi} b_n \cos nx \sin nx\,dx + \ldots.$$

At the limits, the only term on the right which does not vanish is

$$\int_{-\pi}^{\pi} a_n\cos^2 nx\,dx = \pi a_n;$$

$$\therefore\ a_n = \frac{1}{\pi}\int_{-\pi}^{\pi} f(x)\cos nx\,dx. \ \ldots\ldots\ldots\ldots\ldots\ldots\ldots\text{(i)}$$

Taking as an example,

$$y = f(x) = \Big[\pi + x\Big]_{-\pi}^{-\frac{\pi}{2}}$$

$$+\Big[-x\Big]_{-\frac{\pi}{2}}^{\frac{\pi}{2}} + \Big[x - \pi\Big]_{\frac{\pi}{2}}^{\pi} + \text{etc.}$$

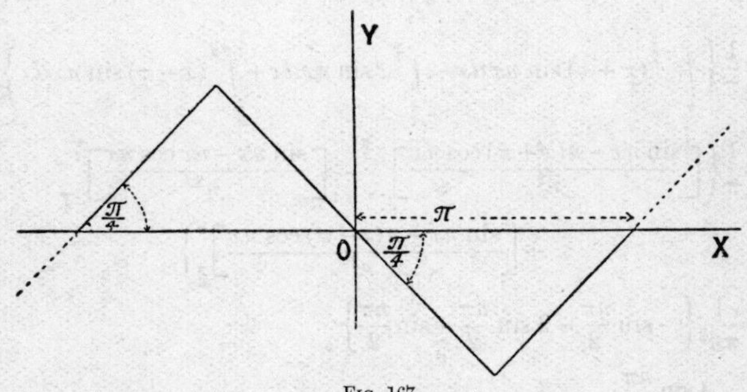

FIG. 167.

A function of x which has

the value $(\pi + x)$ from $x = -\pi$ to $-\frac{\pi}{2}$,

the value $-x$ from $x = -\frac{\pi}{2}$ to $+\frac{\pi}{2}$,

the value $(x - \pi)$ from $x = \frac{\pi}{2}$ to π, and so on.

In this case $$a_n=\frac{1}{\pi}\int_{-\pi}^{\pi}f(x)\cos nx\,dx$$

$$=\frac{1}{\pi}\left\{\int_{-\pi}^{-\frac{\pi}{2}}(\pi+x)\cos nx\,dx-\int_{-\frac{\pi}{2}}^{\frac{\pi}{2}}x\cos nx\,dx+\int_{\frac{\pi}{2}}^{\pi}(x-\pi)\cos nx\,dx\right\}$$

$$=\frac{1}{\pi}\left\{\left[\frac{n(x+\pi)\sin nx+\cos nx}{n^2}\right]_{-\pi}^{-\frac{\pi}{2}}-\left[\frac{nx\sin nx+\cos nx}{n^2}\right]_{-\frac{\pi}{2}}^{\frac{\pi}{2}}\right.$$
$$\left.+\left[\frac{n(x-\pi)\sin nx+\cos nx}{n^2}\right]_{\frac{\pi}{2}}^{\pi}\right\}$$

$$=\frac{1}{\pi n^2}\left\{-\frac{n\pi}{2}\sin\frac{\pi n}{2}+\cos\frac{n\pi}{2}-\cos n\pi-\left(\frac{n\pi}{2}\sin\frac{n\pi}{2}-\frac{n\pi}{2}\sin\frac{n\pi}{2}\right)\right.$$
$$\left.+\frac{n\pi}{2}\sin\frac{n\pi}{2}+\cos n\pi-\cos\frac{n\pi}{2}\right\}$$

$$=0.$$

There are therefore no cosine terms in the expansion,

$$b_n=\frac{1}{\pi}\int_{-\pi}^{\pi}f(x)\sin nx\,dx$$

$$=\frac{1}{\pi}\left\{\int_{-\pi}^{-\frac{\pi}{2}}(\pi+x)\sin nx\,dx-\int_{-\frac{\pi}{2}}^{\frac{\pi}{2}}x\sin nx\,dx+\int_{\frac{\pi}{2}}^{\pi}(x-\pi)\sin nx\,dx\right\}$$

$$=\frac{1}{\pi}\left\{\left[\frac{\sin nx-n(x+\pi)\cos nx}{n^2}\right]_{-\pi}^{-\frac{\pi}{2}}-\left[\frac{\sin nx-nx\cos nx}{n^2}\right]_{-\frac{\pi}{2}}^{\frac{\pi}{2}}\right.$$
$$\left.+\left[\frac{\sin nx-n(x-\pi)\cos nx}{n^2}\right]_{\frac{\pi}{2}}^{\pi}\right\}$$

$$=\frac{1}{\pi n^2}\left\{-\sin\frac{n\pi}{2}-2\sin\frac{n\pi}{2}-\sin\frac{n\pi}{2}\right\}$$

$$=-\frac{4\sin\frac{n\pi}{2}}{\pi n^2}.$$

This is equal to zero for all even values of n, and to $-\frac{4}{\pi n^2}$ for all terms of the type $(4r+1)$, and to $\frac{4}{\pi n^2}$ for all terms where n is of the type $(4r-1)$; finally we have

$$f(x)=-\frac{4}{\pi}\left\{\sin x-\frac{1}{9}\sin 3x+\frac{1}{25}\sin 5x-\frac{1}{49}\sin 7x+\text{etc.}\ldots\right\}.$$

If we put $x=-\frac{\pi}{2}$, $f(x)$ when calculated from the first 16 terms is equal to 1·55, or very approximately $\frac{\pi}{2}$.

Putting $x=-\frac{\pi}{4}$ and using 16 terms, we obtain

$$f(x)=0{\cdot}78 \text{ or } \frac{\pi}{4}.$$

Fourier's theorem.—This important theorem states that any periodic function $f(x)$ may be fully represented by the sum of a constant term and a series of sines and cosines of multiples of that variable, and may be expressed in the form

$$f(x)=a_0+a_1\cos x+a_2\cos 2x+a_3\cos 3x+\dots \text{ etc.}$$
$$+b_1\sin x+b_2\sin 2x+b_3\sin 3x+\dots \text{ etc.},$$

in which the second S.H.M. would have one-half the period of the preceding one, the next one-third, and so on.

The theorem may be written in the form

$$f(x)=a_0+(a_1\cos x+b_1\sin x)+(a_2\cos 2x+b_2\sin 2x)+\text{etc.}$$
$$=a_0+a_{11_1}\sin(x+\alpha_1)+a_{11_2}\sin(2x+\alpha_2)+a_{11_3}\sin(3x+\alpha_3)+\dots,$$

where $a_{11_1}=\sqrt{a_1^2+b_1^2}$ and $\tan\alpha_1=\frac{a_1}{b_1}$, etc.

The series now becomes

$$f(x)=c_0+a\sin(x+\alpha)+b\sin(2x+\beta)+c\sin(3x+\gamma)+\dots.$$

If we divide the period into n equal parts and superpose the parts, we get the constant c_0 increased to nc_0.

Taking the case $y=a\sin(x+\alpha)$ and omitting the case $n=1$, we obtain on superposing

$$\Sigma y=a\left\{\sin\alpha_1+\sin\left(\alpha_1+\frac{2\pi}{n}\right)+\sin\left(\alpha_1+\frac{4\pi}{n}\right)+\text{etc., to } n \text{ terms}\right\}$$

(where $\alpha_1=\alpha+x$ is the x of the first point taken)

$$=a\frac{\sin\left(\alpha_1+\frac{n-1}{n}\pi\right)\sin\pi}{\sin\frac{\pi}{n}},$$

which is zero for all values of n greater than 1.

Therefore, we may split up the given curve into n equal parts, and on superposing we shall find the fundamental vibration to be eliminated.

Now take $y=b\sin(2x+\beta)$.

$$\Sigma y=b\left\{\sin\gamma_1+\sin\left(\gamma_1+\frac{4\pi}{n}\right)+\sin\left(\gamma_1+\frac{8\pi}{n}\right)+\text{etc., to } n \text{ terms}\right\}$$

$$=b\frac{\sin\left\{\gamma_1+\left(\frac{n-1}{n}\right)2\pi\right\}\sin 2\pi}{\sin\frac{2\pi}{n}},$$

which is zero for all values of n, greater than 1, except $n=2$ when it becomes

$$\frac{-b\sin\gamma_1\sin 2\pi}{\sin\pi}=b\frac{-\sin\gamma_1\, 2\cos\pi\sin\pi}{\sin\pi}$$
$$=2b\sin\gamma_1.$$

Therefore, when $n=2$ the fundamental is eliminated, whilst the octave, *i.e.* the vibration with double frequency, remains, but becomes doubled in amplitude.

In the same way, if $y=a\sin(mx+\beta)$, where m is a **prime number**, the superposition will cause the term to vanish for any other value of n than m, and for that particular value we get an expression of the same frequency, but of m times the amplitude.

Now, taking the case $m=12$,

$$y=a\sin(12x+a),$$

$$\Sigma y=a\left\{\sin a_1+\sin\left(a_1+\frac{24\pi}{n}\right)+\sin\left(a_1+\frac{48\pi}{n}\right)+\ldots\text{to } n \text{ terms}\right\}$$

$$=a\frac{\sin\left(a_1+\frac{n-1}{n}12\pi\right)\sin 12\pi}{\sin\left(\frac{12\pi}{n}\right)},$$

where, as before, a_1 is the first value of $12x+a$.

This is equal to zero, except for the values $n=1$, $n=2$, $n=3$, $n=4$, $n=6$, and $n=12$.

Taking the case $n=6$, we obtain

$$\Sigma y=a\frac{\sin(a_1)\sin 12\pi}{\sin 2\pi}=a\frac{\sin a_1\, 12\cos 12\pi}{2\cos 2\pi}=6a\sin a_1,$$

[The second step being obtained by the differential calculus rule for undetermined forms.]

i.e. the amplitude is increased six times, the period remaining the same.

Therefore the effect of dividing into n parts and superposing is to eliminate all terms excepting those of the form $a \sin(rnx+\alpha)$, where $rn=m$, which terms remain of the same periods, but are increased in amplitude n times.

From these results the following method of analysing a curve which represents some periodic motion, such as the movement of a piston or slide valve, is deduced.

Let the relation between x and θ be supposed to be

$$f(x)=a_0+a\sin(\theta+\alpha)+b\sin(2\theta+\beta)+c\sin(3\theta+\gamma)+\text{ etc.}$$

In order to simplify the expressions write $s\theta$ instead of $a\sin(\theta+\alpha)$,

$$f(x)=a_0+s\theta+s2\theta+s3\theta+s4\theta+s5\theta+s6\theta+\text{ etc.}$$

Dividing into two and superposing, calling the result $f(x_2)$,

$$f(x_2)=2(a_0+s2\theta+s4\theta+s6\theta+s8\theta+\text{ etc.});$$

$$\therefore\ 2f(x)-f(x_2)=2(s\theta+s3\theta+s5\theta+s7\theta+\text{ etc.})$$

Dividing into three parts and superposing,

$$f(x_3)=3(a_0+s3\theta+s6\theta+s9\theta+\text{ etc.}).$$

Similarly,

$$f(x_4)=4(a_0+s4\theta+s8\theta+s12\theta+\text{ etc.});$$

$$\therefore\ 4f(x_3)-3f(x_4)=12(s3\theta-s4\theta+s6\theta-s8\theta+\text{ etc.});$$

$$\therefore\ 6\{2f(x)-f(x_2)\}-\{4f(x_3)-3f(x_4)\}$$
$$=12(s\theta+s4\theta+s5\theta-s6\theta+\text{ etc.}).$$

In this way we may eliminate the s-functions on the right, until the uneliminated terms after the first are so small that they may be neglected. We can now calculate the value of the fundamental, then, using this result, proceed to find, in a similar manner, the values of the other s-functions, one by one, so far as may be necessary; when this has been done the curve assumes the form of the sine-curve. The distance between any two points of its intersection with the x-axis is a multiple of the period, π. Measurement of the curve will give very approximately the constants in $Y=12a\sin(x+a_1)$. Thus, $12a$ is equal to the average amplitude; if $x_0, x_1, x_2, \ldots x_n$ are the abscissae of the points of intersection of the curve and the x-axis, then

$$(n+1)\alpha_1 + \frac{n(n+1)}{1 \cdot 2}\pi = x_0 + x_1 + \ldots + x_n,$$

from which α_1 may be determined.

The student has now a choice of three methods of proceeding to determine each of the remaining terms in the Fourier's series:

(1) Determine $s2\theta$ by a process exactly similar to that adopted for $s\theta$.

(2) Subtract from the curve $f(x)$ the part $a\sin(x+\alpha_1)$ as previously found.

(3) Subtract from the curve $f(x)$ a *new calculated* curve $a\sin(x+\alpha_1)$.

When the terms $s\theta$, $s2\theta$, $s3\theta$, etc., have been determined so far as found necessary, it is advisable to re-draw these curves and by adding the ordinates, in the usual manner, to determine the curve $s\theta + s2\theta + s3\theta +$ etc. Comparison of this (calculated) curve with the problem will give some idea as to the accuracy of the calculation and of the hypothesis of the *relative smallness of rejected terms.*

If the form of the calculated curve is sufficiently near that of the problem curve, then there only remains to find k which is the vertical distance between the horizontal axes of the two curves.

If the two curves should be too much unlike, take the difference of the problem curve above the calculated one and proceed to a fresh calculation.

The application of the theorem to a given curve (Fig. 168) may be seen from the following example:

Taking equal intervals $\frac{\pi}{6}$ for θ along the base OX and setting up the twelve ordinates,

$$f(\theta) = k + a\sin(\theta+\alpha) + b\sin(2\theta+\beta) + c\sin(3\theta+\gamma) + \text{ etc.}$$
$$= k + s\theta + s2\theta + s3\theta + \text{ etc. (with the previous notation).}$$

Dividing into two and superposing,

$$f(\theta_2) = 2(k + s2\theta + s4\theta + \text{ etc.}),$$
$$2f(\theta) - f(\theta_2) = 2(s\theta + s3\theta + s5\theta + \text{ etc.});$$

when $\theta=0$, $\qquad f(\theta)=0,$

$$f(\theta_2)=0 \text{ to } 6;$$

which result simply means that to the ordinate passing through 0 must be added the ordinate passing through 6. Similarly, to the 1st ordinate add the 7th and so on; draw a fair curve through the points and obtain $f(\theta_2)$. The sum of the 0 and 6th ordinates is the particular ordinate here mentioned;

$\therefore$ ordinate of $(\theta, 3\theta, 5\theta-)=\frac{1}{2}(6 \text{ to } \theta)$;

when $\theta=\frac{\pi}{6}$, $\qquad f(\theta)=0 \text{ to } 1,$

$$f(\theta_2)=(0 \text{ to } 7)+(0 \text{ to } 1);$$

$$\therefore \text{ ordinate of } (\theta, 3\theta, 5\theta)=\tfrac{1}{2}\{2(0 \text{ to } 1)-(0 \text{ to } 1)-(0 \text{ to } 7)\}$$
$$=\tfrac{1}{2}(7 \text{ to } 1).$$

In this way we get all the ordinates of $(\theta, 3\theta, 5\theta)$ as

$\frac{1}{2}$		
	6 to 0	0 to 6
	7 to 1	1 to 7
	8 to 2	2 to 8
	9 to 3	3 to 9
	10 to 4	4 to 10
	11 to 5	5 to 11

$$f(\theta_2)=2(k+2\theta+4\theta+6\theta+\text{etc.}).$$

Dividing into four parts and superposing,

$$f(\theta_4)=4(k+4\theta+8\theta+\text{ etc.});$$

$$\therefore\ 2f(\theta_2)-f(\theta_4)=4(2\theta+6\theta+10\theta+\text{ etc.});$$

when $\theta=0$, $\qquad f(\theta_2)=0 \text{ to } 6,$

$$f(\theta_4)=(0 \text{ to } 6)+(0 \text{ to } 3)+(0 \text{ to } 9);$$

$$\therefore \text{ ordinate of } (2\theta, 6\theta) \text{ is } \tfrac{1}{4}\{2(0 \text{ to } 6)-(0 \text{ to } 6)+(3 \text{ to } 0)+(9 \text{ to } 0)\}$$
$$=\tfrac{1}{4}(0 \text{ to } 6+3 \text{ to } 0+9 \text{ to } 0)$$
$$=\tfrac{1}{4}(3 \text{ to } 0,\ 9 \text{ to } 6).$$

The ordinates of the $(2\theta, 6\theta)$ are

$\frac{1}{4}$			
	3 to 0,	9 to 6	+ − these
	4 to 1,	10 to 7	
	5 to 2,	11 to 8	
	6 to 3,	0 to 9	
	7 to 4,	1 to 10	
	8 to 5,	2 to 11	

Proceeding in the same manner for $(3\theta, 9\theta)$, we obtain as ordinates

$\frac{1}{6}$	2 to 0, 6 to 4, 10 to 8
	3 to 1, 7 to 5, 11 to 9
	$-$
	$+$
	$-$
	$\pm$

Graphical method of harmonic analysis.—It has already been seen (p. 138) that motion in a straight line, which is compounded of two simple harmonic motions of the same period, is itself a simple harmonic motion of that period. The theorem may be represented by the equation

$$y = a \sin(qt + \alpha) + b \sin(qt + \beta) = A \sin(qt + E), \quad \text{.........(i)}$$

where y is the displacement from mid-position at a time t.

When the component motions a, b, α, β, are given, then for any given value of t, a parallelogram having a and b for its sides can be drawn, and the diagonal will give the amplitude, or radius, A, of the resultant motion. As qt denotes the amount of turning, or angle, in radians it is convenient to write Eq. (i) in the form

$$y = a \sin(\theta + \alpha) + b \sin(\theta + \beta). \quad \text{..................(ii)}$$

The parallelogram is inapplicable when the periods are different, but in such a case two sinuous curves may be separately drawn, and their ordinates added together will give the resultant curve.

Thus, for example, the motion of the slide valve of a steam engine generally proves to be a close approximation to a simple harmonic motion. The deviation from this fundamental motion usually consists of a small superposed octave, or a simple harmonic motion of comparatively small amplitude and of twice the frequency. If y denotes the displacement of the valve from its mean position, the above Eq. (ii) may be written

$$y = a \sin(\theta + \alpha) + b \sin(2\theta + \beta). \quad \text{.................(iii)}$$

The diagrams of displacement consist of two sinuous curves, the first having an amplitude a and angular advance α, the amplitude and angular advance of the second being b and β respectively; the period of the second is one-half that of the first.

Ex. 1. $y=2\sin(\theta+30°)+0\cdot5\sin(2\theta+45°)$.

Let $y_1=2\sin(\theta+30°)$ and $y_2=0\cdot5\sin(2\theta+45°)$,

when $\theta=0°$, $y_1=2\sin 30°=1$;

and when $\theta=30°$, $y_1=2\sin 60°=1\cdot73$.

In a similar manner from $y_2=0\cdot5\sin(2\theta+45°)$,

when $\theta=0°$, $y_2=0\cdot5\sin 45° =\frac{\sqrt{2}}{4}=0\cdot35$;

and when $\theta=30°$, $y_2=0\cdot5\sin 105°=0\cdot5\sin 75°=0\cdot48$.

Other values of θ may be assumed and the values of y_1 and y_2 calculated and tabulated as follows:

Values of θ	0°	30°	60°	90°	120°
y_1	1	1·73	2	1·73	1
y_2	0·35	0·48	0·13	-0·35	-0·48
$y=y_1+y_2$	1·35	2·21	2·13	1·38	0·52

Plot the values of y from the last row, and the curve passing through the plotted points will show the value of y for any value of θ.

Graphical method of composition.—The process may be easily carried out graphically as follows:

Draw a circle with centre C and radius 2″ (Fig. 168); through C draw a horizontal line CL. Make the angle MCA equal to 30°. Divide the circle into 12 equal parts, and from any convenient point N on the line CL measure off 12 equal divisions from N to L; at each point draw the ordinates qp, fh, perpendiculars to CL. Each of the equal divisions on the circle and on NL will denote 30°; number the points on the circle and on NL, 0, 1, 2,... 11 as shown; then, points on the required curve can be found by projection, the projection through 0 on the circle cutting the ordinate through N at E. etc. In this manner the dotted curve (i) can be obtained.

Draw another circle with centre C and radius 0·5″, and make the angle $MCB=45°$. As the point B rotates at twice

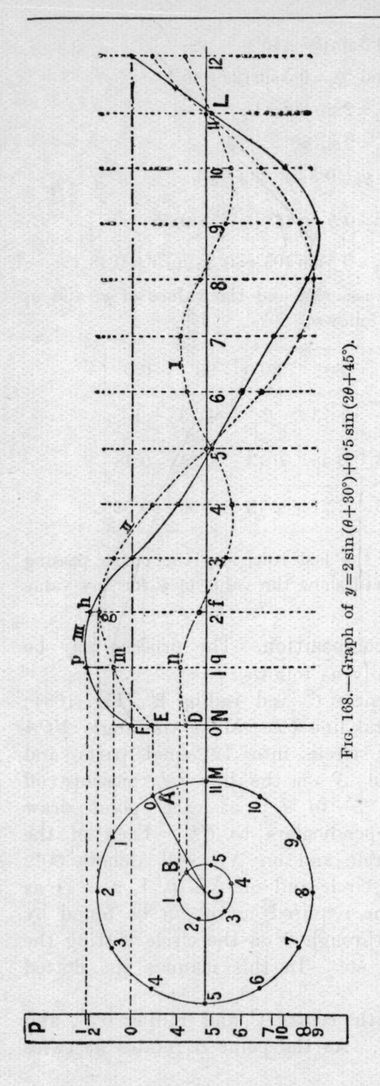

FIG. 168.—Graph of $y=2\sin(\theta+30^\circ)+0{\cdot}5\sin(2\theta+45^\circ)$.

the rate of A, it is only necessary to divide the circle into six equal parts, as shown in Fig. 168.

By projecting as before the curve (ii) may be obtained. The final curve (iii) is obtained by adding the ordinates of the two curves at each point, thus,

$$qp=qm+qn;$$

i.e. by means of a pair of dividers, or the edge of a strip of paper, add qn to qm, and in this manner a series of points is determined; joining these by a fair curve the resultant curve (iii) is obtained.

The converse problem. Resolution.—The converse problem to obtain the elements of the component motions of a curve such as (iii) (Fig. 168) is of great importance. Such a curve is easily set out if the displacements, or ordinates, corresponding to given angular intervals are known. These may be marked on the edge of a strip of paper, or thin cardboard, as indicated at P (Fig. 168). For this purpose a line is drawn through the initial point

F, parallel to the base line NL. If y denotes the displacement, then, supposing the equation of the curve may be expressed by three terms of a Fourier's series, *i.e.*

$$y=k+a\sin(\theta+\alpha)+b\sin(2\theta+\beta)$$

where k is the distance NF.

The analytical process by which the various constants in a Fourier's series are obtained is laborious and to some extent complicated. By a simple graphical method, devised by Mr. J. Harrison, it will be found that any given curve can be readily analysed by merely using a strip of paper as follows:

Let $y=k+a\sin(\theta+\alpha)+b\sin(2\theta+\beta)+c\sin(3\theta+\gamma)+\ldots$ be a complete Fourier's series, which for shortness write

$$y=k+s\theta+s2\theta+s3\theta+s4\theta,\ldots.$$

Let the values of twelve equidistant ordinates, spread over the cycle, be denoted by y_0, y_1, y_2, $y_3 \cdots y_{11}$. From a fixed point on a strip of paper, set off these values along the edge, numbering the points 0, 1, 2, 3, 4, 5 ... 11. These points would represent twelve successive positions of a particle vibrating according to the above law. By employing the principle of superposition we arrive at the results given on p. 460.

The analysis of such a curve as that in Ex. 1 by using a paper strip may be seen from the following example.

Ex. 2. Twelve positions of a slide valve numbered 0, 1, 2, ... 11, corresponding to intervals of 30° of the crank beginning at the inner dead point, are given in Fig. 169. Analyse the motion so as to express the displacement of the valve from its mean position in the form

$$y=a\sin(\theta+\alpha)+b\sin(2\theta+\beta),$$

θ being any crank position measured from the inner dead point. State the actual numerical values of a, b, α, and β in this case.

Mark off the given displacements along the edge of a strip of paper. On a sheet of squared paper mark off twelve equal horizontal distances and number these 0, 1, 2, ... 11, as in Fig. 169. Each of these equal divisions will denote 30°.

On the ordinate through 1, mark off from the paper strip the distance 01; similarly on the ordinate through 2 the distance 02, etc. Proceeding in this manner a series of points on

Table of Analysis.

The complete curve made up of $k, \theta, 2\theta, 3\theta, \ldots$. Call this series of ordinates *A.*	Divide *A* into two equal parts, superpose and add. Some of the terms cancel, and there remain $2(k, 2\theta, 4\theta, 6\theta, \ldots)$. *B.*	Divide *A* into three equal parts, superpose and add. The components remaining are $3(k, 3\theta, 6\theta, 9\theta, \ldots)$. *C.*
y_0 y_1 y_2 y_3 y_4 y_5 y_6 y_7 y_8 y_9 y_{10} y_{11}	y_0+y_6 y_1+y_7 y_2+y_8 y_3+y_9 y_4+y_{10} y_5+y_{11}	$y_0+y_4+y_8$ $y_1+y_5+y_9$ $y_2+y_6+y_{10}$ $y_3+y_7+y_{11}$
Divide *A* into two equal parts, superpose and subtract. There result $2(\theta, 3\theta, 5\theta, \ldots)$. *D.*	Divide *B* into two equal parts, superpose and subtract, obtaining $4(2\theta, 6\theta, 10\theta, \ldots)$. *E.*	Divide *C* into two equal parts, superpose and subtract. $6(3\theta, 9\theta, 15\theta, \ldots)$. *F.*
y_0-y_6 y_1-y_7 y_2-y_8 y_3-y_9 y_4-y_{10} y_5-y_{11} or applying strip of paper inverted 0 to 6 1 to 7 2 to 8 3 to 9 4 to 10 5 to 11	$y_0+y_6-(y_3+y_9)$ $y_1+y_7-(y_4+y_{10})$ $y_2+y_8-(y_5+y_{11})$ that is $(y_0-y_3)+(y_6-y_9)$ $(y_1-y_4)+(y_7-y_{10})$ $(y_2-y_5)+(y_8-y_{11})$ or on the strip 0 to 3+6 to 9 1 to 4+7 to 10 2 to 5+8 to 11	$(y_0+y_4+y_8)-(y_2+y_6+y_{10})$ $(y_1+y_5+y_9)-(y_3+y_7+y_{11})$ that is $y_0-y_2+y_4-y_6+y_8-y_{10}$ $y_1-y_3+y_5-y_7+y_9-y_{11}$ or using the strip 0 to 2+4 to 6+8 to 10 1 to 3+5 to 7+9 to 11
		Deduct $\frac{1}{3}$ of ordinates of curve *F* from those of curve *D*. Then we obtain $D-\frac{F}{3}=2(\theta, 5\theta, 7\theta, 11\theta, \ldots)$.

the curve of displacement is obtained and through these points a fair curve may be drawn.

To obtain the elements of the component motions *the strip is inverted.* Putting 0 on the strip to coincide with 0 on *BN*, mark off on the ordinate through 0, the distance 0 to 6. Similarly, putting 1 on the strip coincident with 1 on *BN*, set off on the ordinate the distance 1 to 7. These processes may be written as 0 to 6, 1 to 7, 2 to 8, etc., as on p. 455. Draw a curve through the points.

Using the contracted notation the equation of the new curve may be written in the form $2(\theta, 3\theta, 5\theta \ldots)$.

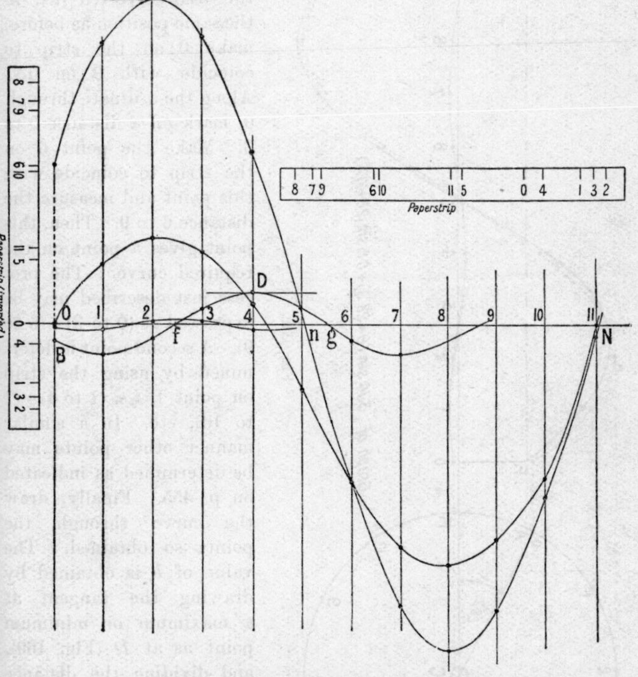

Fig. 169.—Analysis of a displacement curve.

Draw a tangent to this curve at a maximum or minimum point; then the amplitude a is one-half the distance from A to the base line BN, or $6{\cdot}28 \div 2 = 3{\cdot}14$.

The magnitude of the angle α can be obtained by producing the curve to cut the line BN, then, as the distance nN denotes 180°, the distance $0n$ is proportionately $= 151^\circ{\cdot}8$.

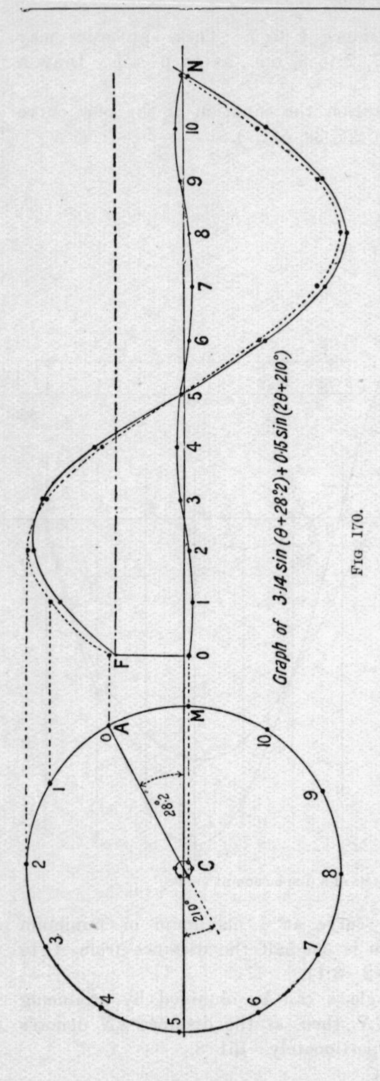

Fig 170.

To obtain the angle α it is only necessary to subtract $151°·18$ from $180°$;

$$\therefore\ \alpha = 28°·2.$$

To obtain the elements of the second term with the strip inverted (*i.e.* in the same position as before) make 0 on the strip to coincide with 0 on $0N$. Along the ordinate through 0, mark off a distance 0 to 3. Make the point 6 on the strip to coincide with this point and measure the distance 6 to 9. Then, this point gives a point on the required curve. The process just described may be expressed as (0 to 3)+(6 to 9). A second point is determined by using the strip on point 1, *i.e.* (1 to 4)+(7 to 10), etc. In a similar manner other points may be determined as indicated on p. 455. Finally, draw the curve through the points so obtained. The value of b is obtained by drawing the tangent at a maximum or minimum point as at D (Fig. 169), and dividing the distance between the tangent and the line $0N$ by 4, *i.e.*

$$b = \frac{0·6}{4} = 0·15''.$$

It will be noticed that the distance fg between the two points where the curve intersects the line $0N$, corresponds to three divisions, hence, each division is 60°. The value of β could be found by producing the curve until the position in the positive direction was obtained, but the value may also be found by noting that the distance between the line passing through 0 and the point f, where the curve intersects the axis, is 2·5 divisions or 150°.

$$\therefore \beta = 360° - 150° = 210°.$$

To find the elements of the third term it would be necessary to proceed in a similar manner, viz. to use the inverted strip and mark off from 0 a point corresponding to the distance 0 to 2; then to shift the strip so that 4 on the strip coincides with the point, and to mark off the distance 4 to 6. Finally, to put 8 at the last point and mark off the distance 8 to 10. The process just described is conveniently written in the form (0 to 2)+(4 to 6)+(8 to 10). Similarly, for the next point we should have (1 to 3)+(5 to 7)+(9 to 11). Proceeding in this manner a series of points is obtained. The curve passing through the plotted points will be expressed, with the present notation, by 6 (3θ, 9θ, 15θ ...). In the present case this practically coincides with the line $0N$, merely showing a slight ripple; also, as the distance from the crest of the curve to the line $0N$ must be divided by 6 to give the magnitude of the amplitude a, it is obvious that the third term in the series is negligible. Hence the equation may be written

$$y = 3 \cdot 14 \sin(\theta + 28° \cdot 2) + 0 \cdot 15 \sin(2\theta + 210°). \quad \text{.................(iii)}$$

It is instructive to reverse the process and obtain, as in Ex. 1, the curve represented by Eq. (iii). Thus, draw a circle radius 3·14 (Fig. 170) and set off an angular advance MCA of 28°·2; also draw a circle concentric with the former, radius 0·15, and set off an angular advance of 210°; project as already described in Ex. 1. Finally, add the ordinates of the two curves. It will be found that the resulting curve will be the same as the given one. This result may be tested by using a piece of tracing paper, or by the paper strip. In the latter case, it is necessary to draw a line through the initial point F parallel to CN. The distance $0F$ is the value of the constant $k = 1 \cdot 4$. Hence, referred to axes of co-ordinates passing through F, the required equation is

$$y = -1 \cdot 4 + 3 \cdot 14 \sin(\theta + 28° \cdot 2) + 0 \cdot 15 \sin(2\theta + 210°).$$

EXERCISES. XLIV.

Integrate the following:

1. $\sin ax \sin bx\, dx$.

2. $x^2 \cos x\, dx$.

3. $\dfrac{x\, dx}{(x-a)(x-b)}$.

4. $\dfrac{(x^2-5x+7)\, dx}{x^2-5x+6}$.

5. $\dfrac{(x^2+7)\, dx}{x^4+5x^2+4}$.

6. $\dfrac{(x^3+2x+4)\, dx}{x^3+2x^2+4x+8}$.

7. $x^3(\log x)^2 dx$.

8. $\dfrac{x^3 dx}{(x-a)(x-b)(x-c)}$.

9. $\dfrac{x\, dx}{(x-3)^2(x+2)}$.

10. $\theta \sin \theta\, d\theta$.

11. $x^3 \cos x\, dx$.

12. $\dfrac{(2x-5)\, dx}{(x+3)(x+1)^2}$.

13. $\dfrac{(6x^2+13x-43)\, dx}{x^3-13x-12}$.

14. The motion of a point in a straight line is compounded of two simple harmonic motions of nearly equal periods, represented by the equation:

$$x = 2{\cdot}1 \sin\left(9t + \frac{\pi}{4}\right) + \sin 8t,$$

where x is the displacement in inches from the mean position, and t is time.

Let the complete period of the vibration be divided into nine equal intervals. Taking only the first, fourth, and seventh of these intervals, in each case draw a curve in which abscissae shall represent times, and ordinates the corresponding displacements of the point.

Let the time of one of the intervals be represented on the paper by a length of 8″. In determining successive ordinates, the method of projection from the resultant crank may be used with advantage.

15. The displacements of a slide valve actuated by a Gooch link were measured at eight intervals each of 45°, and found to be as follows, beginning with the crank on the inner dead centre:

$$2{\cdot}44'',\ 1{\cdot}65'',\ 0,\ -1{\cdot}37'',\ -1{\cdot}87'',\ -1{\cdot}37'',\ 0,\ 1{\cdot}65''.$$

Assuming that the motion of the valve is compounded of two simple harmonic motions, one of double the frequency of the other, as represented by the equation

$$y = k + a \sin(\theta + \alpha) + b \sin(2\theta + \beta),$$

where θ is the crank angle. Find the values of k, a, α, b, β.

CHAPTER XXII.

DIFFERENTIAL EQUATIONS.

Differential equations.—Any equation which connects the variables x and y, and the differential coefficients $\frac{dy}{dx}, \frac{d^2y}{dx^2}, \frac{d^3y}{dx^3}$ etc., is called a **differential equation.** Such equations are of great importance. It will be found, for instance, that the majority of the so-called "laws" in dynamics, etc., can be expressed in their most general form by means of such equations.

It is only possible to give a few of the simpler cases; for further information the student is referred to larger books, such as that of Dr. Forsyth.

A simple form is furnished by the equation

$$y=a+\frac{dy}{dx}x. \quad \text{.............................(i)}$$

The relation expressed by (i) represents a series of straight lines making an intercept a on the axis of y and having slopes $\frac{dy}{dx}=\tan\theta$ **(Fig. 171).**

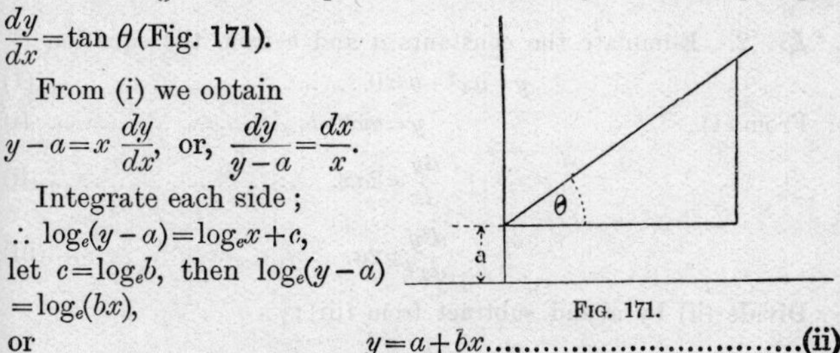

From (i) we obtain

$$y-a=x\frac{dy}{dx}, \text{ or, } \frac{dy}{y-a}=\frac{dx}{x}.$$

Integrate each side;

$\therefore \log_e(y-a)=\log_e x+c$,

let $c=\log_e b$, then $\log_e(y-a)=\log_e(bx)$,

Fig. 171.

or

$$y=a+bx \quad \text{.............................}\mathbf{(ii)}$$

From (ii) $y=a+bx$, the equation to a straight line, we obtain by differentiation

$$\frac{dy}{dx}=b.$$

Hence, we see that b simply denotes the inclination of the line to the axis of x, or, shortly, the **gradient** of the line.

Again, from (ii), $\frac{d^2y}{dx^2}=0$. As both the constants have been eliminated, this is the most general equation of a straight line.

Ex. 1. Given $$\frac{dy}{dx}=b.$$

This may be written $dy=bdx$.

Integrating, $$\int dy=b\int dx;$$

$$\therefore\ y=bx+C. \quad \text{......................(iii)}$$

This equation denotes a family of straight lines with constant gradient. As already indicated, any constant connected by the signs + and − disappears during differentiation, and therefore a constant denoted by C is added to the indefinite integral to give the most general value to it. It will be noticed that it is unnecessary to add a constant to both sides of the equation.

Elimination of constants.—One, two, or more constants may be eliminated from a given equation by introducing $\frac{dy}{dx}$ and $\frac{d^2y}{dx^2}$, etc.

Ex. 2. Eliminate the constants a and b from the equation

$$y-ax^2+b=0. \quad \text{......................(1)}$$

From (1) $$y=ax^2-b, \quad \text{......................(i)}$$

$$\frac{dy}{dx}=2ax, \quad \text{......................(ii)}$$

$$\frac{d^2y}{dx^2}=2a. \quad \text{......................(iii)}$$

Divide (ii) by x and subtract from (iii);

$$\therefore\ \frac{d^2y}{dx^2}-\frac{1}{x}\frac{dy}{dx}=0.$$

The general method of eliminating two arbitrary constants may be carried out as follows:

Let
$$y=f(a, b, x),$$
$$\frac{dy}{dx}=f'(a, b, x),$$
$$\frac{d^2y}{dx^2}=f''(a, b, x),$$
three equations from which to eliminate a and b.

Generally, to eliminate n constants it is necessary to use the first n differential coefficients; and, conversely, a differential equation of the nth order requires for its solution n independent constants.

Ex. 3. Given
$$y^2=ax+bx^2, \quad \text{(i)}$$
eliminate the constants a and b.

Differentiating (i),
$$2y\frac{dy}{dx}=a+2bx. \quad \text{(ii)}$$
Again differentiating,
$$2y\frac{d^2y}{dx^2}+2\left(\frac{dy}{dx}\right)^2=2b. \quad \text{(iii)}$$
Between (i), (ii), and (iii) eliminate a and b; therefore multiply (ii) by x and subtract from (i),
$$y^2-2xy\frac{dy}{dx}+bx^2=0.$$
Substitute for b from (iii),
$$\therefore\ y^2-2xy\frac{dy}{dx}+x^2y\frac{d^2y}{dx^2}+x^2\left(\frac{dy}{dx}\right)^2=0.$$

Ex. 4. If the letters s, v, and t denote space, velocity, and time respectively, then
$$v=\frac{ds}{dt} \text{ and acceleration}=\frac{dv}{dt}=\frac{d^2s}{dt^2}.$$
If the relation between s and t is expressed by
$$s=at^2+bt+c, \quad \text{(i)}$$
the average velocity is obtained from $\frac{\delta s}{\delta t}$ and the actual value is given by $\frac{ds}{dt}$. Thus, from (i)
$$\frac{ds}{dt}=2at+b \text{ and } \frac{d^2s}{dt^2}=2a.$$
Hence, the acceleration is constant and equal to $2a$.

Thus, let $a=\frac{1}{2}g$, $b=V$, and $c=0$, then Eq. (i) becomes by substitution the well-known formula

$$s=\tfrac{1}{2}gt^2+Vt;$$

$$\therefore\ v=\frac{ds}{dt}=gt+V,$$

and $$\text{acceleration}=f=\frac{d^2s}{dt^2}=g;$$

therefore the acceleration is constant and equal to g.

As a simple example consider the differential equation

$$\frac{d^2s}{dt^2}=g.$$

This denotes that the acceleration of a moving body is g.

Integrating, $$\frac{ds}{dt}=v=gt+C.$$

To determine the value of the constant C it is only necessary to know the value of v when $t=0$. Let this be V.

Then, $$v=\frac{ds}{dt}=gt+V. \qquad \text{(i)}$$

Integrating again, $s=\frac{1}{2}gt^2+Vt+C_1$.

If $s=0$ when $t=0$, then $C_1=0$;

$$\therefore\ s=\tfrac{1}{2}gt^2+Vt. \qquad \text{(ii)}$$

Obviously in (ii) the direction of the acceleration and the initial velocity are both vertically downwards; if V is upwards, then the space described in any time t is given by

$$s=Vt-\tfrac{1}{2}gt^2.$$

From the relation Force = mass × acceleration,

$$F=m\frac{dv}{dt}=m\frac{d^2s}{dt^2}. \qquad \text{(iii)}$$

The work done by the force F through a distance ds is $F.ds$;

$$\therefore \text{ from (iii) } F.ds=m\frac{d^2s}{dt^2}ds=mv\,dv=m\frac{ds}{dt}\frac{d^2s}{dt^2}dt.$$

Hence $$F\int ds=m\int v\,dv,$$

or $$Fs=\tfrac{1}{2}mv^2+C. \qquad \text{(i)}$$

If when $s=0$, $v=0$, then (i) becomes $Fs=\frac{1}{2}mv^2$.

" $s=0$, $v=u$, " (i) becomes $Fs=\frac{1}{2}m(v^2-u^2)$.

Ex. 5. Two unequal weights of 2 and 3 lbs. respectively are fastened to the ends of a string passing over a smooth pulley (Fig. 172). The equation of motion is

$$(M+m)\frac{d^2s}{dt^2}=(M-m)g.$$

Find the equation of motion if one weight is 3 ft. from the ground and is moving with a velocity of 2 ft. per sec. at the given instant. Also find the position and velocity one second later, the time which has elapsed since starting from rest, and the position of the weight ($g=32{\cdot}2$).

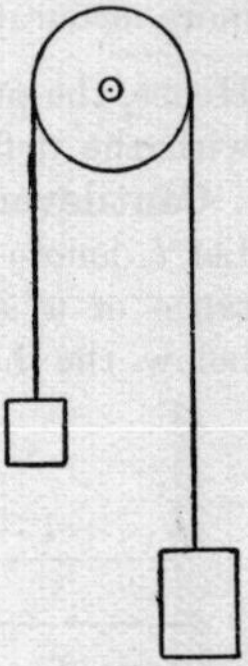

FIG. 172.

From the relation

$$a=\text{acceleration}=\frac{\text{force causing motion}}{\text{mass moved}}\times g$$

we obtain $$\frac{d^2s}{dt^2}=\frac{1}{5}g,$$

$$v=\tfrac{1}{5}gt+C. \quad\text{.........................(i)}$$

Now $v=2$ when $t=0$; $\therefore\ 2=C$,

or $$v=\tfrac{1}{5}gt+2=6{\cdot}44t+2. \quad\text{.....................(ii)}$$

Also $$s=\tfrac{1}{10}gt^2+2t+C_1.$$

But $s=3$ when $t=0$;

$$\therefore\ s=\tfrac{1}{10}gt^2+2t+3=3{\cdot}22t^2+2t+3. \quad\text{.......(iii)}$$

Put $t=1$, $s=8{\cdot}22$ ft., from (iii),

and $v=8{\cdot}44$ ft. per sec., from (ii).

When $v=0$, $$t=-\frac{2}{6{\cdot}44}=-\frac{1}{3{\cdot}22}$$
$$=-0{\cdot}310;$$

$\therefore$ position of the weight is then given by

$$s=3{\cdot}22\times0{\cdot}0961-0{\cdot}620+3$$
$$=2{\cdot}690.$$

Simple differential equations.—The following are a few of the more commonly recurring simple differential equations.

Type 1. $$\frac{d^2y}{dx^2}=A+Bx+Cx^2+Dx^3+\dots.$$

The solution is

$$y=k+k_1x+\frac{Ax^2}{1.2}+\frac{Bx^3}{1.2.3}+\frac{Cx^4}{3.4}+\text{etc.},$$

where k, k_1 are constants of integration.

As already indicated, p. 334, when a curve is very flat and parallel to the axis of x, we may use, instead of the more accurate expression for the curvature, the form $\frac{d^2y}{dx^2}$. Hence, the preceding result may be applied to problems dealing with the deflection of beams.

Cantilever with concentrated load at the free end.—Let l denote the length of the beam (Fig. 173), and x the distance of a section from the fixed end, and y the deflection below the horizontal; then, the bending moment at such a section is $M=W(l-x)$;

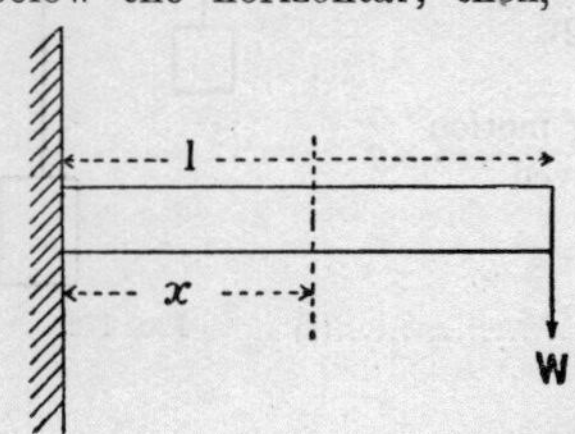

FIG. 173.—Cantilever with concentrated load.

$$\therefore \frac{d^2y}{dx^2}=\frac{W}{EI}(l-x).$$

Where
E = Young's modulus of elasticity,
I = moment of inertia,* and y is measured downwards. Integrating,

$$\frac{dy}{dx}=\frac{W}{EI}\int(l-x)=\frac{W}{EI}\left(lx-\frac{x^2}{2}\right)+C.$$

To find the value of the arbitrary constant C, we notice that, when $x=0$, $\frac{dy}{dx}=0$; $\therefore C=0$.

Again integrating,

$$y=\frac{W}{EI}\int\left(lx-\frac{x^2}{2}\right);$$

$$\therefore y=\frac{W}{EI}\left(\frac{lx^2}{2}-\frac{x^3}{6}\right)+C_1.$$

Again, when $x=0$, $y=0$; $\therefore C_1=0$.

Hence,

$$y=\frac{W}{EI}\left(\frac{lx^2}{2}-\frac{x^3}{6}\right).\quad\text{(i)}$$

In practical cases the maximum value of y is required, and this obviously occurs when $x=l$. Substitute this value in (i);

$$\therefore y=\frac{W}{EI}\left(\frac{l^3}{2}-\frac{l^3}{6}\right)=\frac{1}{3}\frac{Wl^3}{EI}.$$

* [I = Moment of inertia of the cross-section about a line through its centre of area, perpendicular to the plane of bending.]

Cantilever with uniform load.—If l denote the length of the beam (Fig. 174), and w the load per unit length of the beam, the bending moment at a section distant x from the fixed end and y measured downwards

$$=w(l-x)\frac{(l-x)}{2}=\frac{w}{2}(l-x)^2;$$

$$\therefore \frac{d^2y}{dx^2}=\frac{w}{2EI}(l^2-2lx+x^2).$$

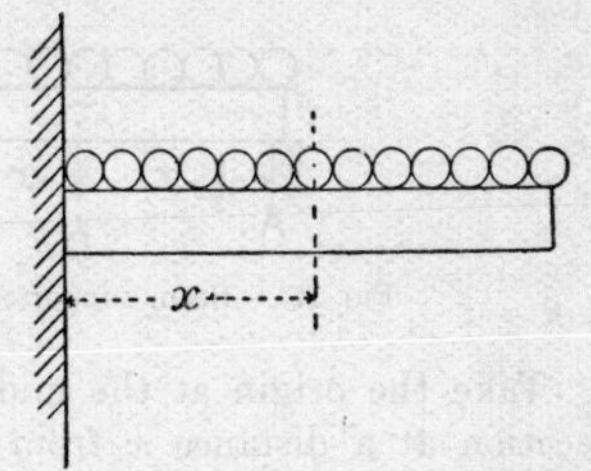

FIG. 174.—Cantilever with uniform load.

Integrating,

$$\frac{dy}{dx}=\frac{w}{2EI}\int(l^2-2lx+x^2)$$

$$=\frac{w}{2EI}\left(l^2x-\frac{2lx^2}{2}+\frac{x^3}{3}\right)+C.$$

To obtain the numerical value of the arbitrary constant C we notice that $\frac{dy}{dx}=0$ when $x=0$; $\therefore$ $C=0$.

Integrating again,

$$y=\frac{w}{2EI}\int\left(l^2x-lx^2+\frac{x^3}{3}\right)$$

$$=\frac{w}{2EI}\left(\frac{l^2x^2}{2}-\frac{lx^3}{3}+\frac{x^4}{12}\right)+C_1.$$

As in the preceding case, $y=0$ when $x=0$, $\therefore$ $C_1=0$.

Hence,

$$y=\frac{w}{2EI}\left(\frac{l^2x^2}{2}-\frac{lx^3}{3}+\frac{x^4}{12}\right). \quad \text{(i)}$$

The maximum value of y obviously occurs when $x=l$.

Substituting this value in (i), we obtain

$$y=\frac{wl^4}{8EI},$$

or, if W denote the total load $=wl$,

then,
$$y=\frac{1}{8}\frac{Wl^3}{EI}.$$

Beam supported at each end and loaded uniformly.—Let AB (Fig. 175) denote a beam carrying a uniform load of magnitude w per unit length; if l denotes the length of the beam, the total load will be wl.

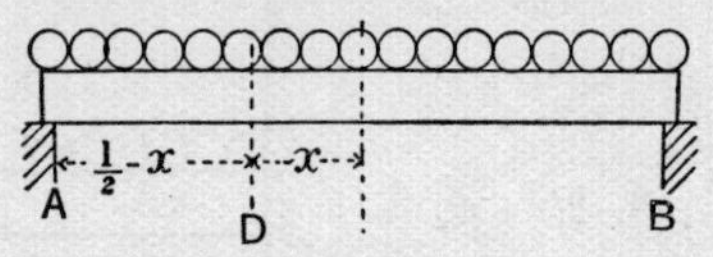

FIG. 175.—Beam supported at each end, uniform load.

Take the origin at the middle of the beam. Let D be a section at a distance x from the origin, y, measured downwards, then the bending moment at D is

$$-\frac{wl}{2}\left(\frac{l}{2}-x\right)+\frac{w}{2}\left(\frac{l}{2}-x\right)^2=-\frac{w}{2}\left(\frac{l^2}{4}-x^2\right);$$

$$\therefore\ \frac{d^2y}{dx^2}=-\frac{1}{EI}\times\frac{w}{2}\left(\frac{l^2}{4}-x^2\right);$$

or, integrating, $$\frac{dy}{dx}=-\frac{1}{EI}\frac{w}{2}\left(\frac{l^2x}{4}-\frac{x^3}{3}\right)+C,$$

when $x=0$, $\frac{dy}{dx}=0$; $\therefore$ C is 0.

Again, integrating,

$$y=-\frac{1}{EI}\frac{w}{2}\left(\frac{l^2x^2}{8}-\frac{x^4}{12}\right)+C_1.$$

Since, when $x=\frac{l}{2}$, $y=0$; $\therefore$ $C_1=\frac{5}{384}\frac{wl^4}{EI}$;

$$\therefore\ y=-\frac{w}{2EI}\left(\frac{l^2x^2}{8}-\frac{x^4}{12}\right)+\frac{5}{384}\frac{wl^4}{EI}.$$

The maximum value of y occurs at the middle of the beam, *i.e* where $x=0$.

Substituting this value for x, we obtain

$$y=\frac{5wl^4}{384EI}=\frac{5}{384}\frac{Wl^3}{EI},$$

where $W=wl$.

Beam fixed at both ends loaded with a uniform load.—Let w be the load per unit length, and l the length of the beam. The forces at one end, such as at A (Fig. 176), consists of a shearing force $\frac{wl}{2}$, and a couple which may be denoted by C. Then, for a section at a distance x from A and y, measured downwards,

$$\frac{d^2y}{dx^2}=\frac{1}{EI}\left(C-\frac{wl}{2}x+\frac{wx^2}{2}\right),$$

$$\frac{dy}{dx}=\frac{1}{EI}\left(Cx-\frac{wlx^2}{4}+\frac{wx^3}{6}\right)+A_1.$$

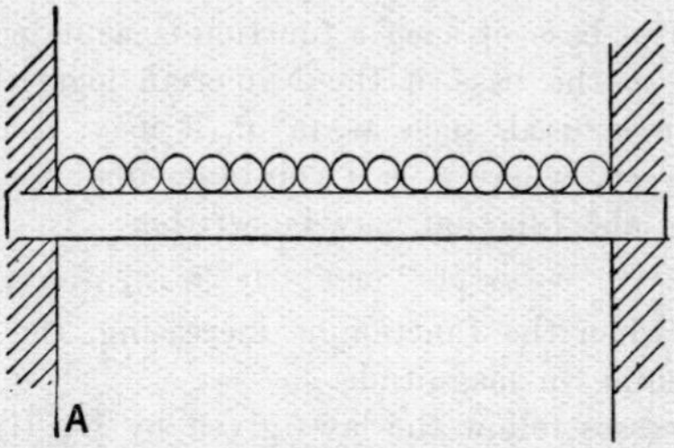

A

FIG. 176.—Beam fixed at both ends, uniform load.

To obtain the numerical values of the constants C and A_1, we notice that when $x=0$, $\frac{dy}{dx}=0$; $\therefore A_1=0$. When $x=l$, $\frac{dy}{dx}$ is again 0;

$$\therefore\ 0=\frac{1}{EI}\left(Cl-\frac{wl^3}{4}+\frac{wl^3}{6}\right);$$

$$\therefore\ C=\frac{1}{12}wl^2.$$

The equation becomes

$$\frac{dy}{dx}=\frac{1}{EI}\left(\frac{wl^2x}{12}-\frac{wlx^2}{4}+\frac{wx^3}{6}\right).$$

Again, by integration,

$$y=\frac{1}{EI}\left(\frac{wl^2x^2}{24}-\frac{wlx^3}{12}+\frac{wx^4}{24}\right)+A_1;$$

when x is 0, y is 0; $\therefore A_1=0$;

$$\therefore y=\frac{w}{24EI}(lx-x^2)^2.$$

Also y is maximum when $x=\frac{l}{2}$; substituting this value,

$$y=\frac{1}{384}\frac{wl^4}{EI}.$$

That is to say, the deflection of a beam fixed at the ends is only $\frac{1}{5}$th of a similar beam the ends of which are merely supported.

Compound interest law.—A class of functions of great importance, such as e^x, e^{-x}, etc., is known as **exponential functions.** The base of such a function is, as indicated, usually taken to be e, the base of the Napierian logarithms. When another base is used, such as in a^x, it may, if necessary, be expressed as e^{kx}, where k is a constant equal to $\log_e a$. In a general form the function may be written

$$y=Ae^{kx} \text{ or } y=Ae^{-kx}, \quad \text{.........................(i)}$$

the former when the function is increasing, the latter when it is diminishing in magnitude.

Many processes follow the laws given by Eq. (i), and it has been very aptly styled by Lord Kelvin the **Compound Interest Law.**

Money lent at compound interest increases in this way, and forms one of the simplest applications of this law. Thus, if £100 is lent at 5 per cent. per annum compound interest, then at the end of the first year the principal and interest amount to £105. This amount is the principal for the second year, and the interest will be charged on £105 instead of on £100; similarly, for the third year, etc. The preceding facts are better expressed symbolically as follows: Let P_0 denote the sum lent at r per cent. per annum, then P_1, the principal for the second year, may be obtained from

$$P_1=P_0\left(1+\frac{r}{100}\right). \quad \text{.........................(ii)}$$

The principal P_2 at the end of the second year is given by

$$P_2=P_1\left(1+\frac{r}{100}\right).$$

Substitute the value of P_1 from (ii) and this becomes

$$P_2 = P_0\left(1+\frac{r}{100}\right)^2.$$

Similarly, at the end of the third year

$$P_3 = P_0\left(1+\frac{r}{100}\right)^3.$$

Hence, in n years $P = P_0\left(1+\frac{r}{100}\right)^n.$

If instead of adding the interest by annual increments the interest is added monthly, then at the end of t years the principal or amount A is given by

$$A = P_0\left(1+\frac{r}{12\times 100}\right)^{12t}.$$

Again, if instead of at monthly intervals, the interest is added at n equal intervals in each year, then in t years

$$A = P_0\left(1+\frac{r}{n\times 100}\right)^{nt}. \quad \text{......................(i)}$$

As the number n is increased, the interval of time t becomes shorter and shorter, and if n be indefinitely great the interest would be added continuously to the principal.

If $n = \frac{rm}{100}$ Eq. (i) may be written

$$A = P_0\left\{\left(1+\frac{1}{m}\right)^m\right\}^{\frac{rt}{100}} \quad \text{.........................(ii)}$$

In the limit when n and therefore m become indefinitely great, Eq. (ii) becomes

$$A = P_0 e^{\frac{rt}{100}}.$$

[The value of $\left(1+\frac{1}{m}\right)^m$ when m is indefinitely great is, on p. 289, shown to be equal to e].

This result may be obtained in a more direct manner as follows:

If P be the principal at the end of t years, then for a small increment of time, denoted by δt, the corresponding increment of P may be denoted by δP.

$$\therefore\ \delta P = \frac{r}{100}P\,\delta t, \quad \text{or,} \quad \frac{\delta P}{\delta t} = \frac{r}{100}P.$$

Hence, when the interval of time is made indefinitely small,

$$\frac{dP}{dt}=\frac{r}{100}P;$$

$$\therefore\ \frac{dP}{P}=\frac{r}{100}dt.$$

Integration gives $\qquad \log_e P=\frac{r}{100}t+C.$

Now, since when $t=0$, $P=P_0$, where P_0 is the principal at the time 0, the constant is $\log_e P_0$;

$$\therefore\ P=P_0e^{\frac{r}{100}t}.$$

Write k for $\frac{r}{100}$, and the preceding result will become

$$P=P_0e^{kt}. \quad \text{..............................(ii)}$$

Friction of a cord or belt on a pulley or cylinder.—Let $ANMB$ (Fig. 177) represent a belt or cord pressed tightly against a surface by forces at its free ends. Then, when the belt is just about to slip on the surface in the direction B to A, the tension at A is greater than at B. The angle AOB may be denoted by θ. Also MN may be taken to be a small portion of AB acted on by the tensions T at M, and $T+\delta T$ at N. Constructing the triangle of forces ABC (Fig. 177), it is readily seen that the radial force

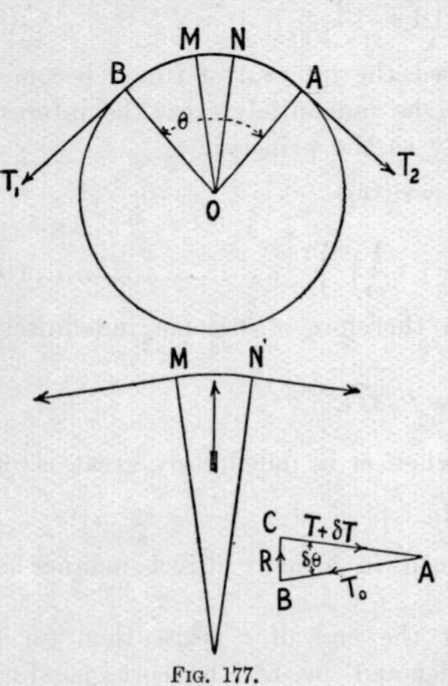

Fig. 177.

$$R=(T+\delta T)\delta\theta.$$

Also friction$=\mu R$, where μ is constant.

Let R denote the reaction of the cylinder, then, resolving tangentially,

$$\frac{dT}{ds}-\mu R=0\,; \quad \text{.............................(i)}$$

resolving normally, $$T\frac{d\theta}{ds}-R=0. \quad \text{.............................(ii)}$$

Eliminating R we have $$\frac{dT}{T}=\mu d\theta.$$

This is the compound interest law.

Integration between the limits T_1 and T_2 of T and 0 and θ of θ, gives

$$\int_{T_1}^{T_2}\frac{dT}{T}=\mu\int_0^{\theta}d\theta,$$

or $$\log T_2-\log T_1=\mu\theta, \quad \text{.............................(iii)}$$

$$\therefore\ \frac{T_2}{T_1}=e^{\mu\theta}. \quad \text{.............................(iv)}$$

If b denotes the width, and t the thickness of a belt, then the area of cross-section is calculated for the maximum tension T_2 with a margin for safety. It will be noticed that when θ, the angle of contact of the belt with the cylinder, and the coefficient of friction μ are known, the ratio of T_2 to T_1 can be calculated from (iv). [The value of t for a single leather belt is usually about $\frac{3}{8}$ inch and the safe stress about 300 to 350 lbs. per sq. in.]

Ex. 6. A rope passes three times round a post and is held by a force of 10 lbs. at one end. What pull at the other end will be necessary to cause the rope to slip, assuming the coefficient of friction μ to be 0·3?

Here, if T_2 denote the force required,

$$\frac{T_2}{T_1}=e^{\mu\theta}=e^{0\cdot 3\times 6\pi},$$

$$\log T_2=0\cdot 3\times 6\pi\log 2\cdot 718+\log T_1$$

$$=5\cdot 656\times 0\cdot 4343+1=3\cdot 4564=\log 2860\,;$$

$$\therefore\ T_2=2860 \text{ lbs.}$$

An electrical example.—If V is the voltage, R the resistance of an electrical circuit in ohms, C the current in ampères, then for a constant current Ohm's law, $V=RC$, applies, but when the current is not constant the law becomes

$$V=RC+L\frac{dC}{dt}, \qquad \text{(1)}$$

$\frac{dC}{dt}$ is the rate of increase of C, and L is called the self-induction of the circuit.

If in (1) $V=0$, then

$$0=RC+L\frac{dC}{dt},$$

or

$$\frac{dC}{dt}=-\frac{R}{L}C;$$

$$\therefore \frac{dC}{C}=-\frac{R}{L}dt.$$

Integrating,

$$\log C=-\frac{R}{L}t+K,$$

where K is a constant.

To find the value of K, let C_0 be the value of C when $t=0$, then

$$\log C_0=0+K;$$

$$\therefore K=\log C_0.$$

Hence, substituting,

$$\log\frac{C}{C_0}=-\frac{R}{L}t;$$

$$\therefore C=C_0e^{-\frac{R}{L}t},$$

again the compound interest law.

Whence

$$V=RC-RC_0e^{-\frac{R}{L}t}.$$

Hence, as t increases, the effect of a constant self-induction decreases.

Ex. 7. The current C ampères in a circuit follows the law, $C=10\sin 600t$; if t is in seconds, and if

$$V=RC+L\frac{dC}{dt}, \qquad \text{(i)}$$

where R is 0·3, and L is 4×10^{-4}, what is V?

From the relation $C=10\sin 600t$ we find

$$\frac{dC}{dt}=6000\cos 600t.$$

Hence, substituting in (i),

$$V=0{\cdot}3\times 10\sin 600t+4\times 10^{-4}\times 6000\cos 600t$$
$$=3\sin 600t+2{\cdot}4\cos 600t. \quad \text{(ii)}$$

Assume that (ii) may be written in the form

$$A\sin(600t+E)$$

This, on expansion, gives (p. 27)

$$A\cos E\sin 600t+A\sin E\cos 600t. \quad \text{(iii)}$$

Hence, comparing (iii) with (ii),

$$A\cos E=3, \quad \text{and} \quad A\sin E=2{\cdot}4.$$

Squaring and adding,

$$A^2(\sin^2 E+\cos^2 E)=3^2+(2{\cdot}4)^2=14{\cdot}76;$$
$$\therefore A^2=14{\cdot}76,$$

or

$$A=3{\cdot}84.$$

Also $\quad E=\tan^{-1}0{\cdot}8=38°\ 39{\cdot}5'.$

Hence, lowest value of $C=-10$,

" " $V=-3{\cdot}84$;

highest value of $C=10$,

" " $V=3{\cdot}84$.

Variation of atmospheric pressure with altitude.—If p_0 is the pressure, ρ_0 the density of the air at sea-level, and p the pressure, and ρ the density at a height h,

$$dp=-\rho dh.$$

The negative sign indicates that the pressure decreases as the altitude increases. Hence

$$\frac{dp}{dh}=-\rho. \quad \text{(i)}$$

To express the density ρ in terms of the pressure and density ρ_0 at sea-level, we have, from Boyle's Law,

$$p\times\rho_0=\rho p_0,$$

or

$$\rho=\frac{p\times\rho_0}{p_0}.$$

Substitute this value in (i), then

$$\frac{dp}{dh} = \frac{-p \times \rho_0}{p_0};$$

$$\therefore \frac{dp}{p} = \frac{-\rho_0}{p_0} dh;$$

$$\therefore \log_e p = \frac{-\rho_0}{p_0} h + \log_e c.$$

Hence $$p = ce^{\frac{-\rho_0}{p_0} h}.$$

To obtain the value of the constant c we notice that at sea-level, where $h=0$, $p=p_0$; $\therefore c=p_0$;

$$\therefore p = p_0 e^{\frac{-\rho_0}{p_0} h}.$$

Differential Equations.—Type II. $\frac{d^2s}{dt^2} = -Fs$, where F is a constant.

To solve equations of this type, assume that $s = A'e^{\alpha t}$ where A' is an arbitrary constant and α a constant to be determined.

By substitution, $$s(\alpha^2 + F) = 0,$$

so that $$\alpha = \pm\sqrt{-F} = \pm i\sqrt{F}, \text{ where } i = \sqrt{-1}$$

$\therefore$ the complete solution is

$$s = A'e^{it\sqrt{F}} + B'e^{-it\sqrt{F}}.$$

But from (i) and (ii), p. 382, by expressing the exponentials in terms of $\sin x$ and $\cos x$, the solution becomes

$$s = A \cos \sqrt{F}t + B \sin \sqrt{F}t,$$

where A and B are written for $A' + B'$ and $i(A' - B')$ respectively.

This is an important equation, and is a typical case of harmonic motion, occurring, for example, in the small oscillations of a spring or of a pendulum. It is also used in the so-called Theory of Struts and may be written in the form

$$\frac{d^2y}{dx^2} = -Cy.$$

The solution is $y = A \sin \sqrt{C}x + B \cos \sqrt{C}x.$

Ex. 8. Let $A=0$, $B=7$, $q=3$. Then the equation becomes

$$s=7\cos 3t;$$

this is referred to on p. 135.

If the differential equation is

$$\frac{d^2s}{dt^2}-k^2s=0,$$

the solution is $$s=Ae^{-kt}+Be^{kt},$$

as may be proved by obtaining the second differential.

A particular solution of this equation is given by

$$s=Ae^{-kt}.$$

The reader should refer to pp. 141, 145 in which are given figures of the curves

$$s=Ae^{\pm kt} \text{ and } y=Ae^{kx}\sin(bx+c).$$

Vibration of a bar or spring.—The deflection of a bar is proportional to the load, and a bar when loaded may be made to vibrate. The periodic time is equal to $2\pi\sqrt{\frac{m}{F}}$, where m is the mass of the load, and F the force required to produce unit displacement.

The periodic time T of a weight P of mass m suspended at one end of a spiral spring, the other end of which is fastened to a suitable support, is in like manner given by

$$T=2\pi\sqrt{\frac{m}{F}}.$$

Let F denote the force required to produce unit displacement. When P is displaced a distance x from its equilibrium position the resultant upward force is Fx. The acceleration in a downward direction (*i.e.* in a direction tending to increase x) is $\frac{d^2x}{dt^2}$.

The acceleration in the upward direction is $-\frac{d^2x}{dt^2}$.

As force = mass × acceleration $=-\frac{md^2x}{dt^2}$,

where m is the mass of the body at P;

$$\therefore\ m\frac{d^2x}{dt^2}=-Fx, \qquad \text{(i)}$$

To solve this, suppose

$$x = A \sin pt + B \cos pt,$$

then
$$\frac{dx}{dt} = Ap \cos pt - Bp \sin pt,$$

and
$$\frac{d^2x}{dt^2} = -Ap^2 \sin pt - Bp^2 \cos pt$$
$$= -p^2x. \quad \text{.........(ii)}$$

Now (i) can be written in the form

$$\frac{d^2x}{dt^2} = -\frac{F}{m}x. \quad \text{.........(iii)}$$

Hence, comparing (ii) and (iii),

$$p = \sqrt{\frac{F}{m}},$$

$$\therefore \; x = A \sin \sqrt{\frac{F}{m}}t + B \cos \sqrt{\frac{F}{m}}t = C \sin\left(\sqrt{\frac{F}{m}}t + a\right); \quad \text{......(iv)}$$

and
$$\frac{dx}{dt} = A\sqrt{\frac{F}{m}} \cos \sqrt{\frac{F}{m}}t - B\sqrt{\frac{F}{m}} \sin \sqrt{\frac{F}{m}}t. \quad \text{.........(v)}$$

Let the initial displacement of the spring be a; $\frac{dx}{dt}$ simply denotes the velocity of P, and, when the displacement is a, the velocity is zero, or P, at the instant considered, is at rest.

Hence $x = a$ when $t = 0$.

Also $\frac{dx}{dt} = 0$ when $t = 0$;

$$\therefore \; a = A \sin\left(\sqrt{\frac{F}{m}} \times 0\right) + B \cos\left(\sqrt{\frac{F}{m}} \times 0\right) \text{ from (iv),}$$

or $a = B$.

Also $0 = A\sqrt{\frac{F}{m}}$ from (v); $\therefore \; A = 0$.

Thus, we obtain

$$x = a \cos \sqrt{\frac{F}{m}}t. \quad \text{.........(vi)}$$

If the constant $\sqrt{\frac{F}{m}}$ be denoted by n, (vi) becomes $x = a \cos nt$.

Substituting various values for nt, we can obtain various data with regard to the motion, thus, when $nt = 0$, $x = a$.

When $nt=\frac{\pi}{2}$, $x=0$; $\therefore$ body is at P.

" $nt=\pi$, $x=a(\cos\pi)=-a$.

" $nt=\frac{3\pi}{2}$, $x=0$.

" $nt=2\pi$, $x=a$.

Hence, as nt increases from 0 to 2π, the body moves through a complete cycle into the initial position;

$$\therefore\ T=2\pi\sqrt{\frac{m}{F}},$$

where T denotes the periodic time.

Similarly, the variations of the velocity can be traced by reference to the values of $\frac{dx}{dt}$.

Ex. 9. The result obtained for the periodic time can easily be verified by experiment. When a load W of 10·5 lbs. is suspended from a spiral spring it is found that 190 swings are made in one minute. Also, 10·8 lbs. is required to stretch the string through unit distance one inch. ($g=32{\cdot}2$ ft. per sec. per sec.)

As 1 minute = 60 seconds,

$$T=\tfrac{60}{190}=\tfrac{6}{19}=0{\cdot}3158 \text{ sec.}$$

Also, $$T=2\pi\sqrt{\frac{m}{F}},$$

where $m=10{\cdot}5\div g=10{\cdot}5\div 32{\cdot}2$

and $F=10{\cdot}8$ lbs.

(as the unit distance is 1 inch, $g=32{\cdot}2\times 12$ ins. per sec. per sec.);

$$T=2\pi\sqrt{\frac{10{\cdot}5}{32{\cdot}2\times 12\times 10{\cdot}8}}=0{\cdot}3152 \text{ sec.}$$

It will be noticed that in the preceding solution the mass of the spring itself has not been taken into account; in fact we have made the assumption that the weight of the spring, and therefore its mass, is negligible in comparison with the vibrating mass at the end of the spring.

Allowance for the weight of the spring may be made by adding a fractional part of the mass of the spring to the vibrating mass at the end of the spring. The numerical value of this fractional part is readily obtained. Thus, if ρ denotes the density of the material of the spring, and if v_1 denotes the velocity of the vibrating spring at a distance x from the point of support, we obtain

$$v_1=\frac{x}{l}v, \text{ where } v \text{ is the velocity of the terminal mass.}$$

$$\therefore \text{ kinetic energy}=\tfrac{1}{2}mv^2+\int_0^l \frac{\rho}{2}\left(\frac{x}{l}v\right)^2 dx=\tfrac{1}{2}mv^2+\left[\frac{\rho}{2}\frac{v^2}{l^2}\frac{x^3}{3}\right]_0^l$$

$$=\tfrac{1}{2}v^2\left(m+\frac{\rho l}{3}\right).$$

Hence, the mass of the spring may be taken into account by adding **one-third its mass** to the mass at the end of the spring.

Ex. 10. A spiral spring is supported at the upper end, and when a weight of 7 lbs. is hung on to the lower end, an extension of 0·1 foot is produced.

Find the time of a vertical oscillation (1) neglecting the mass of the spring, (2) supposing the spring weighs 0·6 lb., and a proper allowance for its mass is added to the 7 lb. weight.

(1) In the formula for the periodic time,

$$t=2\pi\sqrt{\frac{m}{F}},$$

$$m=\frac{7}{32{\cdot}2} \quad\text{and}\quad F=7\times 10=70 \text{ lbs.};$$

$$\therefore\ t=2\pi\sqrt{\frac{7}{32{\cdot}2\times 70}}=2\pi\sqrt{\frac{1}{322}},$$

$$\log t=\log 2+\log\pi-\tfrac{1}{2}\log 322=\bar{1}{\cdot}5443;$$

$$\therefore\ t=0{\cdot}3501 \text{ sec.}$$

(2) Adding $\frac{1}{3}$ the mass of the spring,

$$M=\frac{7}{32{\cdot}2}+\frac{0{\cdot}2}{32{\cdot}2}=\frac{7{\cdot}2}{32{\cdot}2}, \quad\text{also}\quad F=70 \text{ lbs.};$$

$$\therefore\ t=2\pi\sqrt{\frac{7{\cdot}2}{32{\cdot}2\times 70}}=0{\cdot}355 \text{ sec.}$$

Vibration of a beam or rod.—If a bar or rod is supported at its ends A and B and loaded at the centre with a load W, the deflection δ will be given by the formula

$$\delta=\frac{Wl^3}{48EI}, \qquad \text{(i)}$$

where l is the length between supports, E is the modulus of elasticity of the material, and I the moment of inertia. The length and deflection may be expressed in centimetres, in inches, or in feet; W, E, and I must obviously be in the same units. Expressing l and δ in inches, then E will be expressed in pounds per square inch and I in inch units.

If the value of E for a given material is known, from Eq. (i) the numerical value of δ for a given weight W can be calculated. Or, conversely, if δ is carefully measured from experiments, then E can be obtained.

When a bar supported at the ends and loaded at its middle point with a weight W, is made to vibrate, the periodic time of a vibration can be calculated from the formula $T=2\pi\sqrt{\frac{M}{F}}$, where F is the force necessary to produce unit deflection.

A verification of the result may easily be obtained by experiment.

Ex. 11. A wooden rectangular beam or rod rests in a horizontal position on two knife edges 36 inches apart. Find the periodic time of a vibration and the number of vibrations per second when the load at the centre is 11·8 lbs. (Given $E=1{\cdot}865\times10^6$, depth of rod $\frac{1}{2}$ inch, width 1 inch.)

The value of I for a rectangle of sides b and d is $\frac{1}{12}bd^3$ (p. 432).

Substituting in (i), $$\delta=\frac{Wl^3}{4Ebd^3}; \qquad \text{(ii)}$$

$$\therefore \quad W=\frac{4\times1{\cdot}865\times10^6\times1\times(0{\cdot}5)^3\times12}{36^3}\times\delta_1.$$

Obviously, δ_1 must denote the deflection in feet when $g=32{\cdot}2$, and in inches when $g=32{\cdot}2\times12$.

W, the load required to produce unit deflection of 1 foot, is found to be 240 lbs.; the weight of the rod is 8·5 oz., and for the purpose of this calculation $\frac{31}{63}$rds of this may be assumed to act at its middle point;

$$\therefore \text{ mass} = \frac{11\cdot8}{32\cdot2} + \frac{\frac{31}{63} \times 8\cdot5}{16 \times 32\cdot2} = 0\cdot3745\,;$$

$$\therefore \text{ periodic time } T = 2\pi\sqrt{\frac{0\cdot3745}{240}} = 0\cdot2482 \text{ second,}$$

or 4·03 vibrations per second.

The formula used may be readily proved by the student in a manner similar to that used in finding the time of a vibration of a mass suspended from a spring (p. 481). In fact a beam or rod loaded in the manner indicated is only one form of spring.

Simple pendulum.—The nearest approximation to a so-called simple pendulum consists of a small heavy body, such as a leaden bullet, at one end of a fine string, the other end of the string being fixed to a suitable support and the pendulum made to perform small oscillations in a vertical plane. When the arc of vibration is small, the time of vibration may be obtained in a very simple manner as follows :

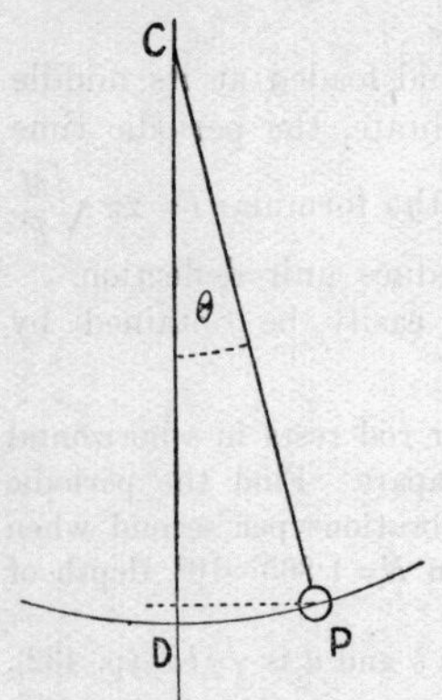

FIG. 178.—Simple pendulum.

Let P (Fig. 178) denote a small mass at one end of a string of length l, the other end of which is fastened to a fixed support C.

Let m denote the mass of the particle at P, and θ the angle DCP.

The two components of the force mg, one along the string PC, the other at right angles to it, may be obtained. The former component, $mg\cos\theta$, produces tension in the string, the latter, $mg\sin\theta$, produces the acceleration of P.

From the relation, force = mass × acceleration

$$\text{acceleration of } P = \frac{mg\sin\theta}{m} = g\sin\theta.$$

The relation between acceleration and displacement in S.H.M. is furnished by

$$\frac{\text{acceleration}}{\text{displacement}} = \omega^2 = \frac{2^2\pi^2}{T^2} \text{ (p. 135)};$$

$$\therefore \frac{2^2\pi^2}{T^2} = \frac{g \sin \theta}{l\theta}.$$

As the angle is supposed to be small, the sine of the angle is very approximately equal to its circular measure (p. 383).

Hence we obtain $$\frac{2^2\pi^2}{T^2} = \frac{g}{l};$$

$$\therefore T = 2\pi\sqrt{\frac{l}{g}}, \quad \text{.........................(i)}$$

where T denotes the periodic time of a vibration.

In the preceding case the arc of swing has been assumed to be very small; when this is not the case, Eq. (i) cannot be used to find the periodic time.

The relation between force and acceleration is

force = mass × acceleration,

or torque = (moment of inertia) × (angular acceleration),

the former being expressed in linear, the latter in angular, motion.

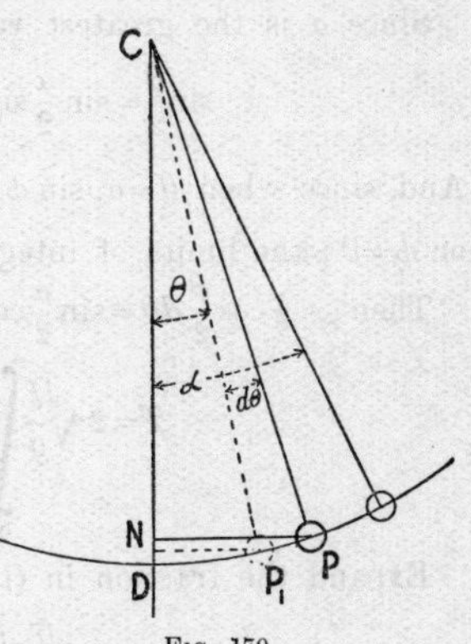

FIG. 179.

Let m be the mass at P (Fig. 179), l the length of CP, P_1 and P two positions of P, the angle $DCP_1 = \theta$, and $P_1CP = d\theta$. Draw PN perpendicular to DC.

Then, $\quad$ torque $= m \times PN = ml \sin \theta$.

Also, moment of inertia of P about C is ml^2;

$$\therefore mgl \sin \theta = -ml^2 \frac{d^2\theta}{dt^2}.$$

The negative sign denotes that θ is decreasing; dividing by ml^2, we obtain

$$\frac{d^2\theta}{dt^2} + \frac{g \sin \theta}{l} = 0. \quad \text{.................................(i)}$$

Multiply by $2\frac{d\theta}{dt}$; and integrate between limits $\left(\frac{d\theta}{dt}=0\right.$, when $\theta=\alpha$, where α is the greatest value of $\left.\theta\right)$;

$$\therefore \frac{d\theta}{dt}=\sqrt{\frac{2g}{l}}(\cos\theta-\cos\alpha)^{\frac{1}{2}},$$

and
$$t=\sqrt{\frac{l}{2g}}\int\frac{d\theta}{(\cos\theta-\cos\alpha)^{\frac{1}{2}}}.$$

As $\cos\theta=1-2\sin^2\frac{\theta}{2}$ and $\cos\alpha=1-2\sin^2\frac{\alpha}{2}$, the periodic time becomes

$$T=\frac{4}{2}\sqrt{\frac{l}{g}}\int_0^\alpha\frac{d\theta}{\sqrt{\left(\sin^2\frac{\alpha}{2}-\sin^2\frac{\theta}{2}\right)}}.$$

Since α is the greatest value of θ, we may assume

$$\sin\frac{\theta}{2}=\sin\frac{\alpha}{2}\sin\phi.$$

And, since when $\theta=\alpha$, $\sin\phi=1$ or $\frac{\pi}{2}$, and when $\theta=0$, $\sin\phi=0$ or $\phi=0$; the limits of integration are $\frac{\pi}{2}$ and 0.

Then $\quad \frac{1}{2}\cos\frac{\theta}{2}\,d\theta=\sin\frac{\alpha}{2}\cos\phi d\phi$;

$$\therefore T=2\sqrt{\frac{l}{g}}\int_0^{\frac{\pi}{2}}\frac{2d\phi}{\left(1-\sin^2\frac{\alpha}{2}\sin^2\phi\right)^{\frac{1}{2}}}\quad\text{.................(ii)}$$

Expand the fraction in (ii) by the Binomial Theorem;

$$\therefore T=4\sqrt{\frac{l}{g}}\int_0^{\frac{\pi}{2}}\left\{1+\frac{1}{2}\sin^2\frac{\alpha}{2}\sin^2\phi+\dots\right\}d\phi$$

$$=4\sqrt{\frac{l}{g}}\left[\phi+\frac{1}{2}\sin^2\frac{\alpha}{2}\left\{\frac{\phi}{2}-\frac{\sin 2\phi}{4}\right\}+\text{etc.}\right]_0^{\frac{\pi}{2}}$$

$$=4\pi\sqrt{\frac{l}{g}}\left(\frac{1}{2}+\frac{1}{8}\sin^2\frac{\alpha}{2}\right)$$

+ terms which may be neglected

$$=2\pi\sqrt{\frac{l}{g}}\left(1+\frac{\alpha^2}{16}\right),\text{ approx.}$$

If θ is small, θ may be written for $\sin\theta$ in Eq. (i), and the formula for a simple pendulum obtained.

Ex. 12. If l is the length of a seconds pendulum, find the number of seconds lost in a day when the arc of vibration is 9°.

We may denote by T the periodic time of a seconds pendulum, and by T' that of a pendulum which swings through an angle of 9° on each side of the vertical.

As 24 hours is 24×3600 seconds;

$$\therefore \text{ loss in seconds} = 24 \times 3600\, T\left(\frac{1}{T} - \frac{1}{T'}\right)$$

$$= 24 \times 3600\left(1 - \frac{T}{T'}\right)$$

$$= 24 \times 3600\left(1 - \frac{1}{1 + \frac{a^2}{16}}\right)$$

$$= 24 \times 3600\left(\frac{a^2}{16 + a^2}\right)$$

$$= \frac{24 \times 3600(0{\cdot}1571)^2}{16 + (0{\cdot}1571)^2} = 133{\cdot}1 \text{ secs.}$$

Ex. 13. A uniform straight plank rests with its middle point upon a rough horizontal cylinder, the axes of the cylinder and plank being perpendicular to each other. Supposing the plank to be slightly displaced so as to remain always in contact with the cylinder without sliding, determine the periodic time.

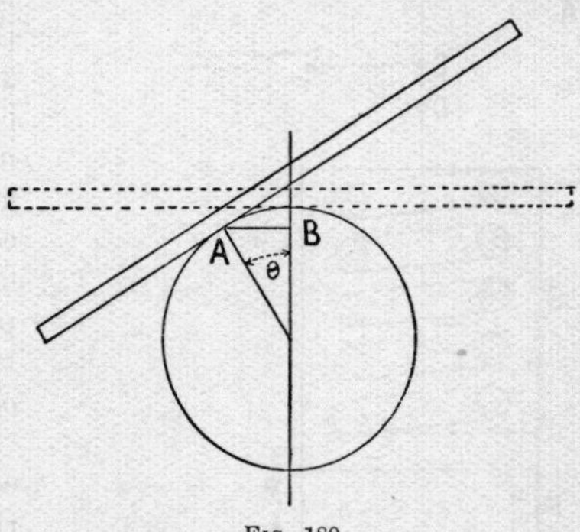

FIG. 180.

Let $2l$ denote the length of the plank and r the radius of the cylinder, and let m denote the mass of the plank.

Assume the plank to be displaced through a small angle θ so that the plank and cylinder are in contact at a point A (Fig. 180). Draw AB perpendicular to the vertical line passing through the centre of the cylinder, then moment of restoring force is $mg \times AB = mgr \sin\theta$ (very approximately);

$$\therefore \; mgr \sin\theta = -I\frac{d^2\theta}{dt^2}. \quad \text{.........................(i)}$$

The value of I for a thin rod, length $2l$, about an axis passing perpendicularly through its middle point is $\frac{ml^2}{3}$ (p. 431).

Hence, substituting in (i),

$$mgr \sin\theta + \frac{ml^2}{3}\frac{d^2\theta}{dt^2} = 0.$$

As the angle is small, $\sin\theta$ is approximately equal to θ;

$$\therefore \; gr\theta + \frac{l^2}{3}\frac{d^2\theta}{dt^2} = 0.$$

Solving as in Type II. (p. 480),

$$\theta = A \sin\sqrt{\frac{3gr}{l^2}}\,t + B\cos\sqrt{\frac{3gr}{l^2}}\,t;$$

$$\therefore \; \text{periodic time} = \frac{2\pi l}{\sqrt{3gr}}.$$

Vibration of an indicator.—In some cases, such as, for example, in a steam engine indicator, the calculation for the frequency of a vibration must include the consideration of two or more vibrating masses. Thus, in Fig. 181, pressure on the piston P compresses a spring S; the motion of the piston rod, by means of suitable links, gives motion to a lever centred at A. The other end C, carrying a pencil point, indicates on an enlarged scale the motion of the piston P.

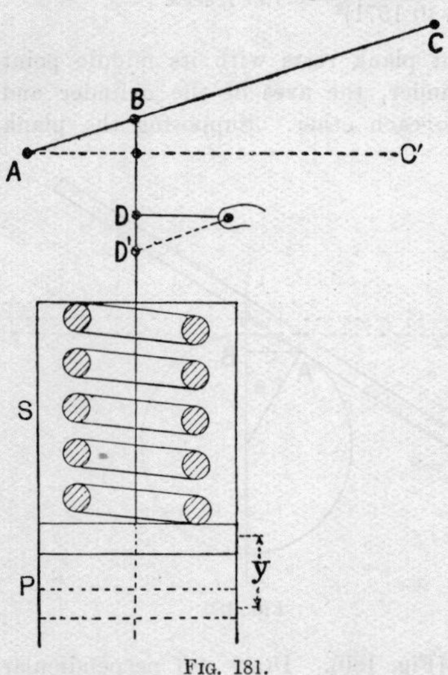

Fig. 181.

The frequency may be calculated by estimating the masses of the moving parts and the shortening produced in the spring by a given pressure. Let M denote the mass in pounds of piston and rod including the link BD and one-third the mass of the spring. Let I denote the moment of inertia (in ft. lbs. units) of the lever ABC. The initial position of the lever is at AC'. When the piston moves through a distance y, the position of the lever may be denoted by the line AC making an angle θ with AC'.

If c denote the compression (in feet) of the spring per pound of load, and a in the same units the initial compression of the spring when the lever is horizontal.

Let F be the compressive force, tending to move AC only, then $\frac{d^2\theta}{dt^2}=\frac{AB.F}{I}$, where I denotes the moment of inertia about A.

$$\therefore F=\frac{I}{AB}\frac{d^2\theta}{dt^2}=\frac{I}{AB^2}\frac{d^2y}{dt^2};$$

if θ is so small that $y=\theta\times AB$, then, from the relation

mass × acceleration = force acting,

we obtain the equation for the whole motion

$$M\frac{d^2y}{dt^2}+\frac{I}{AB^2}\frac{d^2y}{dt^2}=-C\frac{y+a}{a}.$$

This gives for the periodic time

$$T=2\pi\sqrt{\frac{\left(M+\frac{I}{AB^2}\right)a}{C}}$$

$$=\frac{2\pi}{AB}\sqrt{\frac{(M\times AB^2+I)a}{C}}.$$

It will be noticed that the mass of the lever and its length are taken into account in the moment of inertia.

Struts.—A rod of length $2l$ acted on by compressive forces in the direction of its length (Fig. 182) is called a **strut**.

The equation connecting the force F, the deflection y, and the curvature is expressed by

$$\frac{Fy}{EI}=-\frac{d^2y}{dx^2}. \qquad \text{(i)}$$

Let $n^2=\frac{F}{EI}$, then, as in the preceding case, (i) may be written

$$\frac{d^2y}{dx^2}=-n^2y.$$

Hence
$$y=A\sin nx+B\cos nx. \qquad \text{(ii)}$$

From (ii), by differentiation,

$$\frac{dy}{dx}=An\cos nx-Bn\sin nx. \quad \text{(iii)}$$

Now the tangent to the curve is parallel to the axis of x at O, where $x=0$, and at the two ends M and N, where $x=l$ and $x=-l$, respectively, $y=0$.

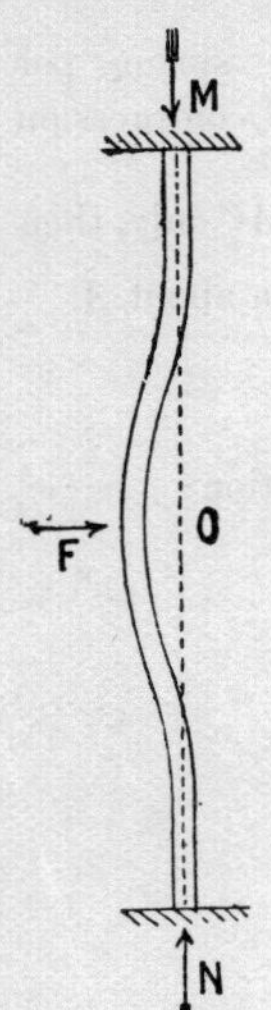

FIG. 182.

Putting $\frac{dy}{dx}=0$ and $x=0$, in (iii),

$$0=An; \quad \therefore A=0.$$

Hence, substituting in (ii),

$$y=B\cos nx=B\cos\sqrt{\frac{F}{EI}}x. \quad \text{(iv)}$$

When $x=0$, $y=B$. Hence, the constant B denotes the maximum deflection, that is, the deflection of the strut in the centre.

Again, when $x=l$, or $-l$, $y=0$. Hence, from (iv),

$$0=B\cos\sqrt{\frac{F}{EI}}l. \quad \text{(v)}$$

It follows at once from Eq. (v) either that $B=0$ or

$$\cos\left(\sqrt{\frac{F}{EI}}l\right)=0.$$

Hence, $\cos\left(\sqrt{\frac{F}{EI}}l\right)$ must be 0, since, from the above considerations, B is not zero, hence the angle must be $\frac{\pi}{2}$, $\frac{3\pi}{2}$, or other odd multiple of $\frac{\pi}{2}$;

$$\therefore \sqrt{\frac{F}{EI}}l=\frac{\pi}{2},$$

or

$$F=\frac{EI\pi^2}{4l^2}.$$

Ends fixed.—The maximum value of F_1 when the ends of a strut are fixed may be obtained as follows:

From (ii),

$$y=A\sin nx+B\cos nx$$

$$=A\sin\sqrt{\left(\frac{F_1}{EI}\right)}x+B\cos\sqrt{\left(\frac{F_1}{EI}\right)}x;$$

$$\therefore \frac{dy}{dx}=\sqrt{\frac{F_1}{EI}}A\cos\sqrt{\frac{F_1}{EI}}x-B\sqrt{\frac{F_1}{EI}}\sin\sqrt{\frac{F_1}{EI}}x.$$

In this case $\frac{dy}{dx}=0$ when $x=0$, also when $x=l$ and when $x=-l$.

Let $x=0$, then

$$0=A\sqrt{\frac{F_1}{EI}};\quad \therefore A=0;\quad \therefore y=B\cos\sqrt{\frac{F_1}{EI}}x.$$

Differentiating,

$$\frac{dy}{dx}=-B\sqrt{\frac{F_1}{EI}}\sin\sqrt{\frac{F_1}{EI}}x.$$

Now, when $x=l$, $\frac{dy}{dx}=0$;

$$\therefore 0=-B\sqrt{\frac{F_1}{EI}}\sin\sqrt{\frac{F_1}{EI}}l.$$

Hence, either $B=0$ or $\sin\sqrt{\frac{F_1}{EI}}l=0.$

Therefore, as B cannot be 0, the angle must be π or 2π, etc.

Taking the smallest value, we have

$$\sqrt{\frac{F_1}{EI}}l=\pi;$$

$$\therefore F_1=\frac{EI\pi^2}{l^2}.$$

The formulae for F and F_1 are known as **Euler's** formulae.

Hence, a strut fixed in direction at both ends is four times as strong as a strut in which one end is not fixed in direction.

Ex. 14. Find the breaking load of a wrought-iron cylindrical pillar or strut, 3 inches diameter and 6 feet long. $E=29\times10^6$.

Here $I=\frac{\pi r^4}{4}=\frac{\pi\times3^4}{4^3}$; $l=6\times12$;

$$\therefore F=\frac{29\times10^6\times\pi^3\times3^4}{4^3\times6^2\times12^2}=\frac{29\times10^6\times\pi^3\times3^4}{4^3\times72^2}\text{ lbs.}$$

$$\log F=\log29+6\log10+3\log\pi+4\log3-(3\log4+2\log72+\log2240);$$

$$\therefore F=98\text{ tons, approx.}$$

Differential Equations: Type III.—The differential equation given by Type II. (p. 480) is of great utility and importance, and is that arrived at in very many problems on vibration. A more general form is, however, sometimes wanted, as in the case of damped vibrations (p. 142), and the equation may be written in the form

$$\frac{d^2s}{dt^2}+2F\frac{ds}{dt}+k^2s=0.$$

We may surmise that $s=Ae^{at}$ will be a solution. Trying this value, we obtain

$$\frac{ds}{dt}=Aae^{at} \quad \text{and} \quad \frac{d^2s}{dt^2}=Aa^2e^{at};$$

$$\therefore \; Aa^2e^{at}+Aae^{at}(2F)+k^2Ae^{at}=0,$$

or

$$s(a^2+2Fa+k^2)=0.$$

Solving the quadratic

$$a=-F\pm\sqrt{F^2-k^2}.$$

Now the solution assumes three forms according as F is greater than, equal to, or less than k.

(i) Let $F>k$, then both values of a are real, and the solution is

$$s=Ae^{(-F+\sqrt{F^2-k^2})t}+Be^{(-F-\sqrt{F^2-k^2})t}$$

$$=e^{-Ft}(Ae^{t\sqrt{F^2-k^2}}+Be^{-t\sqrt{F^2-k^2}}).$$

(ii) Let $F=k$, then the two values of a are equal;

$$\therefore \; s=(A+B)e^{-Ft}=Ke^{-Ft}$$

where $K=A+B$. There is thus only one arbitrary constant instead of two; hence the solution is not complete. To determine the complete solution, let $s=ue^{-Ft}$, where u is a function of t to be determined; then, substituting in the original equation,

$$\frac{d^2u}{dt^2}=0,$$

which, on integration, gives $\frac{du}{dt}=C$,

and, integrating again, $u=Ct+D$, where C, D are the arbitrary constants of integration.

Hence the complete solution becomes

$$s=(Ct+D)e^{-Ft}.$$

(iii) Let $F<k$, then $a=-F\pm i\sqrt{k^2-F^2}$, and the solution is

$$s=e^{-Ft}(Ae^{it\sqrt{k^2-F^2}}+Be^{-it\sqrt{k^2-F^2}}).$$

Using (i) and (ii) from p. 382, the solution becomes

$$s=e^{-Ft}(C\cos\sqrt{k^2-F^2}t+D\sin\sqrt{k^2-F^2}t),$$

where $\quad C=A+B \quad$ and $\quad D=i(A-B).$

If F is zero the solution becomes

$$s=A\sin kt+B\cos kt,$$

and the differential equation is

$$\frac{d^2s}{dt^2}+k^2s=0,$$

i.e. the equation of Type II.

Ex. 15. Solve the differential equation

$$\frac{d^2y}{dx^2}+3\frac{dy}{dx}+2y=0.$$

Put $y=Ae^{ax}$, and we obtain

$$a^2+3a+2=0,$$

or $a=-1$ and $a=-2.$

Solution is $\quad y=Ae^{-x}+Be^{-2x}.$

Ex. 16. Solve the equation

$$\frac{d^2y}{dx^2}-4\frac{dy}{dx}+4y=0$$

Here the roots are equal;

$$\therefore\ y=(A+Bx)e^{-2x}.$$

Ex. 17. $\quad \frac{1}{4}\frac{d^2y}{dx^2}+\frac{dy}{dx}+\frac{y}{2}=0.$

Substituting, we find

$$a^2+4a+2=0;$$

$$\therefore\ y=e^{-2x}\{A\sin\sqrt{2}x+B\cos\sqrt{2}x\}.$$

MISCELLANEOUS EXERCISES. XLV.

Solve the equations:

1. $\frac{d^2y}{dx^2}+7\frac{dy}{dx}+9y=0.$

2. $3\frac{d^2y}{dx^2}+25\frac{dy}{dx}-18y=0.$

3. $\frac{d^2y}{dx^2}-6\frac{dy}{dx}+9y=0.$

4. $2\frac{d^2y}{dx^2}+17\frac{dy}{dx}+40y=0.$

5. In how many years will a sum of money quadruple itself at 5 per cent. per annum?

6. A wet rope touches half way round a rough cylindrical post, and the rope begins to slip when the tensions at the two ends of the rope are 7 lbs. and 56 lbs. respectively. Find the coefficient of friction between the rope and the cylinder. Also find approximately the weight which would be supported if the rope were to make an additional complete turn.

7. Write down the relation between the tensions T_1 and T_2 when a belt or rope is just about to slip on a pulley. If T_1 may be three times T_2 when the angle is 180° without making the rope slip, what will the ratio be when the rope makes a complete turn?

8. If a string, hanging in a vertical plane over a rough horizontal cylinder with 20 lbs. hanging at one end and 2 lbs. at the other, be on the point of slipping, find the coefficient of friction between the cylinder and the string.

9. The slope of a curve at a point whose abscissa is x is given by x^2-x+1. Given that the curve passes through the point $x=1$, $y=2$; find the equation to the curve. Also find the value of y when $x=3$.

10. At what point on the curve $y=2x^3$ is the tangent parallel to the line which touches the curve $y=3x^2-6x+2$ at the point P whose abscissa x is 1·4? Also find the radius of curvature at P.

11. Find the points of intersection of the curves

$$y^2=4ax \text{ and } y^2=\frac{4}{27a}(x-2a)^3.$$

12. Divide 30 into two parts such that the square of the first together with twice the square of the second shall be a minimum.

13. Given the three points (0, 0) (2, 8) (4, 20). Assuming the equation of the curve passing through the three points to be $y=a+bx+cx^2$, find the area between the axis of x and the ordinates $x=0$, $x=4$. If the curve rotates about the axis of x, find the volume.

14. Find the volume of the segment of a sphere the height of the segment being one-half the radius.

15. Draw the graph of $y=\frac{1}{2}(e^x+e^{-x})$. Find the area bounded by the curve and the two ordinates where $x=0$, $x=1·5$. If this area rotates about the axis of x; find the volume described.

EXAMINATION QUESTIONS.

MISCELLANEOUS.

Section I. Arithmetic.

1. The heat developed by one cubic foot of coal gas, one Board of Trade unit of electricity, and by one pound of coal are in the proportion of 1, 5, 24. If the cost of 1000 cubic feet of gas is 3*s.*, what should be paid per ton of coal? If the cost of one unit of electricity is 6*d.*, what should be the price per ton of coal?

Compute by contracted methods without using logarithms:

2. $23{\cdot}07 \times 0{\cdot}1354, \quad 2307 \div 1{\cdot}354.$

Compute by contracted methods to four significant figures only, and without using logarithms or slide rule:

3. $8{\cdot}102 \times 35{\cdot}14, \quad 254{\cdot}3 \div 0{\cdot}09027.$

4. $34{\cdot}05 \times 0{\cdot}009123$ and $3{\cdot}405 \div 0{\cdot}09123.$

5. $0{\cdot}03405 \times 0{\cdot}9123$

and $34{\cdot}05 \div 0{\cdot}09123.$

6. $0{\cdot}01239 \times 0{\cdot}5024, \quad 0{\cdot}1239 \div 50{\cdot}24.$

Section II. Logarithms.

1. Given $a = 3{\cdot}741, \; b = 53{\cdot}92, \; c = 0{\cdot}04168,$

calculate the values of $\dfrac{ab}{\sqrt{c}}, \; \dfrac{c}{ab}, \; \sqrt{abc}.$

2. Evaluate $p^{\frac{3}{5}}(p^2 - q^2)^{-\frac{1}{2}}$

when $p = 11{\cdot}78, \; q = 5{\cdot}67.$

3. Assuming that the squares of the periodic times of the planets vary as the cubes of the semi-major axes of their orbits, determine the semi-major axis of the orbit of Mars about the sun from the following data:

Periodic time of Earth $=365$ days.

" " Mars $=687$ days.

Semi-major axis of Earth's orbit $=93\times10^6$ miles.

Evaluate

4. (i) $(5{\cdot}016)^{2{\cdot}1}$, (ii) $0{\cdot}5016^{-3{\cdot}2}$.

5. (i) $(2{\cdot}345)^{0{\cdot}56}$, (ii) $(0{\cdot}02345)^{-1{\cdot}27}$.

6. (i) $(2{\cdot}308)^{0{\cdot}65}$, (ii) $(0{\cdot}2308)^{-1{\cdot}24}$.

7. $(\sin 59°\,30')^2$.

8. Evaluate $\dfrac{\sqrt[3]{(618)^2}+19\div(38)^{\frac{3}{5}}}{\pi(0{\cdot}0186)^2\times\sqrt[3]{0{\cdot}0125\times10^4}}$.

9. A sum of money doubles itself in 20 years at compound interest, what is the rate per cent?

If a man 60 years old can buy an annuity of £100 a year for £1150, interest being reckoned at 3 per cent., determine what is considered the expectation of life at 60.

10. If the formula $\log\dfrac{H}{V}=a+bV$ represents the relation between H, the horse-power developed by a set of marine engines, and V, the speed of the vessel in knots, then given that speeds of 13 and 22·1 knots correspond to horse-powers of 4738 and 22065 respectively, find the numerical values of the constants a and b.

Also find the horse-power corresponding to a speed of 18 knots.

11. Evaluate $y=e^{-kt}\sin(pt+q)$,

given $k=0{\cdot}1$, $p=0{\cdot}3$, $q=0{\cdot}2$, $e=2{\cdot}718$,

(i) when $t=1$, (ii) when $t=5$.

12. Find values of x to satisfy the expressions:

(i) $\log x=-\frac{7}{4}$, (ii) $x\log 0{\cdot}0612=\log 0{\cdot}3128$.

(iii) $2^x=0{\cdot}034$, (iv) $7^x(7^x-3)=18$.

13. The net yearly profit of a railway may be represented by

$$P=bx+cy,$$

where x is the gross yearly receipt from passengers, and y from goods; b and c being constants.

When $x=520{,}000$ and $y=220{,}000$, P was 330,000, and at a later period when $x=902{,}000$ and $y=700{,}000$, P was 603,000. Find b and c. What will be the probable value of P when $x=1{,}000{,}000$ and $y=800{,}000$?

14. Given $p=a(\theta+b)^5$, where p is the pressure of a certain quantity of steam at a temperature θ,

if $p=28{\cdot}83$ when $\theta=120$,

and $p=52{\cdot}52$,, $\theta=140$,

find the numerical values of a and b. Also find the value of p when θ is 130.

15. Given $y=ae^{bx}$ where $e=2{\cdot}718$,

if $y=7{\cdot}695$ when $x=12$,

$y=12{\cdot}07$,, $x=30$, find a and b.

16. Given $T_2=T_1e^{\mu\theta}$,

if $T_2=65{\cdot}9$ when $\theta=2\pi$,

and $T_2=169$,, $\theta=3\pi$, find μ.

17. If W is the load in tons on a column of length l and diameter d, and $W=cd^{3{\cdot}7}\times l^{-n}$, then given that when

$d=3$, and $l=12$, $W=13{\cdot}57$;

$d=3$, and $l=8$, $W=27{\cdot}03$;

find c and n. Also find W when $l=16$, $d=4$.

18. In a certain country the number of births in any year is $\frac{1}{33}$, and the number of deaths $\frac{1}{46}$ of the population at the beginning of that year. If the number of emigrants in any year is just equal to the number of immigrants in that year, in how many years would the population double itself?

19. Compute

$30{\cdot}56\div4{\cdot}105$, $0{\cdot}03056\times0{\cdot}4105$, $4{\cdot}105^{1{\cdot}23}$, $0{\cdot}04105^{-2{\cdot}3}$.

The answers must be right to three significant figures.

Why do we multiply $\log a$ by b to obtain the logarithm of a^b?

20. Compute $2{\cdot}307^{0{\cdot}65}$ and $23{\cdot}07^{-1{\cdot}25}$ using logarithms. The answers to consist of four significant figures.

Why do we add logarithms to obtain the logarithm of a product?

Suppose we have a scale on a slide rule on which, as usual, the distance to any mark n is $\log n$: and there is another scale on which the distance to any mark m is $\log(\log m)$; show that we can at once read off m^n and also the logarithm of any number to any base.

21. State the logarithms of 37240, 37·24, 0·03724.

Compute, using logarithms,

$\sqrt[3]{37{\cdot}24}$, $\sqrt[2]{3{\cdot}724}$, $372{\cdot}4^{2{\cdot}43}$, $0{\cdot}3724^{-2{\cdot}43}$.

Explain why it is that logarithms are multiplied in computing the powers of numbers.

In using your four-figure logarithm table have you observed that there is more chance of error at some places than at others? How is this? Can you suggest an improvement in such tables?

22. Compute, using logarithms, $\sqrt[3]{0{\cdot}2354 \times 16{\cdot}07}$,

$$(32{\cdot}15)^{0{\cdot}152}, \quad (32{\cdot}15)^{-0{\cdot}152}.$$

Explain why we add logarithms when we wish to multiply numbers.

23. It has been found that if P is the horse-power wasted in air friction when a disc d feet diameter is revolving at n revolutions per minute

$$P = cd^{5{\cdot}5}n^{3{\cdot}5}.$$

If P is 0·1 when $d=4$ and $n=500$, find the constant c.

What is the diameter of a disc which wastes 10 horse-power in air friction when revolving at 580 revolutions per minute?

24. Compute, using logarithms,

$$(2{\cdot}354 \times 1{\cdot}607)^{0{\cdot}315}$$

and

$$(32{\cdot}15)^{-0{\cdot}152}.$$

25. There are two formulae used to calculate ϕ:

$$\phi = \log_e \frac{t}{273},$$

which is only approximate;

$$\phi = 1{\cdot}0565 \log_e \frac{t}{273} + 9 \times 10^{-7}\left(\frac{t^2}{2} - 503t\right) + 0{\cdot}0902,$$

which is correct.

If $t = \theta + 273$ when $\theta = 53$, find the two answers: what is the percentage error in using the approximate formula?

26. If P is the present value of an annuity A, the first payment being due 1 year from now, the last at the end of the nth year from now, the rate of interest on money being at r per cent. per annum; then

$$P = 100\frac{A}{r}\left\{1 - \left(1 + \frac{r}{100}\right)^{-n}\right\}.$$

If the present value of an annuity of 65*l.* is 627*l.* and r is $3\frac{1}{2}$ per cent. per annum, what is the supposed number of years' duration of the annuity?

27. If $a=5$, $b=200$, $c=600$, $g=-0{\cdot}1745$ radian, find the value of

$$ae^{-bt}\sin(ct+g),$$

(i) when $t=0{\cdot}001$, (ii) when $t=0{\cdot}01$, (iii) when $t=0{\cdot}1$.

28. In any class of turbine if P is the power of the waterfall, and R is the average radius at the place where the water enters the wheel, then it is known that for any particular class of turbines of all sizes

$$n \propto H^{1{\cdot}25} P^{-0{\cdot}5},$$

$$R \propto P^{0{\cdot}5} H^{-0{\cdot}75}.$$

In the list of a particular maker I take a turbine at random for a fall of 6 feet, 100 horse-power, 50 revolutions per minute, 2·51 feet radius. By means of this I find I can calculate n and R for all the other turbines of the list. Find n and R for a fall of 20 feet and 75 horse-power.

29. What is the idea on which compound interest is calculated? Explain, as if to a beginner, how it is that

$$A = P\left(1 + \frac{r}{100}\right)^n,$$

where P is the money lent and A is what it amounts to in n years at r per cent. per annum. If A is 130 and P is 100 and n is 7·5, find r. What does the above equation become when we imagine interest to be added on to principal every instant? State two natural phenomena which follow the compound interest law.

30. If pv^k is constant; and if $p=1$, when $v=1$, find for what value of v, p is 0·2. Do this for the following values of k, 0·8, 0·9, 1·0, 1·1. Tabulate your answers.

31. (*a*) If $\theta = 0{\cdot}8\pi$, $\mu = 0{\cdot}3$ and $N = Me^{\mu\theta}$; if $(N-M)V = 33000P$; if P is 30 and V is 520; find N.

(*b*) Find the value of $10e^{-0{\cdot}7t}\sin(2\pi ft + 0{\cdot}6)$, where f is 225 and t is 0·003.

Observe that the angle is stated in *radians*.

(*c*) If $$A = P\left(1 + \frac{r}{100}\right)^n,$$

and if $A = 3P$ when $r = 3\frac{1}{2}$, find n.

32. The population of a country was $4{\cdot}35 \times 10^6$ in 1820, $7{\cdot}5 \times 10^6$ is 1860, $11{\cdot}26 \times 10^6$ in 1890. Test if the population follows the compound interest law of increase. What is the probable population in 1910?

33. At *corresponding* high speeds of modern ships of the same class, if v is the speed in knots, D the displacement in tons, P the indicated horse-power, T the time spent in a particular passage, and C the coal consumed,

$$v \propto D^{\frac{1}{6}}, \quad P \propto D^{\frac{2}{3}}v^3, \quad C \propto PT,$$

show how P, T, and C depend upon D alone.

A cross-Atlantic steamer of 10,000 tons at 20 knots crosses in 6 days, its power being 20,000, using 2,520 tons of coal; what must be the displacement, the speed, the power, and the coal for a vessel which makes the passage in 5 days?

34. The horse-power (H) of an engine is calculated from

$$H = paln \div 33000;$$

where p is the mean pressure, a the area of the piston, l the length of stroke, and n the number of strokes per minute. What is the possible error in the value of H if the following errors in excess are probable? p, 5 %, l, 2 %, n, 1 %, a, 3 %.

Given $p = 80{\cdot}5$, $a = 100$, $l = 1{\cdot}5$, $n = 100$, find the possible error in the calculated value of H.

35. The numerical value of the modulus of elasticity of a steel rod is obtained from the formula $E=\frac{Wl^3}{48DI}$, where $I=\frac{\pi d^4}{64}$, l is the distance between the supports, W is the load on the rod midway between the supports, D is the droop or deflection produced by the load W.

(i) Given $D=0{\cdot}07$, $l=19$, $d=0{\cdot}3724$, $W=14$, find E.

(ii) If there are possible errors of observation so that the measured value of l is 2 per cent. too small, the value of D 1 per cent. too great, and d $1\frac{1}{2}$ per cent. too great, find the value of E.

36. The value of g (acceleration due to gravity) is found from $t=2\pi\sqrt{\frac{l}{g}}$, where t is the periodic time of an oscillation, and l the length of a pendulum. What will be the percentage error in the value of g, if the observed value of t is $1\frac{1}{2}$ per cent. too large?

37. What percentage error will be made in the calculated volume of a sphere, if the measured value of the radius is $1\frac{1}{2}$ per cent. too large? Find the error when the radius is 6 inches.

Section III. Trigonometry.

1. The sides of a triangle are 434, 528, and 619 ft. respectively. Find the greatest angle and the area of the triangle.

2. The angle of elevation of a tower on a horizontal plane passing through the base of the tower is found to be 15°. On walking a distance 75 ft. nearer the angle becomes 20°; find the height of the tower.

3. $$\sin(A+B)=\sin A\cos B+\cos A\sin B.$$

Write down the other three corresponding formulae.

Using $A=50°$, $B=30°$ test these formulae. Write out what the formulae become if

(i) $A=90°$, (ii) if $B=90°$, (iii) if $A=B$.

$$\sin\alpha\cos\beta=\tfrac{1}{2}\{\sin(\alpha+\beta)+\sin(\alpha-\beta)\}.$$

Write down the other three corresponding formulae.

Write out what the formulae become

(i) if $\alpha=90°$, (ii) if $\beta=90°$, (iii) if $\alpha=\beta$.

4. The three sides of a triangle are 2619, 2831, and 4692 feet respectively. Find the three angles and area of the triangle.

5. Two sides and the included angle of a triangle are given; explain how the remaining parts can be found, by dividing the triangle into two right-angled triangles. In a triangle ABC, given

$$b=3251, \quad c=4793, \quad A=71°,$$

find the angles B and C by the method indicated above; the dividing line being drawn from C to AB.

6. The sides of a triangle ABC are $a=77$ mm., $b=51$ mm., $c=40$ mm.

Find values of $\tan\frac{A}{2}$, $\tan\frac{B}{2}$, $\tan\frac{C}{2}$ and of $\sin A$, $\cos B$, $\tan C$.
Draw the triangle to scale and show that the area is 924 sq. mm.

7. Two sides of a triangle are measured and found to be 32·5 and 24·2 inches; the included angle being 57°, find the area of the triangle. Prove the rule used by you. If the true lengths of the sides are really 32·6 and 24·1, what is the percentage error in the answer?

8. If $x=a\sin pt+b\cos pt$ for any value of t where a, b, and p are mere numbers; show that this is the same as $x=A\sin(pt+e)$ if A and e are properly evaluated.

9. Write in a table the values of the sine, cosine, and tangent of the following angles:

$$23°,\ 123°,\ 233°,\ 312°,\ 383°.$$

10. Write down the value of $\sin 23°$ and $\cos 23°$. What is the sum of the squares of these? Explain why you would get the same answer whatever the angle.

11. ABC is a triangle, C being a right angle. AB is 9·82 inches, the angle A is 28°. Find the sides BC and AC, using the Tables.

12. There is a district in which the surface of the ground may be regarded as a sloping plane; its actual area is 3·246 square miles; it is shown on the map as an area of 2·875 square miles; at what angle is it inclined to the horizontal?
Prove the truth of the rule which you use.

13. Assuming the earth to be a sphere, if its circumference is 360×60 nautical miles, what is the circumference of the parallel of latitude 50°? What is the length there of a degree of longitude? If a small map is to be drawn in this latitude, with north and south and east and west distances to the same scale, and if a degree of latitude (which is of course 60 miles) is shown as 10 inches, what distance will represent a degree of longitude?

14. Write down the values of

$$\sin 107°,\quad \cos 148°,\quad \tan 250°.$$

15. (*a*) Prove that

$$\sin(A+B)=\sin A\cos B+\cos A\sin B.$$

You may take the simplest case, where $A+B$ is less than a right angle.
Illustrate the truth of this arithmetically when $A=35°$ and $B=27°$, using your tables.

(*b*) Prove that in a triangle whose sides a, b contain between them the angle C the area is

$$\frac{1}{2}ab\sin C.$$

There is a quadrilateral $ABCD$; A and C being opposite corners. If AB is 16·23 feet, AC 25·4 feet, AD 12·09 feet; if the angle BAC is 41°, and the angle CAD is 35°, find the area of the quadrilateral.

Section IV. Squared Paper.

1. Find a value of x which will satisfy each of the equations

(i) $2x^{2\cdot5} - 5x - 8\cdot34 = 0$, (ii) $x^2 - 10\log_{10}x - 3 = 0$.

2. A chain hangs from two pegs in a horizontal line 10 feet apart in the form of a catenary whose equation is

$$y = \frac{c}{2}\left\{\left(e^{\frac{x}{c}} - e^{-\frac{x}{c}}\right) - 2\right\},$$

$c = 5$, $e = 2\cdot718$.

Draw a diagram of the chain giving its depth below the line joining the pegs at horizontal intervals of 1 foot.

3. If x be the depth to which a floating sphere of radius r and density ρ sinks in water, it is found that

$$x^3 - 3rx^2 + 4r^3\rho = 0.$$

Determine the depth to which a sphere of radius 10 inches and density 0·65 will sink in water.

4. Find a value of x which satisfies the equation

$$\sin x = \frac{1}{3}x.$$

[Hint: plot $y = \sin x$ and $y = \frac{1}{3}x$ and find point of intersection.]

5. In the following table C denotes the maximum current in amperes for rubber-covered wires exposed to ordinary temperatures and A is the area of cross-section of the wire in square inches. Find the law connecting C and A.

C	113	237	354	425	493	624	688
A	0·1	0·25	0·4	0·5	0·6	0·8	0·9

6. The keeper of a restaurant finds when he has G guests in a day, his total daily expenditure is E pounds (for rent, taxes, wages, wear and tear, food and drink), and his total daily receipt is R pounds. The following numbers are averages obtained by examination of his books on many days:

G	E	R
210	16·7	15·8
270	19·4	21·2
320	21·6	26·4
360	23·4	29·8

Using squared paper, find E and R and the day's profits if he has 340 guests.

What number of guests per day just gives him no profit?

What simple algebraical laws seem to connect E, R, P, the profit, and G?

Two of the marks will be given for a correct answer to the following:

If he finds that he has almost too many guests from, say, 1 to 2 o'clock, and from, say, 6 to 7 o'clock, and almost none at other times of the day, what expedient might he adopt to increase his profits?

7. The following quantities are thought to follow a law like $pv^n = \text{constant}$. Try if they do so; find the most probable value of n.

v	1	2	3	4	5
p	205	114	80	63	52

8. At the following draughts in sea water a particular vessel has the following displacements:

Draught h feet, - -	15	12	9	6·3
Displacement T tons,	2098	1512	1018	586

Plot $\log T$ and $\log h$ on squared paper, and try to get a simple rule connecting T and h. If one ton of sea water measures 35 cubic feet, find the rule connecting V and h, if V is the displacement in cubic feet.

9. Preferably to be answered by a Candidate who has already answered Question 8. Find how A the horizontal sectional area of the vessel at the water line depends upon h. At any draught h, what change of displacement V or T is produced by one *inch* difference in h?

10. Work the following three exercises as if in each case one were alone given, taking in each case the simplest supposition which your information permits:

(*a*) The total yearly expense in keeping a school of 100 boys is £2,100; what is the expense when the number of boys is 175?

(*b*) The expense is £2,100 for 100 boys, £3,050 for 200 boys; what is it for 175 boys?

(*c*) The expenses for three cases are known as follows:

£2,100 for 100 boys,
£2,650 for 150 boys,
£3,050 for 200 boys.

What is the probable expense for 175 boys?

If you use a squared paper method, show all three solutions together.

11. For the years 1896-1900, the following average numbers are taken from the accounts of the 34 most important Electric Companies of the United Kingdom.

U means millions of units of electric energy sold to customers. C means the total cost in millions of pence, and includes interest (7 per cent.) on capital, maintenance, rent, taxes, salaries, wages, coal, etc.

U	0·67	1·00	1·366	1·46	2·49
C	4·84	6·25	8·60	9·11	14·25

Is there any simple approximately correct law connecting U and C? If so, what is it? Assume that from the beginning there was the idea of, at some time, reaching a maximum output of 13·9, so that $U \div 13{\cdot}9$ is called f, a certain kind of *load factor*. Let $C \div U$ be called c the total cost per unit; is there any law connecting c and f? You need not plot c and f; it is better to use the law already found.

12. In some experiments in towing a canal boat the following observations were made; P being the pull in pounds and v the speed of the boat in miles per hour.

v	1·68	2·43	3·18	3·60	4·03
P	76	160	240	320	370

Plot $\log v$ and $\log P$ upon squared paper and give an approximate formula connecting P and v.

13. When is $x^{\frac{2}{\gamma}} - x^{1+\frac{1}{\gamma}}$ a maximum, γ being 1·4? Plot the values near the maximum value. For this purpose you need calculate only the maximum value and two others.

14. There is a function

$$y = 5\log_{10}x + 6\sin\tfrac{1}{10}x + 0{\cdot}084(x-3{\cdot}5)^2.$$

Find a much simpler function of x which does not differ from it in value more than 2 per cent. between $x=3$ and $x=6$. Remember that the angle $\frac{1}{10}x$ is in radians.

15. The following are the areas of cross-section of a body at right angles to its straight axis:

A in square inches	250	292	310	273	215	180	135	120
x inches from one end	0	22	41	70	84	102	130	145

What is the whole volume from $x=0$ to $x=145$?

At $x=50$, if a cross-sectional slice of small thickness δx has the volume δv, find $\frac{\delta v}{\delta x}$.

16. Find accurately to three significant figures, a value of x to satisfy the equation

$$0\cdot5x^{1\cdot5} - 12\log_{10}x + 2\sin 2x = 0\cdot921.$$

Notice in *sin* $2x$ that the angle is in radians.

17. The following table records the growth in stature of a girl A (born January, 1890) and a boy B (born May, 1894). Plot these records. Heights were measured at intervals of four months.

TABLE OF HEIGHTS IN INCHES.

Year.	1900.	1901.			1902.			1903.
Month.	Sept.	Jan.	May.	Sept.	Jan.	May.	Sept.	Jan.
A	54·75	55·55	56·6	57·95	59·2	60·2	60·9	61·3
B	48·25	49·0	49·75	50·6	51·5	52·3	53·1	53·9

Find in inches per annum, the average rates of growth of A and B during the whole period of tabulation. What will be the probable heights of A and B at the end of another four months? Plot the *rate* of growth of A at all times throughout the period. At about what age was A growing most rapidly and what was her quickest rate of growth?

18. The New Zealand Pension law for a person who has already lived from the age of 40 to 65 in the colony is:

If the private income I is not more than £34 a year, the pension P is £18 a year. If the private income is anything from 34 to 52, the pension is such that the total income is just made up to 52. If the private income is 52 or more there is no pension.

Show on squared paper, for any income I the value of P, and also the value of the total income. If a person's private income is say £50, how much of it has he an inducement to give away before he applies for a pension? Show on the same paper the total income, if the pension were regulated according to the rule

$$P = 18 - \tfrac{9}{26}I.$$

19. The following table gives corresponding values of two quantities x and y:

y	10·16	12·26	14·70	20·80	24·54	28·83
x	37·36	31·34	26·43	19·08	16·33	14·04

Try whether x and y are connected by a law of the form $yx^n = c$, and if so, determine as nearly as you can the values of n and c.

What is the value of x when $y = 17·53$?

20. The entropy ϕ ranks of a quantity of stuff at the absolute temperature t degrees is known to vary in the following way:

t	443	403	373	343
ϕ	1·584	1·668	1·749	1·850

Plot ϕ horizontally and t vertically.

A rectangle, whose dimension horizontally represents 0·1 rank and whose vertical dimension represents 10 degrees, has an area which represents $0·1 \times 10$ or 1 unit of heat, what heat does each square inch of your diagram represent? The total heat received from beginning to end of the above set of changes is represented by the total area between the curve, the two end verticals and the zero line of temperature: state the amount of it.

You need not, of course, plot the whole of ϕ; you may subtract, say, 1·5 from each of the values. Also, if you want greater accuracy and can estimate areas of rectangles not actually drawn, you need not plot the whole value of t.

21. Find accurately to three significant figures the value of x which satisfies the equation

$$3x^2 - 20 \log_{10} x - 7·077 = 0.$$

Use squared paper.

22. At the following draughts h feet, a particular vessel has the following tonnage T in salt-water:

h	15	12	9	6·3
T	2,100	1,510	1,020	590

Try if there is an approximate connection of the form

$$T = ch^n$$

and if so find c and n.

If a cubic foot of salt water weighs 64 lbs., find a formula connecting D, the displacement in cubic feet, and h.

23. If

$$y=2x+\frac{1 \cdot 5}{x},$$

state what value of x will make y less than any other. An approximate answer, using squared paper, will gain as many marks as the correct answer.

24. The following tests were made upon a Condensing Steam-Turbine-Electric-Generator. There are probably some errors of observation, as the measurement of the steam is troublesome.

Output in Kilowatts K.	Weight W lb. of steam consumed per hour.
1190	23120
995	20040
745	16630
498	12560
247	8320
0	4065

Find if there is a simple approximate law connecting K and W and state what it is algebraically.

State in words what $\frac{W}{K}$ means. Call this w. Express w in terms of K. Calculate w for $K=1,000$ and $K=300$.

25. Find accurately to three significant figures the value of x which satisfies the equation

$$x^2-\frac{20}{3}\log_{10}x=2 \cdot 359.$$

26. The following tests were made upon a Condensing Steam-Turbine-Electric-Generator. There are probably some errors of observation as the measurement of the steam is troublesome:

Output in Kilowatts K - - -	1,190	995	745	498	247	0
Weight W lb. of steam consumed per hour	23,120	20,040	16,630	12,560	8,320	4,065

Find if there is a simple approximate law connecting K and W.

The electric power goes some distance to drive a factory, and it is found by trial that when Y yards of stuff are being woven per hour

$$K=48+0 \cdot 45\,Y.$$

Express W in terms of Y.

State the meaning of W/Y in words, and find its values when Y is 2000 and when Y is 500. What lesson ought to be drawn from this?

Section V. Mensuration.

1. A rectangular plot of grass is surrounded by a gravel walk 4 ft. wide. The area of the plot is 1200 sq. ft. and the area of the walk is 704 sq. ft. Find the length and width of the plot.

2. A cylinder is 4·71 in. diameter and 8·35 in. high. Find its total surface and volume. Also find the diameter of a sphere having the same volume.

3. The height of a conical flue is 6 ft. The plane ends are circular and of diameters 3 ft. and 4 ft. 6 in. respectively. Sketch with dimensions the shape of the sheet that must be cut out of a flat plate to form the flue. Find the weight of the flue if made of $\frac{1}{4}$ in. wrought-iron plate.

4. The weight of a hollow cast-iron sphere 8 in. outside diameter and of uniform thickness is 50 lb. Calculate the diameter of the empty space within the sphere.

5. The rim of a claret glass is 5 cm. diameter, depth 6 cm. Calculate its volume to the nearest integer, assuming the cross-section to be a parabola.

6. A rectangular tank with sloping base and vertical sides is made of thin sheet metal; the length is 2 ft. 9 in., width 2 ft. 3 in., depth at one end 5 ft. and at the other 1 ft. 9 in. Find the area of the sheet iron used and how many gallons of water the tank will hold. Draw a graph showing volume of water for any depth. Use this graph to find depth of water at the deeper end when (*a*) the tank contains 40 gallons, (*b*) when it contains 100 gallons.

7. Find the weight of a hollow steel pillar 12 ft. long, the external and internal diameters being 6 in. and 5 in. respectively. Find the diameter of a solid pillar of the same length and weight.

8. A gasometer in the form of a cylinder with a spherical top has the following dimensions: diameter 28 ft., height at edges 14 ft., height in middle 16 ft. Find the volume.

9. A groove of semi-circular section, of radius r, is cut round the outside of a cylinder of radius R; prove that the volume removed is $\pi^2Rr^2 - \frac{4}{3}\pi r^3$; also show that the surface of the groove is

$$2\pi^2Rr - 4\pi r^2.$$

10. A sphere of radius 6 in. is cut by two parallel planes on opposite sides of the centre at distances 4 in. and 1 in. from the centre respectively. Find the volumes of the zone between the two sections, and of the smaller segment cut off from the sphere by the plane at a distance of 4 in. from the centre.

11. Let a closed curve rotate round a straight line in its own plane and generate a ring; state and prove the two rules for finding the volume and surface of the ring.

12. (*a*) The inside diameter of a hollow sphere of cast iron is the fraction 0·57 of its outside diameter. Find these diameters if the weight is 60 lb. Take one cubic inch of cast iron as weighing 0·26 lb.

If the outside diameter is made 1 per cent. smaller, the inside not being altered, what is the percentage diminution of weight?

(*b*) The cross-section of a ring is an ellipse whose principal diameters are 2 inches and $1\frac{1}{2}$ inches; the middle of this section is at 3 inches from the axis of the ring; what is the volume of the ring?

Prove the rule you use for finding the volume of any ring.

13. (*a*) Prove the rules used in finding the volume and area of a ring. The mean radius of a ring is 2 feet. The cross-section of the ring is an ellipse whose major and minor diameters are 0·8 and 0·5 feet: what is its volume?

(*b*) The length of a plane closed curve is divided into 24 elements, each of 1 inch long. The middles of successive elements are at the distances x from a line in the plane, as follows (in inches): 10, 10·5, 10·91, 11·24, 11·49, 11·67, 12·57, 11·67, 11·49, 11·24, 10·91, 10·5, 10, 10·5, 10·91, 11·24, 11·49, 11·67, 12·57, 11·67, 11·40. 11·24, 10·91, 10·5.

If the curve rotates about the line as an axis describing a ring, find approximately the area of the ring.

14. A hollow circular cylinder of length l, inside radius r, outside radius R; write out a formula for its volume V.

If $V=182$ cubic inches, $l=7{\cdot}23$ inches, $r=2{\cdot}11$ inches, find R.

15. The sum of the areas of two squares is 92·14 square inches, the sum of their sides is 13 inches, find these sides.

16. The area of cross-section* of a prism is 92·30 square inches; what is the area of a section making an angle of 25° with the cross-section?

Section VI. Solid Geometry.

1. The polar or vector co-ordinates of two points A and B are (3″, 30°) and (4·2″, 100°). That is, if O is the pole and OX the line of reference, $OA=3''$, $XOA=30°$; $OB=4{\cdot}2''$, $XOB=100°$.

Draw OX and plot the points A and B. Measure AB and the perpendicular from O on AB, and calculate the area of the triangle OAB. Verify your answer by calculating the value of

$$\tfrac{1}{2}OA\,.\,OB\sin AOB.$$

2. The polar co-ordinates of a point are $r=5$ feet, $\theta=52°$, $\phi=70°$, find the x, y, and z co-ordinates; also find the angles made by r with the axes of co-ordinates.

* The cross-section is the smallest section.

3. There is a point P whose x, y and z co-ordinates are 2, 1·5 and 3. Find its r, θ and ϕ co-ordinates. If O is the origin, find the angles made by OP with the axes of co-ordinates. [1902]

4. Three planes of reference, mutually perpendicular, meet at O. The distances of a point P from the three planes are $x=1·2$, $y=2·7$, $z=0·9$. The distances of a point Q are $x=0·8$, $y=1·8$, $z=1·5$.

Find 1st, the distances OP and OQ;
2nd, the distance PQ;
3rd, the angle between OP and OQ.

5. Three planes of reference mutually perpendicular meet in the lines OX, OY, OZ. The line OP is 6·2 inches long; it makes an angle of 62° with OX and 43° with OY. Call the projections of OP upon OX, OY, and OZ by the names, x, y, and z and calculate their amounts, taking the positive value in the case of z. What angle does OP make with OZ?

The plane containing OZ and OP makes an angle ϕ with the plane containing OZ and OX, what is this angle?

Section VII. Series.

1. From the series $\sin x = x - \frac{x^3}{1.2.3} + \frac{x^5}{1.2.3.4.5} - \ldots$ calculate (using Tables II. and III.) the values of sin 15°, sin 30°, sin 45°.

[x denotes the angle in radians and 15° = 0·2618.]

2. Calculate the numerical values of cos 15°, cos 30°, cos 45°, using the series $\cos x = 1 - \frac{x^2}{1.2} + \frac{x^4}{1.2.3.4} - \ldots$.

3. Find from the series $\tan x = x + \frac{x^3}{3} + \frac{2x^5}{15} + \ldots$ the numerical values of tan 15°, tan 30°, tan 45°.

4. From the series $\log_e(1+x) = x - \frac{x^2}{2} + \frac{x^3}{3} - \frac{x^4}{4} + \frac{x^5}{5} - \ldots$ calculate to base 10 the logarithms of the following:—1·02, 1·04, 1·06, 1·08, 1·1, 1·2, 1·4.

[To calculate $\log_e 1·2$ put $x=0·2$ in the above series then $\log_e 1·2 = 0·1823$ and $\log_{10} 1·2 = 0·1823 \times 0·4343 = 0·7918$.]

5. In the series $e^x = 1 + x + \frac{x^2}{1.2} + \frac{x^3}{1.2.3} + \frac{x^4}{1.2.3.4} + \ldots$ write $(\sqrt{-1})x$ or ix for x.

$$\therefore\ e^{ix} = 1 + ix - \frac{x^2}{1.2!} - \frac{ix^3}{1.2.3} + \frac{x^4}{1.2.3.4}$$

$$= \left(1 - \frac{x^2}{1.2} + \frac{x^4}{1.2.3.4} - \ldots\right) + i\left(x - \frac{x^3}{1.2.3} + \frac{x^5}{1.2.3.4.5} - \ldots\right).$$

$$\therefore\ e^{ix} = \cos x + i \sin x. \quad \ldots\ldots\ldots\ldots\ldots\ldots\text{(i)}$$

Similarly $$e^{-ix} = \cos x - i \sin x. \quad \ldots\ldots\ldots\ldots\ldots\ldots\text{(ii)}$$

From (i) and (ii) $$^{*}\cos x=\frac{e^{ix}+e^{-ix}}{2},$$

$$\sin x=\frac{e^{ix}-e^{-ix}}{2}.$$

6. Express the angle 0·3 radians in degrees; find from the tables its sine. If x is in radians and if

$$\sin x=x-\frac{x^3}{\underline{|3}}+\frac{x^5}{\underline{|5}}-\frac{x^7}{\underline{|7}}+\text{etc.},$$

calculate the sine of this angle to four significant figures. After how many terms are more of them useless in this case when we only need four figures? [Note that $\underline{|5}$ means $1\times2\times3\times4\times5$.]

Section VIII. Vectors.

1. Define carefully what is meant by the Scalar Product of two vectors and by the Vector Product of two vectors, giving one useful example of each.

2. Define carefully what is meant by the Scalar Product and by the Vector Product of two vectors, giving one useful example of each.

3. A mass m of 3 units, moving in a horizontal plane, has a velocity v, of 24_{30° ft. per sec. (directions being measured anticlockwise from the east), its momentum m_1v_1 being $3\times24_{30^\circ}=72_{30^\circ}$ units. A second mass m_2 of momentum m_2v_2 of 128_{70° units. The two bodies collide, moving on with a common velocity v, and a momentum $(m_1+m_2)v$ equal to the vector sum $m_1v_1+m_2v_2=72_{30^\circ}+128_{70^\circ}=a_\alpha$. Show that $a_\alpha=189_{56^\circ}$ also that $v=a_\alpha\div(m_1+m_2)=27_{56^\circ}$.

Section IX. Differentiation.

1. What do you understand by the slope or gradient of a graph? Illustrate your answer by drawing a curve of sines from 0 to π and below it a curve whose ordinate at every point shows the slope at the corresponding point on the sine curve.

2. Given $y=\sqrt[3]{x^5}$, $\cos 3x$, e^{-4x}, $\log\frac{1}{x}$, find in each case $\frac{dy}{dx}$.

3. (i) Define what is meant by $\frac{dy}{dx}$.

(ii) If $y=a^x$, show that $\frac{dy}{dx}$ is proportional to a^x if a be constant.

(iii) Give the value of $\frac{d(10^x)}{dx}$ when $x=3·46$ and (iv) compare it with the value of

$$\frac{10^{3·47}-10^{3·46}}{0·01}.\quad [e=2·718.]$$

* These are known as $\cosh x$ and $\sinh x$ (*read* the latter as shin x).

4. (i) Evaluate $4 \cdot 2(2 \cdot 01^{1 \cdot 7} - 2^{1 \cdot 7}) \div 0 \cdot 01$.

(ii) If $y = 4 \cdot 2x^{1 \cdot 7}$, find $\frac{dy}{dx}$.

Find $\frac{dy}{dx}$ in the following:

5. $y = a + bx + cx^2 + gx^n$.

6. $y = x^{\frac{1}{2}}, \quad y = x^{\frac{2}{3}}, \quad y = \frac{1}{\sqrt{x}}, \quad y = x^3 \sin 2x$.

7. In the curve $y = ae^{bx}$, where $a = 1 \cdot 5$, $b = 0 \cdot 2$, calculate values of y for the following values of x, and fill up the following table:

x	0	0·5	1·0	1·5	2·0	2·5	3·0	3·5	4·0
y									
$\frac{dy}{dx}$ or slope at x, y									

Draw a graph of the curve. Also draw a second graph the abscissae of which are respectively the values of the slope and the values of y you have tabulated. Can you make any inference from this graph? Express your inference in mathematical symbols.

8. At a given instant the radius of a soap bubble is increasing at the rate of 2 inches per minute. What is the rate of increase of volume when the radius is 3 inches?

9. The equation to a curve is $y = ax^{\frac{1}{2}}$. Find a so that $x = 4$, $y = 3$ is a point on the curve. Find the equation to the tangent there and the lengths of the subnormal and subtangent.

10. A piston is at a distance x from one end of a cylinder of diameter d. Steam is admitted to the cylinder at the rate of v cubic feet per second. Show that the rate at which the piston is moving is given by

$$\frac{dx}{dt} = \frac{dx}{dv}\frac{dv}{dt}.$$

If 12 cubic feet of steam per second is admitted into a cylinder 8 inches diameter, find the rate at which the piston is moving.

11. If a particle vibrates according to the law $y = a \sin(pt - e)$, show that the velocity and acceleration at any instant are

$$ap \cos(pt - e) \text{ and } -p^2 y \text{ respectively.}$$

12. At what point on the curve $y = \frac{3}{2}x^{-2}$ is there the slope $\frac{3}{8}$?

13. A piston slides freely in a cylinder 6″ diameter. At what rate does it move when steam is admitted at the rate of 10 cubic feet per second?

14. Callendar's formula for the variation of R the electrical resistance of platinum with t the temperature is

$$R=R_0(1+at+bt^2)$$

where a and b are constants. Find a formula for the increase of resistance for a small rise of temperature.

15. An arc light is at a height of 20 ft. above a straight horizontal road on which a man 6 ft. high is walking at the rate of 4 miles per hour. What is the rate at which the man's shadow is lengthening?

16. For what values of θ between 0° and 180° is $\tan\theta$ increasing four times as fast as θ?

17. In the isothermal expansion of a gas, given $pv=c$, for what value of p will the rate of change of pressure per unit change of volume be double what it was when p was 20?

18. A ladder AB, 13 feet long, rests against a vertical wall, having its lower extremity B distant 5 ft. from the wall. If B be made to slip outwards from the wall at the rate of $1\frac{1}{2}$ ft. per second, find at what rate the upper end A will begin to slide down the wall.

19. The sill of a window in the vertical wall of a house is at a height of 30 feet from the ground. (i) At what rate is a man who is walking at 4 miles per hour on the level ground approaching the sill? (ii) What is the numerical value of the rate when he is 40 feet from the foot of the wall?

20. Find and tabulate from the following values of x and y the values of $\frac{dy}{dx}$ and $\frac{d^2y}{dx^2}$. Find the value of $\frac{d^2y}{dx^2}$ when $x=8{\cdot}2$.

Plot three curves showing (a) the values of y and x, (b) $\frac{dy}{dx}$, (c) $\frac{d^2y}{dx^2}$. Verify by measurement that the slope of (a) is equal to the ordinate of (b) and the slope of (b) is equal to the ordinate of (c).

x	7·8	8·0	8·2	8·4	8·6	8·8
y	6·43	6·95	7·57	8·30	9·21	10·34

21. The relation between s the space passed over by a moving body and the time t is given by

$$s=5e^{\frac{1}{2}t}, \text{ where } e=2{\cdot}718.$$

Find the velocity v and acceleration α at the time $t=2$. Also find the space passed over by the moving body between the times $t=2$, $t=4$.

22. The following values of x and y being given, find by using successive differences the value of $\frac{dy}{dx}$ when $x=3$, [see page 354]:

x	0	1	2	3	4	5
y	2	6·3	18·6	38·9	67·2	103·5

23. A point moves along a line so that its distance s from a fixed point in the line at a time t seconds is given by

$$s=3t-0{\cdot}5t^2+0{\cdot}4t^3.$$

Find expressions for the velocity v, and the acceleration a; find the value in each case when $t=4$.

24. A body weighing 100 lbs. moves along a straight line, its distance s at a time t is given by $s=2{\cdot}7-3{\cdot}5t+3{\cdot}7t^2$.

Find, when $t=4$, the velocity v, the kinetic energy $\frac{1}{2}mv^2$, and momentum mv where m is the mass of the body$=\frac{100}{32{\cdot}2}$.

25. A link of a machine has plane motion; successive positions of its centre of mass G at intervals of $\frac{1}{50}$ second are given by x, y co-ordinates in the following table. Corresponding angular positions are also given, θ being measured from Ox towards Oy.

Position	1	2	3	4	5
x, feet	3·25	2·07	1·09	0·38	0·06
y, feet	0·27	0·7	1·28	1·92	2·57
θ, radians	0·10	0·114	0·153	0·211	0·307

Find the magnitude and direction of the linear acceleration of G and the angular acceleration of the link when in the middle position.

The mass of the link is 115 lbs. and its radius of gyration about G is 0·88 ft. Find the force corresponding to the linear acceleration and the couple corresponding to the angular acceleration of the link for this position.

26. At the time t seconds a body has moved x feet along its path from some fixed point in it. These positions have been found from a skeleton drawing of a mechanism. Find the average speed in each interval. Find also the acceleration in the path at each instant approximately.

t	0	0·1	0·2	0·3	0·4	0·5	0·6
x	0	4	8·175	12·558	17·187	22·094	27·306

27. There is a curve $y=2+0{\cdot}15x^2$.

Prove that for any value of x the slope of the curve or $\frac{dy}{dx}$ is $0{\cdot}3x$.

28. In a certain vessel it happens to be true, within certain limits, that

$$V=1200h^{1\cdot 5}$$

where h is the vertical draught in feet and V is the displacement in cubic feet. If A is the area in square feet of a horizontal section on the water-level, express A in terms of h.

If l and b are the length and greatest breadth of the section and if $A=nlb$ where n is a constant fraction, show that $V=mlbh$ where m is a constant fraction.

29. A quantity y is a function of x, what do we mean by $\frac{dy}{dx}$?

Illustrate your meaning, using a curve. Illustrate your meaning by considering a body which has moved through the space s in the time t. What is $\frac{dy}{dx}$ in the following cases:

$$y=a+bx+cx^2+gx^n, \quad y=a\log x,$$
$$y=ae^{bx}, \quad y=a\sin(bx+c)\,?$$

30. There is a piece of mechanism whose weight is 200 lbs. The following values of s in feet show the distance of its centre of gravity (as measured on a skeleton drawing) from some point in its straight path at the time t seconds from some era of reckoning. Find its acceleration at the time $t=2{\cdot}05$, and the force in pounds which is giving this acceleration to it.

s	0·3090	0·4931	0·6799	0·8701	1·0643	1·2631
t	2·0	2·02	2·04	2·06	2·08	2·10

31. What is meant by the symbol $\frac{dy}{dx}$? Explain how it may be represented by the slope of a curve. State its value in the cases

$$y=ax^n, \quad y=a\epsilon^{bx}, \quad y=a\sin(bx+c),$$
$$y=a\cos(bx+c), \quad y=\log_e(x+b).$$

32. What is meant by the symbol $\frac{dy}{dx}$?

Explain how it may be represented by the slope of a curve.

If $y=2{\cdot}4-1{\cdot}2x+0{\cdot}2x^2$, find $\frac{dy}{dx}$ and plot two curves from $x=0$ to $x=4$, showing how y and $\frac{dy}{dx}$ depend upon x.

33. If the current C ampères in a circuit follows the law $C=10\sin 600t$; if t is in seconds, and if

$$V=RC+L\frac{dC}{dt},$$

where R is 0·3 and L is 4×10^{-4}, what is V?

Show by a sketch how C and V depend upon time, and particularly how one lags behind the other, and also state their highest and lowest values.

34. $y=a+bx^n$ is the equation to a curve which passes through these three points,

$$x=0,\ y=1{\cdot}24;\quad x=2{\cdot}2,\ y=5{\cdot}07;\quad x=3{\cdot}5,\ y=12{\cdot}64;$$

find a, b, and n.

When we say that $\frac{dy}{dx}$ is shown by the slope of the curve, what exactly do we mean? Find $\frac{dy}{dx}$ when $x=2$.

Section X. Maxima and Minima.

1. If $y=2x+\frac{1{\cdot}5}{x}$, find what positive value of x will make y less than any other.

2. A number is added to 1·96 times its reciprocal. For what number is this a minimum?

3. Divide the number 12 into two parts such that twice the square of one part together with three times the square of the other shall be a minimum.

4. Find (i) the strongest, (ii) the stiffest beam that can be cut out of a cylindrical log 12 inches diameter.

5. The power given to an external circuit by a generator of internal resistance r and E.M.F. E is $P=CE-C^2r$ where C denotes the current in ampères.

If $E=40$ volts, $r=2{\cdot}2$ ohms, find for what value of C the power is a maximum.

6. An electric current flowing round a coil of radius r exerts a force F on a small magnet whose axis is on a line through the centre of the coil and perpendicular to its plane. If x is the distance of the magnet from the plane of the coil, then $F=\frac{x}{(x^2+r^2)^{\frac{5}{2}}}$. When is the force a maximum?

7. A battery contains n cells each of E.M.F. v volts and internal resistance r ohms; if x cells are arranged in series and $\frac{n}{x}$ rows in parallel, then the current that the battery will send through an external resistance R is given by

$$C = \frac{vx}{\frac{x^2 r}{n} + R} \text{ ampères.}$$

If there are 20 cells, $v = 1{\cdot}8$ volts, $r = 0{\cdot}2$ ohms, $R = 0{\cdot}36$ ohms, how many cells must be arranged in series to give the greatest possible current?

8. Find the radius and volume of greatest cylinder which can be obtained from a sphere 10 inches diameter.

9. Waves in deep water with crests λ cm. apart travel with velocity $v = c\sqrt{\frac{1}{2}\left(\frac{\lambda}{a} + \frac{a}{\lambda}\right)}$ cm. per second. Where $a = 1{\cdot}73$ cm. and $c = 23{\cdot}2$ cm. per sec. For what distance between the crests do waves travel slowest? Show that this distance gives a minimum and not a maximum speed.

10. Sketch the curve $y = x^2 e^{\frac{1}{x}}$. Show that it has a minimum ordinate of length $1{\cdot}85$ where $x = 0{\cdot}5$.

11. A current is sent through an external resistance R by a battery of internal resistance r and E.M.F. e. The power given to the external circuit is given by

$$P = \frac{Re^2}{(R + r)^2}.$$

Prove that P is a maximum when $R = r$. Given $e = 3{\cdot}5$, $r = 1{\cdot}3$, find the value of R which will give the greatest value of P.

12. A tank with square base and vertical sides is to be made of sheet metal, and to contain 10 cubic feet. Find the length of the side of the base and the height so that the least weight of metal may be used.

13. Given $y = 2\sin x + 3\cos x - 3{\cdot}6$, for what value of x is $y = 0$, and $y = a$ maximum?

14. Find two values of θ between 0 and $\frac{\pi}{2}$, each of which satisfies the equation

$$3\sin\theta + 4\cos\theta = 4{\cdot}25.$$

Find also a value of θ for which the given expression is a maximum.

15. Show how to inscribe the greatest right cone in a given sphere of radius r.

Find the volume of the greatest cone which can be inscribed in a sphere of 10 inches diameter.

16. In a steam engine the mean effective pressure is found to vary with the speed according to the law

$$p = 56 - 0{\cdot}127n,$$

where p denotes the pressure in lbs. per sq. in. and n the speed in revolutions per minute.

Find the speed at which the engine will develop most power.

17. Prove that the least amount of canvas required to make a conical tent of volume V is given by $h = r\sqrt{2}$, where h is the height and r the radius of the base. A conical tent has been constructed so as to enclose the greatest possible volume for a given amount of canvas. Find the number of square feet of canvas used if the tent stands 8 feet high.

18. Given that the combined length and girth of the greatest parcel which may be sent by parcel post must not exceed 6 feet. Find (i) dimensions of a box with square base and vertical sides, (ii) the length of side and volume of a cube, (iii) diameter and volume of a sphere, (iv) diameter, length and volume of a cylinder.

19. Divide a number a into two parts so that twice the square of one part plus three times the square of the other shall be a minimum.

How do you know that you have found a minimum value?

Section XI. Integration.

1. Evaluate (i) $\int_0^4 3x^2 dx$, (ii) $\int_0^{\frac{\pi}{2}} \cos x\, dx$, (iii) $\int_{\frac{1}{3}}^{1} \frac{dx}{x}$.

(iv) Determine the area enclosed between the graph $y = 1{\cdot}5e^{0{\cdot}2x}$, the axis of x and the ordinates $x=0$, $x=4$, by Simpson's rule, by evaluating $\int 1{\cdot}5e^{0{\cdot}2x}$ between the appropriate limits.

2. Given $y = a + bx^n$. If n is $2{\cdot}5$ and a is 0, and if the curve passes through the point $(x=5,\ y=4)$, find b.

What is the area enclosed by the curve, the ordinates at $x=0$, $x=6$, and the axis of x, (i) by Simpson's rule, (ii) by integration?

3. In the curve $y = ax^3$ find a so that $x=5$, $y=10$ is a point on the curve. Find the area between the curve, the axis of x, and the ordinates $x=1$, $x=5$, (i) by Simpson's rule, (ii) by integration.

4. The relation between the velocity v and the time t in a moving body is given by $v = 3t^2$. Show that the displacement of the body from $t=2$ and $t=4$ is given by

$$3\int_2^4 t^2 dt = 56 \text{ ft.}$$

5. The acceleration of a moving body is given by $a=10t$ where t denotes the time in seconds. Find an expression for the velocity at any instant given that the velocity is 10 ft. per sec. when $t=4$.

6. Given $y=e^{\sin x}$, calculate and tabulate values of y for the following values of x : 0°, 15°, 30°, etc.

Find the numerical value of $\int_0^{\frac{\pi}{2}} e^{\sin x}dx$, using Simpson's rule.

7. (i) Plot the curve $y=\cos^2 x$. Use your diagram to determine the value of the definite integral $\int_0^{\frac{\pi}{2}} \cos^2 x\,dx$.

(ii) Find the value by integration.

(iii) Apply Simpson's rule to find approximately the value of

$$\int_0^{\frac{\pi}{2}} \sqrt{\sin x}\,dx.$$

8. Plot the curve $y=0{\cdot}2x^2$. Tabulate the values of y and y^2 for values of x, 0, 1, 2, 3, 4.

Find the area enclosed by the curve, the axis of x, and the ordinates $x=0$, $x=4$, (i) by Simpson's rule, (ii) by integration,

$$i.e.\ A=\int_0^4 y\,dx.$$

Assuming the given curve to rotate about the axis of x, find the volume of the solid between the values $x=0$ and $x=4$, (iii) using Simpson's rule and tabulated values of y^2, (iv) from $V=\pi\int_0^4 y^2dx$.

9. Plot the curve $y=3-5x+2x^2$. Tabulate values of y and y^2 for values of x, 0, 1, 2, 3, 4.

Find the area enclosed between the curve, the axis of x, and the ordinates $x=0$, $x=4$, (i) using Simpson's rule, (ii) by integration.

The curve rotates about the axis of x; find the volume of the solid generated, (iii) by Simpson's rule. (iv) by integration.

10. Integrate (i) $\sqrt[4]{x^3}\,dx$.

(ii) $\frac{dx}{x}$ between the limits 1 and 2.

(iii) $\cos x\,dx$ between the limits 0 and $\frac{\pi}{2}$.

11. A quantity of gas expands so as to satisfy the law $pv=c$. Find the work done in expansion from $v=2$ cub. ft. to $v=8$ cub. ft. Given $p=60$ lbs. per sq. in. $=8640$ lbs. per sq. ft. when $v=2$.

12. Find the work done in the expansion of a quantity of gas from 2 cub. ft. at 8640 lbs. per sq. ft. to 8 cub. ft. The gas expands so as to satisfy the law $pv^{0 \cdot 9}=c$.

13. A quantity of steam expands so as to satisfy the law $pv^{1 \cdot 13}=c$. Find the work done in expansion from $v=3$ cub. ft. to $v=10$ cub. ft. Given $P=8640$ lbs. per sq. ft. when $v=1$.

14. Find in foot pounds the work done when 20 cubic feet of air at an initial pressure of 50 lbs. per sq. in. expands at constant temperature to a volume 100 cub. ft.

15. Plot the curve $y^2=3x$ and find the area enclosed by the curve, the axis of x, and the ordinates $x=0$, $x=3$. Find also the volume of the solid between the same limits when the curve rotates about the axis of x.

16. Find the area enclosed by the curve $x^2=9y$ and the line $x=y$.

17. Find the area enclosed between the curve $y^2=x^3$ and the lines $x=0$, $x=6$.

18. What is the area included between the curve $x^n y=100$, the axis of x, and the lines $x=1$, $x=3 \cdot 5$, when (i) $n=1$, (ii) $n=1 \cdot 3$?

19. $y=a+bx^n$ is the equation of a curve which passes through the three points

$$x=0, \quad y=1 \cdot 2 ; \quad x=1, \quad y=3 \cdot 5 ; \quad x=4, \quad y=5 \cdot 8.$$

Find a, b, and n.

What is the slope of this curve at a point on it whose x co-ordinate is $4 \cdot 6$?

Find the area between the curve, the axis of x, and the ordinates $x=0$, $x=4$.

20. Find the area between the curve $y=\frac{x^2}{4}$, the axis of x, and the ordinates $x=0$, $x=4$.

21. A cylindrical hole of diameter $2c$ is drilled through a solid sphere, diameter $2a$, the axis of the cylinder passing through the centre of the sphere. Show that the volume of the remaining portion of the sphere is

$$\frac{4\pi}{3}(a^2-c^2)^{\frac{3}{2}}.$$

Show that this may be written in the form $V=\frac{\pi}{6}h^3$ where h is the length of the axis of the cylinder.

Find the volume when $a=6$ in., $c=2$ in.

22. Prove that the area between the parabolas $y^2=mx$ and $x^2=ny$ is $\frac{1}{3}mn$.

23. Show that the average height of the ordinate of the curve $y^2=4ax$ between $x=0$ and $x=x'$ is two-thirds of the ordinate y'.

24. The following numbers express the relation between p, the pressure in lbs. per sq. in., and v, the volume of steam in a cylinder during expansion:

p	4·46	4·11	3·78	3·44	3·19	2·96	2·67
v	3·34	3·73	4·12	4·6	5·08	5·58	6·3

p and v are connected by the law $pv^k = c$; find the value of k. Also find the work done from $v = 3·34$ to $v = 6·3$.

25. In the curve $y = a + bx^{\frac{3}{2}}$, if $y = 1·35$ when $x = 0$, and $y = 5·59$ when $x = 4$, find a and b.

Find the area between the curve, the axis of x, and the ordinates $x = 0$, $x = 4$, (i) by Simpson's rule, (ii) by integration.

If the curve rotates about the axis of x, find the volume traced out (iii) using Simpson's rule, (iv) by integration.

26. If the distance s of a body from a fixed point in its path at a time t is given by $s = a \sin pt$, show that the mean velocity v from $t = 0$ to $t = \frac{\pi}{2p}$ is

$$\int_0^{\frac{\pi}{2p}} ap \cos pt \, dt \div \frac{\pi}{2pt} = \frac{2pa}{\pi}.$$

Given $a = 5$, $p = 0·5236$, find v.

27. There is a curve whose shape may be drawn from the following values of x and y:

x in feet	3	3·5	4·2	4·8
y in inches	10·1	12·2	13·1	11·9

Imagine this curve to rotate about the axis of x describing a surface of revolution. What is the volume enclosed by this surface and the two end sections where $x = 3$ and $x = 4·8$?

28. Find $\int p \, . \, dv$, if $pv^s = c$, a constant,

(1) when $s = 0·8$,

(2) when $s = 1$.

29. In the curve $y = cx^{\frac{1}{2}}$, find c if $y = m$ when $x = b$. Let this curve rotate about the axis of x; find the volume enclosed by the surface of revolution between the two sections at $x = a$ and $x = b$. Of course, m, b, and a are given distances.

30. The rate (per unit increase of volume) of reception of heat by a gas is h, p is its pressure, and v its volume; γ is a known constant. If $pv^s=c$, s and c being constants, find h if

$$h=\frac{1}{\gamma-1}\left\{v\frac{dp}{dv}+\gamma p\right\}.$$

Full marks will be given only when the answer is stated in its simplest form.

If h is always 0, find what s must be.

31. Find the area of the curve

$$y=a+bx^n$$

from the ordinate at $x=0$ to the ordinate at $x=m$. If n is 2·5, and a is 0, and if the curve passes through the point $(x=5, y=4)$, find b. What is the area of the curve from the ordinate at $x=0$ to the ordinate $x=5$?

32. In the atmosphere, if p is pressure and h height above datum level, if

$$w=cp^{1/\gamma}$$

where c and γ are constants, and if

$$\frac{dp}{dh}=-w,$$

find an equation connecting p and h.

What is the above c if $p=twR$? Assume $p=p_0$ and $t=t_0$ where $h=0$. R is a known constant for air.

Find the equation connecting h and t.

33. The following values of y and x being given, tabulate $\frac{\delta y}{\delta x}$ and $y\,.\,\delta x$ in each interval, and A or the sum of such terms as $y\,.\,\delta x$. Of course A is the approximate area of the curve whose ordinate is y.

x	0	0·1	0·2	0·3	0·4	0·5	0·6	0·7	0·8	0·9
y	0	·1736	·3420	·5000	·6428	·7660	·8660	·9397	·9848	1·0000

Section XII. Centres of Gravity and Moments of Inertia.

1. A wrought-iron square bar 0·74 inches side is 25·5 inches long. Find its moment of inertia about an axis passing through its centre of gravity and perpendicular to the axis of the bar, (i) using the formula $I_0=\frac{Ml^2}{12}$, (ii) using the more accurate formula

$$I_0=M\left(\frac{l^2}{12}+\frac{b^2}{12}\right),$$

where l denotes the length and b the length of a side.

2. Given $y=2x^{1\cdot7}$ for values of $x=0$, 1, 2, 3, 4, calculate and tabulate values of y and xy. (i) Find by Simpson's rule the area enclosed by the curve, the axis of x, and the end sections $x=0$, $x=4$. (ii) Find the area by evaluating $\int_0^4 2x^{1\cdot7}\,dx$. Find the value of x at the centre of area, (iii) by Simpson's rule, (iv) by

$$\int_0^4 2x^{1\cdot7} \times x\,dx \div \int_0^4 2x^{1\cdot7}\,dx.$$

3. In the curve $y=3-2x+x^2$ for values of $x=0$, 1, 2, 3, 4 find and tabulate values of y, y^2 and xy^2. The curve revolves about the axis of x so as to generate a solid of revolution. Find the centre of gravity of the portion of this solid which lies between the sections at $x=0$, $x=4$, (i) using Simpson's rule to obtain approximately the sum of xy^2 and y^2, (ii) by evaluating $\int_0^4 xy^2\,dx \div \int_0^4 y^2\,dx$.

4. The curve $y=1\cdot35+0\cdot53x^{\frac{3}{2}}$ rotates about the axis of x so as to generate a solid of revolution. Find the centre of gravity of the portion of this solid which lies between the sections $x=0$, $x=4$, (i) by Simpson's rule, (ii) by integration.

5. A curve is given by the following values of x and y, calculate and tabulate corresponding values of y^2 and xy^2. If the curve rotates about the axis of x, find the volume and centre of gravity of the solid of revolution between the end sections $x=0$, $x=4$, using Simpson's rule.

x	0	1	2	3	4
y	0	0·2	0·8	1·8	3·2

6. A sphere radius 5 in. is cut by two parallel planes on opposite sides and at distances 4 in. and 3 in. from the centre respectively. Find the position of the centre of gravity of the zone.

7. Find the moment of inertia of a thin rod, 3 ft. long and weighing 7 lbs., about an axis through one end and perpendicular to its length. Find its kinetic energy ($\frac{1}{2}\omega^2 I$) when it is rotating about this axis at 100 revolutions per minute. ω = angular velocity in radians, I = moment of inertia ($g=32\cdot2$).

8. A rectangular sheet of wrought iron 3 ft. by 4 ft. and $\frac{1}{4}$ in. thick rotates about an axis passing through one of its shorter sides, find its moment of inertia. Also find its kinetic energy when rotating about this axis at 50 revolutions per minute.

9. A cylindrical bar 13 in. long and 2 in. diameter has fixed to its ends two cylinders 10 in. diameter and 2 in. long, the distance between the centres of the cylinders being 11 in. The bar is suspended in a horizontal position by a wire passing through the mid point of its axis. Find the radius of gyration (or swing radius) about the wire.

10. Find the moment of inertia of a hollow right circular cylinder, internal radius R_1, external R_0, length l, about the axis of figure.

Prove the rule by which, when we know the moment of inertia of a body about an axis through its centre of mass, we find its moment of inertia about any parallel axis.

What is the moment of inertia of our hollow cylinder about an axis lying in its interior surface?

Section XIII. Differential Equations.

1. Given that $\frac{dp}{dv} = -\gamma\frac{p}{v}$, where p is the pressure and v the volume of a gas which expands without gain or loss of heat. Show that the law connecting p and v is $pv^{\gamma} = c$, where c is a constant.

2. Given $$\frac{dy}{dx} = by;$$

then $$\frac{dy}{y} = b\,dx;$$

$$\therefore \log_e y = bx + C;$$

$$\therefore y = ae^{bx} \text{ where } a = e^C.$$

3. Given $$\frac{dy}{dx} = n\frac{y}{x};$$

then $$y = ax^n \text{ where } a = e^C.$$

4. A tree trunk is assumed to be in the form of a solid of revolution whose axis is vertical and the area of any cross-section is k times the weight of the portion above that section. Prove that if W is the weight of unit volume of the wood, the area of the section at a height x above the ground is proportional to e^{-kWx}.

5. A thick cylinder internal radius r is subjected to a compressive stress p inside and $p + dp$ outside. Then $\frac{dp}{dr} = -\frac{2(p-a)}{r}$.

Show that $$\log(p-a) = -2\log r + c,$$

$$\text{or } p = a + \frac{k}{r^2} \text{ where } k = e^c.$$

Table I.

USEFUL NUMBERS AND FORMULAE.

$\sqrt{2}=1{\cdot}414$, $\sqrt{3}=1{\cdot}732$, $\sqrt{5}=2{\cdot}236$, $\sqrt{6}=2{\cdot}449$.

$\pi=3{\cdot}1416$ or $3{\cdot}142$ or $\frac{22}{7}$. $\frac{1}{\pi}=0{\cdot}3183$.	
$\pi^2=9{\cdot}87$. 1 inch $=2{\cdot}54$ cm.	$\log \pi = 0{\cdot}4972$
1 lb. $=453{\cdot}6$ grams, $2\frac{1}{5}$ lbs. $=1$ kilogram.	$\log 2{\cdot}718=0{\cdot}4343$
1 gal. of water weighs 10 lbs. $=0{\cdot}1604$ cub. ft.	$\log {\cdot}7854=\bar{1}{\cdot}8951$
1 cubic foot of water weighs 62·3 lbs.	$\log 62{\cdot}3=1{\cdot}7945$
Volts × ampères = watts.	$\log 1728=3{\cdot}2375$
1 horse-power = 33000 ft.-lbs. per min.	$\log {\cdot}5236=\bar{1}{\cdot}7190$
= 746 watts.	$\log {\cdot}1604=\bar{1}{\cdot}2052$

1 radian = 57·3 degrees. To convert common into Naperian logarithms, multiply by 2·3026 ($e=2{\cdot}718$).

Mensuration Formulae. In the following formulae: A denotes area; S, surface; V, volume; a, b, c, the sides of a figure; h, the altitude; l, the slant height; R and r, radii of circles.

Rectangle *or Parallelogram.* $A=ah$.

Triangle. $A=\frac{1}{2}ah$, or $\sqrt{s(s-a)(s-b)(s-c)}$, where $s=\frac{1}{2}(a+b+c)$.

Trapezium. Parallel sides a and b. $A=\frac{1}{2}(a+b)h$.

Circle. Circumference $=2\pi r$, $A=\pi r^2$ or $\pi(R^2-r^2)$.

Ellipse. Semi-axes a and b. $A=\pi ab$.

Simpson's Rule. $A=\frac{s}{3}(A_1+4B+2C)$ where s is the space or distance between two consecutive ordinates. A_1 is the sum of first and last ordinates, B is sum of even, and C is sum of the odd ordinates.

Prismoid. Average section $=\frac{1}{6}(A_1+4B)$, $V=\frac{h}{6}(A_1+4B)$.

Prism. $S=2(ab+bc+ac)$, $V=abc$, diagonal $=\sqrt{a^2+b^2+c^2}$.

Cylinder. $S=2\pi rh+2\pi r^2$, $V=\pi r^2 h$.

Cone. $S=\pi rl+\pi r^2$, $V=\frac{1}{3}\pi r^2 h$.

Sphere. $S=4\pi r^2$, $V=\frac{4}{3}\pi r^3=0{\cdot}5236d^3$.

Ring. $S=4\pi^2 Rr$, $V=2\pi^2 r^2 R$.

Frustum of cone. $S=\pi(R+r)l$, $V=\frac{\pi h}{3}(R^2+r^2+Rr)$.

Frustum of pyramid. $V=\frac{h}{3}(A_1+A_2+\sqrt{A_1A_2})$.

Zone of a sphere. $S=2\pi rh$, $V=\frac{\pi h}{2}\left(R^2+r^2+\frac{h^2}{3}\right)$.

Weight in lbs. per cub. in.:—Cast iron, 0·26; Wrought iron, 0·28; Steel, 0·284; Brass, 0·29; Copper, 0·319; Lead, 0·412.

Table II.

LOGARITHMS.

	0	1	2	3	4	5	6	7	8	9	1	2	3	4	5	6	7	8	9
10	0000	0043	0086	0128	0170						4	9	13	17	21	26	30	34	38
						0212	0253	0294	0334	0374	4	8	12	16	20	24	28	32	36
11	0414	0453	0492	0531	0569						4	8	12	15	19	23	27	31	35
						0607	0645	0682	0719	0755	4	7	11	15	19	22	26	30	33
12	0792	0828	0864	0899	0934						3	7	11	14	18	21	25	28	32
						0969	1004	1038	1072	1106	3	7	10	14	17	20	24	27	31
13	1139	1173	1206	1239	1271						3	7	10	13	16	20	23	26	30
						1303	1335	1367	1399	1430	3	7	10	13	16	19	22	25	29
14	1461	1492	1523	1553	1584						3	6	9	12	15	19	22	25	28
						1614	1644	1673	1703	1732	3	6	9	12	15	17	20	23	26
15	1761	1790	1818	1847	1875						3	6	9	11	14	17	20	23	26
						1903	1931	1959	1987	2014	3	6	8	11	14	17	19	22	25
16	2041	2068	2095	2122	2148						3	5	8	11	14	16	19	22	24
						2175	2201	2227	2253	2279	3	5	8	10	13	16	18	21	23
17	2304	2330	2355	2380	2405						3	5	8	10	13	15	18	20	23
						2430	2455	2480	2504	2529	2	5	7	10	12	15	17	20	22
18	2553	2577	2601	2625	2648						2	5	7	9	12	14	16	19	21
						2672	2695	2718	2742	2765	2	5	7	9	11	14	16	18	21
19	2788	2810	2833	2856	2878						2	4	7	9	11	13	16	18	20
						2900	2923	2945	2967	2989	2	4	6	8	11	13	15	17	19
20	3010	3032	3054	3075	3096	3118	3139	3160	3181	3201	2	4	6	8	11	13	15	17	19
21	3222	3243	3263	3284	3304	3324	3345	3365	3385	3404	2	4	6	8	10	12	14	16	18
22	3424	3444	3464	3483	3502	3522	3541	3560	3579	3598	2	4	6	8	10	12	14	15	17
23	3617	3636	3655	3674	3692	3711	3729	3747	3766	3784	2	4	6	7	9	11	13	15	17
24	3802	3820	3838	3856	3874	3892	3909	3927	3945	3962	2	4	5	7	9	11	12	14	16
25	3979	3997	4014	4031	4048	4065	4082	4099	4116	4133	2	3	5	7	9	10	12	14	15
26	4150	4166	4183	4200	4216	4232	4249	4265	4281	4298	2	3	5	7	8	10	11	13	15
27	4314	4330	4346	4362	4378	4393	4409	4425	4440	4456	2	3	5	6	8	9	11	13	14
28	4472	4487	4502	4518	4533	4548	4564	4579	4594	4609	2	3	5	6	8	9	11	12	14
29	4624	4639	4654	4669	4683	4698	4713	4728	4742	4757	1	3	4	6	7	9	10	12	13
30	4771	4786	4800	4814	4829	4843	4857	4871	4886	4900	1	3	4	6	7	9	10	11	13
31	4914	4928	4942	4955	4969	4983	4997	5011	5024	5038	1	3	4	6	7	8	10	11	12
32	5051	5065	5079	5092	5105	5119	5132	5145	5159	5172	1	3	4	5	7	8	9	11	12
33	5185	5198	5211	5224	5237	5250	5263	5276	5289	5302	1	3	4	5	6	8	9	10	12
34	5315	5328	5340	5353	5366	5378	5391	5403	5416	5428	1	3	4	5	6	8	9	10	11
35	5441	5453	5465	5478	5490	5502	5514	5527	5539	5551	1	2	4	5	6	7	9	10	11
36	5563	5575	5587	5599	5611	5623	5635	5647	5658	5670	1	2	4	5	6	7	8	10	11
37	5682	5694	5705	5717	5729	5740	5752	5763	5775	5786	1	2	3	5	6	7	8	9	10
38	5798	5809	5821	5832	5843	5855	5866	5877	5888	5899	1	2	3	5	6	7	8	9	10
39	5911	5922	5933	5944	5955	5966	5977	5988	5999	6010	1	2	3	4	5	7	8	9	10
40	6021	6031	6042	6053	6064	6075	6085	6096	6107	6117	1	2	3	4	5	6	8	9	10
41	6128	6138	6149	6160	6170	6180	6191	6201	6212	6222	1	2	3	4	5	6	7	8	9
42	6232	6243	6253	6263	6274	6284	6294	6304	6314	6325	1	2	3	4	5	6	7	8	9
43	6335	6345	6355	6365	6375	6385	6395	6405	6415	6425	1	2	3	4	5	6	7	8	9
44	6435	6444	6454	6464	6474	6484	6493	6503	6513	6522	1	2	3	4	5	6	7	8	9
45	6532	6542	6551	6561	6571	6580	6590	6599	6609	6618	1	2	3	4	5	6	7	8	9
46	6628	6637	6646	6656	6665	6675	6684	6693	6702	6712	1	2	3	4	5	6	7	7	8
47	6721	6730	6739	6749	6758	6767	6776	6785	6794	6803	1	2	3	4	5	5	6	7	8
48	6812	6821	6830	6839	6848	6857	6866	6875	6884	6893	1	2	3	4	4	5	6	7	8
49	6902	6911	6920	6928	6937	6946	6955	6964	6972	6981	1	2	3	4	4	5	6	7	8

Table II.

LOGARITHMS.

	0	1	2	3	4	5	6	7	8	9	1	2	3	4	5	6	7	8	9
50	6990	6998	7007	7016	7024	7033	7042	7050	7059	7067	1	2	3	3	4	5	6	7	8
51	7076	7084	7093	7101	7110	7118	7126	7135	7143	7152	1	2	3	3	4	5	6	7	8
52	7160	7168	7177	7185	7193	7202	7210	7218	7226	7235	1	2	2	3	4	5	6	7	7
53	7243	7251	7259	7267	7275	7284	7292	7300	7308	7316	1	2	2	3	4	5	6	6	7
54	7324	7332	7340	7348	7356	7364	7372	7380	7388	7396	1	2	2	3	4	5	6	6	7
55	7404	7412	7419	7427	7435	7443	7451	7459	7466	7474	1	2	2	3	4	5	5	6	7
56	7482	7490	7497	7505	7513	7520	7528	7536	7543	7551	1	2	2	3	4	5	5	6	7
57	7559	7566	7574	7582	7589	7597	7604	7612	7619	7627	1	2	2	3	4	5	5	6	7
58	7634	7642	7649	7657	7664	7672	7679	7686	7694	7701	1	1	2	3	4	4	5	6	7
59	7709	7716	7723	7731	7738	7745	7752	7760	7767	7774	1	1	2	3	4	4	5	6	7
60	7782	7789	7796	7803	7810	7818	7825	7832	7839	7846	1	1	2	3	4	4	5	6	6
61	7853	7860	7868	7875	7882	7889	7896	7903	7910	7917	1	1	2	3	4	4	5	6	6
62	7924	7931	7938	7945	7952	7959	7966	7973	7980	7987	1	1	2	3	3	4	5	6	6
63	7993	8000	8007	8014	8021	8028	8035	8041	8048	8055	1	1	2	3	3	4	5	5	6
64	8062	8069	8075	8082	8089	8096	8102	8109	8116	8122	1	1	2	3	3	4	5	5	6
65	8129	8136	8142	8149	8156	8162	8169	8176	8182	8189	1	1	2	3	3	4	5	5	6
66	8195	8202	8209	8215	8222	8228	8235	8241	8248	8254	1	1	2	3	3	4	5	5	6
67	8261	8267	8274	8280	8287	8293	8299	8306	8312	8319	1	1	2	3	3	4	5	5	6
68	8325	8331	8338	8344	8351	8357	8363	8370	8376	8382	1	1	2	3	3	4	4	5	6
69	8388	8395	8401	8407	8414	8420	8426	8432	8439	8445	1	1	2	2	3	4	4	5	6
70	8451	8457	8463	8470	8476	8482	8488	8494	8500	8506	1	1	2	2	3	4	4	5	6
71	8513	8519	8525	8531	8537	8543	8549	8555	8561	8567	1	1	2	2	3	4	4	5	5
72	8573	8579	8585	8591	8597	8603	8609	8615	8621	8627	1	1	2	2	3	4	4	5	5
73	8633	8639	8645	8651	8657	8663	8669	8675	8681	8686	1	1	2	2	3	4	4	5	5
74	8692	8698	8704	8710	8716	8722	8727	8733	8739	8745	1	1	2	2	3	4	4	5	5
75	8751	8756	8762	8768	8774	8779	8785	8791	8797	8802	1	1	2	2	3	3	4	5	5
76	8808	8814	8820	8825	8831	8837	8842	8848	8854	8859	1	1	2	2	3	3	4	5	5
77	8865	8871	8876	8882	8887	8893	8899	8904	8910	8915	1	1	2	2	3	3	4	4	5
78	8921	8927	8932	8938	8943	8949	8954	8960	8965	8971	1	1	2	2	3	3	4	4	5
79	8976	8982	8987	8993	8998	9004	9009	9015	9020	9025	1	1	2	2	3	3	4	4	5
80	9031	9036	9042	9047	9053	9058	9063	9069	9074	9079	1	1	2	2	3	3	4	4	5
81	9085	9090	9096	9101	9106	9112	9117	9122	9128	9133	1	1	2	2	3	3	4	4	5
82	9138	9143	9149	9154	9159	9165	9170	9175	9180	9186	1	1	2	2	3	3	4	4	5
83	9191	9196	9201	9206	9212	9217	9222	9227	9232	9238	1	1	2	2	3	3	4	4	5
84	9243	9248	9253	9258	9263	9269	9274	9279	9284	9289	1	1	2	2	3	3	4	4	5
85	9294	9299	9304	9309	9315	9320	9325	9330	9335	9340	1	1	2	2	3	3	4	4	5
86	9345	9350	9355	9360	9365	9370	9375	9380	9385	9390	1	1	2	2	3	3	4	4	5
87	9395	9400	9405	9410	9415	9420	9425	9430	9435	9440	0	1	1	2	2	3	3	4	4
88	9445	9450	9455	9460	9465	9469	9474	9479	9484	9489	0	1	1	2	2	3	3	4	4
89	9494	9499	9504	9509	9513	9518	9523	9528	9533	9538	0	1	1	2	2	3	3	4	4
90	9542	9547	9552	9557	9562	9566	9571	9576	9581	9586	0	1	1	2	2	3	3	4	4
91	9590	9595	9600	9605	9609	9614	9619	9624	9628	9633	0	1	1	2	2	3	3	4	4
92	9638	9643	9647	9652	9657	9661	9666	9671	9675	9680	0	1	1	2	2	3	3	4	4
93	9685	9689	9694	9699	9703	9708	9713	9717	9722	9727	0	1	1	2	2	3	3	4	4
94	9731	9736	9741	9745	9750	9754	9759	9763	9768	9773	0	1	1	2	2	3	3	4	4
95	9777	9782	9786	9791	9795	9800	9805	9809	9814	9818	0	1	1	2	2	3	3	4	4
96	9823	9827	9832	9836	9841	9845	9850	9854	9859	9863	0	1	1	2	2	3	3	4	4
97	9868	9872	9877	9881	9886	9890	9894	9899	9903	9908	0	1	1	2	2	3	3	4	4
98	9912	9917	9921	9926	9930	9934	9939	9943	9948	9952	0	1	1	2	2	3	3	4	4
99	9956	9961	9965	9969	9974	9978	9983	9987	9991	9996	0	1	1	2	2	3	3	3	4

Table III.

ANTILOGARITHMS.

	0	1	2	3	4	5	6	7	8	9	1	2	3	4	5	6	7	8	9
·00	1000	1002	1005	1007	1009	1012	1014	1016	1019	1021	0	0	1	1	1	1	2	2	2
·01	1023	1026	1028	1030	1033	1035	1038	1040	1042	1045	0	0	1	1	1	1	2	2	2
·02	1047	1050	1052	1054	1057	1059	1062	1064	1067	1069	0	0	1	1	1	1	2	2	2
·03	1072	1074	1076	1079	1081	1084	1086	1089	1091	1094	0	0	1	1	1	1	2	2	2
·04	1096	1099	1102	1104	1107	1109	1112	1114	1117	1119	0	1	1	1	1	2	2	2	2
·05	1122	1125	1127	1130	1132	1135	1138	1140	1143	1146	0	1	1	1	1	2	2	2	2
·06	1148	1151	1153	1156	1159	1161	1164	1167	1169	1172	0	1	1	1	1	2	2	2	2
·07	1175	1178	1180	1183	1186	1189	1191	1194	1197	1199	0	1	1	1	1	2	2	2	2
·08	1202	1205	1208	1211	1213	1216	1219	1222	1225	1227	0	1	1	1	1	2	2	2	3
·09	1230	1233	1236	1239	1242	1245	1247	1250	1253	1256	0	1	1	1	1	2	2	2	3
·10	1259	1262	1265	1268	1271	1274	1276	1279	1282	1285	0	1	1	1	1	2	2	2	3
·11	1288	1291	1294	1297	1300	1303	1306	1309	1312	1315	0	1	1	1	2	2	2	2	3
·12	1318	1321	1324	1327	1330	1334	1337	1340	1343	1346	0	1	1	1	2	2	2	2	3
·13	1349	1352	1355	1358	1361	1365	1368	1371	1374	1377	0	1	1	1	2	2	2	3	3
·14	1380	1384	1387	1390	1393	1396	1400	1403	1406	1409	0	1	1	1	2	2	2	3	3
·15	1413	1416	1419	1422	1426	1429	1432	1435	1439	1442	0	1	1	1	2	2	2	3	3
·16	1445	1449	1452	1455	1459	1462	1466	1469	1472	1476	0	1	1	1	2	2	2	3	3
·17	1479	1483	1486	1489	1493	1496	1500	1503	1507	1510	0	1	1	1	2	2	2	3	3
·18	1514	1517	1521	1524	1528	1531	1535	1538	1542	1545	0	1	1	1	2	2	2	3	3
·19	1549	1552	1556	1560	1563	1567	1570	1574	1578	1581	0	1	1	1	2	2	3	3	3
·20	1585	1589	1592	1596	1600	1603	1607	1611	1614	1618	0	1	1	1	2	2	3	3	3
·21	1622	1626	1629	1633	1637	1641	1644	1648	1652	1656	0	1	1	2	2	2	3	3	3
·22	1660	1663	1667	1671	1675	1679	1683	1687	1690	1694	0	1	1	2	2	2	3	3	3
·23	1698	1702	1706	1710	1714	1718	1722	1726	1730	1734	0	1	1	2	2	2	3	3	4
·24	1738	1742	1746	1750	1754	1758	1762	1766	1770	1774	0	1	1	2	2	2	3	3	4
·25	1778	1782	1786	1791	1795	1799	1803	1807	1811	1816	0	1	1	2	2	2	3	3	4
·26	1820	1824	1828	1832	1837	1841	1845	1849	1854	1858	0	1	1	2	2	3	3	3	4
·27	1862	1866	1871	1875	1879	1884	1888	1892	1897	1901	0	1	1	2	2	3	3	3	4
·28	1905	1910	1914	1919	1923	1928	1932	1936	1941	1945	0	1	1	2	2	3	3	4	4
·29	1950	1954	1959	1963	1968	1972	1977	1982	1986	1991	0	1	1	2	2	3	3	4	4
·30	1995	2000	2004	2009	2014	2018	2023	2028	2032	2037	0	1	1	2	2	3	3	4	4
·31	2042	2046	2051	2056	2061	2065	2070	2075	2080	2084	0	1	1	2	2	3	3	4	4
·32	2089	2094	2099	2104	2109	2113	2118	2123	2128	2133	0	1	1	2	2	3	3	4	4
·33	2138	2143	2148	2153	2158	2163	2168	2173	2178	2183	0	1	1	2	2	3	3	4	4
·34	2188	2193	2198	2203	2208	2213	2218	2223	2228	2234	1	1	2	2	3	3	4	4	5
·35	2239	2244	2249	2254	2259	2265	2270	2275	2280	2286	1	1	2	2	3	3	4	4	5
·36	2291	2296	2301	2307	2312	2317	2323	2328	2333	2339	1	1	2	2	3	3	4	4	5
·37	2344	2350	2355	2360	2366	2371	2377	2382	2388	2393	1	1	2	2	3	3	4	4	5
·38	2399	2404	2410	2415	2421	2427	2432	2438	2443	2449	1	1	2	2	3	3	4	4	5
·39	2455	2460	2466	2472	2477	2483	2489	2495	2500	2506	1	1	2	2	3	3	4	5	5
·40	2512	2518	2523	2529	2535	2541	2547	2553	2559	2564	1	1	2	2	3	4	4	5	5
·41	2570	2576	2582	2588	2594	2600	2606	2612	2618	2624	1	1	2	2	3	4	4	5	5
·42	2630	2636	2642	2649	2655	2661	2667	2673	2679	2685	1	1	2	2	3	4	4	5	6
·43	2692	2698	2704	2710	2716	2723	2729	2735	2742	2748	1	1	2	3	3	4	4	5	6
·44	2754	2761	2767	2773	2780	2786	2793	2799	2805	2812	1	1	2	3	3	4	4	5	6
·45	2818	2825	2831	2838	2844	2851	2858	2864	2871	2877	1	1	2	3	3	4	5	5	6
·46	2884	2891	2897	2904	2911	2917	2924	2931	2938	2944	1	1	2	3	3	4	5	5	6
·47	2951	2958	2965	2972	2979	2985	2992	2999	3006	3013	1	1	2	3	3	4	5	5	6
·48	3020	3027	3034	3041	3048	3055	3062	3069	3076	3083	1	1	2	3	4	4	5	6	6
·49	3090	3097	3105	3112	3119	3126	3133	3141	3148	3155	1	1	2	3	4	4	5	6	6

Table III.

ANTILOGARITHMS.

	0	1	2	3	4	5	6	7	8	9	1	2	3	4	6	6	7	8	9
50	3162	3170	3177	3184	3192	3199	3206	3214	3221	3228	1	1	2	3	4	4	5	6	7
51	3236	3243	3251	3258	3266	3273	3281	3289	3296	3304	1	2	2	3	4	5	5	6	7
52	3311	3319	3327	3334	3342	3350	3357	3365	3373	3381	1	2	2	3	4	5	5	6	7
53	3388	3396	3404	3412	3420	3428	3436	3443	3451	3459	1	2	2	3	4	5	6	6	7
54	3467	3475	3483	3491	3499	3508	3516	3524	3532	3540	1	2	2	3	4	5	6	6	7
55	3548	3556	3565	3573	3581	3589	3597	3606	3614	3622	1	2	2	3	4	5	6	7	7
56	3631	3639	3648	3656	3664	3673	3681	3690	3698	3707	1	2	3	3	4	5	6	7	8
57	3715	3724	3733	3741	3750	3758	3767	3776	3784	3793	1	2	3	3	4	5	6	7	8
58	3802	3811	3819	3828	3837	3846	3855	3864	3873	3882	1	2	3	4	4	5	6	7	8
59	3890	3899	3908	3917	3926	3936	3945	3954	3963	3972	1	2	3	4	5	5	6	7	8
60	3981	3990	3999	4009	4018	4027	4036	4046	4055	4064	1	2	3	4	5	6	6	7	8
61	4074	4083	4093	4102	4111	4121	4130	4140	4150	4159	1	2	3	4	5	6	7	8	9
62	4169	4178	4188	4198	4207	4217	4227	4236	4246	4256	1	2	3	4	5	6	7	8	9
63	4266	4276	4285	4295	4305	4315	4325	4335	4345	4355	1	2	3	4	5	6	7	8	9
64	4365	4375	4385	4395	4406	4416	4426	4436	4446	4457	1	2	3	4	5	6	7	8	9
65	4467	4477	4487	4498	4508	4519	4529	4539	4550	4560	1	2	3	4	5	6	7	8	9
66	4571	4581	4592	4603	4613	4624	4634	4645	4656	4667	1	2	3	4	5	6	7	9	10
67	4677	4688	4699	4710	4721	4732	4742	4753	4764	4775	1	2	3	4	5	7	8	9	10
68	4786	4797	4808	4819	4831	4842	4853	4864	4875	4887	1	2	3	4	6	7	8	9	10
69	4898	4909	4920	4932	4943	4955	4966	4977	4989	5000	1	2	3	5	6	7	8	9	10
70	5012	5023	5035	5047	5058	5070	5082	5093	5105	5117	1	2	4	5	6	7	8	9	11
71	5129	5140	5152	5164	5176	5188	5200	5212	5224	5236	1	2	4	5	6	7	8	10	11
72	5248	5260	5272	5284	5297	5309	5321	5333	5346	5358	1	2	4	5	6	7	9	10	11
73	5370	5383	5395	5408	5420	5433	5445	5458	5470	5483	1	3	4	5	6	8	9	10	11
74	5495	5508	5521	5534	5546	5559	5572	5585	5598	5610	1	3	4	5	6	8	9	10	12
75	5623	5636	5649	5662	5675	5689	5702	5715	5728	5741	1	3	4	5	7	8	9	10	12
76	5754	5768	5781	5794	5808	5821	5834	5848	5861	5875	1	3	4	5	7	8	9	11	12
77	5888	5902	5916	5929	5943	5957	5970	5984	5998	6012	1	3	4	5	7	8	10	11	12
78	6026	6039	6053	6067	6081	6095	6109	6124	6138	6152	1	3	4	6	7	8	10	11	13
79	6166	6180	6194	6209	6223	6237	6252	6266	6281	6295	1	3	4	6	7	9	10	11	13
80	6310	6324	6339	6353	6368	6383	6397	6412	6427	6442	1	3	4	6	7	9	10	12	13
81	6457	6471	6486	6501	6516	6531	6546	6561	6577	6592	2	3	5	6	8	9	11	12	14
82	6607	6622	6637	6653	6668	6683	6699	6714	6730	6745	2	3	5	6	8	9	11	12	14
83	6761	6776	6792	6808	6823	6839	6855	6871	6887	6902	2	3	5	6	8	9	11	13	14
84	6918	6934	6950	6966	6982	6998	7015	7031	7047	7063	2	3	5	6	8	10	11	13	15
85	7079	7096	7112	7129	7145	7161	7178	7194	7211	7228	2	3	5	7	8	10	12	13	15
86	7244	7261	7278	7295	7311	7328	7345	7362	7379	7396	2	3	5	7	8	10	12	13	15
87	7413	7430	7447	7464	7482	7499	7516	7534	7551	7568	2	3	5	7	9	10	12	14	16
88	7586	7603	7621	7638	7656	7674	7691	7709	7727	7745	2	4	5	7	9	11	12	14	16
89	7762	7780	7798	7816	7834	7852	7870	7889	7907	7925	2	4	5	7	9	11	13	14	16
90	7943	7962	7980	7998	8017	8035	8054	8072	8091	8110	2	4	6	7	9	11	13	15	17
91	8128	8147	8166	8185	8204	8222	8241	8260	8279	8299	2	4	6	8	9	11	13	15	17
92	8318	8337	8356	8375	8395	8414	8433	8453	8472	8492	2	4	6	8	10	12	14	15	17
93	8511	8531	8551	8570	8590	8610	8630	8650	8670	8690	2	4	6	8	10	12	14	16	18
94	8710	8730	8750	8770	8790	8810	8831	8851	8872	8892	2	4	6	8	10	12	14	16	18
95	8913	8933	8954	8974	8995	9016	9036	9057	9078	9099	2	4	6	8	10	12	15	17	19
96	9120	9141	9162	9183	9204	9226	9247	9268	9290	9311	2	4	6	8	11	13	15	17	19
97	9333	9354	9376	9397	9419	9441	9462	9484	9506	9528	2	4	7	9	11	13	15	17	20
98	9550	9572	9594	9616	9638	9661	9683	9705	9727	9750	2	4	7	9	11	13	16	18	20
99	9772	9795	9817	9840	9863	9886	9908	9931	9954	9977	2	5	7	9	11	14	16	18	20

Table IV.

NATURAL SINES.

	0′	10′	20′	30′	40′	50′	1	2	3	4	5	6	7	8	9
0	0000	0029	0058	0087	0116	0145	3	6	9	12	15	17	20	23	26
1	0175	0204	0233	0262	0291	0320	3	6	9	12	15	17	20	23	26
2	0349	0378	0407	0436	0465	0494	3	6	9	12	15	17	20	23	26
3	0523	0552	0581	0610	0640	0669	3	6	9	12	15	17	20	23	26
4	0698	0727	0756	0785	0814	0843	3	6	9	12	15	17	20	23	26
5	0872	0901	0929	0958	0987	1016	3	6	9	12	14	17	20	23	26
6	1045	1074	1103	1132	1161	1190	3	6	9	12	14	17	20	23	26
7	1219	1248	1276	1305	1334	1363	3	6	9	12	14	17	20	23	26
8	1392	1421	1449	1478	1507	1536	3	6	9	12	14	17	20	23	26
9	1564	1593	1622	1650	1679	1708	3	6	9	12	14	17	20	23	26
10	1736	1765	1794	1822	1851	1880	3	6	9	12	14	17	20	23	26
11	1908	1937	1965	1994	2022	2051	3	6	9	11	14	17	20	23	26
12	2079	2108	2136	2164	2193	2221	3	6	9	11	14	17	20	23	26
13	2250	2278	2306	2334	2363	2391	3	6	8	11	14	17	20	23	25
14	2419	2447	2476	2504	2532	2560	3	6	8	11	14	17	20	23	25
15	2588	2616	2644	2672	2700	2728	3	6	8	11	14	17	20	22	25
16	2756	2784	2812	2840	2868	2896	3	6	8	11	14	17	20	22	25
17	2924	2952	2979	3007	3035	3062	3	6	8	11	14	17	19	22	25
18	3090	3118	3145	3173	3201	3228	3	6	8	11	14	17	19	22	25
19	3256	3283	3311	3338	3365	3393	3	5	8	11	14	16	19	22	25
20	3420	3448	3475	3502	3529	3557	3	5	8	11	14	16	19	22	25
21	3584	3611	3638	3665	3692	3719	3	5	8	11	14	16	19	22	24
22	3746	3773	3800	3827	3854	3881	3	5	8	11	14	16	19	21	24
23	3907	3934	3961	3987	4014	4041	3	5	8	11	14	16	19	21	24
24	4067	4094	4120	4147	4173	4200	3	5	8	11	13	16	19	21	24
25	4226	4253	4279	4305	4331	4358	3	5	8	11	13	16	18	21	24
26	4384	4410	4436	4462	4488	4514	3	5	8	10	13	16	18	21	23
27	4540	4566	4592	4617	4643	4669	3	5	8	10	13	15	18	21	23
28	4695	4720	4746	4772	4797	4823	3	5	8	10	13	15	18	20	23
29	4848	4874	4899	4924	4950	4975	3	5	8	10	13	15	18	20	23
30	5000	5025	5050	5075	5100	5125	3	5	8	10	13	15	18	20	23
31	5150	5175	5200	5225	5250	5275	2	5	7	10	12	15	17	20	22
32	5299	5324	5348	5373	5398	5422	2	5	7	10	12	15	17	20	22
33	5446	5471	5495	5519	5544	5568	2	5	7	10	12	15	17	19	22
34	5592	5616	5640	5664	5688	5712	2	5	7	10	12	14	17	19	22
35	5736	5760	5783	5807	5831	5854	2	5	7	10	12	14	17	19	21
36	5878	5901	5925	5948	5972	5995	2	5	7	9	12	14	16	19	21
37	6018	6041	6065	6088	6111	6134	2	5	7	9	12	14	16	18	21
38	6157	6180	6202	6225	6248	6271	2	5	7	9	11	14	16	18	20
39	6293	6316	6338	6361	6383	6406	2	4	7	9	11	13	16	18	20
40	6428	6450	6472	6494	6517	6539	2	4	7	9	11	13	15	18	20
41	6561	6583	6604	6626	6648	6670	2	4	7	9	11	13	15	17	20
42	6691	6713	6734	6756	6777	6799	2	4	6	9	11	13	15	17	19
43	6820	6841	6862	6884	6905	6926	2	4	6	8	11	13	15	17	19
44	6947	6967	6988	7009	7030	7050	2	4	6	8	10	12	15	17	19

Table IV.

NATURAL SINES.

	0′	10′	20′	30′	40′	50′	1	2	3	4	5	6	7	8	9
45	7071	7092	7112	7133	7153	7173	2	4	6	8	10	12	14	16	18
46	7193	7214	7234	7254	7274	7294	2	4	6	8	10	12	14	16	18
47	7314	7333	7353	7373	7392	7412	2	4	6	8	10	12	14	16	18
48	7431	7451	7470	7490	7509	7528	2	4	6	8	10	12	13	15	17
49	7547	7566	7585	7604	7623	7642	2	4	6	8	9	11	13	15	17
50	7660	7679	7698	7716	7735	7753	2	4	6	7	9	11	13	15	17
51	7771	7790	7808	7826	7844	7862	2	4	5	7	9	11	13	14	16
52	7880	7898	7916	7934	7951	7969	2	4	5	7	9	11	12	14	16
53	7986	8004	8021	8039	8056	8073	2	3	5	7	9	10	12	14	16
54	8090	8107	8124	8141	8158	8175	2	3	5	7	8	10	12	14	15
55	8192	8208	8225	8241	8258	8274	2	3	5	7	8	10	12	13	15
56	8290	8307	8323	8339	8355	8371	2	3	5	6	8	10	11	13	14
57	8387	8403	8418	8434	8450	8465	2	3	5	6	8	9	11	12	14
58	8480	8496	8511	8526	8542	8557	2	3	5	6	8	9	11	12	14
59	8572	8587	8601	8616	8631	8646	1	3	4	6	7	9	10	12	13
60	8660	8675	8689	8704	8718	8732	1	3	4	6	7	9	10	11	13
61	8746	8760	8774	8788	8802	8816	1	3	4	6	7	8	10	11	12
62	8829	8843	8857	8870	8884	8897	1	3	4	5	7	8	9	11	12
63	8910	8923	8936	8949	8962	8975	1	3	4	5	6	8	9	10	12
64	8988	9001	9013	9026	9038	9051	1	3	4	5	6	8	9	10	11
65	9063	9075	9088	9100	9112	9124	1	2	4	5	6	7	8	10	11
66	9135	9147	9159	9171	9182	9194	1	2	3	5	6	7	8	9	10
67	9205	9216	9228	9239	9250	9261	1	2	3	4	6	7	8	9	10
68	9272	9283	9293	9304	9315	9325	1	2	3	4	5	6	7	9	10
69	9336	9346	9356	9367	9377	9387	1	2	3	4	5	6	7	8	9
70	9397	9407	9417	9426	9436	9446	1	2	3	4	5	6	7	8	9
71	9455	9465	9474	9483	9492	9502	1	2	3	4	5	6	6	7	8
72	9511	9520	9528	9537	9546	9555	1	2	3	4	4	5	6	7	8
73	9563	9572	9580	9588	9596	9605	1	2	2	3	4	5	6	7	7
74	9613	9621	9628	9636	9644	9652	1	2	2	3	4	5	5	6	7
75	9659	9667	9674	9681	9689	9696	1	1	2	3	4	4	5	6	7
76	9703	9710	9717	9724	9730	9737	1	1	2	3	3	4	5	5	6
77	9744	9750	9757	9763	9769	9775	1	1	2	3	3	4	4	5	6
78	9781	9787	9793	9799	9805	9811	1	1	2	2	3	3	4	5	5
79	9816	9822	9827	9833	9838	9843	1	1	2	2	3	3	4	4	5
80	9848	9853	9858	9863	9868	9872	0	1	1	2	2	3	3	4	4
81	9877	9881	9886	9890	9894	9899	0	1	1	2	2	3	3	3	4
82	9903	9907	9911	9914	9918	9922	0	1	1	2	2	2	3	3	3
83	9925	9929	9932	9936	9939	9942	0	1	1	1	2	2	3	3	3
84	9945	9948	9951	9954	9957	9959	0	1	1	1	1	2	2	2	2
85	9962	9964	9967	9969	9971	9974	0	0	1	1	1	1	2	2	2
86	9976	9978	9980	9981	9983	9985	0	0	1	1	1	1	1	1	2
87	9986	9988	9989	9990	9992	9993	0	0	0	1	1	1	1	1	1
88	9994	9995	9996	9997	9997	9998	0	0	0	0	0	0	1	1	1
89	9998	9999	9999	1·0000	1·0000	1·0000	0	0	0	0	0	0	0	0	0

Table V.

NATURAL COSINES.

Deg.	0′	10′	20′	30′	40′	50′	1	2	3	4	5	6	7	8	9
0	1·0000	1·0000	1·0000	1·0000	9999	9999	0	0	0	0	0	0	0	0	0
1	9998	9998	9997	9997	9996	9995	0	0	0	0	0	0	0	0	0
2	9994	9993	9992	9990	9989	9988	0	0	0	0	0	0	1	1	1
3	9986	9985	9983	9981	9980	9978	0	0	1	1	1	1	1	1	1
4	9976	9974	9971	9969	9967	9964	0	0	1	1	1	1	1	1	2
5	9962	9959	9957	9954	9951	9948	0	1	1	1	1	1	2	2	2
6	9945	9942	9939	9936	9932	9929	0	1	1	1	2	2	2	2	2
7	9925	9922	9918	9914	9911	9907	0	1	1	2	2	2	3	3	3
8	9903	9899	9894	9890	9886	9881	0	1	1	2	2	2	3	3	3
9	9877	9872	9868	9863	9858	9853	0	1	1	2	2	3	3	3	4
10	9848	9843	9838	9833	9827	9822	1	1	2	2	2	3	3	4	4
11	9816	9811	9805	9799	9793	9787	1	1	2	2	3	3	4	4	5
12	9781	9775	9769	9763	9757	9750	1	1	2	2	3	3	4	5	5
13	9744	9737	9730	9724	9717	9710	1	1	2	3	3	4	4	5	6
14	9703	9696	9689	9681	9674	9667	1	1	2	3	4	4	5	5	6
15	9659	9652	9644	9636	9628	9621	1	2	2	3	4	4	5	6	7
16	9613	9605	9596	9588	9580	9572	1	2	2	3	4	5	5	6	7
17	9563	9555	9546	9537	9528	9520	1	2	3	3	4	5	6	7	7
18	9511	9502	9492	9483	9474	9465	1	2	3	4	4	5	6	7	8
19	9455	9446	9436	9426	9417	9407	1	2	3	4	5	6	6	7	8
20	9397	9387	9377	9367	9356	9346	1	2	3	4	5	6	7	8	9
21	9336	9325	9315	9304	9293	9283	1	2	3	4	5	6	7	8	9
22	9272	9261	9250	9239	9228	9216	1	2	3	4	6	6	7	9	10
23	9205	9194	9182	9171	9159	9147	1	2	3	5	6	7	8	9	10
24	9135	9124	9112	9100	9088	9075	1	2	4	5	6	7	8	9	10
25	9063	9051	9038	9026	9013	9001	1	3	4	5	6	7	8	10	11
26	8988	8975	8962	8949	8936	8923	1	3	4	5	6	8	9	10	11
27	8910	8897	8884	8870	8857	8843	1	3	4	5	7	8	9	10	12
28	8829	8816	8802	8788	8774	8760	1	3	4	6	7	8	9	11	12
29	8746	8732	8718	8704	8689	8675	1	3	4	6	7	8	10	11	12
30	8660	8646	8631	8616	8601	8587	1	3	4	6	7	9	10	11	13
31	8572	8557	8542	8526	8511	8496	2	3	5	6	8	9	10	12	13
32	8480	8465	8450	8434	8418	8403	2	3	5	6	8	9	11	12	14
33	8387	8371	8355	8339	8323	8307	2	3	5	6	8	9	11	12	14
34	8290	8274	8258	8241	8225	8208	2	3	5	7	8	10	11	13	14
35	8192	8175	8158	8141	8124	8107	2	3	5	7	8	10	12	13	15
36	8090	8073	8056	8039	8021	8004	2	3	5	7	9	10	12	14	15
37	7986	7969	7951	7934	7916	7898	2	4	5	7	9	10	12	14	16
38	7880	7862	7844	7826	7808	7790	2	4	5	7	9	11	12	14	16
39	7771	7753	7735	7716	7698	7679	2	4	6	7	9	11	13	14	16
40	7660	7642	7623	7604	7585	7566	2	4	6	8	9	11	13	15	17
41	7547	7528	7509	7490	7470	7451	2	4	6	8	10	11	13	15	17
42	7431	7412	7392	7373	7353	7333	2	4	6	8	10	12	13	15	17
43	7314	7294	7274	7254	7234	7214	2	4	6	8	10	12	14	16	18
44	7193	7173	7153	7132	7112	7092	2	4	6	8	10	12	14	16	18

Table V.

NATURAL COSINES.

Deg.	0′	10′	20′	30′	40′	50′	1	2	3	4	5	6	7	8	9
45	7071	7050	7030	7009	6988	6967	2	4	6	8	10	12	15	17	19
46	6947	6926	6905	6884	6862	6841	2	4	6	8	11	13	15	17	19
47	6820	6799	6777	6756	6734	6713	2	4	6	9	11	13	15	17	19
48	6691	6670	6648	6626	6604	6583	2	4	7	9	11	13	15	17	19
49	6561	6539	6517	6494	6472	6450	2	4	7	9	11	13	15	17	20
50	6428	6406	6383	6361	6338	6316	2	4	7	9	11	13	15	18	20
51	6293	6271	6248	6225	6202	6180	2	5	7	9	11	13	16	18	20
52	6157	6134	6111	6088	6065	6041	2	5	7	9	12	14	16	18	20
53	6018	5995	5972	5948	5925	5901	2	5	7	9	12	14	16	18	21
54	5878	5854	5831	5807	5783	5760	2	5	7	9	12	14	16	19	21
55	5736	5712	5688	5664	5640	5616	2	5	7	10	12	14	17	19	21
56	5592	5568	5544	5519	5495	5471	2	5	7	10	12	14	17	19	22
57	5446	5422	5398	5373	5348	5324	2	5	7	10	12	15	17	19	22
58	5299	5275	5250	5225	5200	5175	2	5	7	10	12	15	17	20	22
59	5150	5125	5100	5075	5050	5025	3	5	8	10	13	15	17	20	22
60	5000	4975	4950	4924	4899	4874	3	5	8	10	13	15	18	20	23
61	4848	4823	4797	4772	4746	4720	3	5	8	10	13	15	18	20	23
62	4695	4669	4643	4617	4592	4566	3	5	8	10	13	15	18	20	23
63	4540	4514	4488	4462	4436	4410	3	5	8	10	13	15	18	21	23
64	4384	4358	4331	4305	4279	4253	3	5	8	11	13	16	18	21	23
65	4226	4200	4173	4147	4120	4094	3	5	8	11	13	16	18	21	24
66	4067	4041	4014	3987	3961	3934	3	5	8	11	14	16	19	21	24
67	3907	3881	3854	3827	3800	3773	3	5	8	11	14	16	19	21	24
68	3746	3719	3692	3665	3638	3611	3	5	8	11	14	16	19	21	24
69	3584	3557	3529	3502	3475	3448	3	5	8	11	14	16	19	22	24
70	3420	3393	3365	3338	3311	3283	3	5	8	11	14	16	19	22	25
71	3256	3228	3201	3173	3145	3118	3	6	8	11	14	16	19	22	25
72	3090	3062	3035	3007	2979	2952	3	6	8	11	14	17	19	22	25
73	2924	2896	2868	2840	2812	2784	3	6	8	11	14	17	19	22	25
74	2756	2728	2700	2672	2644	2616	3	6	8	11	14	17	20	22	25
75	2588	2560	2532	2504	2476	2447	3	6	8	11	14	17	20	22	25
76	2419	2391	2363	2334	2306	2278	3	6	8	11	14	17	20	23	25
77	2250	2221	2193	2164	2136	2108	3	6	9	11	14	17	20	23	25
78	2079	2051	2022	1994	1965	1937	3	6	9	11	14	17	20	23	26
79	1908	1880	1851	1822	1794	1765	3	6	9	12	14	17	20	23	26
80	1736	1708	1679	1650	1622	1593	3	6	9	12	14	17	20	23	26
81	1564	1536	1507	1478	1449	1421	3	6	9	12	14	17	20	23	26
82	1392	1363	1334	1305	1276	1248	3	6	9	12	14	17	20	23	26
83	1219	1190	1161	1132	1103	1074	3	6	9	12	14	17	20	23	26
84	1045	1016	0987	0958	0929	0901	3	6	9	12	14	17	20	23	26
85	0872	0843	0814	0785	0756	0727	3	6	9	12	15	17	20	23	26
86	0698	0669	0640	0610	0581	0552	3	6	9	12	15	17	20	23	26
87	0523	0494	0465	0436	0407	0378	3	6	9	12	15	17	20	23	26
88	0349	0320	0291	0262	0233	0204	3	6	9	12	15	17	20	23	26
89	0175	0145	0116	0087	0058	0029	3	6	9	12	15	17	20	23	26

Table VI.

NATURAL TANGENTS.

	0′	5′	10′	15′	20′	25′	30′	35′	40′	45′	50′	55′	1	2	3	4
0°	·0000	0015	0029	0044	0058	0073	0087	0102	0116	0131	0145	0160	3	6	9	12
1	·0175	0189	0204	0218	0233	0247	0262	0276	0291	0306	0320	0335	3	6	9	12
2	·0349	0364	0378	0393	0407	0422	0437	0451	0466	0480	0495	0509	3	6	9	12
3	·0524	0539	0553	0568	0582	0597	0612	0626	0641	0655	0670	0685	3	6	9	12
4	·0699	0714	0729	0743	0758	0772	0787	0802	0816	0831	0846	0860	3	6	9	12
5	·0875	0890	0904	0919	0934	0948	0963	0978	0992	1007	1022	1036	3	6	9	12
6	·1051	1066	1080	1095	1110	1125	1139	1154	1169	1184	1198	1213	3	6	9	12
7	·1228	1243	1257	1272	1287	1302	1317	1331	1346	1361	1376	1391	3	6	9	12
8	·1405	1420	1435	1450	1465	1480	1495	1509	1524	1539	1554	1569	3	6	9	12
9	·1584	1599	1614	1629	1644	1658	1673	1688	1703	1718	1733	1748	3	6	9	12
10	·1763	1778	1793	1808	1823	1838	1853	1868	1883	1899	1914	1929	3	6	9	12
11	·1944	1959	1974	1989	2004	2019	2035	2050	2065	2080	2095	2110	3	6	9	12
12	·2126	2141	2156	2171	2186	2202	2217	2232	2247	2263	2278	2293	3	6	9	12
13	·2309	2324	2339	2355	2370	2385	2401	2416	2432	2447	2462	2478	3	6	9	12
14	·2493	2509	2524	2540	2555	2571	2586	2602	2617	2633	2648	2664	3	6	9	12
15	·2679	2695	2711	2726	2742	2758	2773	2789	2805	2820	2836	2852	3	6	9	13
16	·2867	2883	2899	2915	2931	2946	2962	2978	2994	3010	3026	3041	3	6	9	13
17	·3057	3073	3089	3106	3121	3137	3153	3169	3185	3201	3217	3233	3	6	10	13
18	·3249	3265	3281	3298	3314	3330	3346	3362	3378	3395	3411	3427	3	6	10	13
19	·3443	3460	3476	3492	3508	3525	3541	3558	3574	3590	3607	3623	3	6	10	13
20	·3640	3656	3673	3689	3706	3722	3739	3755	3772	3789	3805	3822	3	7	10	13
21	·3839	3855	3872	3889	3906	3922	3939	3956	3973	3990	4006	4023	3	7	10	13
22	·4040	4057	4074	4091	4108	4125	4142	4159	4176	4193	4210	4228	3	7	10	14
23	·4245	4262	4279	4296	4314	4331	4348	4365	4383	4400	4417	4435	3	7	10	14
24	·4452	4470	4487	4505	4522	4540	4557	4575	4592	4610	4628	4645	4	7	10	14
25	·4663	4681	4699	4716	4734	4752	4770	4788	4806	4823	4841	4859	4	7	11	14
26	·4877	4895	4913	4931	4950	4968	4986	5004	5022	5040	5059	5077	4	7	11	15
27	·5095	5114	5132	5150	5169	5187	5206	5224	5243	5261	5280	5298	4	7	11	15
28	·5317	5336	5354	5373	5392	5411	5430	5448	5467	5486	5505	5524	4	8	11	15
29	·5543	5562	5581	5600	5619	5639	5658	5677	5696	5715	5735	5754	4	8	12	15
30	·5774	5793	5812	5832	5851	5871	5890	5910	5930	5949	5969	5989	4	8	12	16
31	·6009	6028	6048	6068	6088	6108	6128	6148	6168	6188	6208	6228	4	8	12	16
32	·6249	6269	6289	6310	6330	6350	6371	6391	6412	6432	6453	6473	4	8	12	16
33	·6494	6515	6536	6556	6577	6598	6619	6640	6661	6682	6703	6724	4	8	13	17
34	·6745	6766	6787	6809	6830	6851	6873	6894	6916	6937	6959	6980	4	9	13	17
35	·7002	7024	7046	7067	7089	7111	7133	7155	7177	7199	7221	7243	4	9	13	18
36	·7265	7288	7310	7332	7355	7377	7400	7422	7445	7467	7490	7513	5	9	14	18
37	·7536	7558	7581	7604	7627	7650	7673	7696	7720	7743	7766	7789	5	9	14	18
38	·7813	7836	7860	7883	7907	7931	7954	7978	8002	8026	8050	8074	5	10	14	19
39	·8098	8122	8146	8170	8195	8219	8243	8268	8292	8317	8342	8366	5	10	15	20
40	·8391	8416	8441	8466	8491	8516	8541	8566	8591	8617	8642	8667	5	10	15	20
41	·8693	8718	8744	8770	8796	8821	8847	8873	8899	8925	8952	8978	5	10	16	21
42	·9004	9030	9057	9083	9110	9137	9163	9190	9217	9244	9271	9298	5	11	16	21
43	·9325	9352	9380	9407	9435	9462	9490	9517	9545	9573	9601	9629	6	11	17	22
44	·9657	9685	9713	9742	9770	9798	9827	9856	9884	9913	9942	9971	6	11	17	23

Table VI.

NATURAL TANGENTS.

0′	5′	10′	15′	20′	25′	30′	35′	40′	45′	50′	55′	1	2	3	4
1·000	0029	0058	0088	0117	0147	0176	0206	0235	0265	0295	0325	6	12	18	24
1·035	0385	0416	0446	0477	0507	0538	0569	0599	0630	0661	0692	6	12	18	25
1·072	0755	0786	0818	0850	0881	0913	0945	0977	1009	1041	1074	6	13	19	25
1·111	1139	1171	1204	1237	1270	1303	1336	1369	1403	1436	1470	7	13	20	26
1·150	1538	1571	1606	1640	1674	1708	1743	1778	1812	1847	1882	7	14	21	28
1·192	1953	1988	2024	2059	2095	2131	2167	2203	2239	2276	2312	7	14	22	29
1·235	2386	2423	2460	2497	2534	2572	2609	2647	2685	2723	2761	8	15	23	30
1·280	2838	2876	2915	2954	2993	3032	3072	3111	3151	3190	3230	8	16	23	31
1·327	3311	3351	3392	3432	3473	3514	3555	3597	3638	3680	3722	8	16	25	33
1·376	3806	3848	3891	3934	3976	4019	4063	4106	4150	4193	4237	9	17	26	34
1·428	4326	4370	4415	4460	4505	4550	4596	4641	4687	4733	4779	9	18	27	36
1·483	4872	4919	4966	5013	5061	5108	5156	5204	5253	5301	5350	10	19	29	38
1·540	5448	5497	5547	5597	5647	5697	5747	5798	5849	5900	5952	10	20	30	40
1·600	6055	6107	6160	6212	6265	6319	6372	6426	6479	6534	6588	11	21	32	43
1·664	6698	6753	6808	6864	6920	6977	7033	7090	7147	7205	7262	11	23	34	45
1·732	7379	7437	7496	7556	7615	7675	7735	7796	7856	7917	7979	12	24	36	48
1·804	8103	8165	8228	8291	8354	8418	8482	8546	8611	8676	8741	13	26	38	51
1·881	8873	8940	9007	9074	9142	9210	9278	9347	9416	9486	9556	14	27	41	55
1·963	9697	9768	9840	9912	9984	$\overline{0}057$	$\overline{0}130$	$\overline{0}204$	$\overline{0}278$	$\overline{0}353$	$\overline{0}428$	15	29	44	58
2·050	0579	0655	0732	0809	0887	0965	1044	1123	1203	1283	1364	16	31	47	63
2·144	1527	1609	1692	1775	1859	1943	2028	2113	2199	2286	2373	17	34	51	68
2·246	2549	2637	2727	2817	2907	2998	3090	3183	3276	3369	3464	18	37	55	74
2·356	3654	3750	3847	3945	4043	4142	4242	4342	4443	4545	4648	20	40	60	79
2·475	4855	4960	5065	5172	5279	5386	5495	5605	5715	5826	5938	22	43	65	87
2·605	6165	6279	6395	6511	6628	6746	6865	6985	7106	7228	7351	24	47	71	95
2·747	2·760	2·773	2·785	2·798	2·811	2·824	2·837	2·850	2·864	2·877	2·891	3	5	8	10
2·904	2·918	2·932	2·946	2·960	2·974	2·989	3·003	3·018	3·033	3·047	3·063	3	6	9	11
3·078	3·093	3·108	3·124	3·140	3·156	3·172	3·188	3·204	3·221	3·237	3·254	3	6	10	13
3·271	3·288	3·305	3·323	3·340	3·358	3·376	3·394	3·412	3·431	3·450	3·468	4	7	11	14
3·487	3·507	3·526	3·546	3·566	3·586	3·606	3·626	3·647	3·668	3·689	3·710	4	8	12	16
3·732	3·754	3·776	3·798	3·821	3·844	3·867	3·890	3·914	3·938	3·962	3·986	5	9	14	19
4·011	4·036	4·061	4·087	4·113	4·139	4·165	4·192	4·219	4·247	4·275	4·303	5	11	16	21
4·331	4·360	4·390	4·419	4·449	4·480	4·511	4·542	4·574	4·606	4·638	4·671	6	12	19	25
4·705	4·739	4·773	4·808	4·843	4·879	4·915	4·952	4·989	5·027	5·066	5·105	7	15	22	29
5·145	5·185	5·226	5·267	5·309	5·352	5·396	5·440	5·485	5·530	5·576	5·623	9	17	26	35
5·671	5·720	5·769	5·820	5·871	5·923	5·976	6·030	6·084	6·140	6·197	6·255				
6·314	6·374	6·435	6·497	6·561	6·625	6·691	6·758	6·827	6·897	6·968	7·041				
7·115	7·191	7·269	7·348	7·429	7·511	7·596	7·682	7·770	7·861	7·953	8·048				
8·144	8·243	8·345	8·449	8·556	8·665	8·777	8·892	9·010	9·131	9·255	9·383				
9·514	9·649	9·788	9·931	10·08	10·23	10·39	10·55	10·71	10·88	11·06	11·24	Difference columns cease to be useful.			
11·43	11·62	11·83	12·03	12·25	12·47	12·71	12·95	13·20	13·46	13·73	14·01				
14·30	14·61	14·92	15·26	15·60	15·97	16·35	16·75	17·17	17·61	18·07	18·56				
19·08	19·63	20·21	20·82	21·47	22·16	22·90	23·69	24·54	25·45	26·43	27·49				
28·64	29·88	31·24	32·73	34·37	36·18	38·19	40·44	42·96	45·83	49·10	52·88				
57·29	62·50	68·75	76·39	85·94	98·22	114·6	137·5	171·9	229·2	343·8	687·5				

Table VII.

RADIAN MEASURE OF ANGLES.

Deg.	0′	10′	20′	30′	40′	50′
0	0·0000	0029	0058	0087	0116	0145
1	0·0175	0204	0233	0262	0291	0320
2	0·0349	0378	0407	0436	0465	0495
3	0·0524	0553	0582	0611	0640	0669
4	0·0698	0727	0756	0785	0814	0844
5	0·0873	0902	0931	0960	0989	1018
6	0·1047	1076	1105	1134	1164	1193
7	0·1222	1251	1280	1309	1338	1367
8	0·1396	1425	1454	1484	1513	1542
9	0·1571	1600	1629	1658	1687	1716
10	0·1745	1774	1804	1833	1862	1891
11	0·1920	1949	1978	2007	2036	2065
12	0·2094	2123	2153	2182	2211	2240
13	0·2269	2298	2327	2356	2385	2414
14	0·2443	2473	2502	2531	2560	2589
15	0·2618	2647	2676	2705	2734	2763
16	0·2793	2822	2851	2880	2909	2938
17	0·2967	2996	3025	3054	3083	3113
18	0·3142	3171	3200	3229	3258	3287
19	0·3316	3345	3374	3403	3432	3462
20	0·3491	3520	3549	3578	3607	3636
21	0·3665	3694	3723	3752	3782	3811
22	0·3840	3869	3898	3927	3956	3985
23	0·4014	4043	4072	4102	4131	4160
24	0·4189	4218	4247	4276	4305	4334
25	0·4363	4392	4422	4451	4480	4509
26	0·4538	4537	4596	4625	4654	4683
27	0·4712	4741	4771	4800	4829	4858
28	0·4887	4916	4945	4974	5003	5032
29	0·5061	5091	5120	5149	5178	5207
30	0·5236	5265	5294	5323	5352	5381
31	0·5411	5440	5469	5498	5527	5556
32	0·5585	5614	5643	5672	5701	5730
33	0·5760	5789	5818	5847	5876	5905
34	0·5934	5963	5992	6021	6050	6080
35	0·6109	6138	6167	6196	6225	6254
36	0·6283	6312	6341	6370	6400	6429
37	0·6458	6487	6516	6545	6574	6603
38	0·6632	6661	6690	6720	6749	6778
39	0·6807	6836	6865	6894	6923	6952
40	0·6981	7010	7039	7069	7098	7127
41	0·7156	7185	7214	7243	7272	7301
42	0·7330	7359	7389	7418	7447	7476
43	0·7505	7534	7563	7592	7621	7650
44	0·7679	7709	7738	7767	7796	7825

Difference	
for	is
1′	3
2′	6
3′	9
4′	12
5′	15
6′	18
7′	21
8′	24
9′	27

Table VII.

RADIAN MEASURE OF ANGLES.

Deg.	0′	10′	20′	30′	40′	50′
45	0·7854	7883	7912	7941	7970	7999
46	0·8029	8058	8087	8116	8145	8174
47	0·8203	8232	8261	8290	8319	8348
48	0·8378	8407	8436	8465	8494	8523
49	0·8552	8581	8610	8639	8668	8698
50	0·8727	8756	8785	8814	8843	8872
51	0·8901	8930	8959	8988	9018	9047
52	0·9076	9105	9134	9163	9192	9221
53	0·9250	9279	9308	9338	9367	9396
54	0·9425	9454	9483	9512	9541	9570
55	0·9599	9628	9657	9687	9716	9745
56	0·9774	9803	9832	9861	9890	9919
57	0·9948	9977	0007	0036	0065	0094
58	1·0123	0152	0181	0210	0239	0268
59	1·0297	0327	0356	0385	0414	0443
60	1·0472	0501	0530	0559	0588	0617
61	1·0647	0676	0705	0734	0763	0792
62	1·0821	0850	0879	0908	0937	0966
63	1·0996	1025	1054	1083	1112	1141
64	1·1170	1199	1228	1257	1286	1316
65	1·1345	1374	1403	1432	1461	1490
66	1·1519	1548	1577	1606	1636	1665
67	1·1694	1723	1752	1781	1810	1839
68	1·1868	1897	1926	1956	1985	2014
69	1·2043	2072	2101	2130	2159	2188
70	1·2217	2246	2275	2305	2334	2363
71	1·2392	2421	2450	2479	2508	2537
72	1·2566	2595	2625	2654	2683	2712
73	1·2741	2770	2799	2828	2857	2886
74	1·2915	2945	2974	3003	3032	3061
75	1·3090	3119	3148	3177	3206	3235
76	1·3265	3294	3323	3352	3381	3410
77	1·3439	3468	3497	3526	3555	3584
78	1·3614	3643	3672	3701	3730	3759
79	1·3788	3817	3846	3875	3904	3934
80	1·3963	3992	4021	4050	4079	4108
81	1·4137	4166	4195	4224	4254	4283
82	1·4312	4341	4370	4399	4428	4457
83	1·4486	4515	4544	4573	4603	4632
84	1·4661	4690	4719	4748	4777	4806
85	1·4835	4864	4893	4923	4952	4981
86	1·5010	5039	5068	5097	5126	5155
87	1·5184	5213	5243	5272	5301	5330
88	1·5359	5388	5417	5446	5475	5504
89	1·5533	5563	5592	5621	5650	5679

Difference	
for	is
1′	3
2′	6
3′	9
4′	12
5′	15
6′	18
7′	21
8′	24
9′	27

Table VIII.

CHORDS OF ANGLES.

Deg.	0′	10′	20′	30′	40′	50′	Deg.	0′	10′	20′	30′	40′	50′
0	·000	·003	·006	·009	·012	·014	**45**	·765	·768	·771	·773	·776	·779
1	·017	·020	·023	·026	·029	·032	46	·781	·784	·787	·789	·792	·795
2	·035	·038	·041	·044	·046	·049	47	·797	·800	·803	·805	·808	·811
3	·052	·055	·058	·061	·064	·067	48	·813	·816	·819	·821	·824	·827
4	·070	·073	·076	·078	·081	·084	49	·829	·832	·835	·837	·840	·843
5	·087	·090	·093	·096	·099	·102	**50**	·845	·848	·850	·853	·856	·858
6	·105	·108	·110	·113	·116	·119	51	·861	·864	·866	·869	·871	·874
7	·122	·125	·128	·131	·134	·137	52	·877	·879	·882	·885	·887	·890
8	·139	·142	·145	·148	·151	·154	53	·892	·895	·898	·900	·903	·905
9	·157	·160	·163	·166	·168	·171	54	·908	·911	·913	·916	·918	·921
10	·174	·177	·180	·183	·186	·189	**55**	·923	·926	·929	·931	·934	·936
11	·192	·195	·197	·200	·203	·206	56	·939	·941	·944	·947	·949	·952
12	·209	·212	·215	·218	·221	·223	57	·954	·957	·959	·962	·964	·967
13	·226	·229	·232	·235	·238	·241	58	·970	·972	·975	·977	·980	·982
14	·244	·247	·249	·252	·255	·258	59	·985	·987	·990	·992	·995	·997
15	·261	·264	·267	·270	·273	·275	**60**	1·000	1·002	1·005	1·007	1·010	1·013
16	·278	·281	·284	·287	·290	·293	61	1·015	1·018	1·020	1·023	1·025	1·028
17	·296	·298	·301	·304	·307	·310	62	1·030	1·033	1·035	1·037	1·040	1·042
18	·313	·316	·319	·321	·324	·327	63	1·045	1·047	1·050	1·052	1·055	1·057
19	·330	·333	·336	·339	·342	·344	64	1·060	1·062	1·065	1·067	1·070	1·072
20	·347	·350	·353	·356	·359	·362	**65**	1·075	1·077	1·079	1·082	1·084	1·087
21	·364	·367	·370	·373	·376	·379	66	1·089	1·092	1·094	1·097	1·099	1·101
22	·382	·384	·387	·390	·393	·396	67	1·104	1·106	1·109	1·111	1·113	1·116
23	·399	·402	·404	·407	·410	·413	68	1·118	1·121	1·123	1·126	1·128	1·130
24	·416	·419	·421	·424	·427	·430	69	1·133	1·135	1·138	1·140	1·142	1·145
25	·433	·436	·438	·441	·444	·447	**70**	1·147	1·149	1·152	1·154	1·157	1·159
26	·450	·453	·456	·458	·461	·464	71	1·161	1·164	1·166	1·168	1·171	1·173
27	·467	·470	·472	·475	·478	·481	72	1·176	1·178	1·180	1·183	1·185	1·187
28	·484	·487	·489	·492	·495	·498	73	1·190	1·192	1·194	1·197	1·199	1·201
29	·501	·504	·506	·509	·512	·515	74	1·204	1·206	1·208	1·211	1·213	1·215
30	·518	·520	·523	·526	·529	·532	**75**	1·217	1·220	1·222	1·224	1·227	1·229
31	·534	·537	·540	·543	·546	·548	76	1·231	1·234	1·236	1·238	1·240	1·243
32	·551	·554	·557	·560	·562	·565	77	1·245	1·247	1·250	1·252	1·254	1·256
33	·568	·571	·574	·576	·579	·582	78	1·259	1·261	1·263	1·265	1·268	1·270
34	·585	·587	·590	·593	·596	·599	79	1·272	1·274	1·277	1·279	1·281	1·283
35	·601	·604	·607	·610	·612	·615	**80**	1·286	1·288	1·290	1·292	1·294	1·297
36	·618	·621	·624	·626	·629	·632	81	1·299	1·301	1·303	1·305	1·308	1·310
37	·635	·637	·640	·643	·646	·648	82	1·312	1·314	1·316	1·319	1·321	1·323
38	·651	·654	·657	·659	·662	·665	83	1·325	1·327	1·330	1·332	1·334	1·336
39	·668	·670	·673	·676	·679	·681	84	1·338	1·340	1·343	1·345	1·347	1·349
40	·684	·687	·689	·692	·695	·698	**85**	1·351	1·353	1·355	1·358	1·360	1·362
41	·700	·703	·706	·709	·711	·714	86	1·364	1·366	1·368	1·370	1·372	1·375
42	·717	·719	·722	·725	·728	·730	87	1·377	1·379	1·381	1·383	1·385	1·387
43	·733	·736	·738	·741	·744	·746	88	1·389	1·391	1·393	1·396	1·398	1·400
44	·749	·752	·755	·757	·760	·763	89	1·402	1·404	1·406	1·408	1·410	1·412
							90	1·414					

Table IX.

Angle.		Chords.	Sine.	Tangent.	Cotangent.	Cosine.			
Deg.	Radians.								
0°	0	0	0	0	∞	1	1·414	1·5708	90°
1	·0175	·017	·0175	·0175	57·2900	·9998	1·402	1·5533	89
2	·0349	·035	·0349	·0349	28·6363	·9994	1·389	1·5359	88
3	·0524	·052	·0523	·0524	19·0811	·9986	1·377	1·5184	87
4	·0698	·070	·0698	·0699	14·3006	·9976	1·364	1·5010	86
5	·0873	·087	·0872	·0875	11·4301	·9962	1·351	1·4835	85
6	·1047	·105	·1045	·1051	9·5144	·9945	1·338	1·4661	84
7	·1222	·122	·1219	·1228	8·1443	·9925	1·325	1·4486	83
8	·1396	·139	·1392	·1405	7·1154	·9903	1·312	1·4312	82
9	·1571	·157	·1564	·1584	6·3138	·9877	1·299	1·4137	81
10	·1745	·174	·1736	·1763	5·6713	·9848	1·286	1·3963	80
11	·1920	·192	·1908	·1944	5·1446	·9816	1·272	1·3788	79
12	·2094	·209	·2079	·2126	4·7046	·9781	1·259	1·3614	78
13	·2269	·226	·2250	·2309	4·3315	·9744	1·245	1·3439	77
14	·2443	·244	·2419	·2493	4·0108	·9703	1·231	1·3265	76
15	·2618	·261	·2588	·2679	3·7321	·9659	1·217	1·3090	75
16	·2793	·278	·2756	·2867	3·4874	·9613	1·204	1·2915	74
17	·2967	·296	·2924	·3057	3·2709	·9563	1·190	1·2741	73
18	·3142	·313	·3090	·3249	3·0777	·9511	1·176	1·2566	72
19	·3316	·330	·3256	·3443	2·9042	·9455	1·161	1·2392	71
20	·3491	·347	·3420	·3640	2·7475	·9397	1·147	1·2217	70
21	·3665	·364	·3584	·3839	2·6051	·9336	1·133	1·2043	69
22	·3840	·382	·3746	·4040	2·4751	·9272	1·118	1·1868	68
23	·4014	·399	·3907	·4245	2·3559	·9205	1·104	1·1694	67
24	·4189	·416	·4067	·4452	2·2460	·9135	1·089	1·1519	66
25	·4363	·433	·4226	·4663	2·1445	·9063	1·075	1·1345	65
26	·4538	·450	·4384	·4877	2·0503	·8988	1·060	1·1170	64
27	·4712	·467	·4540	·5095	1·9626	·8910	1·045	1·0996	63
28	·4887	·484	·4695	·5317	1·8807	·8829	1·030	1·0821	62
29	·5061	·501	·4848	·5543	1·8040	·8746	1·015	1·0647	61
30	·5236	·518	·5000	·5774	1·7321	·8660	1·000	1·0472	60
31	·5411	·534	·5150	·6009	1·6643	·8572	·985	1·0297	59
32	·5585	·551	·5299	·6249	1·6003	·8480	·970	1·0123	58
33	·5760	·568	·5446	·6494	1·5399	·8387	·954	·9948	57
34	·5934	·585	·5592	·6745	1·4826	·8290	·939	·9774	56
35	·6109	·601	·5736	·7002	1·4281	·8192	·923	·9599	55
36	·6283	·618	·5878	·7265	1·3764	·8090	·908	·9425	54
37	·6458	·635	·6018	·7536	1·3270	·7986	·892	·9250	53
38	·6632	·651	·6157	·7813	1·2799	·7880	·877	·9076	52
39	·6807	·668	·6293	·8098	1·2349	·7771	·861	·8901	51
40	·6981	·684	·6428	·8391	1·1918	·7660	·845	·8727	50
41	·7156	·700	·6561	·8693	1·1504	·7547	·829	·8552	49
42	·7330	·717	·6691	·9004	1·1106	·7431	·813	·8378	48
43	·7505	·733	·6820	·9325	1·0724	·7314	·797	·8203	47
44	·7679	·749	·6947	·9657	1·0355	·7193	·781	·8029	46
45	·7854	·765	·7071	1·0000	1·0000	·7071	·765	·7854	45
								Radians.	Deg.
			Cosine.	Cotangent.	Tangent.	Sine.	Chords.	Angle.	

BOARD OF EDUCATION.

TYPICAL EXAMINATION PAPERS.

I.

1. (*a*) Compute by contracted methods to four significant figures only, and without using logarithms,

$$0{\cdot}01239 \times 5{\cdot}024 \text{ and } 0{\cdot}5024 \div 0{\cdot}01239.$$

(*b*) Compute, using logarithms,

$$\sqrt{0{\cdot}2607}, \quad 26{\cdot}07^{1{\cdot}13}, \quad 26{\cdot}07^{-1{\cdot}13}.$$

(*c*) Explain why we subtract logarithms when we wish to divide numbers.

(*d*) Write down the values of the sine, cosine and tangent of 37°. Explain, from the definitions, why $\sin 37° \div \cos 37° = \tan 37°$. Try by division if this is so.

2. (*a*) Using the tables, find the number of which 0·2 is the Napierian logarithm.

If $$e^x = 1 + x + \frac{x^2}{\underline{|2}} + \frac{x^3}{\underline{|3}} + \text{etc.},$$

calculate e^x when $x = 0{\cdot}2$, to three decimal places.

After how many terms are more of them useless in this case where we only need three decimal places?

[Note that $\underline{|5}$ means $1 \times 2 \times 3 \times 4 \times 5$.]

(*b*) Express $$\frac{0{\cdot}5x + 14{\cdot}09}{x^2 - 3{\cdot}5x - 10{\cdot}26}$$

as the sum of two simpler fractions.

(*c*) The sum of two numbers is 12·54 and the sum of their squares is 81·56; find the numbers.

(*d*) ABC is a triangle, C being a right angle. The side BC is 12·4 feet and the angle A is 65°; find the other sides and angle, using the Tables.

3. x and t are the distance in miles and the time in hours of a train from a railway station. Plot on squared paper. Describe clearly why it is that the *slope* of the curve shows the speed. Where is the speed greatest, and where is it least?

x	0	0·12	0·5	1·52	2·50	2·92	3·05	3·05	3·17	3·50	3·82
t	0	0·05	0·10	0·15	0·20	0·25	0·30	0·35	0·40	0·45	0·50

4. Find x in degrees approximately if

$$3 \sin x + 2 \cos x = 3{\cdot}4.$$

For what value of x is $3 \sin x + 2 \cos x$ a maximum? You may use squared paper.

5. The net yearly profit P of a railway may be represented by

$$P = bx + cy$$

where x is the gross yearly receipt from passengers, and y from goods; b and c being constant numbers.

When $x = 520000$ and $y = 220000$, P was 330000.

And at a later period—

when $x = 902000$ and $y = 700000$, P was 603000.

What will probably be the value of P when $x = 1000000$ and when $y = 800000$?

6. In steamships $c = D^{\frac{2}{3}} v \div I$, where D is the displacement in tons, v the speed in knots, I the indicated horse-power. Now c is not the same for a ship at all speeds but it is nearly the same for two similar ships at corresponding speeds. Corresponding speeds are as the sixth root of the displacements. Find c from each of the following actual measurements made on a ship of 9,764 tons. Tabulate the corresponding speeds for a ship of 12,000 tons and calculate and tabulate the horse-power at each speed.

Speed in knots - -	10·8	14·33
Indicated horse-power	1830	4720

7. State Simpson's rule. An area is divided into ten equal parts by 11 equidistant parallel lines 0·2 inches apart, the first and last touching the bounding curve; the lengths of these lines or ordinates or breadths are, in inches:

0, 1·24, 2·37, 4·10, 5·28, 4·76, 4·60, 4·36, 2·45, 1·62, 0.

Find the area in square inches.

8. If

$$x = a(\phi - \sin\phi)$$
$$y = a(1 - \cos\phi).$$

Take $a = 10$. Calculate the values of x and y for the following values of ϕ:

$$0, \frac{\pi}{6}, \frac{\pi}{4}, \frac{\pi}{3}.$$

Plot points whose co-ordinates are these values of x and y, on squared paper, and draw a curve.

9. When Q cubic feet of water flows per second through a sharp-edged rectangular notch L feet long, the height of nearly still water above the sill being H feet,

$$Q \propto (L - \tfrac{1}{5}H)H^{\frac{3}{2}}.$$

Now, a bad formula is sometimes used which assumes

$$Q \propto LH^{\frac{3}{2}}.$$

Show that for a given L, although a constant may be used to give a correct answer for one value of H, it must give incorrect answers for other values of H.

10. A vessel is shaped like the frustum of a cone; the circular base is 10 inches diameter; the top is 5 inches diameter; the vertical height is 8 inches. What is the height of the imaginary vertex? If x is the height of the surface of a liquid from the bottom, plot a curve showing for any value of x the area of the horizontal section there.

Find from this the whole volume of the vessel in cubic inches.

[Candidates will notice that if d is the diameter of the circular area it is only necessary to plot d^2.]

11. There is a curve $y = 1{\cdot}5 + 0{\cdot}05x^2$.

Prove that for any value of x, the slope of the curve or $\frac{dy}{dx}$ is $0{\cdot}1x$.

12. Find accurately to three significant figures one value of x for which

$$5 \log_{10} x + \frac{2}{x} - 2{\cdot}70 = 0.$$

13. The total cost C of a ship per hour (including interest and depreciation on capital, wages, coal, &c.) is in pounds

$$C = 4 + \frac{s^3}{1000}$$

where s is the speed in knots (or nautical miles per hour).

The time in hours spent in a passage of, say, 3,000 miles is

$$3000 \div s,$$

so that the total cost of the passage is this time multiplied by C. Express this algebraically in terms of s.

Find what this amounts to for various speeds: for what speed is it a minimum?

14. The model of a ship, when being drawn at the following speeds v (in feet per minute), offered the following resistances R (in pounds) to motion:

v	233	287	347	406	466	525	588	646
R	1·08	1·76	2·93	4·26	6·33	9·52	12·74	15·16

It is to be remembered that there are small errors in such measurements.

If we assume a law like $R=av^n$, find n for the smallest and highest speeds; for what value of v does n seem at its greatest?

[Suggestion, plot $\log R$ and $\log v$ on squared paper.]

II.

1. (*a*) Compute by contracted methods to four significant figures only,

$$0·01239\times 0·5024 \text{ and } 0·1239\div 50·24.$$

(*b*) Compute, using logarithms,

$$(0·9415\times 2·304)^{1·72} \text{ and } (0·9415\times 2·304)^{-0·172}.$$

(*c*) Why do we multiply the logarithm of a by b to find the logarithm of a^b?

(*d*) Write down the values of

$$\sin 254°,\quad \cos 124°,\quad \tan 193°,\quad \sin^{-1}(0·2250)$$
$$\cos^{-1}(-0·8192),\quad \tan^{-1}(-4·0108).$$

Only one value to be given in each of the last three cases.

2. (*a*) A quantity y is a function of x; what do we mean by

$$\frac{dy}{dx}?$$

Illustrate your meaning, using a curve.

Illustrate your meaning by considering the speed of a body which has passed through the space s in the time t.

(*b*) Show that if A is the area of a curve from some standard ordinate to the ordinate y corresponding to the co-ordinate x then

$$y=\frac{dA}{dx}.$$

Hence to find A we merely find that function of x of which y is the differential coefficient.

(*c*) If A is the area of the surface of water in a pond when the depth on a given vertical is x and if v is the volume of water; then

$$A=\frac{dv}{dx}.$$

Prove this.

3. Define the scalar product and the vector product of two vectors. Give an illustration of each of these from any part of physical science.

4. The cost C of a ship per hour (including interest and depreciation on capital, wages, coal, etc.) is in pounds

$$C=4+\frac{s^3}{1000}$$

where s is its speed in knots relatively to the water.

Going up a river whose current runs at 5 knots, what is the speed which causes least total cost of a passage?

5. In the curve $y=a+bx^{\frac{3}{2}}$

if $y=1{\cdot}62$ when $x=1$,

and $y=5{\cdot}32$,, $x=4$,

find a and b.

Let this curve rotate about the axis of x.

Find the volume enclosed by the surface of revolution between the two sections at $x=1$, and $x=4$.

6. The following values of y and x being given, tabulate $\delta y/\delta x$ and $y\,.\,\delta x$ in each interval. If $y\,.\,\delta x$ be called δA, tabulate the values of A if A is 0 where $x=0$.

x	0	·1	·2	·3	·4	·5	·6	·7	·8	·9
y	1·428	1·561	1·691	1·820	1·947	2·071	2·193	2·314	2·431	2·547

To facilitate tabulation, it will be found convenient to change these rows into columns.

7. What is Simpson's rule? A circle is drawn of 8 inches diameter. The diameter is divided into eight equal parts and ordinates are drawn at right angles to the diameter. Calculate the lengths of these ordinates, using the tables, and tabulate them. Using Simpson's rule, find the area of the circle.

This answer is in error; what is the percentage error?

8. Find x in degrees if

$$3\sin x+2\cos x=3{\cdot}4\,;$$

x is supposed to be an acute angle. How many answers are there?

Find, using the Calculus, for what value of x is

$$3\sin x+2\cos x$$

a maximum?

9. The following values of p and θ being given, find

$$\frac{dp}{d\theta} \text{ when } \theta = 115.$$

θ	p
100	14·70
105	17·53
110	20·80
115	24·54
120	28·83
125	33·71
130	39·25

10. If
$$x = a \sin pt + b \cos pt$$
for any value of t where a, b and p are mere numbers; show that this is the same as
$$x = A \sin (pt + e)$$
if A and e are properly evaluated.

If
$$V = RC + L\frac{dC}{dt}$$
and if
$$C = 100 \sin 600\, t,$$
R being 2 and L being 0·005, find V.

What is the lag of C in degrees behind V?

11. A vessel is shaped like the frustum of a cone; the circular base is 10 inches diameter; the top is 5 inches diameter; the vertical height is 8 inches. If x is the height of the surface of a liquid from the bottom, express d the diameter there in terms of x; express A the horizontal area there in terms of x; express V the volume of the liquid in cubic inches, in terms of x.

12. Water leaves a circular basin very slowly by a hole at the bottom, every particle describing a spiral which is very nearly circular. Let v be the speed at a point whose distance from the axis is r, and height above some datum level h. Assume no "rotation" or "spin," that is
$$\frac{1}{2}\left(\frac{v}{r} + \frac{dv}{dr}\right) = 0$$
and show that this means
$$v = \frac{c}{r}$$
where c is some constant.

Now at the atmospheric surface

$$\frac{v^2}{2g}+h=C$$

where C is a constant.

Find from this the shape of the surface, that is the law connecting r and h.

13. The model of a ship, when being drawn at the following speeds v (in feet per minute), offered the following resistances R (in pounds) to motion:

V	179	220	259	301	321	341	361
R	1·78	2·76	4·01	5·69	6·39	8·19	11·39

There are small errors in such measurements.

Assume a law $R \propto v^n$, and describe how n changes. What is its greatest value? Show that when v increases by a small percentage, R increases by n times this percentage.

14. The indicated horse-powers of the engines of similar ships similarly loaded may be taken to be proportional to the $1\frac{1}{6}$th power of the displacements at corresponding speeds.

Corresponding speeds are as the sixth roots of the displacements. The following measurements were made at different speeds of a vessel of 1000 tons (The United States S. "Manning"). Find the horse-power at the corresponding speeds of a vessel of 5000 tons; state and tabulate these speeds.

15. A rectangular channel to convey water is to be made from a long strip of metal 6 ft. wide by bending the sides. Find the depth of the channel if the area of its cross-section is 2·5 sq. ft. What would be the depth for a max. area:

16. Find the subtangent and subnormal in the curves:

(i) Ellipse $a^2y^2=b^2(2ax-x^2)$. (ii) Parabola $y^2=4ax$.

(iii) $y=ax^2$. (iv) $y=ax^n$. (v) $y^n=a^{n-1}x$.

(vi) $x^my^n=a$. (vii) $u=x^3-3axy+y^3=0$.

17. The equation to a circle, origin at the centre, is $y^2=a^2-x^2$, show that the curve cuts the axis of x at an angle of 90°.

III.

1. (*a*) Compute by contracted methods to four significant figures only, and without using logarithms,

$$3{\cdot}214 \times 0{\cdot}7423 \div 7{\cdot}912.$$

(*b*) Using logarithms compute,

$$(1{\cdot}342 \times 0{\cdot}01731 \div 0{\cdot}0274)^{0{\cdot}317}.$$

(*c*) Explain why we multiply a logarithm by 3 when we wish to find the cube of a number.

(*d*) Express £18. 17*s.* 3*d.* in pounds.

2. (*a*) If $pu^{1{\cdot}0646} = 479$, find u when p is 120.

(*b*) $y = ax^2 + bx^3$. When x is 1, y is 4·3, and when x is 2, y is 30; find a and b. What is y when x is 1·5?

(*c*) Two men measure a rectangular box; one finds its length, breadth and depth in inches to be 8·54, 5·17 and 3·19. The other finds them to be 8·50, 5·12 and 3·16. Calculate the volume in each case; what is the mean of the two? What is the percentage difference of either from the mean?

3. A body has moved through the distance s feet in the time t seconds and it is known that $s = bt^2$ when b is a constant.

Find the distance when t is 4. Find the distance when the time is $4 + \delta t$. What is the average speed during the interval δt? As

δt is imagined to be smaller and smaller, what does the average speed become?

4. The three parts (*a*), (*b*) and (*c*) must all be answered to get full marks:

(*a*) If

$$\frac{x}{y}=e^{a\theta}$$

where $e=2{\cdot}718$. If $a=0{\cdot}3$ and $\theta=2{\cdot}85$ and if $x-y=550$, find x.

(*b*) When x and y are small we may take

$$\frac{1+x}{1+y}$$

as being very nearly equal to $1+x-y$. What is the error in this when $x=0{\cdot}02$ and $y=0{\cdot}03$?

(*c*) ABC is a triangle, the angle C is a right angle. The side AC is 21·32 feet, the side BC is 12·56 feet, find the angles A and B.

5. A man is 100 feet above the earth which is assumed to be a sphere of 8,000 miles diameter; what is his distance in miles from the furthest point he can see on the surface? Do not give more than three figures in the answer.

6. If $y=x^2-4{\cdot}2x+2{\cdot}93$ calculate y for various values of x and plot on squared paper. What values of x cause y to be 0?

7. x and t are the distance in miles and the time in hours of a train from a railway terminus. Plot on squared paper. Describe why it is that the slope of the curve shows the speed. What is the greatest speed in this case and where approximately does it occur? What is the average speed during the whole time of observation?

x	0	1·5	6·0	14·0	19·0	21·0	21·5	21·8	23·0	24·7	26·8
t	0	0·1	0·2	0·3	0·4	0·5	0·6	0·7	0·8	0·9	1·0

8. A disc rotating with angular velocity a, its density ρ being 8, has an outer radius $r_0=50$. There is a hole in the middle whose radius r_1 is 10. Then at any place whose distance from the centre is r, there is a hoop tensile stress Q where

$$Q=\frac{5}{12}a^2\rho\left(r_1^{\,2}+r_0^{\,2}+\frac{r_0^{\,2}r_1^{\,2}}{r^2}-\frac{3}{5}r^2\right).$$

Taking $a=122{\cdot}5$, and arranging the formula for systematic calculation, find Q for the values of r, 10, 15, 20, 30, 40, and 50. Plot Q and r on squared paper.

9. In the following table A is the area in square feet of the horizontal section of a ship at the level of the surface of the water when the vertical draught of the ship is h feet. When the draught changes from 17·5 to 18·5 feet, what is the increased displacement of the vessel in cubic feet?

h	15	18	21
A	6020	6660	8250

10. In the following table x and y are the co-ordinates of points in a curve, which you need not draw. Tabulate the values of the average slope of the curve in each interval. Also tabulate the area between the two ordinates in each interval. You had better write in columns rather than in rows.

x	1	2	3	4	5
y	1·745	2·618	3·491	4·363	5·236

11. x being distance in feet across a river measuring from one side and y the depth of water in feet, the following measurements were made:

x	0	10	25	33	40	48	60	70
y	0	4	7	8	10	9	6	4

Find the area of the cross section. If the average speed of the water normal to the section is 3·2 feet per second, what is the quantity flowing in cubic feet per second?

12. In a price list I find the following prices of a certain type of steam electric generator of different powers:

K kilowatts	200	600	900
P pounds -	2800	7160	10420

According to what rule has this price list been made up? What is the list price of a generator of 400 kilowatts?

IV.

1. (*a*) Compute by contracted methods to four significant figures only, and without using logarithms,

$$3{\cdot}214 \times 0{\cdot}7423 \div 7{\cdot}912.$$

(*b*) Using logarithms, compute

$$(1{\cdot}342 \times 0{\cdot}01731 \div 0{\cdot}00274)^{-0{\cdot}317}.$$

(*c*) Explain why we multiply the logarithm of a by 3·5 when we wish to find $a^{3\cdot5}$. Start your explanation from the fact that a^3 means $a \times a \times a$.

(*d*) Write down the values of

$$\sin 203°,\ \cos 140°,\ \tan 278°,\ \sin^{-1}(0{\cdot}4226),$$
$$\cos^{-1}(0{\cdot}7547),\ \tan^{-1}(-2{\cdot}7475).$$

2. Define the scalar and vector product of two vectors. Give an illustration of each.

3. The following values of y and x being given tabulate $\delta y/\delta x$ and δA in each interval, δA being the area in the interval between two ordinates. Tabulate the value of A if $A=0$ when $x=3$.

x	3	4	5	6	7	8	9	10	11	12	13
y	1·75	10·45	19·08	27·56	35·84	43·84	51·50	58·78	65·61	71·93	77·71

4. There is a curve, $y = ax^n$,

$$\text{if } y = 2{\cdot}34 \text{ when } x=2$$
$$\text{and } y = 20{\cdot}62 \text{ when } x=5$$

find a and n.

Let the curve rotate about the axis of x, forming a surface of revolution. Find the volume of the slice between the sections at x and $x+dx$. What is the volume between the two sections at $x=2$ and $x=5$?

5. K kilowatts being the average electric power actually delivered to customers from an electric station during an hour and W the weight of coal consumed per hour, the following observations were made :—

K	2560	1520	1300
W	7760	5480	5030

The maximum power which might be delivered being 13060 let $K/13060$ be called f, the load factor. Let W/K be called w, the coal per unit. [The Board of Trade unit is 1 kilowatt hour.] What seems to be the law connecting w and f? Tabulate w and f when f has the values 0·25, 0·20, 0·15, 0·10, 0·05.

6. Assuming the earth to be a sphere, if its circumference is 360×60 miles, what is the circumference of the parallel of latitude 56°? What is the length there of the degree of longitude? If a small map is to be drawn in this latitude with distances all to the same scale, and if a degree of latitude (which is, of course, 60 miles) is shown as 10 inches, what distance will represent a degree of longitude? NOTE.—In this question one mile means one nautical mile.

7. Fifty pounds of shot per second moving horizontally with a velocity of 2500 feet per second due north strike an armour plate and leave the plate horizontally with a velocity of 800 feet per second due east. What force is exerted upon the plate? Note that momentum and force are vectors.

Force is rate of change of momentum per second.

Momentum is mass multiplied by velocity.

The mass of 50 lb. of shot is $50 \div 32{\cdot}2$.

8. There are errors of observation in the following values of y and x :—

x	4	5	6	7	8	9	10	11
y	6·29	5·72	5·22	4·78	4·39	4·06	3·75	3·48

It is found that the following two empirical formulæ seem to be nearly equally good :—

$$y = \frac{a}{b+x} \text{ and } y = \alpha\epsilon^{-\beta x}.$$

Find the best values of a and b, α and β.

9. If $x = a \sin(qt + e)$ expresses simple harmonic motion; what is a? what is q? what is e? Express q in terms of the periodic time. Find expressions for the speed and the acceleration.

10. A sliding piece has a periodic motion. Its distance x from a point in its path is measured at twenty-four equal intervals into which the whole periodic time is divided

16·04, 16·74, 16·66, 15·86, 14·68, 13·42, 12·26, 11·16,
9·98, 8·76, 7·60, 6·68, 5·96, 5·34, 4·68, 4·14,
3·98, 4·50, 5·74, 7·46, 9·36, 11·24, 13·06, 14·70.

Express x in a Fourier Series.

11. When air or steam is flowing through a divergent orifice from a vessel inside which at the still part the pressure is p_1 the cross sectional area A of a steam tube is such that at any place where the pressure is p

$$A^2 \left\{ x^{2/\gamma} - x^{(\gamma+1)/\gamma} \right\}$$

keeps constant x being p/p_1 and γ [1·41 for air and 1·13 for dry or wet steam] being a known number. For what value of x (presumably in the throat) is A a minimum? Find this critical x for air and for steam.

12. The following values of x and y being given, find the most probable value of $\frac{dy}{dx}$ when x is 3.

x	0	1	2	3	4	5	6
y	11·8	16·0	20·0	23·9	27·6	31·1	34·5

If a candidate cannot use *all* the given numbers in finding the answer let him not try this question.

13. The horse-power H, which can be transmitted by a cotton rope (allowing for stress due to centrifugal force) is said to be given by: $H = \left(\frac{62800 - 3v^2}{230000} \right) vd^2$, where v is the speed of the rope (ft. per sec.), d the diameter of the rope in inches. Find the value of v for a maximum value of H.

14. A rectangular playground, area 1600 sq. yds., is to be enclosed by three walls, using an existing wall as one side. Find the remaining sides for minimum cost.

V.

1. (*a*) Without using logarithms, compute by contracted methods, getting four significant figures *correct*,

$$87 \cdot 35 \div (0 \cdot 07568 \times 3 \cdot 501).$$

(*b*) Using logarithms, compute

$$97 \cdot 43 \div (0 \cdot 3524 \times 6 \cdot 321)^{2 \cdot 56}.$$

(*c*) Explain why when we wish to divide numbers we subtract their logarithms.

(*d*) The sum of money £45. 7*s*. 8*d*. is multiplied by 0·3825. What is the answer in pounds?

2. (*a*) A hollow circular cylinder of iron is 10 inches long and weighs 12 lbs.; its internal diameter is 3 inches; what is its external diameter? A cubic inch of iron weighs 0·28 lb.

(*b*) There is a right-angled triangle ABC, the angle ACB is 90°, the angle ABC is 42°. If D is a point in AC; if $AC=3AD$, find the angle DBC.

(*c*) When x is small we may take $(1+x)^{-n}$ as being nearly equal to $1-nx$. What is the percentage error in this when $n=2$ and $x=0 \cdot 01$?

(*d*) What are the factors of $x^2-0 \cdot 4x-4 \cdot 37$?

3. (*a*) 100 lb. of bronze contains 85 per cent. of copper and 15 per cent. of tin. With how much copper must it be melted to obtain a bronze containing 92 per cent. of copper?

(*b*) If $xy^{1 \cdot 37}=25$. If $x=4$, find y.

(*c*) If $\frac{rA}{100a}=\left(1+\frac{r}{100}\right)^n-1$. If $r=5$, if $A=20a$, find n.

4. At the following heights h feet above the ground the wind pressure on a certain occasion was measured as p pounds per square foot on a vertical plane surface.

h	5	15	25	35	50
p	13	22	24	27	31

What is the average value of p between $h=0$ and $h=40$? What is the total force due to wind pressure on a vertical wall 40 feet high and 100 feet long (horizontally)?

5. Find A approximately in degrees, if $2\sin A+3\cos A=3{\cdot}55$. There are two answers between 0° and 90°.

6. Electric lamp filaments of length l, diameter d, made of the same material, kept at the same temperature by the application of v volts, the candle power is proportional to ld and also to v^2d^2/l. There is a 10-candle power lamp whose $l=3$ and $v=100$; we wish to make a 20-candle power lamp with $v=150$; find l for the new lamp.

7. A sliding piece is moving so that at the following times t seconds it has travelled the following distances x feet measured along its path. Plot x and t, measure from the curve the values of x at the times 1·00, 1·01, 1·02, 1·03, etc., and tabulate. Find the accelerations approximately at the times 1·01, 1·02, 1·03, 1·04, and 1·05.

t	1·00	1·01	1·018	1·031	1·045	1·052	1·06
x	3·12	3·305	3·420	3·559	3·664	3·700	3·732

8. L being length in feet and H the height in feet of still water level above the sill of a thin-edged rectangular notch for measuring water, Q being cubic feet per second flowing; it is known that

$$Q=aLH^{\frac{3}{2}}-bH^{\frac{5}{2}}.$$

A notch of length 10 feet was experimented with. When H was 0·51, Q was found to be 5·82, and when H was 0·98, Q was found to be 32·10. What are the values of a and b? What is Q when H is 1·21?

9. The area of the horizontal section of a reservoir A square feet at the height h feet from the lowest point is given in the table below. What is the volume when h is 30? If the water falls in level from $h=15{\cdot}5$ to $h=14{\cdot}5$, what is the loss of volume?

h	0	2·5	4	7	10	12·5	15
A	0	2510	3400	4520	5160	5490	5810
h	17·5	20	23	25	28	30	
A	6210	6890	7810	8270	8670	8780	

10. In a hollow cylindric coil the magnetic field $F \propto nC$, where n is the number of turns and C is the current; $n \propto \frac{1}{d^2}$, where d is the diameter of the wire; $R \propto \frac{1}{d^4}$, where R is the resistance of the wire; $t \propto C^2R$, where t is the permanent maximum temperature produced (above that of the room). Show that when we have the same F we have the same t for any size of wire; but if we double F we quadruple t.

[*Note.*—The above rules are not strictly true, because of the varying thickness of insulation.]

11. Find the area of the parabola

$$y=a+bx+cx^2$$

between the ordinate at $x=\alpha$ and the ordinate at $x=\beta$.

If $\alpha=-h$ and $\beta=h$, what is the answer?

12. The parabola $y=a+bx+cx^2$

passes through three points, whose co-ordinates are

$$-h,\ y_1;\ 0,\ y_2;\ h,\ y_3.$$

Insert these values, and find a, b, and c in terms of the given quantities y_1, y_2, y_3 and h.

13. A machine is in two parts, whose weights are x and y. The cost of the machine is proportional to

$$z=y+4x.$$

The usefulness of the machine is proportional to

$$v=x^2+3xy.$$

If z is 10, what value of x will cause v to be a maximum? For this value of x, what is y?

14. A current C is changing according to the law

$$C=20+21t-14t^2,$$

where t is seconds. The voltage V is such that

$$V=RC+L\frac{dC}{dt},$$

where $R=0·5$ and $L=0·01$; find V as a function of the time.

15. The following numbers are authentic; t seconds is the record time of a trotting (in harness) race of m miles :—

m	1	2	3	4	5	10	20	30	50	100
t	119	257	416	598	751	1575	3505	6479	14141	32153

It is found that there is approximately a law $t=am^b$, where a and b are constants. Test if this is so, and find the most probable values of a and b. The average speed in a race is $s=m/t$; express s in terms of m.

VI.

1. (*a*) Without using logarithms, compute by contracted methods, getting four significant figures *correct*.

$$87·35\div(0·07568\times0·3501).$$

(*b*) Using logarithms compute

$$(0·03524\times6·321)^{-0·256}\times97·43.$$

(*c*) Explain why when we wish to divide numbers we subtract their logarithms.

(*d*) Write down the values of cos 110, sin 213, tan 264, $\sin^{-1}0·3584$, $\cos^{-1}0·6293$.

2. The annual cost of giving a certain amount of electric light to a certain town, the voltage being V and the candle power of each lamp C, is found to be $A=a+\frac{b}{V}$

for electric energy and $B=\frac{m}{C}+n\frac{V^{\frac{2}{3}}}{C^{\frac{5}{3}}}$ for lamp renewals.

The following figures are known when C is 10 :—

V	100	200
A	1500	1200
B	300	500

Find a and b, m and n. If C is 20, what value of V will give minimum total cost?

3. Find A if $2 \sin A + 3 \cos A = 3{\cdot}55$

There are two answers between 0° and 90°, and they must be obtained with no greater inaccuracy than one-fifth of a degree.

4. The basis of Simpson's rule is that if three successive equidistant ordinates (distant h apart), y_1, y_2, y_3, are drawn to any curve, the three points may be taken as lying on the curve

$$y = a + bx + cx^2.$$

Imagine y_2 to be the axis of y so that $-h, y_1$; $0, y_2$, and h, y_3 are the three points. Substitute these values in the equation, and find a and c (b is not needed).

Integrate $a + bx + cx^2$ between the limits h and $-h$ and divide by $2h$; this gives the average value of y. Express it in terms of y_1, y_2, and y_3.

5. If

$$L = t\frac{dp}{dt}c$$

where L is latent heat (in foot-pounds), t is absolute temperature Centigrade, p is pressure in pounds per square foot, c cubic feet is increase of volume if 1 lb. changes from lower to higher state.

Calculate c at $t = 428$, if the following numbers are given for steam. When $t = 428$, L is $497{\cdot}2 \times 1393$.

t	p
413	7563
418	8698
423	9966
428	11380
433	12940
438	14680
443	16580

NOTE. $\frac{dp}{dt}$ is to be found as accurately as possible, using all the given numbers, and not using squared paper.

6. If a crank is at the angle θ from a dead point and $\theta = qt$ where q is angular velocity and t is time in seconds; if x is distance of piston in feet from the end of its stroke; if r is length of crank and l length of connecting rod, then, very nearly

$$x = r(1 - \cos\theta) + \frac{r^2}{4l}(1 - \cos 2\theta).$$

Find the acceleration y of the piston in terms of θ.

If $r = 1$ and $l = 5$, calculate x and y for the following values of θ, 0°, 45°, 90°, 135°, 180°. Plot the values of x and y as co-ordinates of points on squared paper.

7. If a cubic equation is of the form

$$ax^3+bx^2+cx+d=0,$$

show how we can always reduce it to the form

$$x^3+px+q=0.$$

If we have the curve $y=x^3$ and the straight line $y=-px-q$ plotted on a sheet of paper, show that we have the real roots of the equation.

8. Express

$$\frac{x+19}{x^2-2x-15}$$

as the sum of two simpler fractions and integrate.

9. Prove the rule for differentiating the product of two functions and deduce from it the rule for integrating by parts.

10. A closed curve rotates about a straight line in its own plane as an axis and so generates a ring. Prove the rule used for finding the volume of the ring.

11. Prove that in a triangle the ratio of two sides is equal to that of the sines of the opposite angles. Also prove that the area of a triangle is half the product of two sides and the sine of the angle between them.

12. If t seconds is the *record* time of a race of y yards; the law $t=cy^n$ seems to be wonderfully true for all races of men and animals excepting men on bicycles; n is the same number in all cases. c has a special value in each case, men walking, running, skating, swimming, or rowing; horses trotting or galloping or pacing.

(1) For any particular kind of race it is found that when y is increased by 100 per cent., t is increased by 118 per cent.; find n.

(2) For men running, when $y=600$, t is 71; find c in the above formula. Express s, the average speed of each race, in terms of y.

(3) Assume that an animal has a certain amount of endurance E which is exhausted at a uniform rate during the race and that $E=E_0+kt$ where E_0 and k are constants. Calling E/t the rate of fatigue f, express this in terms of s.

Assuming that an animal going at s_0 miles per hour feels no fatigue, or when $s=s_0$, $f=0$; find f in terms of s.

13. The curve $y=a+be^{cx}$ passes through the three points $x=0$, $y=3$; $x=3$, $y=4{\cdot}5$; $x=7$, $y=9{\cdot}5$; find a, b and c. What is $\frac{dy}{dx}$ at the point where $x=3$? It may save time if it is known that c lies between the values $0{\cdot}2$ and $0{\cdot}3$.

14. If compound interest at r per cent. per annum were payable every instant and if at any time t (years) the principal is P, show that

$$\frac{dP}{dt}=\frac{Pr}{100}.$$

Express P in terms of r and t.

In what time will P double itself for any value of r?

VII.

1. (*a*) Without using logarithms, compute by contracted methods to four significant figures

$$9{\cdot}325 \times 0{\cdot}02056 \text{ and } 9{\cdot}325 \div 0{\cdot}02056.$$

(*b*) Using logarithms, compute

$$(6{\cdot}345 \times 0{\cdot}1075)^{2{\cdot}5} \div (0{\cdot}00374 \times 96{\cdot}37)^3.$$

(*c*) Extract the cube roots of

$$20760,\ 207{\cdot}6,\ 0{\cdot}02076,\ 0{\cdot}002076.$$

(*d*) The side of a square is 3 yards 1 foot $9\frac{1}{2}$ inches; find the area of the square in square feet.

2. (*a*) The difference of x and y is 3·14; the sum of x^2 and y^2 is 140; find x and y.

(*b*) The inside of a hollow copper sphere is filled with water whose weight is 10 lb.; what is the inside radius? If the weight of the copper is 30 lb., what is its thickness? A cubic inch of copper weighs 0·32 lb.

(*c*) ABD is a right-angled triangle, B being the right angle. BC is perpendicular to the side AD. The angle A is 56°, BC is 10 inches; find the lengths of AC and CD.

(*d*) What are the factors of $x^2 - 8{\cdot}92x + 18{\cdot}37$?

3. (*a*) If $y = ax^{1{\cdot}46} + bx^{2{\cdot}5}$; if $y = 6{\cdot}3$ when $x = 1$, and if $y = 133$ when $x = 2$, find a and b.

(*b*) 20 lb. of bronze contains 87 per cent. of copper, 13 per cent. of tin. With how much copper must it be melted to obtain a bronze containing 10 per cent. of tin?

(*c*) If $\dfrac{x}{y} = \epsilon^{\mu\theta}$ and if $\mu = 0{\cdot}25$, $\theta = 3$, find x/y. It is known that $x - y = 1000$, find x and y.

4. If i means $\sqrt{-1}$, write down the values of i^2, i^3, i^4, i^5, i^6. Find $\sqrt{17+30i}$, $\sqrt{i}$, $1 \div \sqrt{i}$. Each of the answers is like $a+bi$ where a and b are numbers.

5. x is distance measured along a straight line AB from the point A; the values y are offsets or distances in links measured at right angles to AB to the border of a field. Find the average breadth from AB to the border of the field between the first and last offset. Notice that the intervals in x are not equal.

x	0	1·50	3·00	5·00	7·50	9·00
y	0·53	0·47	0·40	0·42	0·46	0·52

6. There is a root of $x^3-10x^2+40x-35=0$ which lies between 1 and 2; find it, correct to three significant figures.

7. The following numbers give x feet the distance of a sliding piece measured along its path from a certain point to the place where it is at the time t seconds: what (approximately) is its acceleration at all the tabulated times except the first and last? Show in a curve how the acceleration depends upon t.

x	1·000	2·736	4·420	6·000	7·428
t	0	0·1	0·2	0·3	0·4
x	8·660	9·660	10·397	10·848	11·000
t	0·5	0·6	0·7	0·8	0·9

8. The following numbers give v the speed of a train in miles per hour at the time t hours since leaving a railway station. In each interval of time, what is the distance passed over by the train?

v	0	2·4	4·7	7·2	9·6	12·0	14·3
t	·00	0·04	0·08	·12	·16	·20	·24
v	16·9	18·9	20·7	22·2	23·4	24·3	24·9
t	·28	·32	·36	·40	·44	·48	·52

At each of the times tabulated, what is x the distance from the station? Tabulate your answers.

9. Find the area of the parabola $y=a+bx+cx^2$ between the ordinate at $x=\alpha$ and the ordinate at $x=\beta$. If $\alpha=-h$ and $\beta=h$, what is the answer?

10. The parabola $y=a+bx+cx^2$ passes through three points whose co-ordinates are $-h$, y_1; 0, y_2; h, y_3. Insert these values, and find a, b, and c in terms of the quantities y_1, y_2, y_3 and h.

11. The following quantities measured in a laboratory are thought to follow the law $y=ab^{-x}$. Try if this is so, and, if so, find the most probable values of a and b. There are errors of observation.

x	0·1	0·2	0·4	0·6	1·0	1·5	2·0
y	350	316	120	63	12·86	2·57	0·425

12. The equilibrium position for a certain governor is that a ball should be at a certain distance r from an axis about which it revolves, when the centrifugal force is equal to

$$\frac{200+80h}{h}r$$

where $h=\sqrt{2{\cdot}25-r^2}$.

Now a certain mathematical investigation becomes too complex if this law is used, whereas it is known that, if the centrifugal force were equal to $br-a$ where a and b are mere numbers, the investigation would be easy. Find if there is approximately such a law within the limits $r=0{\cdot}5$ and $r=0{\cdot}7$, and what is the maximum error in making such an assumption?

13. One of the three premium systems used in workshops is this:—

If H is the number of hours usually allowed for a job; the man does it in less time, say, h hours. The usual pay in the shop is p pence per hour; the premium paid to the man is

$$P=\frac{(H-h)p}{2},$$

and he is also paid hp.

If r pence per hour is the cost of tools and share of total shop charges, the master would have paid $H(p+r)$ for the job. He now pays $P+h(p+r)$.

If H is 20 and p is 10 and r is 4, find the total payment to the man for the job and by the hour and also the saving to the master on the job; tabulate your answers for the following values of h: 20, 15, 10.

VIII.

1. (*a*) Without using logarithms, compute by contracted methods so that four significant figures *shall be correct*, $9 \cdot 325 \times 0 \cdot 02056$ and $9 \cdot 325 \div 0 \cdot 02056$.

(*b*) Using logarithms, compute

$$(5 \cdot 603 \times 0 \cdot 05723)^{-3 \cdot 437}.$$

(*c*) Write down the values of

$$\sin 207°, \cos 123°, \tan 325°.$$

(*d*) Express $(2x + 1 \cdot 38)/(x^2 + 1 \cdot 38x - 24 \cdot 6)$ as the sum of two simpler fractions.

2. Find, with three significant figures accurate, a root of

$$5x^{\frac{3}{2}} + x \log_{10} x - 4 \cdot 82 = 0.$$

3. The following tests were made on a steam-electric-generator; W is weight of steam in pounds used per hour; K is the output in kilowatts :—

K	3942	3105	1907	910
W	80400	68100	50200	35100

Find if there is a simple approximate law connecting W and K. State the meaning of W/K in words; call it w. Express w in terms of K.

4. By tabulation give, approximately, a table of values of

$$(a)\ \frac{dy}{dx}, \quad (b)\ \int y \, . \, dx$$

if the following values of x and y are given :—

x	0	0·01	0·02	0·03	0·04	0·05	0·06	0·07	0·08	0·09
y	1·2679	1·3640	1·4663	1·5774	1·7002	1·8391	2·0000	2·1918	2·4281	2·7321

5. If r is the radius of a heavenly body E, l the distance of another heavenly body M, of mass m, from E's centre. Then $m/(l+r)^2$ and $m/(l-r)^2$ are the accelerations towards M at points on E farthest from and nearest to M. The tide producing actions at these points are their differences from m/l^2 which is the acceleration at E's centre; prove that the tide producing effect of M is inversely proportional to the cube of the distance when l is large compared with r.

6. If $$\frac{M}{c}=\frac{d^2y}{dx^2}, \text{ and } \frac{dM}{dx}=S, \text{ and } \frac{dS}{dx}=w.$$

Let w be a constant. Find S. Let $S=W$, a constant, when $x=l$. Find M and let $M=0$ when $x=l$.

c is a given constant. Find $\frac{dy}{dx}$,

and let its value be 0 when $x=0$. Find y and let its value be 0 when $x=0$.

7. If $$\frac{dp}{dh}=-w$$

and if $w^c \propto p$ where c is a constant. Find p in terms of h. If $p \propto wt$, express t in terms of h introducing constant.

8. The total cost C of a ship per hour (including interest, depreciation, wages, coal, &c.) is in pounds

$$C=3 \cdot 2+\frac{s^3}{2200}$$

where s is the speed of the ship in knots.

Express the total cost of a passage of 3,000 miles in terms of s. What value of s will make this total cost a minimum? At speeds 10 per cent. less and greater than this, compare the total cost with its minimum value.

9. The curve $y=a+bc^x$ passes through the three points $x=0$, $y=26 \cdot 62$; $x=1$, $y=35 \cdot 70$; $x=2$, $y=49 \cdot 81$, find a, b, and c. What is the area of the curve from the ordinate at $x=0$ to the ordinate at $x=2$?

10. Describe a method of finding whether a given curve follows, approximately, the law $y=a+bx^n$ or $y=b(x+a)^n$ or $y=a+be^{nx}$. Logarithmic paper must not be used; the work can be done on ordinary drawing paper using Tee and set squares.

11. If $y=a \sin qt$ and $x=b \sin (qt-c)$ where t is time and a, q, b, c are constants; if $q=2\pi/T$ where T is the periodic time. Find the average value of xy during the time T.

12. Q being the rate of flow of water per second over a sharp-edged notch of length l, the height of the surface of nearly still water (some distance back) above the sill being h; it has been proved that the empirical formula obtained by Dr. Francis is also a rational formula; it is

$$Q \propto \left(l-\frac{1}{5}h\right)h^{3/2}.$$

Now an incorrect formula is sometimes used

$$Q=clh^{3/2}.$$

Show that for a given l, although a constant c may be found which will give a correct answer for one value of h, it must give incorrect answers for all other values of h.

13. If i is $\sqrt{-1}$, write down the values of i^2, i^3, i^4, i^5. Find $\sqrt{17+30i}$, $\sqrt{i}$, $1 \div \sqrt{i}$ each in the shape $a+bi$.

If $a+bi$ operating upon $\sin qt$ (where t is the variable and q is a constant) gives $a \sin qt + b \cos qt$, find three answers, the effects of operating with $\sqrt{17+30i}$, $\sqrt{i}$ and $1 \div \sqrt{i}$ upon $\sin qt$.

14. Get instructions from Q. **13.**

The voltage applied at the sending end of a long telephone line being $v_0 \sin qt$, the current entering the line is

$$v_0 \sqrt{\frac{s+ikq}{r+ilq}} \sin qt$$

where, per unit length of cable, r is resistance, l is inductance, s is leakance, and k is permittance, or capacity.

If $r=6$ ohms, $l=0{\cdot}003$ Henries, $h=5 \times 10^{-9}$ farads, $s=3 \times 10^{-6}$ Mho, and if $q=6{,}000$, find the current.

NOTE.—There is a quicker method of working than what is indicated in Q. **13**, using Demoivre. You may use it if you please.

15. Air is pumped into an elastic spherical bag at the rate of 5 cub. in. per sec. Find the rate of increase of the diameter and the surface when the diameter is (a) 6·5 in., (b) 9·5 in.

16. (a) A tank having a square base and vertical sides is to be made from 80 sq. ft. of sheet metal. Find side of base and height when the volume is a maximum; (b) find length of side of square base, height, and least amount of material required for a tank if the volume is 13·5 cub. ft.

17. Show that the curve $y=ax^3+bx+c$ (where a, b, and c are constants) can have no max. or min. value if a and b have the same sign. Verify when $a=4$, $b=3$.

18. Find the volume of the solid generated by the revolution of the curve $y^2=5x$ about the axis of x, between the values $x=0$, $x=4$.

19. If V is the volume, r the radius, and h the height of a cylinder, find the rate of increase of volume per unit increase of radius when $r=10{\cdot}5$ in., $h=30$ in. Find the dimensions when $h=r$, so that a change of 1 in. in the radius causes a change of 633 cub. in. in the volume.

IX.

1. (*a*) Compute by contracted methods, correct to four significant figures and without using logarithms,

$$0{\cdot}02351 \times 63{\cdot}02 \quad \text{and} \quad 63{\cdot}02 \div 0{\cdot}02351.$$

(*b*) Compute, using logarithms,

$$(0{\cdot}5673 \times 8{\cdot}421)^{1{\cdot}56}, \quad (0{\cdot}03185)^5, \quad (5{\cdot}731)^{-1{\cdot}64}.$$

(*c*) Find $\log_e 3{\cdot}642$.

(*d*) Write down the values of sin 52°, cos 140°, tan 220°, cos 340°, sin 340°.

2. (*a*) One terrestrial globe is three times the diameter of the other. The area of England on the larger globe is 0·52 square inch; what is the area of England on the other?

(*b*) One cubic inch of copper weighs 0·32 lb. A circular plate of copper 5 inches diameter weighs 0·248 lb.; what is its average thickness?

(*c*) The difference of x and y is 3·56 and the difference of their squares is 18·54, find x and y.

3. (*a*) If

$$A = P\left(1 + \frac{r}{100}\right)^n.$$

If A is 3·25 P when n is 15, find r.

(*b*) xy^n is constant. When x is 1, y is 1; when x is 2, y is 0·6; find n.

(*c*)

$$D = \frac{Wl^3}{4bd^3E}.$$

If $b=1$, $d=2$, $l=20$, $W=100$ and $D=\cdot0008$, find E.

(*d*) If $f = -a + \frac{b}{r^2}$ and $p = a + \frac{b}{r^2}$ where a and b are constants.

If $p=0$ when $r=10$, and $p=100$ when $r=5$, find f when r is 10.

4. In the Hartnell governor, calculate n the revolutions per minute when the balls, each of weight $w=3$ lb., are r feet from the axis. b depends on the stiffness of the spring; make it 200. And a depends on the amount of tightening up of the spring; make it -2. Let f the friction be 1. Calculate the speeds for $r=\cdot55$, $\cdot50$ and $\cdot45$. Find the highest and lowest of these speeds using both + and − signs with f.

$$n=\sqrt{\frac{2936}{w}\left(\frac{a\pm f}{r}+b\right)}.$$

5. If t is the time (in weeks) after the birth of a baby and w is the observed weight of the baby in pounds; show the relation of w to t on squared paper.

t	0	3	6	8
w	6·1	6·75	8	9·1

Draw a curve lying fairly among the points. Choose three points on this curve and find the law

$$w=a+bt+ct^2$$

which satisfies them. Try for one of the observed times how much error there is in the formula.

To show how wrong it is to extrapolate, calculate w from the formula for $t=100$ weeks.

6. In a submarine cable, if d is the diameter of the copper wire and D is the diameter of the gutta-percha covering; the distance to which readable signals may be sent is greater as

$$y=d^2\log\frac{D}{d}\text{ is greater.}$$

Take D as 10. For various values of d calculate y and plot on squared paper. What value of d is best?

7. Forty-four students were supposed to attend a certain drawing class from 10 a.m. to 1 p.m., Saturday, February 5th, 1909. The numbers x entering the building and signing the attendance book and presumably staying, and the number of real workers y, are as follows:

Time	10.0	10.15	10.30	10.45	11.0	11.30	12.0	12.15	12.30	12.45	1.0
x	4	7	10	11	17	18	19	20	20	20	20
y	4	7	10	11	15	16	14	14	8	7	6

Plot x and time and y and time on squared paper. In each case find the total number of student-hours and find each as a percentage of 132, the greatest possible number.

8. A steamship at the following speeds (v knots) uses the following Indicated Horse Power P.

v	10	12	14	16	18	20
P	1066	1912	3216	4951	7361	10355

Find if there is a law of the form $P=av^n$, and if so, what are the most probably correct values of a and n. There are experimental errors in the observed values of v and P.

9. A copper wire of radius r_1 is coated with iron to an outside radius r_0. The self-induction l Henries per mile is

$$l=3{\cdot}11\times 10^{-4}\mu \log_e \frac{r_0}{r_1},$$

where μ the permeability may be taken to be 300. If l is to be 0·04 and r_1 is 0·0122 inch, find r_0.

10. Draw the curve $y=10\sqrt{x}$ from $x=1$ to $x=9$. The curve rotates about the axis of x generating a surface of revolution. Imagine the solid divided up into a sufficient number of thin slices by planes at right angles to x; add up the volumes of these slices from $x=1$ to $x=9$.

11. There is a value of x between 15 and 20 which satisfies the following equation:

$$2{\cdot}5 \log x + \frac{x^2}{100} = 6{\cdot}35;$$

find it. Log x is the common logarithm of x.

12. A lever moves about a pin; its angular displacement from a certain position is θ at the time t seconds.

θ	·587	·759	·923	1·074	1·207	1·319
t	0	0·01	0·02	0·03	0·04	0·05

Find its average angular velocity during each interval of time and the probable angular acceleration at the time 0·03. The angle θ is in radians.

13. If $s=12t^2$, where s is the space in feet which has been passed through by a body in t seconds, find s when $t=10$, find the space when $t=10+m$. What is the distance passed through in the interval of m seconds after $t=10$? What is the average speed during this interval? What is this as m gets to be very small?

X.

1. (*a*) Compute by contracted methods, correct to four significant figures and without using logarithms,

$$0{\cdot}02351 \times 0{\cdot}1367 \quad \text{and} \quad 6{\cdot}321 \div 0{\cdot}01367.$$

(*b*) Compute, using logarithms $(0{\cdot}1972 \div 1{\cdot}567)^{-0{\cdot}12}$.

(*c*) If

$$\phi = \log_e \frac{t}{273},$$

where t is $273+\theta$, find ϕ for these values of θ, 20, 100, 150.

(*d*) Write down the values of sin 150°, cos 150°, cos 220°, tan 220°.

2. A telephonic current of frequency $\frac{p}{2\pi}$ becomes of the value

$$C = C_0 e^{-hx} \sin(pt - gx)$$

in the distance x miles, where

$$\sqrt{\frac{kpr}{2}}\sqrt{\sqrt{1+\frac{p^2l^2}{r^2}} \mp \frac{pl}{r}}$$

gives the value of h if the minus sign be taken and the value of g if the + sign be taken; t is time in seconds; the frequency is 600; k is $0{\cdot}05 \times 10^{-6}$ farads per mile, r is 88 ohms per mile. Find the distance in which the amplitude $C_0 e^{-hx}$ is halved, first when $l=0$, second when $l=0{\cdot}2$ Henries per mile. In each case find the lag gx.

3. It is thought that there is a law $y = a \log cx$ connecting the following experimental quantities. Try if it is so, and if so, find the probable values of a and c.

x	10	14	20	35	56	98
y	0·956	1·034	1·076	1·194	1·255	1·373

4. t weeks being the age of a baby, its weight w lb. was measured; show the relation of w to t on squared paper.

t	0	3	6	8
w	6·1	6·75	8	9·1

It is supposed that there is a law

$$w = a + bt + ct^2.$$

Find the probable values of a, b and c. If this law holds for three more weeks, find w when t is 11. When the baby is 11 weeks old, what will be the rate per week at which its weight is increasing?

5. The curve $y = 10\sqrt{x}$ rotates about the axis of x generating a surface of revolution. Find the volume between the plane cross-sections at $x = 1$ and $x = 9$.

6. A vector a is changing in direction and magnitude; what is $\frac{da}{dt}$ if t is time? Illustrate this by one example, say, by centripetal acceleration of a point moving with constant speed in a circular path.

7. By tabulation give, approximately, a table of values of

$$A = \int y \, . \, dx$$

if the following values of x and y are given. Let A be 0 when x is 0. Plot y and x on squared paper.

x	0	·1	·2	·3	·4	·5	·6
y	1·5663	1·6774	1·8002	1·9391	2·1000	2·2918	2·5281

Draw a curve showing A and x.

8. Describe a method of finding whether a given curve follows approximately the law

$$y = a + bx^n$$

$$\text{or} \quad y = b(x + a)^n$$

$$\text{or} \quad y = a + be^{nx}.$$

Logarithmic paper must not be used; the work can be done on ordinary drawing paper using tee and set squares.

9. Simplify to the form $\alpha + \beta i$ (where i means $\sqrt{-1}$) the expression

$$\sqrt{\frac{5 + 3i}{2 - 5i}}.$$

10. If $y = a \sin qt$ and $x = b \sin (qt - c)$, where t is time and a, q, b, c are constants; if $q = 2\pi/T$, where T is the periodic time; find the average value of xy during the time T.

11. A quantity of air changes in volume and pressure in the following way:

v	7	7·4	7·6	7·8	8	9
p	65·2	143·2	177·7	201·7	208·2	186·2

It is known that if H is the heat received by it,

$$h=\frac{dH}{dv}=\frac{1}{\gamma-1}\left(v\frac{dp}{dv}+\gamma p\right).$$

Compute this approximately at the middle of each interval δv. Plot the values of both p and h as ordinates on squared paper, plotting v horizontally. The value of γ is 1·4.

12. The time of oscillation of the pendulum of a clock is

$$T=\sqrt{\frac{a}{W}},$$

where a is a constant and W is the weight of the pendulum. If the bob is a coil of wire through which a current c flows; if there is another coil fixed to the bottom of the case through which the current C flows, so that the weight of the pendulum is increased by an amount proportional to cC, this being a small fraction of W; show that the gain of the clock per hour represents the time integral of cC. Usually cC is proportional to electrical power, so that the clock indicates energy.

13. If a crank of an ordinary engine turns at a uniform rate, show that the motion of the crosshead is approximately a simple harmonic motion plus its octave.

14. From the corners of a square sheet of metal of 12 in. side small squares are cut out and the edges turned up to make a box. Find the length of side of the small squares so that the volume of the box is a maximum.

15. Find the max. and mean ordinates of curve $y=x-x^2$.

16. A box with lid, sides vertical, volume 5·6 cub. ft. is to be made from the smallest amount of sheet metal, thickness of base twice the lid and sides. Find dimensions. (Square base.)

XI.

1. (*a*) Without using logarithms, compute by contracted methods to four significant figures

$$5{\cdot}306 \times 0{\cdot}07632 \div 73{\cdot}15.$$

(*b*) Using logarithms, compute

$$(22{\cdot}15 \div 4{\cdot}139)^{0{\cdot}86}.$$

(*c*) The value of g, the acceleration (in centimetres per second per second) due to gravity in latitude l, is (approximately)

$$980{\cdot}62 - 2{\cdot}6 \cos 2l.$$

Calculate this for the latitude 52°.

(*d*) The gunners' rule is that one halfpenny (the diameter of a halfpenny is one inch) subtends an angle of one minute at the distance of 100 yards. What is the percentage error in this rule?

2. (*a*) A hollow cylinder of outside diameter D and radial thickness t is of length l. What is its volume? If D is 4 inches and $t = 0{\cdot}5$ inch, if the volume is 20 cubic inches, find l.

(*b*) Two similar ships A and B are loaded similarly. B is twice the length of A. The wetted area of A is 12,000 square feet and its displacement 1500 tons. State the wetted area and displacement of B.

(*c*) The cross-section of a stream divided by the wetted perimeter of the channel in which it flows is called its Hydraulic Mean Depth. What are the Hydraulic Mean Depths when water flows in a pipe of diameter d (i) when the water fills the pipe, (ii) when it only half fills the pipe?

(*d*) What is the number of which ·6314 is the Naperian logarithm?

3. (*a*) If $xy^n = a$; if x is 5 when y is 10, and if x is 11 when y is 8, find n and a. What is the value of y when x is 7?

(*b*) The velocity of sound in air is $66{\cdot}3\sqrt{t}$ feet per second where t is the absolute temperature Centigrade, that is the ordinary temperature plus 273. What is the velocity at 10° C., and by what fraction must this be multiplied to give the velocity at 15° C.?

(*c*) Assuming the earth to be a sphere of 8000 miles diameter, what is the circumference of the parallel of latitude 52°? The earth makes one revolution in 24 hours (approximately); what is the speed at latitude 52° in miles per hour?

4. There is a natural reservoir with irregular sides. When filled with water to the vertical height h feet above the lowest point, the following is the area A of the water surface in thousands of square feet:

h	0	5	10	20	30	42	50	65	75
A	0	220	322	435	505	560	586	617	624

Find the average value of A between $h=10$ and $h=65$.

What is A when h is 36? Find the volume of water which would raise the surface from $h=35\frac{1}{2}$ to $h=36\frac{1}{2}$.

5. The energy stored in similar fly-wheels is $E=ad^5n^2$, where d is the diameter and n the revolutions per minute; a is a constant. A wheel whose diameter is 5 feet, revolving at 100 revolutions per minute, stores 18,500 ft.-lb., find a. What is the diameter of a similar fly-wheel which will increase its store by 10,000 ft.-lb. when its speed increases from 149 to 151 revolutions per minute?

6. There is a root of $x^3+5x-11=0$ between 1 and 2: find it, using squared paper, accurately to four significant figures.

7. A steamer is moving at 20 feet per second towards the east; the passengers notice that the smoke from the funnel streams off apparently towards the south-west with a speed of 10 feet per second; what is the real speed of the wind and what is its direction? If solved by actual drawing, the work must be accurately done.

8. If $y=20+\sqrt{30+x^3}$, take various values of x from 10 to 50 and calculate y. Plot on squared paper. What straight line agrees with the curve most nearly between these values? Express it in the shape $y=a+bx$.

9. If the force which retards the falling of an object in a fluid is proportional to vs, where v is the velocity of falling and s is the area of the surface of the object, and if the force which accelerates falling is the weight of the object, show that as objects are smaller they fall more and more slowly.

Recollect that of similar objects made of the same materials the weights are as the cubes, the surfaces are as the squares of like dimensions.

10. A sliding piece is at the distance s feet from a point in its path at the time t seconds. Do not plot s and t. What is the average speed in each interval of time? Assume that this is really the speed in the middle of the interval, and now plot time and speed on squared paper.

s	1·0000	1·1054	1·2146	1·3246	1·4432	1·5624	1·6857	1·8118
t	0	0·1	0·2	0·3	0·4	0·5	0·6	0·7

(i) What is the approximate increase in speed between $t=0·25$ and $t=0·35$? (ii) What is approximately the acceleration when $t=0·3$?

11. The sections of the two ends of a barrel are each 12·35 square feet; the middle section is 14·16 square feet; the axial length of the barrel is 5 feet; what is its volume?

12. There is a machine consisting of two parts, whose weights are x and y. The cost of the machine in pounds is $12x+5y$. The power of the machine is proportional to xy. Find x and y if the cost is 100*l.* and if we desire to have the greatest power possible. Use squared paper if you please.

13. According to a certain hypothesis the tensile stress in a rectangular section of an iron hook at a distance y from a certain line through the centre of the section is proportional to

$$p=\frac{y+c}{1-\frac{y+c}{R}}.$$

When $R=10$ and $c=1$, calculate p for various values of y from $y=5$ to $y=-5$, and plot on squared paper. (i) What is the average value of p? (ii) For what value of y is the stress zero?

XII.

1. (*a*) Without using logarithms, compute by contracted methods so that four significant figures *shall be correct*,

$$5·306 \times 0·07632 \div 73·15.$$

(*b*) Using logarithms, compute

$$(22·15 \div 4·139)^{-0·86}.$$

(*c*) The lengths of a degree of latitude and longitude, in centimetres, in latitude l are

$$(1111{\cdot}317 - 5{\cdot}688 \cos l)\,10^4$$

and

$$(1111{\cdot}164 \cos l - {\cdot}950 \cos 3l)\,10^4.$$

The length of a sea mile (or 6082 feet) is 185,380 cm. What are the lengths of a *minute* of latitude and of a minute of *longitude* in sea miles in the latitude 52°?

2. A telephonic current of frequency $\frac{p}{2\pi}$ becomes of the value

$$C = C_0 e^{-hx} \sin(pt - gx)$$

in the distance of x miles, where

$$\sqrt{\frac{kpr}{2}}\sqrt{\sqrt{1+\frac{p^2l^2}{r^2}} \pm \frac{pl}{r}}$$

gives the value of h if the minus sign be taken and the value of g if the plus sign be taken. When $\frac{pl}{r}$ is very large, what are the values of h and g approximately? If $k = 0{\cdot}05 \times 10^{-6}$, $r = 88$, and $p = 5000$, take two cases, (i) when $l = 0$, and (ii) when $l = 0{\cdot}3$, and in each case find the distance x in which the amplitude C is halved.

3. Find the value of $\cosh 0{\cdot}1(1+i)$, where i means $\sqrt{-1}$.

4. To find the volume of part of a wedge, the frustum of a pyramid, or of a cone, of part of a railway cutting or embankment, etc., we use the "Prismoidal Formula," which is "The sum of the areas of the end sections and four times the mid section, all divided by 6, is the average section; this multiplied by the total length is the whole volume." Under what circumstances is this rule perfectly correct? Prove its correctness.

5. If $z = y + 2\frac{dy}{dx}$, and if y is as tabulated, find z approximately. Show both y and z as functions of x in curves.

x	4·0	4·1	4·2	4·3	4·4	4·5
y	3·162	3·548	3·981	4·467	5·012	5·623

6. A body capable of damped vibration is acted on by simply varying force which has a frequency f. If x is the displacement of the body at any instant t, and if the motion is defined by

$$\frac{d^2x}{dt^2} + b\frac{dx}{dt} + n^2x = a \sin 2\pi ft,$$

we wish to study the forced vibration.

Take $a=1$, $b=1{\cdot}5$, $n^2=4$; find x (i) when $f=0{\cdot}2547$, (ii) when $f=0{\cdot}3820$.

7. The following values of x and y being given, tabulate $\frac{\delta y}{\delta x}$ in each interval, also $\delta A = y\delta x$, and $A=\int y\,dx$. Show in curves how the value of y, $\frac{dy}{dx}$ and A depend on x.

x	0·0	0·1	0·2	0·3	0·4	0·5	0·6	0·7	0·8
y	6·428	7·071	7·660	8·192	8·660	9·063	9·397	9·659	9·848

8. There is a table giving values of y in terms of x and another giving values of u in terms of y. What is u when $x=8{\cdot}3$?

x	y	y	u
7	14·914	15	·8169
8	16·128	16	·7118
9	17·076	17	·5543

9. If $pv=100t$, and $p=3000$ when $t=300$, find v. If $p=3010$ and $t=302$, find the new v. If the second set of values be called $3000+\delta p$, $300+\delta t$, and $v+\delta v$, what is δv? Now use the formula

$$\delta v = \left(\frac{dp}{dv}\right)\delta p + \left(\frac{dv}{dt}\right)\delta t,$$

and calculate δv in the new way. Why is there an error in the answer?

10. The value of y, a periodic function of t, is here given for 12 equidistant values of t covering the whole period. Express y in a Fourier Series.

13·602	18·468	20·671	20·182	17·820	14·346
10·130	5·612	1·877	·486	2·500	7·506

It ought not to be necessary to say that 18·468 is the second value.

11. To solve $x^3-20x+9=0$ graphically, it is evident that we desire the value of x which will cause x^3 to be equal to $20x-9$; plot therefore the curve $y=x^3$, and plot the straight line $z=20x-9$. Where they intersect we have the value of x desired. When the trial is made it will be found that there are three answers; what are they?

12. On the indicator diagram of a gas engine the following are some readings of p pressure and v volume. The rate of reception of heat (if the gases are supposed to be receiving heat from an outside source and not from their own chemical action) is

$$\frac{dH}{dv}=p+\frac{k}{K-k}\left(p+v\frac{dp}{dv}\right),$$

where k and K, the important specific heats, are such that

$$\frac{k}{K-k}=2+\frac{pv}{300}.$$

v	2·0	2·1	2·2	2·3	2·4	2·5	2·6	2·7	2·8	2·9	3·0	3·1
p	84·5	110	176	215	231	234	226	213	202	192	183	175

v	3·2	3·3	3·4	3·5	3·6
p	167	159	152	146	140

Find $\frac{dH}{dv}$ at three places; where $v=2{\cdot}05$, $3{\cdot}55$ and at the place of highest pressure.

13. When a shaft fails under the combined action of a bending moment M and a twisting moment T, according to what is called the internal friction hypothesis,

$$M+a\sqrt{M^2+T^2}$$

ought to be constant where a is a constant. Test if this is so, using the following numbers which have been published. Considerable errors in the observations must be expected.

M	0	0	0	1200	1160	1240	2800	2840	2760
T	4320	4360	4308	4338	4326	4368	3836	3846	3804

M	4400	4320	4600	5020	5180	5360
T	2416	2438	2060	0	0	0

XIII.

1. (*a*) Without using logarithms, compute by contracted methods, to four significant figures,

$$0{\cdot}009216 \times 116{\cdot}06 \div 13{\cdot}014.$$

(*b*) Using logarithms, find the value of

$$0{\cdot}009216 \times 116{\cdot}1 \div 13{\cdot}01.$$

Then raise your answer to the power 0·4343.

(*c*) Write down the values of the sine, cosine and tangent of

$$170^\circ \text{ and } 1{\cdot}4\pi \text{ radians}.$$

(*d*) Find the two square roots of $2{\cdot}6 - 3{\cdot}1i$ by first reducing it to the form $r(\cos\theta + i\sin\theta)$. The symbol i stands for $\sqrt{-1}$.

2. Simpson's second rule is based on the property that for any four equidistant ordinates of the curve

$$y = a + bx + cx^2 + dx^3$$

the mean ordinate is given by the formula

$$y_m = \tfrac{1}{8}(y_1 + 3y_2 + 3y_3 + y_4)$$

Prove this. State the rule.

3. Calculate p, u and $\dfrac{dp}{dt}$ when $t = 344$, having given

$$\log_{10} p = 6{\cdot}1007 - \frac{1518}{t} - \frac{122500}{t^2},$$

$$pu^{1{\cdot}0646} = 479.$$

4. The following measurements were made from the expansion curve of an indicator diagram :

x	1	2	3	4	5	6
y	231	151	109	84	67	56

It is desired to represent the curve approximately by the equation

$$y(x + a)^n = b.$$

Try whether this is permissible, and, if so, find good average values for a, b and n.

5. A rectangular plot of ground, 40 yards by 30 yards, is divided into twelve equal squares in plan. The heights of the ground at the corners of the squares, in feet above datum level, are given systematically in the following table:

4·8	3·9	2·9	1·8	1·0
5·1	6·0	4·7	3·5	1·8
4·0	7·2	6·7	4·6	2·8
2·0	4·5	5·8	4·6	2·5

Estimate the mean height of the plot.

Draw a plan to a scale of 1 inch to 10 yards, and on it show a horizontal contour or section of the ground at the level of 4 feet.

6. Suppose y to be some known function of x and let Y be its integral $\int y\,dx$. Sketch approximately, on a common base, any such pair of y and Y curves, and point out some relationships that exist between them.

Give the values of $\frac{dy}{dx}$ and $\int y\,dx$ in the two following cases:

$$y = a(bx+c)^{-1}; \quad y = x\cos 2x.$$

7. A surface of revolution is formed by the rotation of the curve $y = 1 + 2\sin x$ about the axis of x.

Find the volume enclosed by the surface between the transverse planes at $x = -\frac{\pi}{6}$ and $x = \frac{7}{6}\pi$.

8. Compute $\sinh x$, (a) when $x = 1·5$; (b) when $x = 1 + 0·7i$. The symbol i means $\sqrt{-1}$.

9. The following equation refers to a forced vibration, with damping:

$$\frac{d^2x}{dt^2} + 2f\frac{dx}{dt} + n^2x = n^2y.$$

State the meanings to be attached to the various terms of the equation. You may take either a mechanical or an electrical illustration.

Find the motion, after the natural vibration has been damped out, for conditions in which $f = 1$, $n^2 = 10$ and $y = 3\sin 2t$.

10. What is meant by $\frac{dA}{dt}$, the rate of increase of A with time, where A is a vector quantity?

A point moving in a plane had the positions, at successive intervals δt each of 0·01 second, given by the vectors:

$$R_1 = 0·427'_{15°}, \quad R_2 = 0·396'_{32·9°}, \quad R_3 = 0·364'_{52·2°},$$

where the angles define direction.

Find approximately the velocity $\frac{dR}{dt}$ of the point when in the given middle position.

11. Find the moment of inertia of a right-angled isosceles triangle, each equal side of which is a, about an axis through its centre of gravity parallel to one of its equal sides.

The section of a chimney shaft consists of two concentric regular octagons. The radii of the inscribed circles are R and r; the thickness of the brickwork is thus $R-r$. Determine the moment of inertia of the section about a symmetrical axis in its plane parallel to pairs of sides.

12. A line OR, 3 inches long, makes acute angles α, β and γ with three mutually perpendicular axes of reference OX, OY and OZ. If $\alpha=52°$, $\beta=63°$, find γ.

A plane through R, perpendicular to OR, has the equation

$$\frac{x}{a}+\frac{y}{b}+\frac{z}{c}=1.$$

Find a, b and c.

What is the area of the triangle formed by the traces of this plane on the three planes of reference YZ, ZX and XY?

13. An electrically propelled car was fitted with a recording accelerometer, the drum of which was driven by gearing connected to the wheels.

When the car had travelled x feet from its position of rest, the acceleration, y ft./sec.^{2}, was measured from the diagram as follows:

x	0	10	20	30	40	50	60
y	3·60	2·19	1·35	0·80	0·51	0·41	0·32

Show by a diagram how y varies with x.

Determine approximately the speed v of the car for various values of x, using the equation

$$v^2=2\int_0^x y\,dx.$$

Draw a curve showing v as a function of x, and measure the speed when $x=60$.

14. In a portion of an electric circuit let c be the current and v the voltage difference at the ends. Then it is known that

$$v=\left(R+L\theta+\frac{1}{K\theta}\right)c,$$

where for this portion R is the ohmic resistance, L the self-induction, K the capacity of a condenser, and θ means the operator $\frac{d}{dt}$.

Solve this equation for the alternating current $c=c_0\sin qt$. Illustrate your answer by a vector diagram.

Show that by suitably proportioning L and K, the effects of the self-induction and condenser may be made to neutralise one another.

APPENDIX.

MENSURATION (*Continued*).

Prismoidal formulae.—Two closed curves or irregular polygons in parallel planes, joined by a developable surface, such as the frustum of a cone, or pyramid, form a **prismoid.**

If y_0 and y_2 denote the areas of the two ends and y_1 the area midway between them,

$$\textbf{Average section} = \tfrac{1}{6}(y_0 + 4y_1 + y_2). \quad \ldots\ldots\ldots\ldots(1)$$

$$\textbf{Volume of solid} = (\text{average section}) \times (\text{length}).$$

Referring to p. 417, it will be seen that (1) and (2) are merely Simpson's Rule for three ordinates,

$$\textit{i.e.}\ \textbf{average ordinate} = \frac{s}{3}(y_0 + 4y_1 + y_2) \div 2s = \tfrac{1}{6}(y_0 + 4y_1 + y_2).$$

Ex. 1. The base of a square pyramid is a square of 4 in. side, upper face 2 in. side, height of frustum 5 in. Find the volume.

$$\text{Length of side of mid-section} = \tfrac{1}{2}(4+2) = 3 \text{ in.}$$

$$\text{Average section} = \tfrac{1}{6}(4^2 + 4 \times 3^2 + 2^2) = \tfrac{56}{6}.$$

$$\text{Volume} = \tfrac{56}{6} \times 5 = 46 \cdot 67 \text{ cub. in.}$$

Ex. 2. The base of the frustum of a cone is 4 in. diameter, the upper face 2 in. diameter, height of frustum 5 in. Find the volume.

$$\text{Average section} = \tfrac{1}{6}(4^2 + 4 \times 3^2 + 2^2)\frac{\pi}{4} = \frac{7\pi}{3}.$$

$$\text{Volume} = \frac{7\pi}{3} \times 5 = 36 \cdot 66 \text{ cub. in.}$$

The results in both cases are the same as those obtained by using equations (ii) and (iv), p. 210.

Ex. 3. In a railway cutting the cross-sections 15 yds. apart are 90, 80 and 70 square yards respectively. Find the total volume of earthwork.

$$\text{Average section} = \tfrac{1}{6}(90 + 4 \times 80 + 70) = 80 \text{ sq. yds.}$$

$$\text{Volume} = 80 \times 30 = 2400 \text{ cub. yds.}$$

Ex. 4. The top of a reservoir with plane sides is a rectangle 400 ft. by 70 ft. and the bottom a rectangle 100 ft. by 50 ft. Find the volume if the depth of the reservoir is 18 ft.

$$\text{Mid-section} = \tfrac{1}{2}(400 + 100) \text{ and } \tfrac{1}{2}(70 + 50).$$

$$\therefore \text{ area} = 250 \times 60 = 15000 \text{ sq. ft.},$$

$$400 \times 70 = 28000 \text{ sq. ft.}, \quad 50 \times 100 = 5000 \text{ sq. ft.}$$

$$\text{Average section} = \tfrac{1}{6}(28000 + 4 \times 15000 + 5000)$$

$$= \frac{93000}{6} \text{ sq. ft.}$$

$$\text{Volume} = \frac{93000}{6} \times 18 = 279000 \text{ cub. ft.}$$

Harmonic motion.—Many expressions can be reduced to the form $y = a \sin(bx + c)$ given on p. 137.

Ex. 1. If $x = a \sin pt + b \cos pt$, where a, b and p are constants, show that this is the same as $x = A \sin(pt + e)$, if A and e are properly evaluated.

Using the formula for $\sin(A + B)$, p. 27, we obtain

$$x = A \sin pt \cos e + A \cos pt \sin e.$$

Also $\quad x = a \sin pt + b \cos pt.$

Comparing coefficients, we obtain $A \cos e = a$, $A \sin e = b$.

Squaring and adding, $A^2(\sin^2 e + \cos^2 e) = a^2 + b^2$;

$$\therefore A = \sqrt{a^2 + b^2}, \quad \frac{\sin e}{\cos e} = \tan e = \frac{b}{a}.$$

Ex. 2. Express $x = 6 \sin 4t + 5 \cos 4t$ in the form $A \sin(4t + e)$.

$$A = \sqrt{6^2 + 5^2} = 7{\cdot}81, \quad \tan e = \tfrac{5}{6}; \quad \therefore e + 39^\circ{\cdot}8 \text{ or } 0{\cdot}6946 \text{ radians};$$

$$\therefore x = 7{\cdot}81 \sin(4t + 0{\cdot}6946).$$

Ex. 3. If $V = RC + L\dfrac{dC}{dt}$, and if $C = 100 \sin 600t$, find V when R is 2 and $L = 0{\cdot}005$. What is the lag of C (in degrees) behind V?

As $C = 100 \sin 600t$, $\quad \therefore \dfrac{dC}{dt} = 60000 \cos(600t)$.

Substituting, $V=200 \sin 600t+300 \cos 600t$,

$$A=\sqrt{200^2+300^2}=360{\cdot}6.$$

$$A \cos e=200, \quad A \sin e=300; \quad \therefore \tan e=\tfrac{300}{200};$$

$$\therefore e=56^\circ{\cdot}3=0{\cdot}983 \text{ radian},$$

$$V=360{\cdot}6 \sin(600t+0{\cdot}983),$$

lag of $C=56^\circ{\cdot}3$.

Demoivre's theorem.—For any value of n, $\cos n\theta \pm i \sin n\theta$ is one of the values of $(\cos\theta+i\sin\theta)^n$ (where i denotes $\sqrt{-1}$).

Multiplying $\cos\alpha+i\sin\alpha$ by $\cos\beta+i\sin\beta$, the product is $\cos(\alpha+\beta)+i\sin(\alpha+\beta)$.

Again, multiplying by $\cos\gamma+i\sin\gamma$, the product is

$$\cos(\alpha+\beta+\gamma)+i\sin(\alpha+\beta+\gamma).$$

In this manner the product of any number of factors of the form $\cos\alpha+i\sin\alpha$ may be obtained.

If there are n such factors, each factor being $\cos\theta+i\sin\theta$, we obtain $(\cos\theta+i\sin\theta)^n=\cos n\theta+i\sin n\theta$.

Operators and imaginaries.—An expression of the form $a \pm ib$, where a and b are any real numbers and i denotes $\sqrt{-1}$ (p. 112), may be assumed to be obtained by an **operator** which will rotate a line through a definite angle about an axis perpendicular to the line.

If a line $CA=a$, then $CA'=-a$ (Fig. 31, p. 135). Also, if i is an **operator** which will rotate the line CP from CA to CB, *i.e.* through 90°, then $CB=ia$.

The operator applied to CB will bring the line into the position CA';

$$\therefore CA'=iCB=i\times ia \quad \text{or} \quad i^2a=-a;$$

$$\therefore i^2=-1 \quad \text{or} \quad i=\sqrt{-1}.$$

Distances parallel to AA' may be denoted by letters, but distances perpendicular to AA' are denoted by letters preceded by $\sqrt{-1}$ or i. Hence, as on p. 113, $i^2=-1$, $i^3=-i$, $i^4=1$, etc.

Any complex quantity of the form $a \pm bi$ may be expressed in the form $r(\cos\theta+i\sin\theta)$ by choosing the values of r and θ so that $r\cos\theta=a$, $r\sin\theta=b$. Squaring and adding,

$$r^2(\sin^2\theta+\cos^2\theta)=a^2+b^2;$$

$$\therefore r=\sqrt{a^2+b^2}, \quad \tan\theta=\frac{b}{a}.$$

Ex. 1. Express $5+4i$ in the form $r(\cos\theta+i\sin\theta)$, extract the square root and express it in the form $a+bi$.

$$r=\sqrt{5^2+4^2}=6{\cdot}403, \quad \tan\theta=\tfrac{4}{5}; \quad \therefore \theta=38^\circ 40'.$$

Hence $$5+4i=6{\cdot}403(\cos 38^\circ 40'+i\sin 38^\circ 40')$$

and $$\sqrt{5+4i}=\sqrt{6{\cdot}403}\left(\frac{\cos 38^\circ 40'}{2}+i\frac{\sin 38^\circ 40'}{2}\right)$$

$$=2{\cdot}53(\cos 19^\circ 21'+i\sin 19^\circ 20')$$

or $$2{\cdot}53(0{\cdot}9436+i\times 0{\cdot}3310)=2{\cdot}388+0{\cdot}8375i.$$

Ex. 2. Express $-2{\cdot}35+1{\cdot}96i$ in the form $r(\cos\theta+i\sin\theta)$, and extract the fourth root.

$$r=\sqrt{2{\cdot}35^2+1{\cdot}96^2}=3{\cdot}061, \quad \tan\theta=\frac{1{\cdot}96}{-2{\cdot}35}; \quad \therefore \theta=140^\circ 10'.$$

$$-2{\cdot}35+1{\cdot}96i=3{\cdot}061(\cos 140^\circ 10'+i\sin 140^\circ 10'),$$

$$\sqrt[4]{-2{\cdot}35+1{\cdot}96i}=\sqrt[4]{3{\cdot}061}\left(\frac{\cos 140^\circ 10'}{4}+i\frac{\sin 140^\circ 10'}{4}\right)$$

$$=1{\cdot}322(\cos 35^\circ 3'+i\sin 35^\circ 3').$$

The results may also be written in the forms

$$3{\cdot}061[140^\circ 10']; \quad 1{\cdot}322[35^\circ 3'] \quad \text{or} \quad 3{\cdot}061[140^\circ{\cdot}17].$$

Ex. 3. Express $5+4i$ in the form $re^{i\theta}$.

As in Ex. 1, $r=6{\cdot}403$, $\theta=38^\circ 40'=0{\cdot}675$ radian;

$$\therefore 5+4i=6{\cdot}403e^{0{\cdot}675i}.$$

Ex. 4. Express $6{\cdot}403(\cos 38^\circ 40'+i\sin 38^\circ 40')$ in the form $a+bi$.

$$6{\cdot}403(\cos 38^\circ 40'+\sin 38^\circ 40')$$

$$=6{\cdot}403(0{\cdot}7822+0{\cdot}6248i)=5+4i.$$

An expression of the form $(a+bi)\times(m+ni)$ may be written in the form

$$r(\cos\theta+i\sin\theta)\times r_1(\cos\theta_1+i\sin\theta_1)$$

$$=rr_1\{\cos(\theta+\theta_1)+i\sin(\theta+\theta_1)\}.$$

Similarly an expression of the form $\dfrac{(a+bi)}{m+ni}$ may be written

$$\frac{r}{r_1}\{\cos(\theta-\theta_1)+i\sin(\theta-\theta_1)\}.$$

Ex. 5. Express $5+3i$ in the form $r(\cos\theta+i\sin\theta)$, express $2-5i$ also in this form. Divide the first of these by the second, extract the square root and write the answer in the form $a+bi$.

$$r=\sqrt{5^2+3^2}=5\cdot831, \quad \tan\theta=\tfrac{3}{5}; \quad \therefore\ \theta=30^\circ\ 58'.$$

$$r_1=\sqrt{2^2+5^2}=5\cdot385, \quad \tan\theta_1=-\tfrac{5}{2}; \quad \therefore\ \theta_1=-68^\circ\ 12'.$$

$$\frac{5+3i}{2-5i}=\frac{5\cdot831}{5\cdot385}\{\cos(30^\circ\ 58'+68^\circ\ 12')+i\sin(30^\circ\ 58'+68^\circ\ 12')\}$$

$$=1\cdot082(\cos 99^\circ\ 10'+i\sin 99^\circ\ 10'),$$

$$\sqrt{\frac{5+3i}{2-5i}}=\sqrt{1\cdot082}\left(\cos\frac{99^\circ\ 10'}{2}+i\sin\frac{99^\circ\ 10'}{2}\right)$$

$$=1\cdot041(\cos 49^\circ\ 35'+i\sin 49^\circ\ 35');$$

$$\therefore\ 1\cdot041(0\cdot6483+0\cdot7613i)=0\cdot6748+0\cdot7925i.$$

Ex. 6. Show that (i) $\sqrt{i}=0\cdot707+0\cdot707i$; (ii) $1\div\sqrt{i}=0\cdot707-0\cdot707i$.

As $i=1(\cos 90^\circ+i\sin 90^\circ)$,

$$\therefore\ \sqrt{i}=1(\cos 45^\circ+i\sin 45^\circ) \quad \text{or} \quad \sqrt{i}=0\cdot707+0\cdot707i.$$

Ex. 7. A fly-wheel is rotating at a radians per second at the time t seconds. If M is the moment acting, if fa is a fluid friction and is the only resistance, and I the moment of inertia of the wheel,

$$M=fa+I\frac{da}{dt}.$$

Take $f=200$ and $I=5000$; find M if $a=20+0\cdot1\sin 12t$.

As $a=20+0\cdot1\sin 12t$, $\quad \frac{da}{dt}=1\cdot2\cos 12t$.

Substituting these values, we obtain

$$M=f(20+0\cdot1\sin 12t)+5000\times1\cdot2\cos 12t$$

$$=4000+20\sin 12t+6000\cos 12t.$$

As $a+bi$ may be put in the form $r(\cos\theta+i\sin\theta)$, if this operates upon $n\sin qt$ the result is $nr\sin(qt+\theta)$.

Ex. 8. Operate with $5+4i$ upon $5\sin qt$.

From Ex. 1, $5+4i=6\cdot403(\cos 38^\circ\ 40'+i\sin 38^\circ\ 40')$.

Hence the result is $5\times6\cdot403\sin(qt+38^\circ\ 40')=32\sin(qt+38^\circ\ 40')$.

Ex. 9. Show that the values of $\sqrt{17+30i}$, $\sqrt{i}$, and $1\div\sqrt{i}$ are $5\cdot073+2\cdot956i$, $\frac{1}{\sqrt{2}}+\frac{i}{\sqrt{2}}$, and $\cos 45^\circ-i\sin 45^\circ$ respectively.

Ex. 10. If $a+bi$ operating upon $\sin qt$ (where t is the variable and q is constant) gives $a \sin qt + b \cos qt$, show that the effects of operating with $\sqrt{17+30i}$, $\sqrt{i}$, and $1 \div \sqrt{i}$ upon $\sin qt$ are

$$5{\cdot}062 \sin qt + 2{\cdot}963 \cos qt, \quad \cos 45^\circ \sin qt + \sin 45^\circ \cos qt,$$

and $\sin\left(qt - \frac{\pi}{4}\right)$ respectively.

Ex. 11. Show that the value of $\cosh 0{\cdot}1\,(1+i)$ is $1{\cdot}0002 + 0{\cdot}01001i$.

Ex. 12. The numerical value of $\cosh x$ when x is $0{\cdot}3154$ is $1{\cdot}050$.

Ex. 13. Express $3-4i$ in the form $r(\cos\theta + i\sin\theta)$.

Express $-5+6i$ also in this form. Divide the first of these by the second, and show that the result is $0{\cdot}6395 + 0{\cdot}0324i$.

Ex. 14. Show that the cube root of $-2{\cdot}35 + 1{\cdot}961$ is

$$0{\cdot}9951 + 1{\cdot}056i.$$

Differentiation and integration.—The methods indicated in Chapters XV. to XIX. will enable the differentiation or integration of any ordinary expression to be effected. As it is difficult to remember the various integrals, it is advisable for a student to compile a complete list of them.

Ex. 1. If $y = Ae^{ax}$, what is $\frac{dy}{dx}$? An electric condenser, of capacity K farads and leakage resistance R ohms, has been charged, and the voltage is diminishing according to the law

$$\frac{dv}{dt} = -\frac{v}{AK}.$$

Express v in terms of the time t sec. If $K = 0{\cdot}8 \times 10^{-6}$ farad, if v is noted to be 30, and 15 sec. afterwards to be 26·43, find R.

If $y = Ae^{ax}$,

$$\frac{dy}{dx} = Aae^{ax} = ay, \quad \frac{dv}{dt} = -\frac{v}{AK}; \quad \therefore\ v = v_0 e^{-\frac{t}{KR}},$$

or $$\log\frac{v_0}{v} = \frac{t}{KR}.$$

If $t=0$ when $v=30$, $\quad \therefore\ v_0 = 30.$

Hence $$\log\frac{30}{26{\cdot}43} = \frac{15}{KR},$$

or $$R = \frac{15}{KR\log\frac{30}{26{\cdot}43}}.$$

The Napierian log of $\frac{30}{26 \cdot 43} = 0 \cdot 1266$;

$$\therefore R = \frac{15 \times 10^6}{0 \cdot 8 \times 0 \cdot 1266} = 148 \times 10^6 \text{ ohms.}$$

Ex. 2. The curve $y = ae^{bx}$ passes through the points $x = 1$, $y = 3 \cdot 5$, and $x = 10$, $y = 12 \cdot 6$. Find a and b. This curve rotates about the axis of x. Find the volume between the sections $x = 1$, $x = 10$.

The given equation may be written $\log y = \log a + bx \log e$.

Hence, substituting the given values, we obtain

$$\log 12 \cdot 6 = \log a + 10b \log e, \quad \ldots\ldots(1)$$

$$\log\ 3 \cdot 5 = \log a + \ b \log e. \quad \ldots\ldots(2)$$

From (1) and (2), $a = 3 \cdot 036$, $b = 0 \cdot 1423$.

Hence $y = 3 \cdot 036 e^{0 \cdot 1423x}$.

$$\text{Volume} = \pi \int y^2 dx = \pi \int_1^{10} (3 \cdot 036 e^{0 \cdot 1423})^2 dx$$

$$= \pi \int_1^{10} (9 \cdot 217 e^{0 \cdot 2846}) dx;$$

$$\therefore \frac{\pi \times 9 \cdot 217}{0 \cdot 2846} \left[e^{0 \cdot 2846} \right]_1^{10} = 1617.$$

Ex. 3. If the curve $y = 1 + 0 \cdot 2x^2$ rotates round the axis of x, the volume between the cross-section at $x = 0$ and $x = 10$ is 2963.

Approximate differentiation.—By the methods already indicated in Chapters XIV. and XV. it is possible to differentiate a given expression when the relation between two variables is known. Approximate values may be obtained from tabulated values of two variables.

Ex. 1. Values of s and t are as tabulated; find $\frac{ds}{dt}$ in the middle of each interval. Find the value of $\frac{ds}{dt}$ and $\frac{d^2s}{dt^2}$ when $s = 0 \cdot 03$ and $s = 0 \cdot 07$.

t	0	·01	·02	·03	·04	·05	·06	·07	·08	·09
s	·2734	·3108	·3263	·3382	·3482	·3570	·3650	·3723	·3792	·3856

The values of ds are found by subtracting consecutive values of s thus, $0{\cdot}3108 - 0{\cdot}2734 = 0{\cdot}0374$. Proceeding in this manner, the following values may be obtained; also, as dt is 0·01, the values of $\frac{ds}{dt}$ may be tabulated as follows:

t	0	·01	·02	·03	·04	·05	·06	·07	·08	·09
s	·2734	·3108	·3263	·3382	·3482	·3570	·3650	·3723	·3792	·3856
ds	·0374	·0155	·0119	·0100	·0088	·0080	·0073	·0069	·0064	
$\frac{ds}{dt}$	3·74	1·55	1·19	1·00	·88	·80	·73	·69	·64	

To find the value of $\frac{ds}{dt}$ when $s = 0{\cdot}03$, it is only necessary to obtain the mean value thus, $\frac{1}{2}(1{\cdot}19 + 1{\cdot}00) = 1{\cdot}095$.

Similarly, when $s = 0{\cdot}07$, $\frac{ds}{dt} = 0{\cdot}71$.

By subtracting consecutive values of $\frac{ds}{dt}$ and dividing by dt^2, values of $\frac{d^2s}{dt^2}$ may be obtained thus, $0{\cdot}0119 - 0{\cdot}0155 = -0{\cdot}0036$; hence when $t = 0{\cdot}03$, $\frac{d^2s}{dt^2} = -36$.

Ex. 2. On the indicator diagram of a gas engine the following are some readings of p pressure and v volume. The rate of reception of heat (if the gases are supposed to be receiving heat from an outside source and not from their own chemical action) is

$$\frac{dH}{dv} = p + \frac{k}{K-k}\left(p + v\frac{dp}{dv}\right),$$

where k and K, the important specific heats, are such that

$$\frac{k}{K-k} = 2 + \frac{pv}{300}.$$

v	2·0	2·1	2·2	2·3	2·4	2·5	2·6	2·7	2·8
p	84·5	110	176	215	231	234	226	213	202
v	2·9	3·0	3·1	3·2	3·3	3·4	3·5	3·6	
p	192	183	175	167	159	152	146	140	

Find $\frac{dH}{dv}$ at three places; where $v=2{\cdot}05$, $3{\cdot}55$, and at the place of highest pressure.

When $v=2{\cdot}05$, $\quad p=\frac{1}{2}(84{\cdot}5+110)=97{\cdot}25,$

$$dp=110-84{\cdot}5=25{\cdot}5, \quad \frac{dp}{dv}=255;$$

$$\frac{dH}{dv}=97{\cdot}25+\left(2+\frac{97{\cdot}25\times2{\cdot}05}{300}\right)(97{\cdot}25+2{\cdot}05\times255)$$

$$=97{\cdot}25+2{\cdot}6646\times620=1749{\cdot}3.$$

When $v=3{\cdot}55$, $\quad p=\frac{1}{2}(146+140)=143,$

$$\frac{dp}{dv}=-60;$$

$$\therefore \frac{dH}{dv}=143+\left(2+\frac{143\times3{\cdot}55}{300}\right)(143-3{\cdot}55\times60)$$

$$=143-3{\cdot}692\times70=-115{\cdot}4.$$

At the place of highest pressure, where $p=234$, $v=2{\cdot}5$ and $\frac{dp}{dv}=0$;

$$\therefore \frac{dH}{dv}=234+\left(2+\frac{234\times2{\cdot}5}{300}\right)\times234$$

$$=1158{\cdot}3.$$

Approximate integration.—If corresponding values of x and y are tabulated, where y is a quantity which depends upon x, then by tabulating $\frac{\delta y}{\delta x}$ for each interval and also tabulating $y\,\delta x$, an approximation to the value of the integral of y may be obtained.

Ex. 1. Given the following values of x and y, find by tabulation a table of values of $A=\int y\,dx$:

x	0	0·1	0·2	0·3	0·4	0·5	0·6
y	1·5663	1·6774	1·8002	1·9391	2·10	2·2918	2·5281

Find the area between $x=0$ and $x=0{\cdot}6$. Verify by using Simpson's Rule.

Values of δy are obtained by subtracting consecutive values of y thus, $1{\cdot}6774 - 1{\cdot}5663 = 0{\cdot}1111$ as $\delta x = 0{\cdot}1$; hence $\frac{\delta y}{\delta x} = 1{\cdot}111$. To obtain values of $y\,\delta x$ it is only necessary to find mean values of y and multiply by 0·1 thus, $\frac{1}{2}(1{\cdot}5663 + 1{\cdot}6774) \times 0{\cdot}1 = 0{\cdot}16218$. The values of $A = \int y\,dx$ are found by adding the values of $y\,\delta x$ thus, $0{\cdot}16218 + 0{\cdot}17388 = 0{\cdot}33606$. Other values may be obtained and tabulated as follows:

x	0	·1	·2	·3	·4	·5	·6
y	1·5663	1·6774	1·8002	1·9391	2·10	2·2918	2·5281
$\frac{\delta y}{\delta x}$	1·111, 1·228, 1·389, 1·609, 1·918, 2·363						
$y\,\delta x$	·16218, ·17388, ·18696, ·20195, ·21959, ·24099						
$\int y\,dx$	0, ·16218, ·33606, ·52302, ·72497, ·94456, 1·18555						

The area can also be obtained by Simpson's Rule, p. 199.

Sum of end ordinates = 4·0944,
,, even ,, = 5·9083,
,, odd ,, = 3·9002.

$$A = \frac{0{\cdot}1}{3}(4{\cdot}0944 + 4 \times 5{\cdot}9083 + 2 \times 3{\cdot}9002) = 1{\cdot}1842.$$

Ex. 2. The following values of x and y being given, tabulate $\delta y/\delta x$ and δA in each interval, δA being the area in the interval between two ordinates:

x	3	4	5	6	7	8
y	1·75	10·45	19·08	27·56	35·84	43·84
x	9	10	11	12	13	
y	51·5	58·78	65·61	71·93	77·71	

Show that the area $A = \int y\,dx$ is 424·49, by Simpson's Rule 424·58.

Average values.—The average value of $\sin^2 x$ from $x=0$ to $x=2\pi$ may be found as follows:

As $\cos 2x = 1 - 2\sin^2 x$, $\quad \therefore \sin^2 x = \frac{1}{2}(1 - \cos 2x)$,

$$\int \tfrac{1}{2}(1-\cos 2x)\,dx = \Big[\tfrac{1}{2}x - \tfrac{1}{4}\sin 2x\Big]_0^{2\pi} = \pi.$$

Hence $\quad$ average value = area $\div 2\pi = \frac{1}{2}$.

In a similar manner the average value of $\cos^2 x$ from $x=0$ to $x=2\pi$ is found to be $\frac{1}{2}$.

Ex. 1. If $y = a\sin qt$ and $x = b\sin(qt - c)$, where t is time and a, q, b and c are constants; if $q = 2\pi/T$, where T is the periodic time, find the average value of xy during the time T.

$$xy = ab\sin qt\sin(qt-c).$$

Let $qt = \theta$; $\quad \therefore xy = ab\sin\theta\sin(\theta - c)$

$$= ab\sin\theta(\sin\theta\cos c - \cos\theta\sin c)$$

$$= ab\sin^2\theta\cos c - ab\sin\theta\cos\theta\sin c.$$

The average value of $\sin^2\theta = \frac{1}{2}$. Average value of $\sin\theta\cos\theta$ is 0.

$\therefore$ average value of xy is $\frac{1}{2}ab\cos c$.

Solution of triangles (*continued*).—The solution of triangles has been explained in Chap. VIII.; in practice, however, it is better to use the simple trigonometrical ratios. The methods adopted may be seen from the following example; further exercises are given in Ex. XVII. and Ex. XVIII.

Ex. The three sides of a triangle are $a = 39{\cdot}38$, $b = 51{\cdot}38$, $c = 47{\cdot}48$. Find the remaining parts and the area. As in Fig. 46 (p. 166), take the longest side as base, let p denote the length of the perpendicular BD, $x = AD$ and $y = DC$. Then, from the triangles ABD, DBC,

$$x^2 + p^2 = 47{\cdot}48^2. \qquad y^2 + p^2 = 39{\cdot}38^2.$$

$$\therefore x^2 - y^2 = 86{\cdot}86 \times 8{\cdot}1\text{; also } x + y = 51{\cdot}38.$$

$$x - y = \frac{86{\cdot}86 \times 8{\cdot}1}{51{\cdot}38} = 13{\cdot}7.$$

Hence $\quad x = 32{\cdot}54, \quad y = 18{\cdot}84.$

$$\cos A = \frac{32{\cdot}54}{47{\cdot}48}. \quad \therefore A = 46^\circ\ 44'.$$

$$\cos C = \frac{18{\cdot}84}{39{\cdot}38}. \quad \therefore C = 61^\circ\ 25' \text{ and } B = 71^\circ\ 51'.$$

$$\text{Area} = \tfrac{1}{2}(47{\cdot}48 \times 51{\cdot}38 \sin 46^\circ\ 44') = 888{\cdot}2.$$

Miscellaneous Exercises XLVI.

1. If the volume V of a sphere is decreasing at the rate of 2 cub. ft. per sec., show that the rate of decrease of the radius is $1 \div 2\pi$ when r is 1 ft.

2. If the radius of a soap bubble increases at the rate 0·1 in. per sec.; find rate of increase of volume when the radius is 3·5 in.

3. Air is pumped into a spherical rubber bag at the rate of 5·5 cub. in. per sec.; find rate of increase of the diameter when the diameter is 7·5 in.

4. The slope of a curve is given by

$$\frac{dy}{dx}=(x^2-1)^2+4x; \text{ find } y \text{ and } \frac{d^2y}{dx^2}.$$

5. For what value of x will the slope of the curve $y=x^3$ have the value 12 ?

6. The slope of a curve is $\frac{dy}{dx}=x^3+2x+3$; if the curve passes through (4, 10), find its equation.

7. Find (i) the least value of x^2-x+1; (ii) the slope at $x=1{\cdot}4$.

8. The gradient of a curve is given by $(2-3x)$. If the curve passes through $(2, -4)$, find its equation.

9. If $\frac{dy}{dx}=\frac{20}{\sqrt{x}}$; find the increase in y when x increases from 4 to 9.

10. Find (i) the first and second derivatives of x^3-4x^2+5x-3, (ii) find the max. and min. values.

11. A pit is in the form of an inverted cone, the apex at a distance $1{\cdot}6r$ (where r is the radius at the surface). If the radius at the surface of the water is 5 ft., and increasing at 6 in. per sec., at what rate is the volume of water increasing ?

12. In a cylinder $r=h$ where r denotes the radius and h the height; find the dimensions so that a change of 1 in. in the radius produces a change of 200 cub. in. in the volume, h remaining constant.

13. If $V=5+7t$ where V is the velocity of a body at a time t sec.; find distance described from $t=3$, to $t=5$.

14. The displacement of a moving body at a time t is:

$$s=6-9t+2t^2.$$

Find the speed when $t=5$; also find time when speed is zero.

15. If s denotes the space described in t sec. of a moving body; find the velocity and acceleration when $t=3$.

(i) $s=10t^2-30t+6$; (ii) $s=t^4+3t^3-t^5+10$; $s=8{\cdot}2-6{\cdot}2t+4t^2$.

16. Explain how the operation denoted by $\frac{d^2y}{dx^2}$ is used to distinguish between the max. and min. values of a function. Determine the max. and min. values of:

$$y=8-2x+3x^2-x^3.$$

Table X.

NATURAL COTANGENTS.

[Numbers in difference columns to be subtracted, not added.]

	0′	5′	10′	15′	20′	25′	30′	35′	40′	45′	50′	55′	1	2	
0°	Inf.	687·5	343·8	229·2	171·9	137·5	114·6	98·22	85·94	76·39	68·75	62·50			
1	57·29	52·88	49·10	45·83	42·96	40·44	38·19	36·18	34·37	32·73	31·24	29·88			
2	28·64	27·49	26·43	25·45	24·54	23·69	22·90	22·16	21·47	20·82	20·21	19·63			
3	19·08	18·56	18·07	17·61	17·17	16·75	16·35	15·97	15·60	15·26	14·92	14·61			
4	14·30	14·01	13·73	13·46	13·20	12·95	12·71	12·47	12·25	12·03	11·83	11·62	Differen column cease to useful		
5	11·43	11·24	11·06	10·88	10·71	10·55	10·39	10·23	10·08	9·931	9·788	9·649			
6	9·514	9·383	9·255	9·131	9·010	8·892	8·777	8·665	8·556	8·449	8·345	8·243			
7	8·144	8·048	7·953	7·861	7·770	7·682	7·596	7·511	7·429	7·348	7·269	7·191			
8	7·115	7·041	6·968	6·897	6·827	6·758	6·691	6·625	6·561	6·497	6·435	6·374			
9	6·314	6·255	6·197	6·140	6·084	6·030	5·976	5·923	5·871	5·820	5·769	5·720			
10	5·671	5·623	5·576	5·530	5·485	5·440	5·396	5·352	5·309	5·267	5·226	5·185			
11	5·145	5 105	5·066	5·027	4·989	4·952	4·915	4·879	4·843	4·808	4·773	4·739			
12	4·705	4·671	4·638	4·606	4·574	4·542	4·511	4·480	4·449	4·419	4·390	4·360	6	12	1
13	4·331	4·303	4·275	4·247	4·219	4·192	4·165	4·139	4·113	4·087	4·061	4·036	5	11	1
14	4·011	3·986	3·962	3·938	3·914	3·890	3·867	3·844	3·821	3·798	3·776	3·754	5	9	1
15	3·732	3·710	3·689	3·668	3·647	3·626	3·606	3·586	3·566	3·546	3·526	3·507	4	8	1
16	3·487	3·468	3·450	3·431	3·412	3·394	3·376	3·358	3·340	3·323	3·305	3·288	4	7	1
17	3·271	2·254	3·237	3·221	3·204	3·188	3·172	3·156	3·140	3·124	3·108	3·093	3	6	1
18	3·078	3·063	3·047	3·033	3·018	3·003	2·989	2·974	2·960	2·946	2·932	2·918	3	6	
19	2·904	2·891	2·877	2·864	2·850	2·837	2·824	2·811	2·798	2·785	2·773	2·760	3	5	
20	2·747	2·735	2·723	2·711	2·699	2·687	2·675	2·663	2·651	2·639	2·628	2·616	2	5	
21	2·605	2·594	2·583	2·571	2·560	2·550	2·539	2·528	2·517	2·507	2·496	2·485	2	4	
22	2·475	4648	4545	4443	4342	4242	4142	4043	3945	3847	3750	3654	20	40	6
23	2·356	3464	3369	3276	3183	3090	2998	2907	2817	2727	2637	2549	18	37	5
24	2·246	2373	2286	2199	2113	2028	1943	1859	1775	1692	1609	1527	17	34	5
25	2·145	1364	1283	1203	1123	1044	0965	0887	0809	0732	0655	0579	16	31	4
26	2·050	0428	0353	0278	0204	0130	0057	1·9984	1·9912	1·9840	1·9768	1·9697	15	29	4
27	1·963	9556	9486	9416	9347	9278	9210	9142	9074	9007	8940	8873	14	27	4
28	1·881	8741	8676	8611	8546	8482	8418	8354	8291	8228	8165	8103	13	26	3
29	1·804	7979	7917	7856	7796	7735	7675	7615	7556	7496	7437	7370	12	24	3
30	1·732	7262	7205	7147	7090	7033	6977	6920	6864	6808	6753	6698	11	23	3
31	1·664	6588	6534	6479	6426	6372	6319	6265	6212	6160	6107	6055	11	21	3
32	1·600	5952	5900	5849	5798	5747	5697	5647	5597	5547	5497	5448	10	20	3
33	1·540	5350	5301	5253	5204	5156	5108	5061	5013	4966	4919	4872	10	19	2
34	1·483	4779	4733	4687	4641	4596	4550	4505	4460	4415	4370	4326	9	18	2
35	1·428	4237	4193	4150	4106	4063	4019	3976	3934	3891	3848	3806	9	17	2
36	1·376	3722	3680	3638	3597	3555	3514	3473	3432	3392	3351	3311	8	16	2
37	1·327	3230	3190	3151	3111	3072	3032	2993	2954	2915	2876	2838	8	16	2
38	1·280	2761	2723	2685	2647	2609	2572	2534	2497	2460	2423	2386	8	15	2
39	1·235	2312	2276	2239	2203	2167	2131	2095	2059	2024	1988	1953	7	14	2
40	1·192	1882	1847	1812	1778	1743	1708	1674	1640	1606	1571	1538	7	14	2
41	1·150	1470	1436	1403	1369	1336	1303	1270	1237	1204	1171	1139	7	13	2
42	1·111	1074	1041	1009	0977	0945	0913	0881	0850	0818	0786	0755	6	13	1
43	1·072	0692	0661	0630	0599	0569	0538	0507	0477	0446	0416	0385	6	12	1
44	1·036	0325	0295	0265	0235	0206	0176	0147	0117	0088	0058	0029	6	12	1

Table X.

NATURAL COTANGENTS.

[Numbers in difference columns to be subtracted, not added.]

0′	5′	10′	15′	20′	25′	30′	35′	40′	45′	50′	55′	1	2	3	4
1·0000	9971	9942	9913	9884	9856	9827	9798	9770	9742	9713	9685	6	11	17	23
0·9657	9629	9601	9573	9545	9517	9490	9462	9435	9407	9380	9352	6	11	17	22
0·9326	9298	9271	9244	9217	9190	9163	9137	9110	9083	9057	9030	5	11	16	21
0·9004	8978	8952	8925	8899	8873	8847	8821	8796	8770	8744	8718	5	10	16	21
0·8693	8667	8642	8617	8591	8566	8541	8516	8491	8466	8441	8416	5	10	15	20
0·8391	8366	8342	8317	8292	8268	8243	8219	8195	8170	8146	8122	5	10	15	20
0·8098	8074	8050	8026	8002	7978	7954	7931	7907	7883	7860	7836	5	9	14	19
0·7813	7789	7766	7743	7720	7696	7673	7650	7627	7604	7581	7558	5	9	14	18
0·7536	7513	7490	7467	7445	7422	7400	7377	7355	7332	7310	7288	5	9	14	18
0·7265	7243	7221	7199	7177	7155	7133	7111	7089	7067	7046	7024	4	9	13	18
0·7002	6980	6959	6937	6916	6894	6873	6851	6830	6809	6787	6766	4	8	13	17
0·6745	6724	6703	6682	6661	6640	6619	6598	6577	6556	6536	6515	4	8	13	17
0·6494	6473	6453	6432	6412	6391	6371	6350	6330	6310	6289	6269	4	8	12	16
0·6249	6228	6208	6188	6168	6148	6128	6108	6088	6068	6048	6028	4	8	12	16
0·6009	5989	5969	5949	5930	5910	5890	5871	5851	5832	5812	5793	4	8	12	16
0·5774	5754	5735	5715	5696	5677	5658	5639	5619	5600	5581	5562	4	8	12	15
0·5543	5524	5505	5486	5467	5448	5430	5411	5392	5373	5354	5336	4	8	11	15
0·5317	5298	5280	5261	5243	5224	5206	5187	5169	5150	5132	5114	4	7	11	15
0·5095	5077	5059	5040	5022	5004	4986	4968	4950	4931	4913	4895	4	7	11	15
0·4877	4859	4841	4823	4806	4788	4770	4752	4734	4716	4699	4681	4	7	11	14
0·4663	4645	4628	4610	4592	4575	4557	4540	4522	4505	4487	4470	4	7	10	14
0·4452	4435	4417	4400	4383	4365	4348	4331	4314	4296	4279	4262	3	7	10	14
0·4245	4228	4210	4193	4176	4159	4142	4125	4108	4091	4074	4057	3	7	10	13
0·4040	4023	4006	3990	3973	3956	3939	3922	3906	3889	3872	3855	3	7	10	13
0·3839	3822	3805	3789	3772	3755	3739	3722	3706	3689	3673	3656	3	7	10	13
0·3640	3623	3607	3590	3574	3558	3541	3525	3508	3492	3476	3460	3	6	10	13
0·3443	3427	3411	3395	3378	3362	3346	3330	3314	3298	3281	3265	3	6	10	13
0·3249	3233	3217	3201	3185	3169	3153	3137	3121	3105	3089	3073	3	6	10	13
0·3057	3041	3026	3010	2994	2978	2962	2946	2931	2915	2899	2883	3	6	9	13
0·2867	2852	2836	2820	2805	2789	2773	2758	2742	2726	2711	2695	3	6	9	13
0·2679	2664	2648	2633	2617	2602	2586	2571	2555	2540	2524	2509	3	6	9	12
0·2493	2478	2462	2447	2432	2416	2401	2385	2370	2355	2339	2324	3	6	9	12
0·2309	2293	2278	2263	2247	2232	2217	2202	2186	2171	2156	2141	3	6	9	12
0·2126	2110	2095	2080	2065	2050	2035	2019	2004	1989	1974	1959	3	6	9	12
0·1944	1929	1914	1899	1883	1868	1853	1838	1823	1808	1793	1778	3	6	9	12
0·1763	1748	1733	1718	1703	1688	1673	1658	1644	1629	1614	1599	3	6	9	12
0·1584	1569	1554	1539	1524	1509	1495	1480	1465	1450	1435	1420	3	6	9	12
0·1405	1391	1376	1361	1346	1331	1317	1302	1287	1272	1257	1243	3	6	9	12
0·1228	1213	1198	1184	1169	1154	1139	1125	1110	1095	1080	1066	3	6	9	12
0·1051	1036	1022	1007	0992	0978	0963	0948	0934	0919	0904	0890	3	6	9	12
0·0875	0860	0846	0831	0816	0802	0787	0772	0758	0743	0729	0714	3	6	9	12
0·0699	0685	0670	0655	0641	0626	0612	0597	0582	0568	0553	0539	3	6	9	12
0·0524	0509	0495	0480	0466	0451	0437	0422	0407	0393	0378	0364	3	6	9	12
0·0349	0335	0320	0306	0291	0276	0262	0247	0233	0218	0204	0189	3	6	9	12
0·0175	0160	0145	0131	0116	0102	0087	0073	0058	0044	0029	0015	3	6	9	12

17. A rectangular box without a lid, 9 in. long, is to be made of sheet metal; its volume to be 81 cub. in. Find dimensions when the least amount of material is used.

18. An open cylindrical tank, made of sheet iron with a flat base, is to hold 20,000 gallons of water. Find the dimensions when the least amount of metal is used.

19. A rectangular playground, area 800 sq. yd., is to be enclosed by three walls, using an existing wall for one side; find lengths of sides for least cost.

20. A lidless box is made from a rectangular piece of sheet metal 5 ft. by 4 ft. by cutting small squares out of each corner and bending remaining pieces through a right angle. Find the size of the squares when the box has the greatest volume.

21. The consumption of petrol is found to be proportional to $\left(\frac{V^3}{3} - 6V^2\right)$. Find the speed V at which the consumption is least.

22. A cylinder made of sheet metal is required to hold 300 gallons of water; find the dimensions for the least amount of material, (i) no cover, (ii) closed top and bottom.

23. The volume of water in a hemispherical vat of radius r ft. is $\pi(rx^2 - \frac{1}{3}x^3)$, where x is the depth. Water is poured in at the rate of 5 cub. ft. per min. Find the rate of increase of x when $r=6$ ft., $x=2{\cdot}5$ ft.

24. In t sec. after its projection from the ground, a bullet reaches a height h given by $h=130t-16t^2$. What is $\frac{dh}{dt}$? Find (i) value of $\frac{dh}{dt}$ at $t=1{\cdot}2$, $t=4{\cdot}7$. (ii) Find the time to reach the greatest height and to reach the ground again.

25. In the following *differential equations* given $\frac{dy}{dx}$, find y:

(i) $4x^2 - 3x + 4$; (ii) $4x^4 + a^4 - 4a^2x^2 + 2$;

(iii) $ac - bx^2 + cx^3 - x^4 + 6$; (iv) $x(2x-1)^2$;

(v) $(x-4)(x+2)$; (vi) $3x^2 + \frac{3}{x^2}$.

26. Given $\frac{dy}{dx} = 2x - 6x^2$, find y. If when $x=5$ the value of the function is 390, find the value when $x=8$.

27. Show, by integration, that the volume of that part of a sphere of radius 10 in., cut off by a plane at 3 in. from the centre, is $\frac{1127\pi}{3}$.

28. Find the area between the axes and the curve $y=20+3x-2x^2$ from $x=0$ to $x=4$.

29. Determine the function of x which has $6x+4$ for its derivative and is 40 when $x=3$.

ANSWERS.

Exercises I., p. 10.

1. $4x(x^2+1)\{(x^2+1)^2-x^2\}$; 3·5174. 2. 0·236.

3. $\frac{a^{\frac{3}{2}}}{8}+\frac{ab^{\frac{1}{2}}}{12}-\frac{a^{\frac{1}{2}}b}{18}-\frac{b^{\frac{3}{2}}}{27}$; 3·146. 4. $\frac{14x}{1-9x^2}$; $2\frac{1}{3}$.

5. $\frac{x+2}{x^2+1}$; 0·5590. 6. 5·268. 7. 3·46.

8. 0·2397. 11. 0·2236; 0·0556. 12. $\frac{2}{ab}$.

13. 1·0557. 14. $8a^3$. 15. $\frac{6\sqrt{x}+3x}{1+\sqrt{x}-2x}$; 4·902.

17. $\frac{4}{x^2-1}$; 0·6188. 18. $-\frac{c}{e}$. 19. 1. 20. $(4x-3y)(3x-4y)$.

21. $(a^2+ab+b^2)(a^2-ab+b^2)(a^4-a^2b^2+b^4)$.

22. $(x^2+y^2+xy+1)(x^2+y^2-xy-1)$.

24. $(4x-5)(5x+6)$. 25. $(2y+7)(x+3)$. 26. $(5x-7)(x-3a)$.

27. $(x-1)^2(x^2+2x+3)$. 28. a. 29. $x+1$.

30. 0·9659. 31. 9. 34. $\frac{1}{x-2}+\frac{1}{x-3}$.

35. $\frac{4}{1-3x}-\frac{5}{1-2x}$. 36. $\frac{1}{x-1}-\frac{1}{x+2}-\frac{3}{(x+2)^2}$. 37. $\frac{2}{x+3}-\frac{1}{x-5}$.

38. $\frac{2}{x+1}-\frac{1}{x-2}$. 39. $\frac{4}{x-3}-\frac{3}{x+7}$. 40. $\frac{3}{x-3}+\frac{2}{x-4}$.

41. $\frac{3x}{x-2}+\frac{2}{x-4}$. 42. $\frac{2x}{x-1}+\frac{3}{x-2}-\frac{4}{x-3}$. 43. $\frac{1}{x-1}-\frac{4}{x+1}$.

44. $(x-1{\cdot}9)(x+2{\cdot}3)$. 45. $-(a-b)(b-c)(c-a)$.

46. $(x-20)(x+26)$. 47. $(x+2\sqrt{6})(x-2\sqrt{6})$.

48. $21(2x+5y)(2x-5y)$. 49. $(x-5{\cdot}68)(x-3{\cdot}24)$. 50. $\frac{2}{x-3}$.

51. $\frac{(x+2)(x-1)}{x^2-2}$. 52. $\frac{1-x}{(1-3x)(1+x)}$; $\frac{1}{2(1-3x)}+\frac{1}{2(1+x)}$.

53. $\frac{4}{x^2-1}$, 0·619. 54. $\frac{7}{3x-5}-\frac{5}{4x+3}$.

Exercises II., p. 20.

1. $\frac{7\pi}{32}$. 2. 47° 45′. 3. $\frac{4\pi}{3}$, 120°.

4. 1·0872, 0·9128. 5. 435·7. 6. 0·3927 miles.

7. 0·7431, −0·6947, −0·6745. 8. 0·2588, −0·6691, 0·3249.

9.

angle	23°	123°	233°	312°	383°
sine	0·3907	0·8387	−0·7986	−0·7431	0·3907
cosine	0·9205	−0·5446	−0·6018	0·6691	0·9205
tangent	0·4245	−1·5399	1·3270	−1·1106	0·4245

6·702 radians. **11.** 43° 35′, 136° 25′.
13. 71° 36·6′ **14.** 31·42, 47·13. **15.** 5·237 ft. per sec.
17. 0·6283. **18.** 0·3704, 21° 13′. **19.** 687·6 ft.

Exercises III., p. 35.

1. $\frac{63}{65}$; $\frac{16}{65}$. **2.** $\frac{63}{65}$; $-\frac{16}{65}$. **6.** 0·6561. **7.** 0·9898; $\frac{1}{2}$.

8. 0·28; 0·96. **10.** $\frac{\sqrt{7}}{4}$; $\frac{\sqrt{7}}{3}$; $\frac{3\sqrt{7}}{7}$. **12.** Infinity. **19.** 18·72.

20. 0·39; 112° 52′. **22.** 4·359. **26.** $-\frac{7}{25}$; $\frac{24}{25}$; $\frac{2}{5}\sqrt{5}$.

Exercises IV., p. 41.

1. 60°, 120°. **2.** 45°, 135°. **3.** 30°, 150°.
4. 45°, 71° 33′. **5.** 120°. **6.** 60°, 15°, etc.
7. (i) 52° 1′, 127° 58′; (ii) 134° 45′; (iii) 70° 52′, 160° 52′.
8. 45°, 60°. **9.** 70° 32′. **10.** 120°, 0°.
11. 30°, 60°. **12.** 30°, 150°. **13.** 45°, 60°.
14. 90°, 45°. **15.** 216° 52′. **16.** 270°.
17. 69° 18′. **18.** (i) 120°; (ii) 135°; (iii) 13° 20′, 166° 40′.
19. 45°, 60°, 120°, 135°. **20.** −0·4446, −0·4446.
21. 28° 9′, 61° 51′, 118° 9′, 151° 51′.
22. 71° 2′, 108° 58′, 251° 2′, 288° 58′.
23. $A=39°\ 48'$, $B=27°\ 54'$. **24.** 38° 20′. **25.** 29° 17′.
26. 45°, $n\pi \pm \frac{\pi}{4}$. **27.** 122° 18′. **28.** 54°, 126°, 198°, 342°.
30. (*a*) 60°; (*b*) 30°. **31.** 30°. **32.** 9° 53′, 19° 10′.
34. 19° 9′. **36.** 7° 54′. **37.** $\frac{\pi}{4}$, $\frac{\pi}{5}$, $\frac{2\pi}{3}$.

Exercises V., p. 47.

1. $-\frac{3}{16}$. **3.** $x^{\frac{3}{n}} - x^{-\frac{3}{n}}$. **4.** $x^6 + \frac{1}{x^6} + 3\left(x^2 + \frac{1}{x^2}\right)$.

5. $3 + 2x^{-\frac{1}{4}}y^{\frac{1}{4}} + x^{-\frac{1}{2}}y^{\frac{1}{2}} + 2x^{\frac{1}{4}}y^{-\frac{1}{4}} + x^{\frac{1}{2}}y^{-\frac{1}{2}}$. **6.** $a^3bc^{\frac{1}{6}}$.

7. $\frac{1}{b^3}$. **8.** $x=2$, $y=3$. **9.** (*b*) $x^2y^{\frac{3}{2}}$; (*c*) $x^{-\frac{1}{6}}$.

10. $x^{\frac{1}{4}}y^{\frac{3}{4}}(x^{\frac{3}{4}}-4x^{\frac{1}{2}}y^{\frac{3}{4}}+16x^{\frac{1}{4}}y^{\frac{3}{2}}-64y^{\frac{9}{4}})$. **11.** $a^{\frac{3}{2}}+b+c^{\frac{3}{4}}-3a^{\frac{1}{2}}b^{\frac{1}{3}}c^{\frac{1}{4}}$.

12. 12. **13.** 1·285. **14.** $a^{-\frac{27}{20}}b^{-\frac{7}{12}}$.

15. $a^{\frac{11}{12}}b^2$. **16.** (i) $\left(\frac{p}{q}\right)^{\frac{2}{3}}+\left(\frac{p}{q}\right)^{\frac{1}{3}}+\left(\frac{q}{p}\right)^{\frac{1}{3}}+\left(\frac{q}{p}\right)^{\frac{2}{3}}$; $x^{-1}y^{\frac{1}{6}}$.

17. x^2. **18.** $a^{\frac{4}{3}}+a^{\frac{2}{3}}b^{\frac{3}{2}}+b^3$; 84·96. **19.** 25·2.

Exercises VI., p. 62.

1. 0·5540. **2.** 3·123, 1704. **3.** 12.
4. 0·3722. **5.** (i) 0·4722; (ii) 0·9557. **6.** $\frac{9}{32}$.
7. 15·5. **8.** 1·7022. **9.** 55·16.
10. 303. **11.** $6·504\times10^5$. **12.** 3·514, 9·02.
13. 1·027. **14.** 1133. **15.** 245·5, 280.
16. $p=0·4286$, 0·3952, 0·3642; $v=3$, 2·806, 2·643.
17. 14407, 16604, 18557, 18815. **18.** 1·722, 0·0198.
19. $\sqrt{10}$. **20.** 39·98. **21.** 254·6.
22. 74·98. **23.** $x=0·9625$, $y=0·5668$.
24. 0·5. **25.** 2·078. **26.** 0·2184, 0·2993.
27. 3·17. **28.** 2·885. **29.** $29·2\times10^6$.
30. 1·613. **31.** 0·9895. **32.** 0·1556, 0·2100, 1·1810.
33. (i) 0·4315; (ii) $\bar{4}·8596$; (iii) $\bar{1}·8210$. **35.** −0·8899.
36. $G=·4516$, $D=3$. **37.** 1·0572. **38.** −3·221.
39. (i) $V=48·5$, $v=59·28$; (ii) $V=76·92$, $v=98$. **40.** −0·9266.
41. (i) 33280; (ii) 33570; (iii) 38410;
(iv) 33440; (v) 44910; (vi) 40500.
42. 31518 gallons. **43.** −9·897. **44.** 50·9443.
45. 133·6. **46.** 2·971. **47.** 1·8136, 4·255, ∞. **48.** 5·491.
49. (i) 3·786; (ii) 0·2641. **50.** $1·737\times10^{-6}$.
51. 0·4338, 0·6015. **52.** $c=816$, $y=866$, $x=284·1$. **53.** 0·04467, 2.

Exercises VII., p. 71.

1. 30. **2.** 11. **3.** $1\frac{1}{2}$. **4.** 13. **5.** $3\frac{1}{2}$. **6.** $\frac{2}{3}$.
7. 106. **8.** 111. **9.** $\frac{1}{3}$. **10.** −4. **11.** 3. **12.** 1.
13. 7. **14.** $4\frac{2}{3}$. **15.** $\frac{7}{8}$. **16.** 4. **17.** $\frac{a^2+c^2}{2c}$.
18. 9. **19.** $\frac{1}{ab}$. **20.** $\frac{a^2+b^2+c^2}{a+b+c}$. **21.** $\frac{a}{2}$. **22.** ab.
23. $\frac{ab+bc-b^2}{a}$. **24.** 5, 0. **25.** −4. **26.** $\frac{4}{7}$. **27.** 3

Exercises VIII., p. 74.

1. 2 hours. 2. 120, 80. 3. 25, 24.
4. A, 45; B, 60. 5. A's share, £4; B's, £6; C's, £480.
6. 42. 7. £3. 8. 60 miles.
9. 4 miles per hour. 10. £175, £225. 11. £411, rate 10·95%.
12. £7. 10*s*., £9., £7. 4*s*. 13. £5000. 14. £1050.

Exercises IX., p. 81.

1. 13, 11. 2. 10, 2. 3. 3, 6.
4. $x=3,\ y=2,\ z=5$. 5. $\frac{11}{12}, \frac{1}{11}$. 6. 9, 12.
7. 8, 12. 8. $\frac{p-a}{7}, \frac{p-b}{4}$. 9. 6, 9.
10. 2, 3. 11. $2\frac{1}{7}, \frac{3}{7}$. 12. $x=1, y=-1, z=6$.
13. 0·02, 2·9. 14. am^2, $2am$. 15. $\frac{3}{2}b, -\frac{a}{2}$. 16. a, b.
17. $\frac{a^2+b^2}{bef+acd}, \frac{a^2+b^2}{bcd-aef}$. 18. $\frac{b(b-a)}{a+b}, \frac{a(a+b)}{a-b}$.
19. $x=1, y=2, z=3$. 20. $3a, -2b$.
21. $x=\frac{n(a-b-c)}{a-3b+c},\ y=\frac{n(b-c-a)}{a-3b+c},\ z=\frac{n(c-a-b)}{a-3b+c}$.
22. $x=a,\ y=2a,\ z=3a$.
23. (i) $\frac{p}{4m^2}, \frac{p}{2m}$; (ii) $x=12,\ y=-60,\ z=60$.

Exercises X., p. 87.

1. $\frac{31}{43}$. 2. £11·018. 4. $\frac{5}{3}$. 5. £10, £5, £1000.
6. 120 lbs. 7. £1666$\frac{2}{3}$, £1000, £333$\frac{1}{3}$. 8. $76\frac{1}{2}, 202\frac{1}{2}$.
9. 4. 10. £411, 10·95%. 11. $\frac{3}{10}, \frac{7}{10}$.
12. 325, 175. 13. 9. 14. 7062.

Exercises XI., p. 98.

1. 4, 1. 2. 4, 2. 3. $-4, -3$. 4. 2·73, 4·35.
5. 2·74, 3·35. 6. 2, -12. 7. 3, $1\frac{10}{11}$. 8. ± 3.
9. $-3\pm\sqrt{44}$. 10. $\pm\frac{3\sqrt{34}}{34}$. 11. $\pm\sqrt{\frac{(m-n)}{m+n}}$.
12. $0, \pm\sqrt{\frac{a^2+b^2}{2}}$. 15. $\frac{5}{3}, -\frac{3}{5}$. 16. $\frac{3}{2}, \frac{2}{3}, -2, -\frac{1}{2}$.

17. $x=3, -1, y=4, -2$. **18.** $4{\cdot}2426, -14{\cdot}142$.

19. x^2-6x+7. **20.** $0, 5a, -a$. **21.** $2{\cdot}5, -1, \frac{3\pm\sqrt{17}}{4}$.

22. $\pm\sqrt{3}, \pm 1$. **23.** $1, 2a-1$. **24.** $\frac{5}{2}\pm\frac{\sqrt{65}}{2}$.

25. $1+\sqrt{2}\pm\sqrt{(2+2\sqrt{2})}$. **26.** $-2\pm\sqrt{10}, -2\pm\sqrt{3}$.

27. $0, -\frac{243}{193}$. **28.** $\pm\sqrt{23}-1, \pm\sqrt{7}-1$.

29. $\pm\frac{\sqrt{4ac+c^2}+c}{2(a+b)}$. **30.** $4{\cdot}3$ or $-1{\cdot}376$. **31.** $20{\cdot}06-1{\cdot}86$.

32. $x=12$ or 3, $y=6$, $z=3$ or 12. **33.** $1, \frac{1\pm\sqrt{17}}{2}$. **34.** $3{\cdot}42, 1{\cdot}75$.

35. $\pm\sqrt{2}$. **36.** $\pm\frac{1}{2}\sqrt{10}, 0$. **37.** $1, \frac{3\pm\sqrt{5}}{2}$.

38. $3{\cdot}217, 2{\cdot}233$. **39.** $\sqrt{3}\pm 1=2{\cdot}732, 0{\cdot}732$.

40. $x^2-14x-351=0$. **42.** $1{\cdot}932, 0{\cdot}5176$.

Exercises XII., p. 101.

1. $x=5, 1, y=1, 5$. **2.** $x=6\frac{1}{3}, 3, y-2\frac{5}{6}, \frac{1}{2}$.

3. $x=5, -\frac{78}{19}, y=4, -\frac{118}{57}$. **4.** $x=6{\cdot}8, 4, y=-5{\cdot}4, 3$.

5. $x=\pm 3, y=\pm 1$. **6.** $x=4, 3, \mp 2\sqrt{6}-6$; $y=3, 4, \pm 2\sqrt{6}-6$.

7. $x=5, \frac{3}{4}$; $y=3, -\frac{5}{4}$. **8.** $x=3, -4\frac{1}{3}$; $y=\frac{1}{2}, -3\frac{1}{6}$.

9. $x=\pm 7, \pm\sqrt{51}$; $y=2$; 0. **10.** $x=8, y=\pm\frac{5}{2}\sqrt{7}$.

11. $x=3, 1{\cdot}5$; $y=-1, 5{\cdot}75$.

12. $x=\frac{1}{3}, -\frac{1}{8}$; $y=\frac{1}{4}, -\frac{1}{7}, z=\frac{1}{6}, \frac{1}{28}$.

13. $x=\frac{b^2}{\sqrt[3]{b^3-a^3}}, y=\frac{a^3-b^3}{b\sqrt[3]{b^3-a^3}}, z=-\frac{a^3}{b\sqrt[3]{b^3-a^3}}$.

14. $x=5, y=4$ or 3, $z=3, 4$. **15.** $x=1, -3, y=3, -5, z=3\frac{1}{2}, -5\frac{1}{2}$.

16. $x=0{\cdot}5, 0{\cdot}4, y=0{\cdot}4, 0{\cdot}5$.

17. $x=\pm\sqrt{\frac{9\pm\sqrt{33}}{12}}$; $y=\pm\sqrt{\frac{15\pm\sqrt{33}}{12}}$.

Exercises XIII., p. 107.

1. 15*s.* per dozen. **2.** 9, 16. **3.** $x=16, -3$; $y=3, -16$.

4. 108 yds., 45 yds. **5.** £100. **6.** 5 ft.

7. 12 and 8. **8.** 13 and 7. **9.** 12 in., 27 in.

10. $x=\frac{5}{2}(\pm\sqrt{3}-1)$, $y=\frac{5}{2}(\mp\sqrt{3}+3)$. **11.** 27, 54, 81.

Exercises XIV., p. 112.

1. 16, -8, 4. **2.** 1, $\frac{1 \pm \sqrt{17}}{2}$. **3.** $-0{\cdot}5$, 1, $0{\cdot}25$.
4. $2a$, a. **5.** 5, -2, -3. **6.** $-3{\cdot}732$, $-0{\cdot}268$, 4.
7. 11, -5, -6. **8.** 7, $\frac{5 \pm \sqrt{21}}{2}$. **9.** 1·13.
10. 2. **11.** 2·0945. **12.** 2·327.
13. 1·44354. **14.** 3·9575. **15.** 4, -2.
16. 1·73. **17.** 1·203, 2·622, $-0{\cdot}825$. **18.** 2·012.

Exercises XV., p. 150.

1. (i) $R=1{\cdot}42+4{\cdot}66E$; (ii) $E=0{\cdot}295R+0{\cdot}87$;
(iii) $E=0{\cdot}062R+0{\cdot}132$; (iv) $E=0{\cdot}109R+4$.
2. $c=8{\cdot}5$, $d=-30$; $F=8{\cdot}5R-30$. **3.** 1686.
6. $n=1{\cdot}042$, $pu^{1{\cdot}042}=\text{const.}$ **7.** $n=1{\cdot}35$, $c=441$, $p=59{\cdot}77$.
8. $a=3{\cdot}25$, $b=0{\cdot}2$, $y=3{\cdot}25+0{\cdot}2x^2$. **9.** $c=2{\cdot}6$, $n=2{\cdot}546$.
10. 102, 14700. **11.** $a=2$, $b=0{\cdot}05$, $y=2+0{\cdot}05x^2$.
12. $a=2$, $b=-0{\cdot}2$, $c=0{\cdot}05$. **13.** 1·2, 3; $y=3x^{1{\cdot}2}$.
14. $n=1{\cdot}172$, $pv^{1{\cdot}172}$. **16.** $A=47{\cdot}6B-300$; 0·52 %.
17. $a=0{\cdot}3$, $b=2{\cdot}5$, $y=0{\cdot}3x^2+2{\cdot}5$, 71·4.
18. $A=0{\cdot}5$, $b=-1$, $y=0{\cdot}5e^{-x}$.
19. (*a*) £3675, (*b*) £2812·5, (*c*) £2860. **20.** 7440, 540.
21. (i) $a=32{\cdot}26$, $b=-4844$, $n=-0{\cdot}94$; (ii) $a=32{\cdot}04$, $b=-7200$.
22. $13{\cdot}08h=v^{1{\cdot}8}$. **23.** 14790, 14360, 13540.
24. $a=2{\cdot}5$, $b=0{\cdot}25$, $n=0{\cdot}35$. **25.** $c=7{\cdot}6$, $n=0{\cdot}4229$, $a=0{\cdot}1669$.
27. 1590 sq. ft. **28.** $A^2=a^2+b^2$, $\tan e=\frac{b}{a}$.
30. values of y are: 2·45, 3·656, 5·453, 8·136, 12·13, 18·1, 27·01, 40·29, 60·12: aver. val. = 17·89, slope at $x=4$ is 4·854.
33. 247400 ft.-lbs., 73·4 ft. per sec. **34.** 8 miles per hour.
37. 0·5885, 3·0965. **38.** $\mu=0{\cdot}000125V^{0{\cdot}56}$.

Exercises XVI., p. 161.

1. 3·021, 41° 37′, 53° 23′. **2.** 1·814 in., 2·446 in. **3.** 255·5.
4. 97° 44′, 31° 16′. **5.** 519·6, 854·2. **6.** 40·44 ft. **7.** 89·66 yds.
8. 1 : 0·8318. **10.** 695 yds., 1·62 min. **11.** 117·7 ft.

Exercises XVII., p. 168.

1. $A=60°$, $B=45°$, $C=75°$. 3. 53° 8′, 0·54 sq. ft.
4. 55° 46′. 5. 73° 24′. 6. 0·5999, 73° 44′.
7. 109° 28′, 38° 58′, 31° 34′. 8. 90°, 210 sq. ft. 9. 0·7670, 74° 58′.
10. 42°. 11. 41° 24′. 12. 37° 22′.
13. 38° 56′. 14. 50° 28′. 15. 34° 8′, 4114 sq. ft.
16. $A=51°$ 54′, $B=104°$ 44′, $C=23°$ 22′. 18. 36° 52′, 53° 8′, 90°.
19. 64° 38′, 1·538 ft. 20. 0·6 ft. 21. 5314 sq. ft.
22. 1959 sq. ft. 23. 454·1 sq. ft. 24. 28·45 sq. in.
25. 67° 24′, 59° 28′, 53° 8′. 26. 29·4°, 31·9°, 118·7°.

Exercises XVIII., p. 173.

1. $B=72°$ 31′, $C=56°$. 2. $B=101°$ 29′, $C=14°$ 11′. 3. $\frac{\sqrt{3}}{12}$.
4. $B=79°$ 6′, $C=40°$ 54′. 5. $B=71°$ 40′, $C=48°$ 20′.
6. 4° 56′, 168° 27′. 7. 93°, 27°, 9·54. 8. 108° 58′, 6° 2′.
9. 6 sq. ft. 10. 72° 12′, 47° 48′. 11. 23·68, 826·6, 111° 24′, 36° 36′.
12. 97·3°, 28·7°, 595 ft. 13. 128·3°, 18·7°.

Exercises XIX., p. 175.

1. 68° 25′, 395·6 ft. 2. 516·3, 3003.
3. 32·62 ft., 10°, 151° 23′; 138 ft., 28° 37′, 132° 46′.
4. 81° 45′. 5. 60° 55′.
6. $c=6·68$, $B=125°$ 49′, $C=1°$ 52′; $c=196·9$, $B=54°$ 11′, $C=73°$ 30′.
7. $B=51°$ 17′ or 128° 43′. 8. $B=41°$ 42′ or 138° 18′.
10. $C=62°$ 31′ or 117° 29′, $A=102°$ 18′ or 47° 20′.
11. $C=45°$ or 135°, $B=105°$ or 15°, $b=\sqrt{3}\pm1$. 12. 32° 26′.
13. $C=60°$ or 120°, $a=300$ or 86·6, $A=90°$ or 30°.
(iii) No. $C=90°$, 173·2.

Exercises XX., p. 182.

1. 105 ft. 2. 488·5 ft. 3. $BP=240·9$ ft., $BAQ=29°$ 4′.
4. 367·8 ft. 5. 1701 ft. 7. 86·6 ft. 10. 624·7 yds.
11. 1·152. 12. 106 ft. 13. 229·7 yds. 14. 114·41 ft.
15. $h=0·7432l$. 16. 1000 ft. 17. 27·8 yds. 18. 73·2 ft.
19. 0·8166 miles. 20. 1034 ft. 21. 8769 yds.
22. 56·5 ft., 94 ft. 23. 114 ft. 27. 0·4803 : 1.

Exercises XXI., p. 189.

1. 18 yds. **2.** £68. 17*s*. 4·6*d*. **3.** 4·686 ft.
4. 31·11, 62·22. **5.** 1428 sq. ft. **6.** 3 ac. 1 r.
7. 374·122 sq. ft. **8.** 10 ft. 6 in. **9.** 210 sq. in.
10. 109·81 sq. ft. **12.** 3·338, 3·343, mean 3·340 acres.
13. 6 chains, $2\frac{1}{2}$ chains. **14.** 721721 sq. ft. **15.** 892·92 yds.
16. 1764. **17.** 2·576 acres. **18.** 7 ch. 50 links.
19. 6 ac. 3 r. **20.** 3·849 yds.

Exercises XXII., p. 199.

1. 8·168, 1·3 ft. **2.** 468 ft. **3.** 112·6 sq. in.
4. 1·819 ft. **5.** 2240·14 sq. ft. **6.** 104·7 ft.
7. 10·5 ft. **8.** 143 yds. **9.** 183·26 sq. in.
10. 20·106 sq. ft. **11.** 15·187 ft. **12.** 12 in.
13. 11·55 ft. **14.** 333 sq. ft. **15.** £164. 2*s*.
16. 22·8 ins. **17.** 15 ft. **18.** 23·22 sq. in.
19. $a:b=3{\cdot}414:1$. **20.** £833. 17*s*. 3*d*. **21.** 1612·5 sq. ft.
22. 2732·4 sq. ft. **23.** 5373 sq. ft. **24.** 1808 sq. ft.
25. 14400. **26.** 14·95 sq. in. **27.** 32·78, 32·598.
28. $293{\cdot}1 \times 2$ sq. ft. **29.** 169·85 sq. ft.

Exercises XXIII., p. 205.

1. (i) 402·176 sq. ft., 1608·704 cub. ft.; (ii) 2·125 ft.
(iii) 678·5 lbs.; (iv) 280 ft.
2. 1812·1 cub. in., 905·52 sq. in., 21·7.
3. (i) 402·2 sq. in., 402·2 cub. in., 104·6 lbs.; (ii) 0·3 in.; (iii) 30 ft.
4. 190·76 sq. ft., 187·1 cub. ft. **5.** 2·18 lbs.
6. 7392 lbs. **7.** 122·4 lbs. **8.** 2300 cub. in., 598·1 lbs.
9. 879·8 sq. in., 754·1 cub. in. **10.** 20.
11. 3·398 in. **12.** 19736640. **13.** 165·748.
14. 37·65 hrs. **15.** 95·5 tons. **16.** 53·56 sq. in.

Exercises XXIV., p. 211.

1. 10 ft., 400 sq. ft. **2.** 47·124 cub. in., 54·95 sq. in.
3. 6 ft. **4.** 278·6 cub. in., 114·8 lbs.
5. 138·5 sq. in., 96 cub. in., 1·83 lbs.
6. 924 cub. ft. **7.** 19 : 7 : 1. **8.** £5. 10*s*.
9. 14·4 ft. **10.** 11315·9 cub. in.; 3464·4 sq. ft.
11. 173·2 cub. in. **12.** 125·7 sq. ft.

Exercises XXV., p. 215.

1. (i) 491 sq. in., 1023 cub. in.; (ii) 7·444 in.; (iii) 3·385 in.
2. 213·6 sq. in., 592·8 cub. in.
3. 1756 cub. in., 570·2 sq. in., 1117·8 sq. in.
4. 8·502 ft.
5. 59·57 cub. ft.
6. 648000.
7. 2723 cub. in.
8. 0·5198 in., 0·828 in.

Miscellaneous Exercises XXVI., p. 223.

1. 38·5 sq. in., 9·629 sq. in.
2. 2130·7 sq. ft., 12016·58 cub. ft.
3. 19·43 lbs.
4. 1232 cub. ft.
5. 1256·63 sq. ft., 5321 cub. ft.
6. 16·18.
7. 171·7 sq. ft., 249·4 cub. ft.
8. 4210 grams.
9. 151·78 cub. ft.
10. 1·83 to 1.
11. 10 ft.
12. 36372 cub. ft.
13. 4·243 cm.
14. 4 in.
15. 2267 lbs.
16. 16 in.
17. 11·62 in.
18. 1·628 in.
19. 11·1 in.
20. 3 : 5.
21. 2087·96 lbs.
22. 100·6 lbs.
23. 24·25 ft.
24. 58·91 sq. in.
25. $217\frac{7}{33}$ yds., 7·7 lbs.
26. 99·9 sq. ft.
27. 4·06 in.
28. 0·2209 cub. in.
29. 12 lbs. 6·6 oz.
30. 3412 lbs.
31. 15·52 ft., 4774 cub. ft.
32. 50480 cub. ft. 22·93 ft.
33. 10 ft.

Exercises XXVII., p. 241.

1. $z=1·732$.
2. 7·071, 64° 54′, 55° 33′, 45°.
3. 2·45.
4. 7·071, 45°, 53° 8′, 0·4242, 0·5657, 0·7071.
5. 1·75, 2·082, 1·268.
6. 3·4, 0·5882, 0·4413, 0·6764.
7. 8·775, 0·4559, 0·5699, 0·6839.
8. $x=1·348$, $y=3·728$, $z=3·078$.
9. 3·776, 0·5041, 0·6101, −0·6101.
10. 14·45, 39·71, 90·63.
11. 3·283, 0·4568, 0·7004, 0·5483.
12. 3·624, 9·959, 16·96
13. 8·55, 23·49, 43·3, 80° 3′, 62°.
14. 9·063, 4·226.
15. 5, 53° 8′.
16. 9·434, 58°.
17. 96·59, 25·88.
18. 46·98, 17·1.

Exercises XXVIII., p. 261.

1. 20·7 lbs., 121° 15′, 4·43.
2. 39·4, 188° 49′; 114, 277°.
3. 328·5, 101°·3, 2·12; 257, 60°, 1·7.
4. 3·9, 61°.
5. 11·35 knots, 12° 15′.
6. 30° N. of E., 47° N. of W.
7. (*a*) 14·5, 73°; (*b*) 23, 27°.

8. $a^2=b^2+c^2-2bc\cos\alpha$, $a^2+b^2+c^2-2ab\gamma-2bc\cos\alpha-2ac\cos\beta$.
9. 6·75 knots, 21° S. of E.
10. (*a*) S.E., (*b*) 23° E. of N., (*c*) N., (*d*) 23° E. of S., (*e*) no wind.
14. 30·47, 173° 52′. **15.** $A=22{\cdot}4$, $B=29{\cdot}6$. **16.** $\alpha=49°$, $\beta=141°$.
17. $C=4$, 46, $\gamma=2{\cdot}5°$, 80°. **18.** 25, 45°; 24·2, 2° 36′.
20. 4·368, 76° 42′. **21.** 1·8, 55° 18′.
22. 27, 141°. **24.** 14·6, 161° 30′, 4·534.
25. 6 ft. per. sec. − 210 f.s.s. **26.** 24·2, 2° 36′.
27. (*a*) 6000 ft.-lbs. per sec., (*b*) 2645 ft.-lbs. per. sec., (*c*) 0, (*d*) − 1060 ft.-lbs. per sec.
28. $A=22{\cdot}5$, $B=30{\cdot}4$.
29. 2·035, 7·5° W. of S.; 5·77, 25° E. of N.; 6·5, 11·5° W. of S. $A.B=2{\cdot}472$, $AC=2{\cdot}863$.
30. $\theta=60{\cdot}3°$, 60·7°, 81°; 66·54, $\alpha=107°\,38'$, $\beta=69°\,14'$, $\theta=27°\,28'$.
31. 14·1 f.s. at 135°. **32.** 5·736, 8·192 miles per hour.
34. 1966 dynes.

Exercises XXIX., p. 269.

1. $-62\frac{1}{2}$. **2.** 0. **3.** 13·5. **4.** $22\frac{2}{3}$. **5.** 9, 8, 7 ....
6. 6, 8, 10, or 10, 8, 6. **7.** 10. **8.** 25. **9.** $\frac{3}{4}$. **10.** $18\frac{16}{27}$, $\frac{29}{27}$.
11. 973. **12.** $\frac{2(2a+d)}{3d}$, $\frac{2a+d}{3d}$. **13.** 62. **14.** 1, 3, 5 ....
16. 20. **17.** 5. **18.** $a=10$, $d=-2$. **19.** 77.

Exercises XXX., p. 273.

1. $86\frac{1}{4}$. **2.** $18\left\{\left(1-\frac{1}{3}\right)^{10}\right\}$. **3.** $-0{\cdot}592\left\{\left(\frac{3}{10}\right)^{10}-1\right\}$.
4. − 185. **5.** 9780. **6.** 45920. **7.** 80.
8. $16\left\{1-\left(\frac{1}{4}\right)^{10}\right\}$. **9.** − 16·7728. **10.** − 136·5.
11. 18, 54, 162 ..., or − 18, − 54, − 162, etc. **12.** 4, 8, 16, 32, 64.
13. 1, 4, 16. **14.** $-\frac{211}{8}(\sqrt{3}-\sqrt{2})$. **16.** impossible $r>1$.
17. $\frac{3}{5}$. **18.** 9. **19.** $74\frac{2}{3}$.
20. $\frac{3}{2}$. **21.** 16, 24, 36 .... **23.** $r=\pm 2$, $a=3$.

Exercises XXXI., p. 275.

1. $2\frac{2}{5}$, 3, 4, 6. **2.** 5, 4, 3·2. **3.** 7. **4.** 5.
5. $\frac{1}{2}$, $\frac{1}{3}$, $\frac{1}{4}$. **6.** 4, 16. **7.** 1, $\frac{6}{5}$, $\frac{3}{2}$. **8.** 24.
9. $2\frac{2}{11}$, $2\frac{2}{5}$, $2\frac{2}{3}$. **10.** $\frac{13}{4}$, ± 3, $\frac{36}{13}$; 2, $\frac{13}{4}$, $\frac{9}{2}$; 2, ± 3, $\frac{9}{2}$; 2, $\frac{36}{13}$, $\frac{9}{2}$.

Exercises XXXII., p. 277.

1. 38·4. 2. 57·6. 3. $\frac{3}{2}$. 4. $\frac{16}{7}$.
5. 100·8. 6. $74\frac{2}{3}$. 7. $\frac{4}{9}$. 8. $\frac{14}{3}$.
9. $\frac{14}{3}$. 11. $-\frac{19}{6}$, $\frac{16}{3}\times\left(\frac{15}{3}\right)^3$, $1\frac{7}{33}$.
12. -154, -148, -142. 13. $22\frac{2}{3}$, $22\frac{2}{3}$.
14. -70, 110, 290, 470, 650, 830, 1010, 1190.
15. $r=1·5$, 768, 1152, 1728, etc. 16. $4n(n+1)$, $(2n+1)^2$.
17. (a) $\frac{x^{n-1}}{x-1}$; (b) $\frac{2^{n+1}x^{n+1}-1}{2x-1}$; (c) $\frac{nx^{n+1}-(n+1)x^n+1}{(x-1)^2}$.
19. $y^2\times\frac{y^{2n}-1}{y^2-1}+bn(n+1)$.

Exercises XXXIII., p. 287.

1. -4. 2. $\frac{1}{3}$. 3. 5. 5. $\frac{2048}{675}x^3$.
6. $55a^9b^2$, $462a^5b^6$, $462a^6b^5$.
7. $x^6\pm6x^5a+15x^4a^2\pm20x^3a^3+15x^2a^4\pm6xa^5+a^6$.
8. $625-200x+2400x^2-1280x^3+256x^4$.
9. $1820x^{12}a^4$. 10. $2-\frac{1}{3.2^2}-\frac{1}{3.6.2^4}$; 1·913.
11. $a^2+6ax+x^2\pm(4a+4x)\sqrt{ax}$.

Exercises XXXV., p. 308.

1. $4x^3+9x^2-2x$. 2. nAx^{n-1}. 3. $a\cos ax$.
4. $Aa\cos ax$. 5. $-Aa\sin ax$. 6. $\frac{3}{2}\sqrt{x}$.
7. v_0+at. 9. $\cos x$; $-\sin x$; $\sec^2 x$.
10. $ab\cos bx$, $-ab\sin bx$, nax^{n-1}.
11. $-ab\sin(bx+c)$; $\frac{b}{a+bx}$. 12. $-\frac{x}{\sqrt{a^2-x^2}}$.
13. $-\operatorname{cosec}^2 x$. 14. $\frac{1}{x}$. 15. $a^x\log_e a$.
16. $nax^{n-1}\cos ax^n$. 17. $-\frac{a}{t^2}$. 18. $-\frac{t}{\sqrt{a^2-t^2}}$.
19. $\frac{2}{x}$. 20. $8x+13$. 21. $10x-9$. 22. $5x^4+12x^2$.
23. $-3x^{-\frac{5}{2}}$. 24. $-1·408cv^{-2·408}$. 25. ft. 26. f.

Exercises XXXVI., p. 322.

1. $14x$. **2.** $3\cos x$. **3.** $-3\sin 3x$. **4.** $-10\sin(2x+3)$.

5. $\frac{1}{x}$. **6.** $\frac{3A}{x}$. **7.** $6e^{2x}$. **8.** $-kAe^{-kx}$.

9. $6t-4$. **10.** $2At+B$. **11.** $12\cos(4t+9)$.

12. $-63\sin 2(6t^3+9t+5)\times(2t^2+1)$. **13.** $\frac{14}{8}e^{\frac{t}{8}}+72\cos 8t$.

14. $11e^t\sin(6t+7)+66e^t\cos(6t+7)$.

15. $Abe^{bt}\sin(ct+f)+Ace^{bt}\cos(ct+f)$.

Exercises XXXVII., p. 334.

1. $40x^3$. **2.** $\frac{8a^2x^3-4x^5}{(a^2-x^2)^2}$. **3.** $\frac{2x(a-2x^3)}{(a+x^3)^3}$.

4. $\sec^2 x$. **5.** $-\frac{1+x}{(1+x^2)^{\frac{3}{2}}}$. **6.** $\frac{mq-pn}{(px+q)^2}$, $-\frac{n}{x^{n+1}}$.

7. $\frac{1-x}{(1+x^2)^{\frac{3}{2}}}$, $x^{a-1}(a\log x+1)$. **8.** $\frac{2(1-x^2)}{(1+x^2)^2}$.

9. $e^{\sin x}\cos x$. **10.** $\frac{\log_e e}{\sin^{-1}x\sqrt{1-x^2}}$. **11.** $\frac{-x\sin\sqrt{x^2+a^2}}{\sqrt{x^2+a^2}}$.

12. $\frac{x\cos\sqrt{x^2+a^2}}{\sqrt{x^2+a^2}}$. **13.** $\frac{x}{x^2+a^2}$. **14.** $\frac{2x}{\sqrt{1-x^4}}$.

15. $3x^2+2x+1$. **16.** $\frac{2}{1+x^2}$. **17.** $\frac{1}{1-x^4}$.

18. $\frac{2a}{x^2-a^2}$. **19.** $-\operatorname{cosec}^2 x$. **20.** $\frac{1}{\sqrt{a^2+x^2}}$.

21. $\frac{2}{1+x^2}$. **22.** $-3x\sqrt{a^2-x^2}$. **23.** $\frac{2x(2-x^2)}{\sqrt{x^2-1}(x^4-x^2+1)}$.

24. $\frac{m\cos(m-1)x}{(\cos x)^{m+1}}$. **25.** $\frac{1}{1+x^2}$. **26.** $(4bx+3a)x^2$.

27. $\frac{x}{\sqrt{x^2+a^2}}$. **28.** $2\sin x\cos x$. **29.** $\sin^2 x(3\cos^2 x-\sin^2 x)$.

30. $2(a+2x)(ax+x^2)$. **31.** $e^x(\cos x-\sin x)$. **32.** $x^{c-1}(\log_a x^c+\log_a e)$.

33. $\frac{a^2-2x^2}{\sqrt{a^2-x^2}}$. **34.** $-\frac{1}{x\sqrt{x^2-1}}$. **35.** $\frac{1}{1-x^2}+\frac{x\sin^{-1}x}{(1-x^2)^{\frac{3}{2}}}$.

Exercises XXXVIII., p. 351.

1. 10·4, 10·004, 10·0004, 10. **2.** $5+4{\cdot}2t$; 26.

3. $150-10t$; 80 f.s.; -10 f.s.s., 31·06 lbs. **4.** 1·6 miles.

5. (i) 52·01, (ii) 50·201, (iii) 50·0201; 50 ft. per sec.

7. 3·4 f.s.s., 5·279 lbs. 8. 14·26 f.s.; 40 f.s.s.; 124·3 lbs.

Exercises XXXIX., p. 370.

1. Each 16·5. 2. $x \pm \frac{1}{2}$. 3. $x = -1$ max., $x = +1$ min

4. 6·25 sq. ft. 5. Line is bisected. 6. Max. none, min. $= -64$.

7. Max. 6, min. $1\frac{10}{27}$. 8. Max. $-\frac{a}{2}$, min. $\frac{a}{2}$.

10. (i) 8, 4; (ii) 9, 3. 11. $y = \pm 1$. 12. $x = \sqrt{\frac{a}{b}}$, 2.

13. (i) $x = 0$ max.; (ii) $x = 3$ min.; (iii) $x = 0$ min.

14. $x = 0$ max. $= 2\sqrt{a}$. 15. $h = r = 147 \cdot 1$ ft.; area $= 203907$ sq. ft.

16. 2·55 cub. ft. 17. $\frac{1}{2}\left(\frac{\pi}{2} + a\right)$, $\frac{1}{2}\left(\frac{3\pi}{2} + a\right)$. 18. $3\frac{1}{3}$, 4.

19. $\frac{a(5 + \sqrt{13})}{6}$ max., $\frac{a(5 - \sqrt{13})}{6}$ min. 20. 360·8 sq. ft.

22. Each side $= \frac{c}{\sqrt{2}}$ where c is the length of the hypotenuse.

23. (i) 1 max., 3 min.; (ii) $\frac{8a^2}{3\sqrt{3}}$ max., 0 min.

24. (a) $r = h = 2 \cdot 484$ ft.; (b) $r = 1 \cdot 971$ ft., $h = 3 \cdot 942$ ft.

Exercises XL., p. 376.

1. $12x^2 + 18x - 2$; $24x + 18$. 2. $a \cos ax$; $-a^2 \sin ax$.

3. $Aa \cos ax$, $-Aa^2 \sin ax$. 4 $-Aa \sin ax$, $-Aa^2 \cos ax$, or $-a^2 y$.

5. $\frac{3}{4} \frac{1}{\sqrt{x}}$. 6. a.

Exercises XLI., p. 387.

1. $x - \frac{x^2}{2} + \frac{x^3}{3} - \frac{x^4}{4} + \frac{x^5}{5} - \dots$.

2. (i) $\log a + \frac{x}{a} - \frac{1}{2} \frac{x^3}{3a^3} + \frac{1 \cdot 3}{2 \cdot 4} \frac{x^5}{5a^5} + \dots$; $2^n \left\{1 + \frac{nx^2}{2!} + n(3n - 2)\frac{x^4}{4!}\right\}$.

3. $x^4 + \frac{4}{3}x^6 + \frac{6}{5}x^8 +$ etc. 4. $x^x(1 + \log x)$; $x^x\{(1 + \log x)^2 + x^{-1}\}$.

5. $e^{\tan x}(1 + x \sec^2 x)$; $e^{\tan x} \sec^2 x\{2 + x(\sec^2 x + 2 \tan x)\}$.

6. $\frac{1}{1 + x^2}$; $\frac{-2x}{(1 + x^2)^2}$. 7. $2(-1)^{n-1}\frac{(n-3)!}{x^{n-2}}$.

8. $e^{x}\{x^3+3nx^2+3n(n-1)x+n(n-1)(n-2)\}$.

9. $x-\frac{x^3}{3}+\frac{x^5}{5}-\frac{x^7}{7}+\dots$.

10. $\sin^{-1}x+\frac{h}{(1-x^2)^{\frac{1}{2}}}+\frac{x}{(1-x^2)^{\frac{3}{2}}}\frac{h^2}{2!}+\frac{1+2x^2}{(1-x^2)^{\frac{5}{2}}}\frac{h^3}{3!}+\dots$.

11. $x+\frac{x^2}{2!}+\frac{2x^3}{3!}+\frac{9x^5}{5!}+\dots$.

12. $x-\frac{x^3}{3!}+\frac{x^5}{5!}$.

Exercises XLII., p. 418.

1. 21, 1·0987.

2. $\frac{x^3}{3}$; $\frac{1}{b}\sin bx$; $\log v=\log 3=1\cdot0987$; $\frac{x^3}{3}=\frac{1728-729}{3}=333$.

3. $\left[2cx+x^2\right]_{10}^{20}=560-180=380$.

4. $\left[(c+nx^2)^3\right]_a^b=76^3-36^3=392320$.

5. $\frac{1}{a}\sin ax$.

6. $\frac{1}{a}\tan ax$.

7. $\frac{1}{a}\tan^{-1}ax$.

8. $y=\frac{l^{ax}}{a\log_e l}$.

9. $\frac{A}{b}\sin(a+bx)$.

10. $\frac{1}{b}\tan^{-1}(a+bx)$.

11. $\frac{1}{3q}(p+qx)^3$.

12. $\frac{1}{b}\sin^{-1}(a+bx)$.

13. $\frac{a}{m+1}x^{m+1}$; $ax+\frac{b}{n+1}x^{n+1}$; $\frac{\sin(a+bx)}{b}$; $\log x$; $\frac{1}{b}\log(a+bx)$.

14. $\frac{1}{a}\tan^{-1}\frac{x}{a}$.

15. $-\frac{1}{2}\log(a^2-x^2)$.

16. $\frac{1}{a}\sec^{-1}\frac{x}{a}$.

17. $\frac{q}{p+q}x^{\frac{p+q}{q}}$.

18. $\frac{1}{2}\sin^{-1}\left(\frac{x^2}{a^2}\right)$. (Hint, put $\frac{x^2}{a^2}=z$.)

19. $\log\sqrt{\frac{(x+3)^3}{x+1}}$.

20. $\frac{1}{2}\log\tan\left(\frac{\pi}{4}+\theta\right)$. (Hint, put $\tan\theta=\phi$ and then split into two fractions.)

21. $\log(\theta+\sin\theta)$.

22. $\frac{1}{-5(a^2-x^2)^{\frac{5}{2}}}$.

23. $x-\tan^{-1}\tan\frac{x}{2}$. (Hint, divide into two fractions.)

24. $\frac{x^6}{6}$; $\frac{2}{3}x^{\frac{3}{2}}$; $\frac{4}{3}x^{\frac{3}{2}}$; $\frac{3}{5}x^{\frac{5}{3}}$.

25. $\frac{2}{3}x^3+\frac{3}{2}x^2+5x$.

26. $-\cos x+\sin x$.

27. $-\frac{1}{6}\cos 6x-\frac{1}{2}\cos 2x$.

28. $-\frac{1}{12}\cos 6x+\frac{1}{4}\cos 2x$.

29. $\frac{1}{2}\sin 2x-\frac{1}{6}\sin 6x$.

30. $\frac{1}{6}\sin 6x+\frac{1}{2}\sin 2x$.

31. $\frac{1}{a}e^{av}$.

32. $-\frac{a}{0\cdot37}v^{-0\cdot37}$.

33. $\frac{1}{3}at^3+\frac{1}{2}bt^2+ct+g$.

34. $\log\{x+\sqrt{x^2+a^2}\}$. (Hint, put $z=x+\sqrt{x^2+a^2}$.)

35. $\frac{a^{m+x}}{\log a}$.

36. $\frac{1}{a}\log\frac{x}{\sqrt{x^2+a^2}+a}$.

37. $\frac{1}{3}(1+x^2)^{\frac{1}{2}}(x^2-2)$. (Hint, put $z^2=1+x^2$.)

38. $\frac{1}{2a^2}\tan^{-1}\frac{x^2}{a^2}$.

39. $\frac{2bx-a}{2a^2x^2}-\frac{b^2}{a^3}\log\frac{a+bx}{x}$. $\left(\text{Hint, put } z=\frac{1}{x}.\right)$

40. $-\frac{1}{3}(1-x^2)^{\frac{1}{2}}(x^2+2)$.

41. $\frac{1}{2}(x-\sin x\cos x)$.

42. $x+\frac{3}{4}\log\frac{x-2}{x+2}$.

43. $\frac{1}{2\log_e 2\cdot4}2\cdot4^{2x}$.

44. $\log\tan\frac{1}{2}\left(\frac{\pi}{2}+x\right)$.

45. $\log\tan\frac{x}{2}$.

46. $y=1\cdot25x^2$; vol. $=32180$.

47. 18682 cub. units.

Exercises XLIII., p. 439.

1. 1·3″, 2·983.
2. 21″.
3. 1778.
4. $4\frac{1}{2}$″, 241·5.
5. 8·9 sq. in.; 1·9″, $I=22\cdot5$, $k=1\cdot59$.

Exercises XLIV., p. 464.

1. $-\frac{1}{2}\left\{\frac{\sin(a+b)x}{a+b}-\frac{\sin(a-b)x}{a-b}\right\}$.
2. $x^2\sin x+2(x\cos x-\sin x)$.
3. $\frac{1}{(a-b)}\{a\log(x-a)-b\log(x-b)\}$.
4. $x+\log\frac{x-3}{x-2}$.
5. $2\tan^{-1}x-\frac{1}{2}\tan^{-1}\frac{x}{2}$.
6. $x-\log(x+2)-\frac{1}{2}\log(x^2+4)$.
7. $\frac{x^4}{4}\left\{(\log x)^2-\frac{1}{2}\log x+\frac{1}{8}\right\}$.

8. $x+\frac{a^3\log(x-a)}{(a-b)(a-c)}+\frac{b^3\log(x-b)}{(b-c)(b-a)}+\frac{c^3\log(x-c)}{(a-c)(b-c)}$.

9. $\frac{2}{25}\log\frac{x-3}{x+2}-\frac{3}{5(x-3)}$.

10. $\sin\theta-\theta\cos\theta$.

11. $x^3\sin x+3x^2\cos x-6x\sin x-6\cos x$.

12. $\frac{7}{2}\frac{1}{x+1}+\frac{11}{4}\log\frac{x+1}{x+3}$.

13. $5\log(x+1)-2\log(x+3)+3\log(x-4)$.

Miscellaneous Exercises XLV., p. 496.

1. $y=e^{-\frac{7}{2}x}\left(Ae^{\sqrt{\frac{13}{4}}x}+Be^{-\sqrt{\frac{13}{4}}x}\right)$.

2. $y=Ae^{\frac{2}{3}x}+Be^{-9x}$.

3. $y=e^{3x}(Ax+B)$.

4. $y=e^{-\frac{17}{4}x}\left(A\sin\sqrt{\frac{31}{16}}x+B\cos\sqrt{\frac{31}{16}}x\right)$.

5. 28·41.

6. 0·662, 3584 lbs.

7. 9.

8. 0·733.

9. $y=\frac{x^3}{3}-\frac{x^2}{2}+x+\frac{7}{6}$; $8\frac{2}{3}$.

10. $x=\pm0·6324$, 2·929, 2·315.

11. $x=8a$; $y=\pm4a\sqrt{2}$, $\pm2a\sqrt{-1}$.

12. 20, 10.

13. $y=3x+\frac{x^2}{2}$; 1368.

14. $\frac{5}{24}\pi r^3$.

15. 2·1295, 10·22.

Miscellaneous Exercises, p. 497.

Section I. Arithmetic.

1. £8. 1*s*. 3*d*., £268. 16*s*. 0*d*.

2. 3·123, 1704.

3. 284·7, 2817.

4. 0·3106, 37·32.

5. 0·03106, 373·2.

6. 0·006224, 0·002466.

Section II. Logarithms.

1. 988·3, 0·0002065, 2·899.

2. 0·4255.

3. $14·18\times10^7$.

4. (i) 29·55, (ii) 9·099.

5. (i) 1·612, (ii) 117·4.

6. (i) 1·720, (ii) 6·179.

7. 0·742.

8. 4·093.

9. $3\frac{1}{2}$ %, 10·55 years.

10. $a=1·937$, $b=0·04806$, $H=11410$.

11. 0·4338, 0·6015.

12. (i) 0·01778, (ii) 0·416, (iii) −4·877, (iv) 0·9206.

13. $b=0·594$, $c=0·096$, $P=670800$.

14. $a=3·023\times10^{-10}$, $b=37·01$, $p=39·25$.

15 $y=5·7^{0·025x}$.

16. 0·3.

17. $c=15·92$, $n=1·7$, $W=24·15$.

18. 79·2.

19. 7·446, 0·01254, 5·68, 1546. **20.** 1·722, 0·0198.
21. 4·5710, 1·5710, $\bar{2}$·5710, 3·339, 1·93, 1768000, 11·03.
22. 1·558, 1·694, 0·59. **23.** $1·746 \times 10^{-14}$, $d=8·409$.
24. 1·521, 0·59. **25.** $\phi=0·1773$, 0·1778, Error 0·28 %.
26. 12. **27.** 1·69, 0·2987, $1·387 \times 10^{-9}$.
28. $n=260$, $R=0·881$; see p. 57. **29.** $r=3·5$.
30. 7·478, 5·98, 5·0, 4·32. **31.** (*a*) 3596, (*b*) −9·908, (*c*) 32.
32. $14·78 \times 10^6$. [Hint: assume $P=ae^{nx}$.]
33. $P \propto D^{\frac{7}{6}}$, $T \propto D^{-\frac{1}{6}}$, $C \propto D$; $D=29880$, $v=24$, $P=71710$, $C=7530$.
34. 11 per cent., 3·88. **35.** (i) $30·28 \times 10^6$, (ii) $34·49 \times 10^6$.
36. 3 per cent. **37.** 4·5 per cent., 40 cub. in.

SECTION III. TRIGONOMETRY.

1. 79° 26′, 112700 sq. ft. **2.** 76·12 ft.
4. 29° 20′, 31° 56′, 118° 44′, 3248000 sq. ft.
5. $B=39° 27'$, $C=69° 33'$.
6. 1·571, 0·3334, 0·25, 0·9057, 0·8, 0·5333.
7. 329·8 sq. in., 0·12 %. **8.** $A^2=a^2+b^2$, $\tan e=\frac{b}{a}$.
10. 0·3907, 0·9205. **11.** $BC=4·612$, $AC=8·672$.
12. 27° 38′. **13.** 13884 miles, 38·57, 6·428 inches
14. 0·9563, −0·848, 2·7475. **15.** (*b*) 223·3 sq. ft.

SECTION IV. SQUARED PAPER.

1. (i) 2·572, (ii) 2·72. **3.** 12·03 inches. **4.** 2·28. **5.** $C=770A^{0·87}$.
6. $E=22·5$, $R=28$, $P=$ £5. 5*s*., 230, vary the price (see p. 120).
7. 0·86. **8.** $T=36·29h^{1·5}$, $V=1271h^{1·5}$.
9. $A=\frac{dV}{dh}=1906h^{0·5}$, $\delta V=158·8h^{0·5}$. **10.** £3675, £2812·5, £2860.
11. $c=5·56+\frac{0·06}{f}$, $U=0·18C-0·15$. **12.** $P=31·6v^{1·78}$ (see p. 126).
13. $x=0·5282$ (see p. 369). **14.** $y=1·22x+0·49$ (see p. 131).
15. 33420 cub. in., 304. **16.** 1·22.
17. Aver. rates, A, 2·8, B, 2·4. A's age $11\frac{1}{2}$ years, 4·2, 1·5.
18. Any amount up to £16. **19.** $yx^{1·1}=553$; 22·39. **20.** 106·3.
21. 2·134, 0·4793. **22.** $T=36·29h^{1·5}$; $D=1271h^{1·5}$. **23.** 0·866.
24. $W=16K+4400$, $w=\frac{4400}{K}+16$; 20·4, 30·7. **25.** 2·134, 0·4793.
26. $W=4400+16K$, $W \div Y=5168Y^{-1}+7·2$; 9·784, 17·54.

SECTION V. MENSURATION.

1. 60 ft., 20 ft. **2.** 158·45 sq. in., 145·5 cub. in., 6·525 in.
3. 718 lbs. **4.** 5·25 in. **5.** 59 c.c. **6.** 130·1 galls., 43·33 sq. ft.
7. 360·8 lbs., 3·316 in. **8.** 9240 cub. ft. **10.** 497·4, 67·04.
12. (*a*) 8·148 in., 4·644 in., 3·64 %; (*b*) 44·43 cub. in.
13. (*a*) 3·95 cub. ft.; (*b*) 1687 sq. in. **14.** 3·53 in.
15. 8·4545, 4·5455. **16.** 101·9.

SECTION VI. SOLID GEOMETRY.

1. $AB=4{\cdot}25$ in., 2·79 in., area = 5·92.
2. 1·348, 3·702, 3·078, $\alpha=74°\ 22'$, $\beta=42°\ 14'$.
3. $r=3{\cdot}905$, $\theta=39°\ 48'$, $\phi=36°\ 52'$, $\alpha=59°\ 12'$, $\beta=67°\ 24'$.
4. $OP=3{\cdot}09$, $OQ=2{\cdot}48$, $PQ=1{\cdot}15$, angle $POQ=20°\ 6'$.
5. $x=2{\cdot}9$, $y=4{\cdot}535$, $z=3{\cdot}066$, 60° 22′, 57° 18′.

SECTION VII. SERIES.

1. 0·25882, 0·50001, 0·70715. **2.** 0·96594, 0·86603, 0·70713.
3. 0·26794, 0·57728, 0·99668.
4. 0·008598, 0·01702, 0·02527, 0·03335, 0·0410, 0·1463.
6. 17°·19. 0·2955.

SECTION IX. DIFFERENTIATION.

2. $\frac{5}{3}x^{\frac{2}{3}}$, $-3\sin 3x$, $-4e^{-4x}$, $-\dfrac{1}{x}$.

3. (i) Rate of increase of y per unit increase of x.
(ii) $\dfrac{dy}{dx}=a^x\log_e a$. (iii) 6642. (iv) 6700.

4. (i) 11·76. (ii) 11·6. **5.** $b+2cx+ngx^{n-1}$.

6. $\dfrac{1}{2x^{\frac{1}{2}}}$, $\dfrac{2}{3}\dfrac{1}{x^{\frac{1}{3}}}$, $-\dfrac{1}{2x^{\frac{3}{2}}}$, $x^2(2x\cos 2x+3\sin 2x)$.

7. values of y 1·5, 1·658, 1·832, 2·025, 2·238, 2·473, 2·733, 3·021, 3·338.

$$\frac{dy}{dx}=0{\cdot}3e^{0{\cdot}2x}=0{\cdot}2y=0{\cdot}3,\ 0{\cdot}3316,\ \text{etc.}$$

8. 226·2 cub. in. per min. **9.** $a=\frac{3}{2}$, $\frac{3}{8}x+\frac{3}{2}$, $\frac{9}{8}$, 8.
10. 34·38 ft. per sec. **12.** $x=-2$. **13.** 50·93 f.s.
14. $\dfrac{dR}{dt}=R_0(a+2bt)$. **15.** $\frac{88}{35}$ f.s. **16.** 60° or 120°.
17. 40. **18.** 0·625 f.s.

19. $\frac{x}{50}\frac{dx}{dt}$, $3\frac{1}{5}$ miles per hour, [x=distance from wall]. **20.** 3·562.

21. $v=6·795$ f.s., $a=3·398$ f.s.s., $s=23·36$ ft. **22.** 24·3.

23. $v=3-t+1·2t^2$, $a=2·4t-1$; 18·2 f.s., 8·7 f.s.s.

24. $v=7·4t-3·5$, 26·1, $\frac{1}{2}mv^2=1058$, $mv=81·04$.

25. 932 f.s.s., 9° 13′, 47·5 radians per sec., per sec., 3329 lbs. 131·3 ft. lbs.

[Hint. Find $\delta^2x/\delta t^2=925$, $\delta^2y/\delta t^2=150$;

$\therefore$ $a=\sqrt{150^2+925^2}=932$ f.s.s., also $\delta^2\theta/\delta t^2=47·5$.

$$\text{Couple}=\frac{115}{32·2}\times(0·88)^2\times 47·5.]$$

28. $A=dV/dh=1800h^{0·5}$.

29. $b+2cx+ngx^{n-1}$, ax^{-1}, abe^{bx}, $ab\cos(bx+c)$.

30. 9·25 f.s.s., 57·5 lbs. (see p. 343).

31. nax^{n-1}, abe^{bx}, $ab\cos(bx+c)$, $-ab\sin(bx+c)$, $\frac{1}{x+b}$.

32. $0·4x-1·2$ (see p. 341).

33. $V=3\sin(600t)+2·4\cos(600t)$, $C=10$, -10, $V=3·84$, $-3·84$ (see p. 478).

34. $a=1·24$, $b=0·6019$, $n=2·348$, 3·596.

Section X. Maxima and Minima.

1. $\frac{\sqrt{3}}{2}$. **2.** ±1·4. **3.** 7·2, 4·8.

4. (i) 6·9 in., 9·8 in.; (ii) 6 in. **5.** 9 amp.

6. $x=\pm\frac{r}{2}$. **7.** 6. **8.** 4·083 in., 302·6 cub. in.

9. $\lambda=1·73$. **11.** 1·3. **12.** width 2·71 ft., depth 1·36 ft.

13. 32°, 33° 41′. **14.** 5° 4′, 68° 40′, 36° 52′.

15. Distance of base of cone from centre of sphere $=\frac{r}{3}$; 155·2 cub. in.

16. $n=220·5$ **17.** 174 sq. feet.

18. (i) 1 ft., 2 ft. high, 2 cub. ft.; (ii) $\frac{6}{5}$ ft., 1·728 cub. ft.; (iii) 1·449 ft., 1·592 cub. ft.; (iv) 1·274 ft.. 2 ft., 2·55 cub. ft.,

19. $0·6a$, $0·4a$.

Section XI. Integration.

1. (i) 64; (ii) 1; (iii) 1·0986; (iv) 9·192, 9·19.

2. $b=0·04535$; (i) 6·8565; (ii) 6·858.

3. $a=\frac{10}{125}$; (i) 12·46; (ii) 12·5. **5.** $v=5t^2-70$. **6.** 3·11.

7. (i) 0·7847 ; (ii) 0·7854 ; (iii) 1·1877.

8. (i) 4·267 ; (ii) 4·267 ; (iii) 25·8 ; (iv) 25·75.

9. (i) 14·67 ; (ii) 14·67 ; (iii) 398 ; (iv) 393.

10. (i) $\frac{4x^{\frac{7}{4}}}{7}$; (ii) 0·693 ; (iii) 1.

11. Work done $= \int_2^8 p\,dv = 23960$ ft. lbs.

12. 25640 ft. lbs. **13.** 83540 ft. lbs. **14.** 231753·6.

15. 6, 42·41. **16.** 13·5. **17.** 70·56. **18.** 125·28, 105·4.

19. $y = 1{\cdot}2 + 2{\cdot}3x^{\frac{1}{2}}$, slope $= 0{\cdot}5362$. By Simpson's rule 16·873. Integration 17·063.

20. $5\frac{1}{3}$. **21.** 758·2 cub. in. **24.** $k = 0{\cdot}8$, 1450 ft. lbs.

25. $a = 1{\cdot}35$, $b = 0{\cdot}53$: (i) 12·19 ; (ii) 12·18 ; (iii) 137 ; (iv) 137.

26. 1·67. **27.** 6 cub. ft., see p. 427.

28. $5cv^{0\cdot2}$, $c \log_e v$, see p. 403. **29.** $\frac{\pi m^2(b^2 - a^2)}{2b}$, see p. 415.

30. $h = \frac{p(\gamma - s)}{\gamma - 1}$, $s = \gamma$, see p. 403. **31.** $am + \frac{bm^{n+1}}{n+1}$, 0·07155, 5·714.

32. $p^{\frac{\gamma-1}{\gamma}} = \frac{1-\gamma}{\gamma} ch + p_0^{\frac{\gamma-1}{\gamma}}$, $c = p_0^{\frac{\gamma-1}{\gamma}} \div t_0 R$, $t = \frac{1-\gamma}{\gamma R} h + t_0$.

33. $A = 0{\cdot}5714$.

Section XII. Centre of Gravity and Moment of Inertia.

1. (i) 0·04566 ; (ii) 0·04566 + 0·00003846.

2. (i) 31·29 ; (ii) 31·28 ; (iii) 2·916 ; (iv) 2·919.

3. (i) $\bar{x} = 3{\cdot}0$; (ii) $\bar{x} = 3{\cdot}1$. **4.** (i) $\bar{x} = 2{\cdot}86$; (ii) 2·8.

5. 25·8, $\bar{x} = 3{\cdot}352$.

6. $\int_{-4}^{3} y^2 x\,dx \div \int_{-4}^{3} y^2\,dx = 1{\cdot}577$ inches from centre.

7. 0·652, 35·77. **8.** 20·03, 274·8. **9.** 0·5517 ft. units.

10. $\frac{M}{2}(R_0^2 + R_1^2)$, $M\left(\frac{R_0^2 + R_1^2}{2} + R_1^2\right)$.

I., p. 542.

1. (*a*) 0·06224, 40·55 ; (*b*) 0·5105, 39·82, 0·02511 ; (*d*) 0·6018, 0·7986, 0·7536.

2. (a) 1·2213, 4th ; (b) $\frac{2\cdot3}{x-5\cdot4}-\frac{1\cdot8}{x+1\cdot9}$; (c) 7·473, 5·067 ;
(d) 25°, 5·782, 13·69.

4. 36° 52′, 75° 45′, 56° 18′. **5.** $b=0\cdot594$, $c=0\cdot096$, $P=670800$.

6. $c=2\cdot696$, 1·387, $v=11\cdot18$, 14·83, $I=2173$, 5604. **7.** 6·248 sq. in.

8. $x=0$, 0·237, 0·783, 1·812 ; $y=0$, 1·34, 2·929, 5·0.

10. 16 in., 366·6 cub. in. **12.** $x=2\cdot34$.

13. $1200/s+3s^2$, 12·6 knots. **14.** $n=2\cdot3$, 2·6, 500 ft. per min.

II., p. 545.

1. (a) 0·006224, 0·002466 ; (b) 3·786, 0·2641 ;
(d) −0·9613, −0·5592, 0·2309, 13°, 145°, 104°.

4. 15·65 knots. **5.** $a=1\cdot0915$, $b=0\cdot5285$, 112.

7. 49·33 sq. in., 1·89 per cent. **8.** 75° 45′, 36° 52′, 56° 18′.

9. 0·80 (see p. 354). **10.** $V=360\cdot6\sin(600t+56\cdot3)$; 56°·3.

11. $d=\frac{5}{8}(16-x)$, $A=\frac{\pi}{4}\left\{\frac{5}{8}(16-x)\right\}^2$, $V=\frac{\pi}{12}\left\{1600-\frac{25}{64}(16-x)^3\right\}$.

12. $r^2=\frac{c^2}{2g}\times\frac{1}{C-h}$. **14.** Speeds, 7·847, 14·38, 20·92.
Horse-power, 653·9, 3178, 14270.

15. 2·5 ft. or 6 in., 1·5 ft. **16.** (i) $\frac{2ax-x^2}{a-x}$, $\frac{b^2}{a^2}(a-x)$;

(ii) $2x$, $2a$, (iii) $\frac{x}{2}$, $2a^2x^3$, (iv) $\frac{x}{2}$, na^2x^{2n-1},

(v) nx, $\frac{y^2}{nx}$, (vi) $-\frac{nx}{m}$, $-\frac{m}{n}\frac{y^2}{x}$, (vii) $\frac{y^3-ayx}{ay-x^2}$, $\frac{ay^2-x^2y}{y^2-ax}$.

III., p. 549.

1. (a) 0·3015 ; (b) 0·9488 ; (d) £18·8626.

2. (a) $u=3\cdot671$; (b) $a=1\cdot1$, $b=3\cdot2$, $y=13\cdot275$;
(c) 140·9, 137·5, mean 139·2, 1·2 per cent.

3. $s=16b$; aver. speed $=b(8+\delta t)$; $8b$.

4. (a) $x=957\cdot2$; (b) 0·000292 ; (c) $A=30°\ 30'$, $B=59°\ 30'$.

5. 12·31 miles. **6.** 3·316, 0·884.

7. 80 miles per hour, $t=0\cdot2$ hour, aver. $=26\cdot8$ miles per hour.

8. $2\cdot522\times10^8$, $1\cdot789\times10^8$, $1\cdot493\times10^8$, $1\cdot169\times10^8$, $8\cdot989\times10^7$, $6\cdot005\times10^7$.

9. 6660 cub. ft. **11.** 449 sq. ft., 1436·8 cub. ft.

12. Linear law ; £4978.

IV., p. 552.

1. (*a*) 0·3015; (*b*) 0·5078; (*d*) $-0·3907$, $-0·766$, $-7·11\dot{5}$, 25°, 155° ..., 41°, 319° ..., 110°, 290°.

3. 424·58.

4. $a=0·4514$, $n=2·374$, vol. $=1155$.

5. $w=2·167+\dfrac{0·1689}{f}$.

f	0·25	0·2	0·15	0·1	0·05
w	2·843	3·012	3·293	3·856	5·545

6. 12078 miles, 33·55 miles, 5·92 ins.

7. 4076, 17·8 E. of N.

8. $a=54·53$, $b=4·67$, $\alpha=8·706$, $\beta=0·08399$.

9. Speed $=aq\cos(qt+e)$; accel. $=-q^2x$.

10. $x=10+6\sin(\theta+57°)+\cos 2\theta+0·18\sin 4\theta$.

11. 0·5270, 0·5779.

12. 3·813.

13. 83·5 ft. per sec.

14. 56·56 yds., 28·29 yds.

V., p. 555.

1. (*a*) 329·6, (*b*) 12·54, (*d*) £17·359.

2. (*a*) 3·802 in., (*b*) 31°, (*c*) 0·0306 %, (*d*) $(x+2·3)(x-1·9)$

3. (*a*) 87·5 lb., (*b*) $y=3·811$, (*c*) $n=14·2$.

4. 21·3 lb. per sq. ft., 85200 lb.

5. 23°·6, 43°·8.

6. 4·953.

8. $a=-0·258$, $b=-36·4$, $Q=55·2$.

9. $1·748\times10^5$ cub. ft., 5810 cub. ft.

11. $a(\beta-\alpha)+\dfrac{b}{2}(\beta^2-\alpha^2)+\dfrac{c}{3}(\beta^3-\alpha^3)$; $2h\left(a+\dfrac{ch^2}{3}\right)$.

12. $a=y_2$, $b=\dfrac{y_3-y_1}{2h}$, $c=\dfrac{y_1-2y_2+y_3}{2h^2}$.

13. $x=1·\dot{3}\dot{6}$, $y=4·\dot{5}\dot{4}$.

14. $V=10·21+10·22t-7t^2$.

15. $a=100$, $b=1·25$, $s=a^{-1}\times m^{1-b}$.

VI., p. 558.

1. (*a*) 3296, (*b*) 143·1, (*d*) $-0·342$, $-0·5446$, 9·5144, 21°, 51°.

2. $a=900$, $b=60{,}000$, $m=-403$, $n=733·3$, $V=358·4$.

3. See Paper V. No. 5.

5. $c=5·45$.

6. $y=q_2\left[r\cos\theta+\frac{r^2}{l}\cos 2\theta\right]=\left(\cos\theta+\frac{\cos 2\theta}{5}\right)$ if $q=1$.

θ	0°	45°	90°	135°	180°
x	0	0·343	1·0	1·757	2·0
y	1·2	0·707	0·2	– 0·707	– 0·8

8. $\log\frac{(x-5)^3}{(x+3)^2}$.

13. $a=1·698$, $b=1·3$, $c=0·256$.

14. $P=P_0e^{\frac{r}{100}t}$; $69·3\div r$.

VII., p. 561.

1. (*a*) 0·1917, 453·5, (*b*) 8·206, (*c*) 27·48, 5·920, 0·2748, 0·1276, (*d*) 116·4.
2. (*a*) $x=\pm 9·788$ or $\pm 6·648$; $y=\pm 6·648$ or $\pm 9·788$, (*b*) 4·045 in., 0·412 in., (*c*) 6·745 in., 14·826 in., (*d*) $(x-5·6935)(x-3·2265)$.
3. (*a*) $a=-33·50$, $b=39·80$, (*b*) 6 lb., (*c*) 2·116, 1896·1, 896·1.
4. -1, $-i$, 1, i, -1, $5·062+2·963i$, $0·7071+0·7071i$, $0·7071-0·7071i$.
5. 4·05 sq. ch.

6. 1·1843.

7. – 5·2, – 10·4, – 15·2, – 19·6, – 23·2, – 26·3, – 28·6, – 29·9.
8. Total distance 7·562 miles.
9. $a(\beta-\alpha)+\frac{b}{2}(\beta^2-\alpha^2)+\frac{c}{3}(\beta^3-\alpha^3)$; $2h\left(a+\frac{ch^2}{3}\right)$.
10. $a=y_2$, $b=\frac{y_3-y_1}{2h}$, $c=\frac{y_1-2y_2+y_3}{2h^2}$.
11. $y=550(36·14)^{-x}$.
12. $y=257·14r-18·57$; max. error $\frac{2}{3}$% nearly.
13.

h	Total payment.	Hourly payment.	Master's saving.
20	200	10	0
15	175	11·67	25
10	150	15	50

VIII., p. 564.

1. (*a*) 0·1917, 453·55, (*b*) 49·86, (*c*) −0·4540, −0·5446, −0·7002, (*d*) $\frac{1}{x+5\cdot697}+\frac{1}{x-4\cdot317}$.

2. 0·97716.

3. $W=14\cdot67K+22333$; $w=14\cdot67+\frac{22333}{K}$.

4. (*b*) 0·16567.

6. $S=w(x-l)+W$; $M=\frac{w}{2}(x^2+l^2)-wlx+W(x-l)$;

$$\frac{dy}{dx}=\frac{w}{2c}\left(\frac{x^3}{3}+l^2x-lx^2\right)+\frac{W}{c}\left(\frac{x^2}{2}-lx\right);$$

$$y=\frac{w}{2c}\left(\frac{x^4}{12}-\frac{lx^3}{3}+\frac{l^2x^2}{2}\right)+\frac{W}{c}\left(\frac{x^3}{6}-\frac{lx^2}{2}\right).$$

7. $p^{\frac{c-1}{c}}-p_0^{\frac{c-1}{c}}=k\frac{c-1}{c}h$; $t-t_0=ch$.

8. 15·212 knots, 1·06 % and 1·11 % greater.

9. $y=10\cdot42+16\cdot2(1\cdot554)^x=10\cdot42+16\cdot2e^{0\cdot4409x}$; 72·4.

11. $\frac{1}{2}ab\cos c$.

13. −1, $-i$, 1, i, $5\cdot062+2\cdot963i$; $\frac{1}{\sqrt{2}}+\frac{i}{\sqrt{2}}$; $\cos 45^\circ - i\sin 45^\circ$;

$5\cdot062\sin qt+2\cdot963\cos qt$; $\cos\frac{\pi}{4}\sin qt+\sin\frac{\pi}{4}\cos qt$; $\sin\left(qt-\frac{\pi}{4}\right)$.

14. $v_0\{0\cdot001253\sin qt+0\cdot0001396\cos qt\}$.

15. (*a*) 0·07534 in., 3·077 sq. in., (*b*) 0·03527 in., 2·105 sq. in.

16. (*a*) 5·164 ft., 2·582 ft., (*b*) 3 ft., 1·5 ft.

18. 125·7 cub. in. **19.** 1979 cub. in., $h=r=10\cdot03$ in.

IX., p. 567.

1. (*a*) 1·4816, 2680·5; (*b*) 11·48, $3\cdot277\times10^{-8}$, 0·05707; (*c*) 1·2924. (*d*) 0·788, −0·766, 0·8391, 0·9397, −0·342.

2. (*a*) 0·0578; (*b*) 0·0395; (*c*) $x=4\cdot384$, $y=0\cdot824$.

3. (*a*) 8·1; (*b*) 1·357; (*c*) $3\cdot125\times10^7$; (*d*) $66\frac{2}{3}$.

4.

r	n	
0·55	440·3	436·3
0·50	440·1	435·7
0·45	440·0	435·0

5. $w=6\cdot1+0\cdot14t+0\cdot03t^2$. When t is 3 error is 0·6 %. When t is 100, $w=320$ lbs. or 23 stones nearly.

6. $d=6\cdot065$.

7. Student-hours, 36, 26, 27·3 %, 19·7 %.

8. $n=3{\cdot}28$, $a=0{\cdot}56$. **9.** 0·01873. **10.** $4000\pi=12566$.

11. 17·93. **12.** 180 rad. per (sec.)^2.

13. $s=1200$, $\delta s=240m+12m^2$: aver. speed $=240+12m$; 240.

X., p. 570.

1. (*a*) 0·003214, 462·4 ; (*b*) 1·282.

(*c*)

θ	20	50	100
ϕ	0·0715	0·3127	0·4376

(*d*) 0·5, −0·866, −0·766, 0·8391.

2. $x=7{\cdot}612$ miles, lag$(gx)=39{\cdot}7^\circ$; $x=10{\cdot}13$ miles, lag$(gx)=222{\cdot}4^\circ$.

3. $a=0{\cdot}3997$; $c=24{\cdot}6$.

4. $a=6{\cdot}1$, $b=0{\cdot}14$, $c=0{\cdot}03$ when t is 11 ; $w=11{\cdot}27$ lbs. ; rate 0·8 lb.

5. $4000\pi=12566$. **9.** $0{\cdot}6744+0{\cdot}7927i$.

14. 8 in. **15.** $\frac{1}{4}$, $\frac{1}{6}$. **16.** 1·552 ft., height 2·327 ft.

XI., p. 573.

1. (*a*) 0·005533 ; (*b*) 4·232 ; (*c*) 981·25 ; (*d*) 4·47 %.

2. (*a*) $\frac{\pi}{4}\{D^2-(D-2t)^2\}l$, 3·638 in. ; (*b*) 48000 sq. ft., 12000 tons.

(*c*) (i) $\frac{d}{4}$, (ii) $\frac{d}{4}$; (*d*) 1·88.

3. (*a*) $n=3{\cdot}534$, $a=17100$; (*b*) 1115 ft. per sec., 1·009.
(*c*) 15470 miles, 644·8 miles per hour.

4. Aver. $A=519{\cdot}5$; when h is 36, A is 536 ; vol. $=536000$ cub. ft.

5. $a=0{\cdot}0005919$, $d=7{\cdot}761$ ft. **6.** 1·5106.

7. 14·74 ft. per sec., 28·68° N. of W. **8.** $y=21{\cdot}8+0{\cdot}964x$.

10. (i) 0·042, (ii) 0·42 ft. (sec.)^2. **11.** 67·78 cub. ft.

12. $x=4\frac{1}{6}$, $y=10$. **13.** (i) 2·55, (ii) $p=0$ when $y=-1$.

XII., p. 575.

1. (*a*) 0·005536 ; (*b*) 0·2363 ; (*c*) 0·9868 mile, 0·616 mile.

2. (i) $h=0{\cdot}1049$, $g=0$, $x=6{\cdot}612$ miles.
(ii) $h=0{\cdot}01817$, $g=0{\cdot}6127$, $x=38{\cdot}15$ miles.

3. $1{\cdot}0002+i\times0{\cdot}01001$.

4. See *Elementary Practical Mathematics for Technical Students*, p. 256.

5. Values of z are 11·075, 12·424, 13·944, 15·639, 17·538.

6. (i) $x=\frac{8}{12 \cdot 3}(\cos 1 \cdot 6t - 0 \cdot 6 \sin 1 \cdot 6t)$; (ii) $x=\frac{2}{11}(\sin 2 \cdot 4t - 2 \cos 2 \cdot 4t)$.

7.

$\frac{\delta y}{\delta x}$	6·43	5·89	5·32	4·68	4·03	3·34	2·62	1·89
A	0·675	1·4116	2·2042	3·0468	3·933	4·856	5·8088	6·7842

8. When $x=8 \cdot 3$, $u=0 \cdot 652$.

9. $\delta v=0 \cdot 03322$; $\delta v=0 \cdot 03333$. Error occurs because latter method is only an approximation.

10. $y=11 \cdot 1+10 \sin (\theta+10°)+0 \cdot 83 \sin (2\theta+50°)$.

11. 4·23, 0·455, −4·68.

12.

v	2·05	3·55	2·5
$\frac{dH}{dv}$	1709·7	−115·4	1158·3

13. Plot M and $\sqrt{M^2+T^2}$.

XIII., p. 579.

1. (*a*) 0·082189; (*b*) 0·08228, 0·338; (*c*) 0·1736, −0·9848, −0·1763, −0·9511, −0·3090, 3·0777; (*d*) $4 \cdot 046(\cos 310° + i \sin 310°)$; $\pm(1 \cdot 823 - 0 \cdot 8498i)$.

3. 4·494; 80·1; 0·0847.

4. $a=0 \cdot 17$, $b=316 \cdot 4$, $n=0 \cdot 95$.

5. 4·71.

6. $\frac{-ab}{(bx+c)^2}$; $\cos 2x - 2x \sin 2x$; $\frac{a}{b}\log(bx+c)+k$;

$\frac{x}{2}\sin 2x+\frac{1}{4}\cos 2x+k$.

7. 55·82.

8. 2·1293; $0 \cdot 8968+0 \cdot 9926i$.

9. $4 \cdot 5 \sin 2t - 1 \cdot 5 \cos 2t$.

10. $13 \cdot 32_{135 \cdot 4°}$.

11. $\frac{a^4}{36}$.

12. 49° 54′; $a=4 \cdot 87$, $b=6 \cdot 61$, $c=4 \cdot 66$; 25 sq. in.

13. $y_m=1 \cdot 18$; $v=11 \cdot 9$

Miscellaneous Exercises XLVI., p. 592A.

2. 15·4 cub. in. **3.** 0·6223 in. per sec.

4. $\frac{x^5}{5}-\frac{2x^3}{3}+2x^2+x+c$; $4x^3-4x+4$. **5.** $x=\pm 2$.

6. $\frac{x^4}{4}+x^2+3x-82$. **7.** $x=0{\cdot}5,\ 1{\cdot}8$. **8.** $2x-\frac{3}{2}x^2-2$.

9. 40. **10.** $3x^2-8x+5$; $6x-8$; $1,\ \frac{5}{3}$.

11. 62·84 cub. ft. per sec. **12.** $r=h=5{\cdot}64$ ft.

13. 66 ft. **14.** 11, $2\frac{1}{4}$ sec.

15. (i) 30, 20 ; (ii) $-216,\ -378$; (iii) 17·8, 8. **16.** $1\pm\frac{1}{\sqrt{3}}$.

17. 4·243 in., 2·12 in. **18.** $r=h=10{\cdot}07$ ft. **19.** 40 yd., 20 yd.

20. 8·835 in. **21.** $V=12$.

22. (i) $r=h=2{\cdot}48$ ft. ; (ii) $r=1{\cdot}97$ ft. : $h=3{\cdot}94$ ft.

23. 0·067 ft. per min. **24.** (i) 91·6 ; $-20{\cdot}4$; (ii) 4.0625 sec., 8·125 sec.

25. (i) $\frac{4x^3}{3}-\frac{3x^2}{2}+4x+c$; (ii) $\frac{4x^5}{5}+a^4x-\frac{4a^2x^3}{3}+2x+c$;

(iii) $acx-\frac{bx^3}{3}+\frac{cx^4}{4}-\frac{x^5}{5}+6x+c$; (iv) $x^4-\frac{4}{3}x^3+\frac{x^2}{2}+c$;

(v) $\frac{x^3}{3}-x^2-8x+c$; (vi) $x^3-\frac{3}{x}+c$. **26.** -345.

28. $61\frac{1}{3}$. **29.** $3x^2+4x+1$.

INDEX.

PRINTED IN GREAT BRITAIN BY ROBERT MACLEHOSE AND CO. LTD.
THE UNIVERSITY PRESS, GLASGOW.